THE AMINO SUGARS

The Chemistry and Biology of Compounds Containing Amino Sugars

Volume IIB

Metabolism and Interactions

THE AMINO SUGARS

The Chemistry and Biology of Compounds Containing Amino Sugars

EDITED BY

ROGER W. JEANLOZ and ENDRE A. BALAZS

Volume IA Chemistry of Amino Sugars

Volume IB Glycosaminoglycans, Glycoproteins, and Glycosaminolipids

Volume IIA Distribution and Biological Role

Volume IIB Metabolism and Interactions

THE AMINO SUGARS

The Chemistry and Biology of Compounds Containing Amino Sugars

VOLUME IIB

METABOLISM AND INTERACTIONS

EDITED BY

ENDRE A. BALAZS and ROGER W. JEANLOZ

Institute of Biological and Medical Sciences–Retina Foundation and Harvard Medical School Boston, Massachusetts

Harvard Medical School and Massachusetts General Hospital Boston, Massachusetts

1966

ACADEMIC PRESS New York and London

ACADEMIC PRESS INC.
111 Fifth Avenue, New York, New York 10003

United Kingdom Edition published by
ACADEMIC PRESS INC. (LONDON) LTD.
Berkeley Square House, London W.1

Library of Congress Catalog Card Number: 62-13092

PRINTED IN THE UNITED STATES OF AMERICA

LIST OF CONTRIBUTORS

Numbers in parentheses refer to the pages on which the authors' contributions begin.

ENDRE A. BALAZS (229, 361), *Department of Connective Tissue Research, Institute of Biological and Medical Sciences, Retina Foundation; Department of Ophthalmology, Harvard Medical School, Boston, Massachusetts*

PETER BERNFELD (213, 251), *Bio-Research Institute, Cambridge, Massachusetts*

HARRY BOSTRÖM (45), *Department of Metabolic Research, The Wenner-Gren Institute, University of Stockholm, and the Department of Medicine, Serafimerlasarettet, Karolinska Institutet, Stockholm, Sweden*

EUGENE A. DAVIDSON (1), *Department of Biochemistry, Duke University Medical Center, Durham, North Carolina*

K. S. DODGSON (201), *Department of Biochemistry, University of Wales, Cardiff, Wales*

HEINZ GIBIAN (181), *Schering AG, Berlin, Germany*

ALFRED GOTTSCHALK (337), *Max-Planck-Institut für Virusforschung, Tübingen, West Germany*

BERNARD JACOBSON (361), *Department of Connective Tissue Research, Institute of Biological and Medical Sciences, Retina Foundation, Boston, Massachusetts*

MAX E. RAFELSON, JR. (171), *Department of Biochemistry, Presbyterian–St. Luke's Hospital, and the University of Illinois College of Medicine, Chicago, Illinois*

LENNART RODÉN (45), *La Rabida–University of Chicago Institute, and the Department of Biochemistry, The University of Chicago, Chicago, Illinois*

MICHAEL SCHNEIR (171), *Department of Biochemistry, Presbyterian–St. Luke's Hospital, and the University of Illinois College of Medicine, Chicago, Illinois*

GEORG F. SPRINGER (267), *Department of Immunochemistry Research, Evanston Hospital Association and Department of Microbiology, Northwestern University Medical School, Evanston, Illinois*

LARS SUNDBLAD (229), *Department of Clinical Chemistry, Södersjukhuset, Stockholm, Sweden*

J. A. SZIRMAI (129), *Research Laboratories, Department of Rheumatology, University Hospital, Leiden, The Netherlands*

PETER G. WALKER (155), *The Institute of Orthopaedics, Royal National Orthopaedic Hospital, Stanmore, Middlesex, England*

VANNIE W. WILSON, JR. (171), *Department of Biochemistry, Presbyterian–St. Luke's Hospital, and the University of Illinois College of Medicine, Chicago, Illinois*

IKUO YAMASHINA (81), *Faculty of Pharmaceutical Sciences, Kyoto University, Sakyo-Ku, Kyoto, Japan*

PREFACE

The rapid increase of knowledge in the field of amino sugar-containing compounds has inspired this treatise. It was felt that a summary of the present knowledge, with a comprehensive review of the literature, prepared by scientists currently working in this field, would provide a starting point for the newcomer to the field and would also serve the expert in the broadening of his interest.

The purpose of this treatise is twofold: (1) to survey the chemistry, physical chemistry, and biochemistry of all naturally occurring and synthetically prepared amino sugars and amino sugar-containing molecules and (2) to present a critical and interpretative account of the biological and medical importance of these molecules. The broad scope of the work has resulted in a progressive extension of the subject into diverse areas, including such fields as protein, carbohydrate, and lipid chemistry, immunochemistry, histochemistry, bacteriology, virology, and pathology. It is hoped that this first attempt to present a comprehensive and integrated account of this excitingly expanding field of knowledge will serve as a valuable tool for research and teaching, extending, in its usefulness, well beyond the main subject matter.

The organization of this treatise was dictated by the systematic treatment of this broad subject. Volume IA (Chapters 1–5) is devoted to the chemistry of amino sugars, including oligosaccharides, nucleotide derivatives, and glycosides of amino sugars. Volume IB (Chapters 6–17) presents the chemical and physicochemical structure of amino sugar-containing polysaccharides (glycosaminoglycans), peptides (glycopeptides), proteins (glycoproteins), and lipids (glycolipids), and the methods for their isolation, determination, and histochemical localization. Volume IIA (Chapters 18–37) deals with the distribution and biological role of amino sugars and amino sugar-containing macromolecules in plants and animals.

The present volume was prepared with two main purposes in mind. One was to review the metabolism of the amino sugars and the amino sugar moieties of macromolecules. Not only are the biosynthetic processes presented in detail, but also the degradation of these macromolecules by enzymes, oxidation–reduction systems, and radiation. Inasmuch as this treatise is focused on amino sugars, the biosynthetic and degradation processes which involve the protein, peptide, or lipid part of the macromolecules are not reviewed.

The second purpose of this volume is to review the interaction of amino sugars, glycosaminoglycans, glycoproteins, and glycolipids with other macromolecules, as well as with viruses, cells, and the whole organism. This objective presented the editors with the difficult task of carefully selecting the subjects to be included. Several amino sugar-containing macromolecules are involved in biological processes and pharmacological reactions of great importance, such as the blood-group reactions of some glycoproteins and the prevention of blood coagulation by heparin; a review of all the biological and pharmacological aspects of these interactions would, however, have needed several additional volumes and would have led to an undesirable dilution of the main theme. The editors, therefore, decided to cover the pharmacological aspects of the interaction of amino sugars and their compounds only superficially and to refer the reader to recent reviews dealing with the subject in detail.

The editors regret that the present volume, which represents the last in the series of four comprising this treatise, is only the second to appear in print. The delay of the publication of Volumes IA and IB has been caused by the rapid growth of the field and the subsequent compelling desire of the editors and authors to incorporate this never-ending expansion of knowledge in a systematic and comprehensive way.

In the Preface to Volume IIA, the editors recorded their appreciation for the cooperation and patience of the contributors to this treatise. It is appropriate to reiterate our thanks to the sixteen authors of the fourteen chapters of Volume IIB who had not only the difficult chore of reviewing a prolific field but often the pioneering task of canvassing and compiling the literature according to new points of view.

ENDRE A. BALAZS
ROGER W. JEANLOZ

Boston, Massachusetts
January, 1966

NOMENCLATURE

The nomenclature used in this volume is identical to that used in Volume IIA of this treatise. In order to avoid repetition, the reader is referred, for details, to "A Guide to the Nomenclature" on page xiii of Volume IIA of *The Amino Sugars.*

For immediate accessibility, some old terms and the few new ones are listed below.

Chondroitin 4-sulfate	— formerly called chondroitin sulfate A
Chondroitin 6-sulfate	— formerly called chondroitin sulfate C
Dermatan sulfate	— formerly called chondroitin sulfate B
Galactosaminoglycans	— polysaccharides that contain galactosamine
Glucosaminoglycans	— polysaccharides that contain glucosamine
Glycoproteins	— proteins that contain sugars
Glycosaminoglycans	— polysaccharides that contain amino sugars
Glycosaminoglycuronans	— polysaccharides that contain amino sugars and uronic acid moieties
Glycosaminolipids	— lipids that contain amino sugars
Heparan sulfate	— formerly called heparitin sulfate
Keratan sulfate	— formerly called keratosulfate

CONTENTS

CHAPTER 40

Metabolism of Glycoproteins, Glycopeptides, and Glycolipids

Ikuo Yamashina

CHAPTER 41

Effect of Steroid Hormones on the Glycosaminoglycans of Target Connective Tissues

J. A. Szirmai

CHAPTER 42

Hexosaminidases

P. G. Walker

CHAPTER 43

Neuraminidases

Max E. Rafelson, Jr., Michael Schneir, and Vannie W. Wilson, Jr.

CHAPTER 44

Enzymes Degrading Glycosaminoglycans

Heinz Gibian

CHAPTER 45

Sulfatases of Glycosaminoglycans

K. S. Dodgson

CHAPTER 46

Activation and Inhibition of Enzymes by Polyanions Containing Amino Sugars

Peter Bernfeld

CHAPTER 47

Chemical and Physical Changes of Glycosaminoglycans and Glycoproteins Caused by Oxidation–Reduction Systems and Radiation

Lars Sundblad and Endre A. Balazs

CHAPTER 48

Interaction of Polyanions with Blood Components

Peter Bernfeld

CHAPTER 49

Immunochemistry

Georg F. Springer

CHAPTER 50

Interaction between Glycoproteins and Viruses

Alfred Gottschalk

CHAPTER 51

Interaction of Amino Sugars and Amino Sugar-Containing Macromolecules with Viruses, Cells, and Tissues

Endre A. Balazs and Bernard Jacobson

CONTENTS OF OTHER VOLUMES

VOLUME IIA

Distribution and Biological Role

Edited by Endre A. Balazs and Roger W. Jeanloz

Chapter 38

METABOLISM OF AMINO SUGARS

Eugene A. Davidson

The presence of amino sugars in natural products has been known since 1878, when a nitrogenous reducing substance ("glykosamin") was isolated from chitin and appropriately termed chitosamine (Ledderhose, 1878). Shortly thereafter, a second amino sugar was isolated from several animal sources, shown to be isomeric with chitosamine, and was given the name chondrosamine. Much of the early biochemical work on both the amino sugars and compounds related to them is reviewed in the monograph by Levene (1925).

The tremendous increase in enzymic studies of hexosamine metabolism in recent years is manifest. The results have been impressive; pathways for the synthesis of many hexosamine derivatives have been well defined, and considerable detailed information is available regarding the enzymic reactions involved in the degradation of the amino sugars and their derivatives.

There are, however, a considerable number of unanswered questions. These include the mechanism of the fructose-6-phosphate L-glutamine transamidase reaction; the mode of transfer of amino sugar derivatives (and, in fact, virtually all sugar derivatives that are involved in heteropolymer structures) to polymers, such as hyaluronic acid, chondroitin sulfate, and the like; the nature of the sulfate acceptor involved in sulfated-polysaccharide synthesis; and the detailed mode of biosynthesis of muramic acid and the possible occurrence of this sugar in higher organisms. Also, the biological formation of a wide variety of new amino sugars (such as D-fucosamine, 2-amino-2-deoxy-D-galacturonic acid, diaminohexoses, and the like) and their possible distribution in other sources have not as yet received any serious attention. The catabolic pathways of the connective-tissue polysaccharides have not been satisfactorily defined, and the resolution of glucosaminidase and galactosaminidase activities remains to be clarified. The possible direct oxidative metabolism of hexosamine in mammalian systems needs to be reinvestigated, as does the ability of such systems to utilize substrates such as glucosaminic acid. The pathways for galactosamine formation appear to be satisfactorily defined, although the substrate specificity of the L-glutamine fructose-phosphate transamidase reaction has not been investigated with substrates such as tagatose 6-phosphate. The further metabolic utilization of *N*-acetylgalactosamine 6-phosphate has not been studied, nor has the metabolism of galactosamine 1-phosphate been investigated, especially with regard to such enzymes as uridyl transferases and pyrophosphorylases.

The following material should be regarded as a progress report rather than a compilation of all information in this field.

I. Energy-Utilizing Reactions

A. Hexosamine Synthesis

1. Origin of the Carbon Skeleton

The structure of the most common amino sugars, that of 2-amino-2-deoxyaldohexoses, suggested two alternative pathways for their biosynthetic origin. The first such synthetic route would involve dissimilation of a carbohydrate precursor, such as glucose, to glycolytic intermediates by known reactions, followed by the condensation of an appropriate fragment (dihydroxyacetone phosphate, for example) with a nitrogen-containing compound such as serine or a serine derivative. A second plausible hypothesis would involve the direct amination of either a hexose or activated hexose, with a possible additional requirement for an oxidation or reduction step. The resolution of this question was not possible until the advent of isotopic tracers permitted the individual carbon atoms in question to be specifically tracked through the operative biological pathway.

The biological systems that have been utilized in studies aimed at definition of the origin of the hexosamine carbon chain included capsular hyaluronic acid synthesis by group-A hemolytic streptococci, ovomucoid formation in eggs, and serum hexosamine synthesis by growing mammals. The general approach adopted depended on the incorporation of specifically labeled glucose (most often glucose-1-C^{14}, which, at the time, was readily available via the cyanohydrin synthesis) as a precursor. The isotope was either included in the growth medium of the microorganisms or administered as a single radioactive dose to animals. The synthesized hexosamine was isolated after the usual hydrolytic procedures, characterized by direct crystallization or by formation of the 2-hydroxy-1-naphthaldehyde Schiff base and subjected to degradation procedures designed to isolate carbon-1 free from the remaining carbons of the chain. In this manner, it was possible to ascertain whether extensive randomization of the carbon chain had occurred or whether direct conversion of the glucose carbon skeleton to that of the amino sugar had been effected.

Becker and Day (1953) reported the results of such studies in which glucose-1-C^{14} or glucosone-1-C^{14} was examined as a potential precursor of serum hexosamine in rats. The experimental methods and techniques employed were virtually identical to those described in the preceding paragraph. Since 90% of the isotopic label was found to be retained in carbon-1 of the synthesized glucosamine, it was concluded that the precursor glucose was converted to the hexosamine without cleavage of the carbon chain. Specific-activity measurements indicated that glucosone was somewhat more efficiently utilized as a precursor for the hexosamine than was glucose; a suggested pathway involved oxidation of glucose to glucosone, followed by a conventional transamination-like reaction. Glucosone is known to exert a marked toxicity when given subcutaneously, intravenously, or orally (Herring and Hynd, 1928). This toxic effect, which appears to be highly stereospecific—D- or L-arabinosone, D- or L-xylosone, D-galactosone, L-glucosone, and L-gulosone are nontoxic at comparable levels (Bayne, 1952)—may be due to the competitive inhibition by glucosone of the phosphorylation of glucose by hexokinase (Eeg-Larsen and Laland, 1954); glucosone may also interfere with the transport of glucose into cells. In view of the effects which glucosone is known to produce, and, since the pool sizes and transport rates of glucosone and glucose are widely different, the definitive involvement of glucosone as an intermediate in hexosamine synthesis could not be considered established by the results just mentioned.

Topper and Lipton (1953) studied hexosamine synthesis in group-A hemolytic streptococci grown in the presence of glucose-1-C^{14}. Their conclusions regarding the origin of the hexosamine carbon chain were similar to those reached by Becker and Day, inasmuch as the isotopic label was largely retained in carbon-1 of the hexosamine. They also examined the possible role of glucosone as an intermediate, and their findings with glucosone as a substrate were also equivocal. These studies were extended by experiments in which the dilution of the specific radioactivity of the newly synthesized hexosamine was examined as a function of the presence of several unlabeled, potential precursors. As a result of such experiments, it was concluded that both glucosamine and *N*-acetylglucosamine were able to function as precursors of the amino sugar moiety of the synthesized hyaluronic acid, whereas D-glucuronic acid and D-galactosamine were ineffective in this capacity.

A more extensive and rigorous series of investigations along the same lines was simultaneously carried out in Dorfman's laboratory (Roseman *et al.*, 1953; Roseman *et al.*, 1954; Dorfman *et al.*, 1955; Dorfman *et al.*, 1955a). Using group-A hemolytic streptococci, these workers obtained results which were generally similar to those found by Becker and Day and by Topper and Lipton. Thus, the specific activity of the C-1 of the amino sugar was essentially identical to the specific activity of the C-1 of the medium glucose. Since the growth medium contained a high percentage of unlabeled amino acids, it could be concluded that compounds such as serine do not play any significant role in hexosamine biogenesis. Studies with glucosamine or *N*-acetylglucosamine as potential precursors of hyaluronate glucosamine demonstrated that both of these sugars could function in this capacity. Additional experiments utilizing C^{14}-labeled and N^{15}-labeled glucosamine demonstrated that the amino sugar is incorporated without prior deamination. These authors also investigated the possibility of glucosone as an intermediate in the glucose-to-glucosamine conversion. Since the results indicated that glucosone was not a precursor for hexosamine synthesis, and were, therefore, at variance with those previously reported by Becker and Day (1953) and by Topper and Lipton (1953), elucidation of the actual role of glucosone depended on the more definitive studies carried out with cell-free enzyme systems.

The radioactivity-distribution pattern found in the synthesized hyaluronic acid was such that the glucose carbons appeared both in the amino sugar and in the uronic acid moieties. Degradation of the uronic acid fraction strongly suggested that the glucose precursor was also converted to this sugar without randomization. The acetyl group was studied for its origin and was found to be either in equilibrium with, or to arise from a common precursor with, the acetate present in the medium. The distribution of label in the acetyl group could be accounted for by synthesis from D-glucose via conventional biochemical pathways.

Rieder, studying hexosamine incorporation into ovomucoid during synthesis of this glycoprotein in eggs of laying hens, arrived at conclusions identical to those just mentioned (Rieder, 1953; Rieder and Buchanan, 1958).

A more recent study of similar nature was carried out by Spiro (1959), who examined carbohydrate precursors of serum glycoprotein hexosamine in rats. His studies indicated that the ability of various tissues to incorporate glucose carbon into hexosamine varied considerably; the highest rate of synthesis was found in liver, which is the primary site of glycoprotein synthesis. The isotopic data obtained confirmed the direct conversion of the hexose carbon to that of hexosamine without the intermediary formation of triose fragments.

2. Origin of the Amino Group

The studies just reported were concerned primarily with the origin of the carbon skeleton of the amino sugar. Several comparable studies were carried out in an attempt to ascertain the origin of the amino group. Rieder concluded that ammonia was a more efficient precursor of the hexosamine nitrogen of ovomucoid than were amino acids (Rieder, 1953; Rieder and Buchanan, 1958a).

A more extensive study was carried out by Lowther and Rogers (1955, 1956) utilizing N^{15}-labeled substrates. They were able to demonstrate that resting cell suspensions of group-A hemolytic streptococci were able to form hyaluronic acid from glucose and L-glutamine if the suspending medium was supplemented with inorganic phosphate and magnesium. Glutamine could be replaced by ammonium L-glutamate or by a number of other amino acids in combination with L-glutamate, although aged cells required glutamine. Inhibitor studies carried out with methionine sulfoxide also suggested that glutamine was an obligatory precursor of the hexosamine nitrogen in this system. The incorporation of N^{15}-labeled ammonium ions into the amino group of glucosamine proceeded at a very efficient rate in the presence of a large unlabeled pool of either L-glutamate or other amino acids, but could be diluted out by L-glutamine. Finally, it was demonstrated that cell-free extracts of these organisms catalyzed the synthesis of glucosamine phosphate from hexose phosphate and glutamine but not from hexose phosphate and ammonium L-glutamate. As a result of the experiments just described, Lowther and Rogers concluded that glutamine is an essential intermediate in the synthesis of glucosamine by hemolytic streptococci.

During studies of the incorporation of inorganic sulfate into chondroitin sulfuric acid by cartilage slices, it was found that a liver factor exerted a marked stimulatory effect on this conversion (Boström and Månsson, 1953a; Boström *et al.*, 1955; Rodén, 1956). Similar effects of L-glutamine were demonstrated on the incorporation of sulfate into the glycosaminoglycans synthesized in the nucleus pulposus (Rodén, 1956a). Purification studies resulted in the identification of glutamine as the sole activating agent; the conclusion was drawn that this was a result of its effect on the level of hexosamine synthesis in the tissue.

In an extension of these studies, it was demonstrated that glucosamine could be directly incorporated into the amino sugar moiety of cartilage chondroitin sulfuric acid and that this incorporation was far more efficient for glucosamine than for galactosamine. In view of the fact that the amino sugar in the synthesized chondroitin sulfate was galactosamine rather than glucosamine, the implication from these studies is that the system examined did not have the ability to activate preformed galactosamine, and, therefore, the galactosamine was obtained via a glucosamine derivative, probably by some epimerization reaction (Rodén, 1956b; Tessari, 1959). Although the effect of L-glutamine on glycosaminoglycans production is not uniform in all systems examined (Morris, 1960), it may be safely concluded from the studies just reported that, in general, biological systems derive the amino group of hexosamines from L-glutamine.

3. Cell-Free Systems

A strong stimulus to studies in this field was provided by the now classic paper of Leloir and Cardini (1953), in which the first demonstration of hexosamine synthesis catalyzed by a cell-free system was reported. They reported that cell-free extracts of *Neurospora crassa,* a mold which contains chitin as part of its cell wall, could catalyze the conversion of hexose phosphate and L-glutamine to a compound which was tentatively identified as D-glucosamine 6-phosphate. The identification of the amino sugar product was based upon colorimetric behavior in the Elson–Morgan reaction and retention of reducing properties (both of which indicated that the carbonyl function was still intact), precipitability with barium hydroxide–zinc sulfate, and the formation of free glucosamine after treatment with phosphatase. Because of the extreme lability of the enzyme system under study, it was not possible to determine whether the hexose phosphate utilized was glucose 6-phosphate or fructose 6-phosphate, since the extracts contained an active phosphoglucoisomerase. Several other substrates were tested as possible precursors of the hexosamine carbon chain. These included altrose, glucose, fructose, mannose, a mixture of trioses, fructose 1-phosphate, and glucose diphosphate, and all were found to be inactive. Materials which were tested for amino-group-donor ability included asparagine, aspartic acid, glutamic acid, ammonium acetate, urea-cycle intermediates, and ammonium ion in the presence of adenosine triphosphate. The system was highly specific; only L-glutamine could provide the amino group of the synthesized hexosamine. Several seemingly possible cofactors, such as pyridoxal phosphate, failed to exert any stimulatory effect under the conditions studied. The equation written by Leloir and Cardini for hexosamine biosynthesis was as follows:

$$\text{hexose 6-phosphate} + \text{L-glutamine} \rightarrow \text{glucosamine 6-phosphate} + \text{L-glutamic acid} \quad (1)$$

This enzyme system was subsequently investigated by several authors. Pogell, studying extracts obtained from rat liver, came to the conclusion that glucose 6-phosphate was a more immediate precursor of the hexosamine carbon chain than was fructose 6-phosphate (Pogell, 1956; Pogell and Gryder, 1957). This conclusion was not based on the exclusion of fructose 6-phosphate as a substrate after enzyme fractionation to remove phosphoglucoisomerase, but rather on decreased inactivation and increased stability of the enzyme in the presence of glucose 6-phosphate as compared with results obtained with fructose 6-phosphate. Since it was not possible to obtain a satisfactory balance for the conversion in these experiments, and since phosphoglucoisomerase was still present, these results must be regarded as equivocal.

A more definitive study was carried out by Roseman and co-workers, who purified the hexosamine-synthesizing enzyme system from several sources, including *Neurospora crassa, Escherichia coli,* and rat liver (Blumenthal *et al.*, 1955; Roseman *et al.*, 1958; Ghosh *et al.*, 1960). These studies revealed that each of the enzymes was specific for fructose 6-phosphate and that glucose 6-phosphate was completely inactive as a substrate for purified preparations. The unusual assay problems that arise in colorimetric amino sugar determinations under conditions of enzymic assay were discussed, and a rather specific procedure was described which permits reliable estimation of hexosamine synthesis in such systems. During the course of the fractionation studies, it was frequently noted that activities with fructose and glucose phosphates were comparable in the early stages of purification. Activities toward glucose 6-phosphate always disappeared as fractionation proceeded, however, and fractions which were inactive with fructose 6-phosphate were also inactive when tested with glucose 6-phosphate. Since virtually identical results were found for all of the systems examined, the conclusion was reached that fructose 6-phosphate served as the immediate precursor of the hexosamine carbon chain. L-Glutamine was the only satisfactory amino-group donor, and the enzyme was inhibited by diazo L-norleucine and, less effectively, by azaserine. A subsequent report confirmed these results for an enzyme preparation from *Bacillus subtilis* and stated that the glutamine analogues, methionine sulfoxide and γ-glutamyl hydrazide, were noninhibitory (Clarke and Pasternak, 1962). In neither study was the mode of inhibition determined (presumably, competitive inhibition with glutamine) nor were K_i values reported.

Balance studies were reported for both the rat-liver and the *Escherichia coli* enzymes, and, although the *Neurospora crassa* preparation still contained appreciable glutaminase activity, fructose-phosphate disappearance was readily accounted for by hexosamine-phosphate formation. The synthesized hexosamine phosphate was isolated and characterized as the crystalline sugar which exhibited an X-ray diffraction pattern identical to that of synthetic glucosamine 6-phosphate. Additional evidence adduced for the structure of the biosynthetic material was obtained from the role of glucosamine phosphate as a substrate for other enzyme systems, as well as from chromatographic procedures. The enzymic reaction was not detectably reversible, starting with glucosamine 6-phosphate and glutamic acid, even in the presence of phosphohexoisomerase, glucose 6-phosphate dehydrogenase, and triphosphopyridine nucleotide. The equilibrium constant was not measured, nor was the conversion of N^{15}-glutamine to hexosamine studied. It is of considerable interest to note that, of all systems since examined, the organism originally studied by Leloir and Cardini was that which has always provided the most active crude extracts. The net reaction may be depicted as follows:

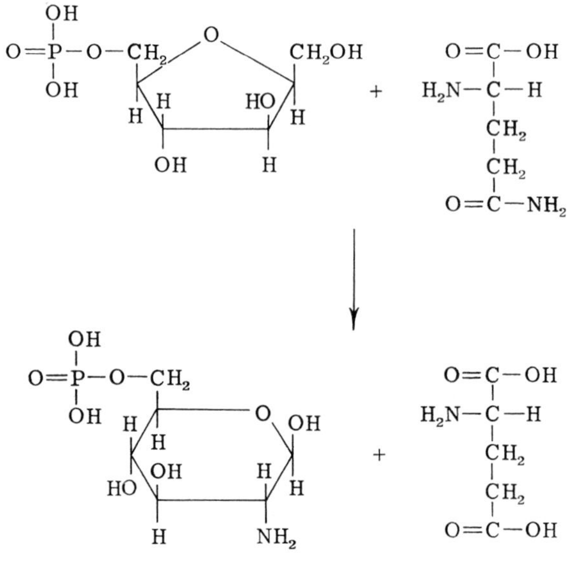

OH
O=P—O—CH$_2$ O CH_2OH
OH H H HO H
OH H
+
O=C—OH
H_2N—C—H
CH_2
CH_2
O=C—NH_2

↓

OH
O=P—O—CH_2
OH H O OH
H
OH H
HO H
H NH_2
+
O=C—OH
H_2N—C—H
CH_2
CH_2
O=C—OH

4. Distribution in Normal and Lathyritic Tissues

The distribution of the hexosamine-synthesizing enzyme system has been studied by several authors and it was found to be present in extracts of cartilage, epiphyseal plates, bone callus, mucous membranes, and lung, as well as in liver and kidney (Castellani, Perri, and Zambotti, 1955; Castellani and Zambotti, 1956; Zambotti, Castellani, and Schiatti, 1956; Priest, 1960). A report of interest appeared, disclosing that the level of the hexosamine-synthesizing enzyme system was found to be markedly decreased in animals treated with lathyrogenic factors (Pedrini and Pedrini-Mille, 1959). It was demonstrated that there was approximately a 75% decrease in the ability of extracts of the epiphyseal plates of treated animals to form hexosamine phosphate from hexose phosphate and L-glutamine. Lathyrogenic agents, such as β-aminopropionitrile or aminoacetonitrile, which alter amino sugar metabolism in whole animals (Kulonen *et al.*, 1961) are without effect in cell-free systems. There was no demonstration of any inhibitor, but the absolute level of enzyme is not known because the experiments were based on the wet weight of the tissue, and, in this condition, there is a marked change in the amount of soluble protein. Although no attempt was made to correlate the enzyme activity with cell content, the extent of the effect observed suggests that the lathyritic defect may occur at the enzymic level. These studies certainly merit further investigation.

5. Induction and Repression

The addition of *N*-acetylglucosamine to growing cultures of a suitable microorganism causes two effects. The first is the repression of L-glutamine D-fructose-6-phosphate transamidase and the second is the induction of glucosamine-6-phosphate deaminase (Clarke and Pasternak, 1962). The substrate for the latter enzyme is glucosamine 6-phosphate, but the possible simultaneous induction of a specific kinase for either glucosamine or *N*-acetylglucosamine, as well as of a deacylase, was not reported.

The induction of the deaminase may be controlled by the availability of glucose, as happens with several other inducible enzymes (Neidhardt, 1960; Mandlestam, 1962). The implication of these experiments is that exogenous hexosamine is a preferential source of amino sugars for the bacterial cell, and, if the glucose concentration simultaneously falls, the cells may respond by adaptively utilizing the amino sugar as a carbon and energy source.

6. Mechanism

The conversion of fructose 6-phosphate to glucosamine 6-phosphate involves, besides an amide transfer, an internal oxidation–reduction proceeding from an intermediate which would not also be formed from glucose 6-phosphate. Any proposed mechanism must also account for the apparent lack of reversibility of this conversion.

Since present information on the homogeneity of the best enzyme preparations obtained does not exclude the possibility that the reaction is catalyzed by more than a single enzyme, it is impossible to state rigorously how many steps must be involved in this conversion or what the rate-limiting process should be. A possible mechanism for this transformation is illustrated in Fig. 1.

The cleavage of the amide bond of glutamine would be essentially an irreversible step, since the amination reaction does not result in the formation of a C—N bond of sufficient energy to allow resynthesis of glutamine. Evidence for the proposed pathway might be obtained by the use of appropriately labeled substrates in a manner analogous to the

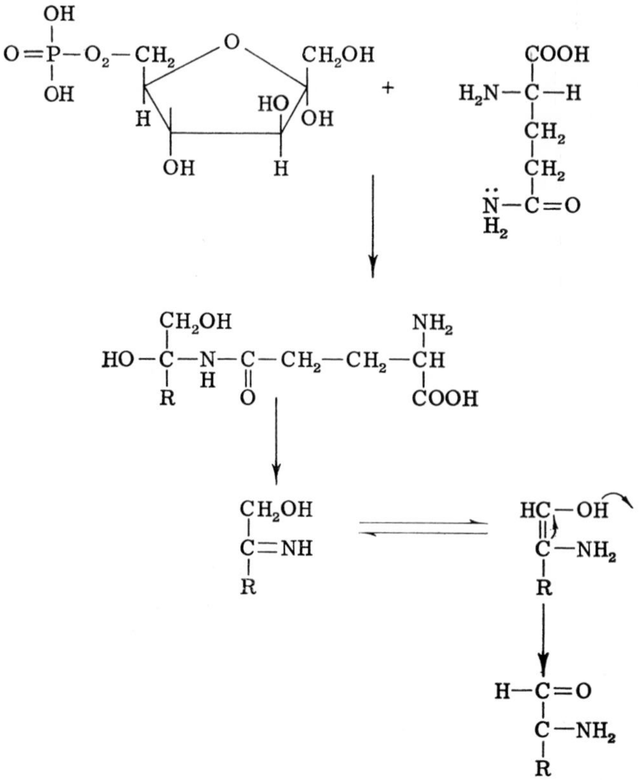

FIG. 1. Postulated mechanism for fructose-6-phosphate glutamine transamidase.

study of the mechanism of action of phosphoglucoisomerase (Topper, 1957). The formation of an intermediate imine (as may be seen, with ammonia as a substrate, this reaction would be reversible) is followed by tautomerization via an isomerase type of mechanism. Thus, one of the hydrogens at C-1 of the fructose 6-phosphate would ultimately appear bound to C-2 of the hexosamine phosphate; this could be determined by the use of tritium-labeled substrate. Either the glutaminyl residue is cleaved after addition to the carbonyl group, or the intermediate imine which would result from the initial amination should be enzyme bound; otherwise, hydrolysis by solvent to release ammonia might occur.

The driving force of the over-all conversion might be the formation of the carbonyl group at C-1, as well as the cleavage of the amide bond of glutamine.

It should be noted that direct chemical synthesis of glucosamine from fructose and ammonia has been achieved (Heyns and Meinecke, 1953), and the behavior of D-glucosamine in aqueous solutions in the presence of alkali has also been examined (Heyns, Koch, and Koch, 1954; Zimmerman, 1959). Kinetic investigation indicated that the decomposition of glucosamine in alkaline solution was a two-step process, with the rate of the initial step independent of alkali concentration. The proposed mechanism suggested a proton shift from carbon to nitrogen, followed by rearrangement of the resulting complex. The biological amination reaction may proceed with opening of the furanose ring followed by tautomerizations similar to those just mentioned, thus yielding the hexosamine end product.

The facts that cell-free extracts of a wide variety of biological systems are able to form hexosamine from hexose phosphate and that *in vitro* systems are able to produce heteropolysaccharides when augmented with a precursor such as D-glucose strongly suggest that these cells have the entire enzymic complement necessary for *de novo* synthesis of the polysaccharide molecules. Therefore, no prior conversion of simple precursor substrates is expected to take place in liver or comparable tissues. The generally higher specific activity of the hexosamine-synthesis system found in liver is probably a reflection of the increased synthetic demand on this tissue, the high cellularity, and the relative ease of extraction of soluble protein. The levels of activity found in cartilage, skin, and bone reflect the general metabolic activity of such tissues and should not be taken to indicate that the synthesis of glycosaminoglycans by these tissues is dependent on delivery of some preformed metabolite synthesized at some other site.

B. N-Acetylation

The vast majority of glycosaminoglycans contain hexosamines as the *N*-acetyl derivatives. The *N*-sulfate group in heparin, the *N*-glycolyl group in neuraminic acid derivatives, and a partially deacetylated galactosaminan represent virtually all the exceptions. The initial report on hexosamine metabolism by Leloir and Cardini (1953) stated that an enzyme system was present in their crude extracts which was able to catalyze the acetylation of either glucosamine or glucosamine 6-phosphate to form the respective *N*-acetyl derivatives. Acetyl coenzyme A was implicated as the acetyl donor in this system, but was not definitively identified, since a generating system was employed. The high level of phosphatase activity present in their crude extracts did not permit a differentiation between the free amino sugar and its phosphorylated derivative as substrate for the acetylating system. A prior report by Chou and Soodak (1952) described the *N*-acetylation of glucosamine catalyzed by extracts of "pigeon liver acetone powder." The lack of inhibition by penicillin suggested that this enzyme was not identical with the aromatic amine acetylase. Microbial acetylating systems which were active with naturally occurring amino acid substrates were also able to utilize glucosamine, with the concomitant formation of the acetylamino sugar (Tabor, Mehler, and Stadtman, 1953).

A partially purified yeast preparation was reported to specifically acetylate glucosamine 6-phosphate without action on the free amino sugar (Brown, 1955). These results, as were those reported previously, were somewhat complicated by the utilization of an acetyl coenzyme A–generating system which, in addition to containing amine-acetylating activities, also contained a source of high-energy phosphate. Thus, it appeared that mammalian enzyme systems were able to acetylate glucosamine, whereas yeast enzymes required glucosamine 6-phosphate as substrate.

A later investigation of the *N*-acetylation reaction revealed that both mammalian and microbial systems, as well as that system originally studied in *Neurospora crassa,* were specific for glucosamine 6-phosphate, and the significance of the acetylation of the free amino sugar was questioned (Davidson, Blumenthal, and Roseman, 1957). Crude preparations obtained from mammalian liver were active with either glucosamine or glucosamine phosphate as substrate, although activity with the phosphorylated substrate was appreciably higher. Purification of the extracts resolved this nonspecificity; acetylation of glucosamine was catalyzed by the aromatic amine acetylase, whereas those enzyme fractions catalyzing the acylation of the phosphorylated substrate were inactive with the free amino sugar. It thus appears likely that the activity demonstrated by crude extracts with glucosamine probably reflects the lack of specificity of the enzyme originally identified as an aromatic amine acetylase, since the rate of acetylation of glucosamine is approximately 4% of that found with *p*-nitroaniline as substrate. Hexosamine phosphate *N*-acetylase has been found in extracts of many tissues, including liver, kidney, spleen, cartilage; in a wide variety of molds and fungi; and in several microorganisms. The enzyme has also been purified from extracts of sheep brain (Pattabiraman and Bachhawat, 1961). The reaction is effectively irreversible, owing to the cleavage of the high-energy thiol ester bond of acetyl coenzyme A.

hexosamine 6-phosphate + acetyl coenzyme A →
N-acetylhexosamine 6-phosphate + coenzyme A (2)

Preparations obtained from *Neurospora crassa* acetylate both glucosamine and galactosamine 6-phosphates at comparable rates throughout purification. The significance of the galactosamine phosphate acetylation is not understood at present and may represent a lack of specificity of the enzyme preparation, although it should be pointed out that an acid-stable phosphate ester of galactosamine has been reported to occur in cartilage (Di Stefano, Neuman, and Rouser, 1953). The purified enzyme, hexosamine phosphate *N*-acetylase, is inactive with mannosamine 6-phosphate as a substrate and thus exhibits specificity for the configuration about carbon-2 but no specificity for the configuration at carbon-4. Hexosamine 1-phosphates appear to be inactive with this enzyme, but substrates such as uridine diphosphoglucosamine have not been tested.

C. Kinases

The primary mechanism for the synthesis of glucosamine and, subsequently, galactosamine by both mammalian and microbial systems appears to be the pathway described in Section B, leading to the formation of glucosamine 6-phosphate as the first product having the 2-deoxy-2-aminohexose structure. There are, however, alternate pathways for the formation of both glucosamine 6-phosphate and *N*-acetylglucosamine 6-phosphate which involve kinase activities of a variety of specificities and distributions.

1. Nonspecific Kinases

The first indication that hexosamines could serve as a substrate for enzymes normally involved in hexose activation was the report by Harpur and Quastel (1949) that brain extracts phosphorylate D-glucosamine and D-galactosamine. The identity of the enzymes carrying out these phosphorylations was not resolved, nor were the products of the reactions identified. In another communication (1949a), these authors reported that glucosamine appeared to compete with glucose for brain hexokinase, whereas acetylglucosamine not only was inactive in this system but functioned as a competitive inhibitor. These results were subsequently extended and confirmed during a study of the substrate specificity of brain hexokinase (Sols and Crane, 1954).

The ability of glucosamine to serve as a substrate for glucokinase received additional support in a report of the phosphorylation of glucosamine by partially purified (Grant and Long, 1952) or crystalline (Brown, 1951) yeast hexokinase; in the latter study the product was characterized, by periodate-oxidation methods, as glucosamine 6-phosphate. Glucosamine functions as a glucose antagonist in yeast, and it was suggested that the two sugars compete either for the same site during transport to the interior of the cell or for the hexokinase system (Woodward and Hudson, 1953, Woodward, Cramer, and Hudson, 1953). A similar study measured the effects of various glucose analogues on plant respiration and ion-transport activities; glucosamine was able to interfere with normal energy-yielding pathways which involved glucose as a primary phosphorylation substrate (Stenlid, 1954).

The problem of the transport of glucosamine from the endogenous environment to the interior of cells has been studied with Ehrlich ascites cells (Crane, 1955), and the effect of insulin has also been assayed (Wick *et al.*, 1955). The latter report stated that the site of insulin action is similar for glucosamine and glucose, and that the mechanism of insulin facilitation of glucose utilization may also be operative for glucosamine, since there is increased metabolism of this sugar in the presence of insulin. Several other systems have been described, in which there is competition between glucosamine and glucose, either in transport or in kinase systems. These include the Walker 256 carcinoma (Ball, Wick, and Sanders, 1957), a hexokinase isolated from *Neurospora crassa* (Medina and Nicholas, 1957), kinase preparations of intestinal mucosa (Sols, 1956), and a report that glucosamine is able to exert a Crabtree effect on isolated ascites cells (Günther and Greiling, 1960).

Crude kinase preparations from galactose-adapted *Saccharomyces fragilis* phosphorylate galactosamine (Cardini and Leloir, 1953). The product was identified as the 1-phosphate by the loss of characteristic color in the Elson–Morgan reaction, as well as by the disappearance of reducing sugar. Although these preparations were quite crude, it was suggested that the activity with galactosamine as substrate reflected the lack of specificity of the induced galactokinase. A more recent study confirmed this, since the rates of phosphorylation of galactose and galactosamine were in constant ratio throughout considerable purification of the kinase (Alvarado, 1960).

Galactokinase has been used as the basis for large-scale preparation of galactosamine α-1-phosphate (Wheat and Davidson, 1963), *N*-acetyl galactosamine α-1-phosphate, and uridine diphospho-*N*-acetylgalactosamine (Davidson and Wheat, 1963).

Phosphorylation of both glucosamine and galactosamine to form the respective 6-phosphates was reported to be catalyzed by a hexokinase preparation from *Aspergillus parasiticus,* a chitin-containing mold that produces an extracellular polymer containing exclusively galactosamine residues (Davidson, 1960).

The recent report of the occurrence of amino sugars of the D-manno configuration as constituents of *N*-acetylneuraminic acid and related compounds prompted a study of the ability of mannosamine to act as a substrate for glucokinase preparations. Crystalline yeast hexokinase phosphorylates D-mannosamine to yield an acid-stable ester which was tentatively identified as D-mannosamine 6-phosphate (Jourdian and Roseman, 1960). Further metabolic reactions of this amino sugar have not been reported.

The ability of these systems just indicated to handle the hexosamines as substrates seems to be entirely owing to the nonspecificity of the endogenous hexokinase systems present. There are several reports, however, indicating more specific kinase activities for glucosamine, galactosamine, and the acetylamino sugars as well.

2. Specific Kinases

Schistosoma mansoni contains a kinase which is specific for glucosamine, forming the 6-phosphate ester (Bueding, Ruppender, and MacKinnon, 1954). No further reports on this interesting enzyme have appeared, and it is not known whether this specificity indicates an unusual pathway for subsequent hexosamine metabolism. Carter and Peters (1958) studied glucosamine clearance in dogs and found the rate equal to the glomerular-filtration rate. The phosphorylation of the amino sugar by kidney cortex was examined *in vitro* and found to proceed at twice the rate of that of D-glucose. This is not necessarily an indication of the presence of a specific kinase in kidney, but, more likely, reflects a difference in the permeability and transport into kidney cells of the two sugars.

A hexokinase of *Pseudomonas* has been reported to be active with galactosamine, presumably forming galactosamine 1-phosphate, although the product was not definitively characterized (Klein, 1953).

Several reports have described the direct phosphorylation of *N*-acetylhexosamines. Soodak (1955) indicated that cell-free extracts prepared from glucose-grown *Escherichia coli* 26 can phosphorylate both glucosamine and *N*-acetylglucosamine in the presence of adenosine triphosphate. Similarly, cells grown on lactose or galactose produced active kinases for galactosamine. The product of the galactosamine kinase reaction was not further characterized, and it was not stated whether the 1- or 6-phosphate was formed; the product of the acetylglucosamine kinase reaction was stated to be *N*-acetylglucosamine 6-phosphate.

A more recent report has indicated that the acetylhexosamines are phosphorylated by preparations of kidney, heart, spleen, liver, and brain. Acetylglucosamine and acetylgalactosamine are both substrates but yield the 6-phosphate and the 1-phosphate, respectively. Although definitive data were not obtained in this series of experiments, the nature of the products indicates that a specific kinase is involved for each of the acetylamino sugars (Leloir, Cardini, and Olavarría, 1958). Similar kinase activities have been reported by Asensio and Sols (1958).

The ability of glucosamine to compete with glucose for hexokinase in ascites cells was mentioned previously. Acetylglucosamine does not function similarly in this system. Since these experiments were conducted with whole cells, and the conclusions were based on inhibition of oxygen consumption in the presence of various substrates, it is conceivable that the apparent inability of acetylglucosamine to compete in this system may reflect failure of the sugar to penetrate the cell, prior deacetylation of the sugar at a site removed from that of glucokinase, or specific phosphorylation of the acetylhexosamine substrate.

Extracts of *Lactobacillus bifidus* convert alkyl β-glycosides of *N*-acetylglucosamine to *N*-acetyl-α-glucosamine 1-phosphate in the presence of a phosphate source such as inorganic phosphate. This appears to be a conventional bimolecular displacement reaction, and the suggestion has been offered that a phosphorylase type of mechanism might be involved. This would be similar to maltose phosphorylase (Fitting and Doudoroff, 1952), but different from sucrose or glycogen phosphorylase (Cori and Cori, 1945). This enzyme should not catalyze the exchange of labeled *N*-acetylglucosamine with its 1-phosphate derivative; this reaction, however, has not been studied. These extracts also catalyze phosphorylation of *N*-acetylglucosamine to yield *N*-acetylglucosamine 1-phosphate, but no additional reports have appeared (O'Brien, Glick, and Zilliken, 1960,a).

It is very difficult to evaluate the physiological significance of the various reported kinase activities for the free amino sugars and their acetylated derivatives. The relative lack of specificity of glucokinase for glucosamine, regardless of source, and the similar lack of specificity of galactokinase for galactosamine probably indicate only the discrimination of these enzymes rather than a significant physiological role. Considerable evidence is accumulating, however, which indicates that specific kinases for both the amino sugars and the *N*-acetylamino sugars exist in natural sources. Substrates such as glucosamine or galactosamine can arise by a series of degradative enzymic reactions, and it is possible that they could be salvaged and reutilized exactly as if they had been synthesized *de novo*.

Several structural components of connective tissue are known to consist of alternating *N*-acetylamino sugar and uronic acid residues. The degradation products of these polymers, oligosaccharides with this repeating structure, can ultimately yield the constituent monosaccharides by the action of glucuronidase or glucosaminidase (Meyer, Linker, and Rapport, 1951). Similarly, it is well known that chitin-derived oligosaccharides can be degraded by hexosaminidase to yield free acetylglucosamine. Similar studies have not been carried out with *N*-acetylgalactosamine-containing substrates, since either the requisite oligosaccharides have not been isolated or the presence of the sulfate group has inhibited glycosidase activity. It has been established, however, that relatively highly purified hexosaminidase preparations obtained from a variety of sources hydrolyze both *N*-acetyl-β-glucosaminides and *N*-acetyl-β-galactosaminides (Woollen, Walker, and Heyworth, 1961). Thus, it is likely that oligosaccharides which contain galactosamine residues could also yield the free *N*-acetylamino sugar. A wide variety of naturally occurring oligosaccharides present in milk contain *N*-acetylglucosamine residues that can be liberated by glycosidase action. Thus, significant quantities of the free *N*-acetylamino sugars and perhaps of the amino sugars themselves (enzymic deacylations will be discussed later) are likely to be formed, and the kinases in question probably exert a physiologically significant role under rather specific conditions. The major pathway of hexosamine synthesis and utilization, however, undoubtedly occurs via the intermediacy of fructose 6-phosphate.

D. Mutases

The ultimate conversion of the acetylated amino sugar derivatives to the structures in which they are found in natural systems wherein they are always linked in glycosidic bonds to other residues is effected through a uridine diphospho sugar derivative with a structure analogous to uridine diphosphoglucose. The synthesis of these UDP derivatives is effected by reaction between uridine triphosphate (UTP) and the respective sugar 1-phosphate, with liberation of inorganic pyrophosphate. The systems are reversible, and the enzymes are named for the reverse reaction, such as uridine-diphospho-*N*-acetylglucosamine pyrophosphorylase. The equilibrium is shifted in the synthetic direction by the irreversible action of inorganic pyrophosphatase.

Phosphoglucomutase acts on D-glucosamine 6-phosphate to catalyze the formation of an equilibrium mixture of the 6- and 1-phosphates; the properties of this system are quite similar to those found with glucose 6-phosphate as substrate (Brown, 1953; Roseman, 1956). Although this reaction does not appear to be catalyzed by a specific enzyme, subsequent reaction of the glucosamine 1-phosphate with uridine triphosphate is possible and will be discussed later.

The conversion of *N*-acetylglucosamine 6-phosphate into *N*-acetylglucosamine 1-phosphate has been studied in extracts of *Neurospora crassa* (Reissig, 1956) and is as follows:

$$N\text{-acetylglucosamine 6-phosphate} + \text{phospho-enzyme} \rightleftharpoons N\text{-acetylglucosamine 1,6-diphosphate} + \text{enzyme} \quad (3)$$

$$N\text{-acetylglucosamine 1,6-diphosphate} + \text{enzyme} \rightleftharpoons N\text{-acetylglucosamine 1-phosphate} + \text{phospho-enzyme} \quad (4)$$

Whereas a similar mutase activity has been reported to be catalyzed by phosphoglucomutase preparations (Leloir and Cardini, 1953), the report by Reissig (1956) indicates that the *N*-acetylglucosamine phosphate mutase is a specific enzyme. The ratio of phosphoglucomutase to phospho-*N*-acetylglucosamine mutase activity in the various fractions obtained varied approximately 2000-fold, strongly suggesting that different proteins were involved. The composition of the equilibrium mixture was similar to that obtained with the glucose substrates in that it contained 86% of the 6-phosphate. The enzyme required either glucose 1,6-diphosphate or *N*-acetylglucosamine 1,6-diphosphate for activity, indicating that a phospho–enzyme complex is formed, and thus the mechanism is analogous to that of phosphoglucomutase. Formation of *N*-acetylglucosamine diphosphate by the enzyme was demonstrated, and the reversal of this catalyzed the formation of glucose diphosphate from *N*-acetylglucosamine diphosphate. Under the conditions studied, it was not possible to decide whether the α- or β-*N*-acetylglucosamine 1-phosphate was the substrate utilized. On the basis of relative-stability studies, it was suggested that the inactive sugar was the β isomer. This has subsequently been confirmed both by synthesis and by conversion of the *N*-acetyl-α-glucosamine 1-phosphate to UDP-*N*-acetylglucosamine.

Similar mutase activities have also been identified in extracts from several animal sources, but were not purified, so the existence of a specific mutase in mammalian systems has not been confirmed, although its presence seems quite likely.

E. Synthesis and Reactions of UDP Sugars

1. UDP-*N*-ACETYLGLUCOSAMINE

The conjugated nucleotide sugar, UDP-*N*-acetylglucosamine, was first isolated from baker's yeast approximately 10 years ago (Cabib, Leloir, and Cardini, 1953). The structure of this material was deduced from the release of *N*-acetylamino sugar after mild acid hydrolysis; identification of the nucleotide portion as UDP; the failure of the complex to give any detectable reducing or *N*-acetylhexosamine value; and electrometric-titration behavior. Based on these data, it was concluded that the UDP-*N*-acetylglucosamine structure was similar to that found in uridine diphosphoglucose.

Since that time, the role of these derivatives in transfer reactions and in the synthesis of glycosidically linked compounds has prompted a study of the nucleotide pool present in various biological systems. UDP-*N*-acetylglucosamine has been detected in mung-bean seedlings (Solms and Hassid, 1957); liver (Smith and Mills, 1954); cell nuclei (Osawa, Allfrey, and Mirsky, 1957); *Staphylococcus aureus* (Ito, Ishimoto, and Saito, 1958); group-A hemolytic streptococci (Cifonelli and Dorfman, 1957); and *Neurospora crassa* (Smith and Wheat, 1960). It appears that this sugar derivative is ubiquitous in natural sources and claims a central role in the synthesis of not only *N*-acetylglucosaminides but *N*-acetylgalactosamine-containing polymers and cell-wall polysaccharides, as well.

The synthesis of UDP-*N*-acetylglucosamine is catalyzed by a pyrophosphorylase acting on UTP in the presence of *N*-acetyl-α-glucosamine 1-phosphate:

$$\text{UTP} + N\text{-acetyl-}\alpha\text{-glucosamine 1-phosphate} \rightleftharpoons \text{UDP-}N\text{-acetylglucosamine} + \text{inorganic pyrophosphate} \quad (5)$$

The enzyme catalyzing this reaction appears to be independent of UDP-glucose pyrophosphorylase, although it has not been extensively studied.

A similar enzyme isolated from mast cells has been reported to catalyze the formation of uridine-diphospho-*N*-glucosamine from UTP and α-D-glucosamine 1-phosphate (Silbert and Brown, 1961).

The synthetic reaction has also been studied in yeast extracts (Glaser and Brown, 1955). The reverse reaction, the formation of UTP, is catalyzed by liver extracts in the presence of UDP-*N*-acetylglucosamine and inorganic pyrophosphate (Smith and Mills, 1954). Similar activities were reported to be present in extracts of rat-liver nuclei and yeast; the products were identified after preliminary separation by ion-exchange chromatography (Maley, Maley, and Lardy, 1956).

During studies of the specificity of the UDP-*N*-acetylglucosamine pyrophosphorylase reaction, it was found that glucosamine 1-phosphate could be converted to UDP-glucosamine in the presence of UTP and a cell-free extract of yeast. It is not known whether formation of this nucleotide sugar is of biological significance, although it is conceivable that this product could function as an intermediate in heparin synthesis or as a precursor for the formation of galactosaminans via UDP-galactosamine.

2. Transfer Reactions Involving UDP-*N*-acetylglucosamine

The transfer of *N*-acetylglucosamine from UDP-*N*-acetylglucosamine to chemically prepared chitodextrin acceptors catalyzed by extracts of *Neurospora crassa* was reported by Glaser and Brown (1957). The product formed was tentatively identified as chitin by its solubility characteristics and repeating structure. There were several interesting features of this enzyme system, including the apparent requirement for an activator, in this case, *N*-acetylglucosamine itself. Stimulations as large as tenfold were observed under optimal conditions, and studies with carbon-14-labeled substrates indicated that the *N*-acetylglucosamine that functioned as activator was not incorporated into the synthesized polymer, nor could *N,N′*-diacetylchitobiose inhibit the transfer reaction or serve to trap radioactivity from carbon-14-labeled UDP-*N*-acetyl-glucosamine. *N*-Acetylgalactosamine was unable to function as an activator in this system. Data such as these suggested that simple oligosaccharides did not function as intermediates in the transfer reaction, and the mechanism of activation by the free *N*-acetylglucosamine remains obscure.

The mechanism of inversion of the anomeric center during this transfer process is not understood. The UDP-*N*-acetylglucosamine is formed exclusively from *N*-acetyl-α-D-glucosamine 1-phosphate and is, therefore, α-linked at the glycosidic carbon, whereas synthesized chitin is exclusively β-linked. Displacement by acceptor substrate in a conventional bimolecular reaction would lead to inversion of the anomeric center; prior transfer to some intermediate such as a diacetyltrehalosamine type of compound may be required, with the second transfer reaction effecting the actual inversion. The mechanism of this epimerization probably also applies to the synthesis of hyaluronic acid, chondroitin sulfate, and the like.

3. UDP-*N*-acetylglucosamine 4′-epimerase

The original isolates of UDP-*N*-acetylglucosamine obtained from mammalian liver were found to contain, in addition to this nucleotide, a significant proportion of a second amino sugar nucleotide which was subsequently identified as UDP-*N*-acetylgalactosamine (Pontis [Videla], 1955). Leloir (1956) suggested that the UDP-*N*-acetylgalactosamine was derived from the corresponding glucosamine derivative by an epimerase type of reaction analogous to that operative in the glucose–galactose interconversion catalyzed by UDP-glucose 4′-epimerase.

$$\text{UDP-}N\text{-acetylglucosamine} \xrightleftharpoons[]{\substack{\text{catalytic}\\ \text{nicotinamide-adenine}\\ \text{dinucleotide}\\ \text{(oxidized)}}} \text{UDP-}N\text{-acetylgalactosamine} \quad (6)$$

Extracts of rat liver were reported to catalyze the conversion of the nucleotide-linked *N*-acetylglucosamine, not to UDP-*N*-acetylgalactosamine but, rather, to free *N*-acetylgalactosamine (Cardini and Leloir, 1957). Subsequent studies, however, have demonstrated that the product of this reaction was *N*-acetylmannosamine and not *N*-acetylgalactosamine (Comb and Roseman, 1958a). The formation of *N*-acetylmannosamine probably takes place with the help of a mechanism which will be discussed later.

The epimerization reaction originally suggested by Leloir has also, however, been described by Glaser (1959,a). He reported that partially purified extracts obtained from *Bacillus subtilis* contained an epimerase which was able to catalyze the interconversion of the *N*-acetylglucosamine and *N*-acetylgalactosamine nucleotides. The activity of this enzyme could be completely separated from comparable activities against UDP-glucose as substrate and, therefore, represents a specific epimerase. It should be noted that the strain of *Bacillus subtilis* utilized in this study was known to form polymeric material which contained bound galactosamine; galactosamine polymers have also been isolated from mold sources (Distler and Roseman, 1960). A similar reaction was catalyzed by liver extracts although not resolved from UDP-glucose 4′-epimerase.

A purified UDP-glucose 4′-epimerase preparation obtained from yeast also catalyzed the *N*-acetylhexosamine epimerization, but no separation of the activities against the hexose or hexosamine substrates was described (Maley and Maley, 1959). Skin extracts contain UDP-acetylglucosamine 4-epimerase but are inactive with UDP-glucose as substrate, thus strengthening the probability that UDP-glucose and UDP-*N*-acetylglucosamine epimerase activities are catalyzed by separate protein entities (Jacobson and Davidson, 1963).

Epimerization of thymidine diphosphoglucosamine and *N*-acetylglucosamine to form the respective galactosamine derivatives has been reported to be catalyzed by extracts of *Pseudomonas aeruginosa* (Kornfeld and Glaser, 1962).

The mechanism of these reactions has not been intensively studied, but appears to be similar to that suggested for UDP-glucose 4′-epimerase (de Robichon-Szulmajster, 1961), although the role of nicotinamide-adenine dinucleotide (oxidized) is still obscure (Jacobson and Davidson, 1963).

Subsequent reactions of the UDP-*N*-acetylgalactosamine have not been described, although it is reasonable to assume that a nucleotide of this type functions in chondroitin sulfate synthesis, in the synthesis of other amino sugars with the D-*galacto* configuration, and in the synthesis of cell-wall structures of bacteria.

The ability of kinases from various sources to catalyze the formation of galactosamine 1-phosphate and *N*-acetylgalactosamine 1-phosphate raises some question as to the possibility of a specific pyrophosphorylase or uridyl transferase for these sugars which would lead to the direct formation of the UDP-galactosamine derivatives. Such enzymes have not as yet been described, although it is reasonable to assume that both exist.

4. Other Reactions Involving UDP-*N*-acetylglucosamine or UDP-*N*-acetylgalactosamine

Strominger (1955) reported the isolation of two unusual nucleotide-linked hexosamine derivatives: UDP-*N*-acetylglucosamine phosphate and UDP-*N*-acetylgalactosamine sulfate. A more detailed report has recently appeared (Strominger, 1962). The former compound apparently arises via an isolation artifact, and the original nucleotide has the following structure: uridine diphosphate *N*-acetylglucosamine 6-phospho-1-galactose (Gabriel and Ashwell, 1962; Suzuki, 1962). The latter nucleotide rapidly incorporated sulfate *in vivo,* but transfer of sulfate from phosphoadenosine phosphosulfate to UDP-*N*-acetylgalactosamine could not be demonstrated *in vitro*. Neither the transfer of the hexosamine sulfate to acceptor substrates nor any other reactions for this compound have been described.

The reaction of UDP-*N*-acetylglucosamine to form a highly fluorescent compound of unknown structure but still containing the *N*-acetylhexosamine carbon chain has been described to be catalyzed by extracts of a Vi antigen-producing strain of *Escherichia freundii* (Wheat, 1956). Several strains of *Escherichia coli* and a Vi antigen-producing *Paracolobactrum ballerup* yielded inactive extracts. Although this reaction, which is presumably an oxidation, has not been further elucidated, it should be noted that a sugar contained in the Vi antigen molecule has been identified as 2-amino-2-deoxy-D-galacturonic acid (Heyns *et al.*, 1959).

5. Muramic Acid Synthesis

A considerable advance in the understanding of microbial cell-wall synthesis and the mechanism of action of antibiotics was provided by the pioneering work of Park (1952,a), who described the accumulation of a series of unusual nucleotidyl hexosamine-containing compounds produced by *Staphylococcus aureus* allowed to metabolize in the presence of penicillin. Structural studies on these compounds indicated that they contained the conventional UDP-sugar type of structure, but that the amino sugar was neither glucosamine nor galactosamine (see Volume I, Chapter 4). In addition, the derivatives contained covalently bound peptide fragments whose composition appeared to reflect the amino acid composition of the bacterial cell wall. The structure of the amino sugar, muramic acid, a constituent of virtually all gram-positive bacterial cell walls, was resolved by Strange and Kent (1959) and it is discussed in detail in Volume I, Chapter 2, of this book.

Muramic acid has also recently been isolated and identified from cell walls of *Chromobacterium violaceum,* a gram-negative organism (Wheat and Rollins, 1962). The possible occurrence of this material in structural components of higher organisms has not been investigated.

The incorporation of glucose carbon directly into muramic acid and the incorporation of C^{14}-labeled *N*-acetylglucosaminides into the muramic acid structure have been demonstrated (O'Brien, Glick, and Zilliken, 1960). The isolation from cell walls of protein-bound muramic acid which contains a phosphate group attached to the sugar residue has also been reported (Ågren and DeVerdier, 1958). The detailed mechanisms involved in this transformation are still unknown, however.

Extracts of several bacterial species were reported to catalyze a condensation reaction between UDP-*N*-acetylglucosamine and phosphoenol pyruvate (Strominger, 1958). The resulting compound was thought to be a 3-substituted enol ether because of its characteristic behavior in the Morgan–Elson color reaction for acetylamino sugars. The conversion of this compound to muramic acid, a step which requires a reduction, has not been demonstrated, and neither has the net synthesis of the enol ether or of muramic acid been reported. Thus, the conversion of UDP-*N*-acetylglucosamine and an appropriate 3-carbon fragment to muramic acid remains unsubstantiated, and it is possible that this condensation takes place at the sugar-phosphate level.

F. Neuraminic Acid Synthesis

The 9-carbon structure of muramic acid which contains the building blocks of *N*-acetylhexosamine and pyruvate is mirrored, to a certain extent, in the structures of the sialic acids. The most widely distributed compound of this series, *N*-acetylneuraminic acid, arises as the result of an aldol type of condensation between the methyl carbon of pyruvate and the carbonyl carbon of an acetylamino sugar.

The discovery of an aldolase type of enzyme from *Vibrio cholerae* (Heimer and Meyer, 1956) permitted the ultimate resolution of the structure of *N*-acetylneuraminic acid. The key observation was made by Comb and Roseman (1958), when they identified the hexosamine moiety of *N*-acetylneuraminic acid as *N*-acetylmannosamine (2-acetamido-2-deoxymannose) rather than *N*-acetylglucosamine and demonstrated that an aldol type of condensation between the methyl carbon of pyruvate and C-1 of *N*-acetylmannosamine yielded *N*-acetylneuraminic acid. These results were confirmed by chemical and synthetic studies (Kuhn and Brossmer, 1958; Carroll and Cornforth, 1960).

1. *N*-Acetylglucosamine-6-phosphate 2-epimerase

The *N*-acetylmannosamine structure may arise as a result of the enzymic epimerization of *N*-acetylglucosamine 6-phosphate. This reaction is catalyzed by extracts of *Escherichia coli* (Roseman, Hayes, and Ghosh, 1960). Chemical studies on the *N*-acetylamino sugars have shown ready epimerization at pH 11. The enzymic transformation takes place at pH 7.2 and may involve some type of proton displacement. In contrast to several other carbohydrate epimerizations, there was no demonstrated requirement for a pyridine nucleotide cofactor. Active preparations have also been obtained from liver extracts.

2. *N*-Acetylglucosamine 2-epimerase

Incubation of UDP-*N*-acetylglucosamine with crude preparations of mammalian liver gave rise to UDP and an acetylhexosamine originally thought to be *N*-acetylgalactosamine (Cardini and Leloir, 1957) but subsequently shown to be *N*-acetylmannosamine (Comb and Roseman, 1958a). Although the pathway for this conversion has not been exactly ascertained, recent studies suggest that the initial reaction involved cleavage of the sugar nucleotide to UDP and *N*-acetylglucosamine followed by epimerization of the free sugar (Ghosh and Roseman, 1962). *N*-Glycolylglucosamine is also a substrate. This unusual reaction is characterized by a highly specific requirement for catalytic quantities of ATP. The adenine nucleotide is inactive as a substrate. This suggests an effect of ATP on enzyme conformation, but no further studies have been reported.

3. *N*-Acetylmannosamine Kinase

Activation of free *N*-acetylmannosamine to form the 6-phosphate derivative is carried out by a kinase which appears to be relatively specific for this substrate. Active preparations have been obtained from liver and from bovine submaxillary gland (Warren and Felsenfeld, 1961; Ghosh and Roseman, 1962). This enzyme appears to be activated by potassium ions and has the conventional divalent-cation requirement.

4. *N*-Acetylmannosamine-6-phosphate-phosphoenolpyruvate Aldolase

The formation of the characteristic neuraminic acid structure from *N*-acetylmannosamine 6-phosphate involves an aldol type of condensation of that sugar and phosphoenolpyruvate. This reaction is catalyzed by enzyme preparations from liver, *Escherichia coli,* and bovine submaxillary gland (Roseman *et al.,* 1961; Warren and Felsenfeld, 1961a, 1962). The aldolase appears to require a sulfhydryl agent, as well as Mg^{++}, for optimal activity, and demonstration of the net reaction is difficult unless considerable precaution is taken in preparation of the extracts. The equilibrium constant is largely in the synthetic direction. The reaction is depicted as follows:

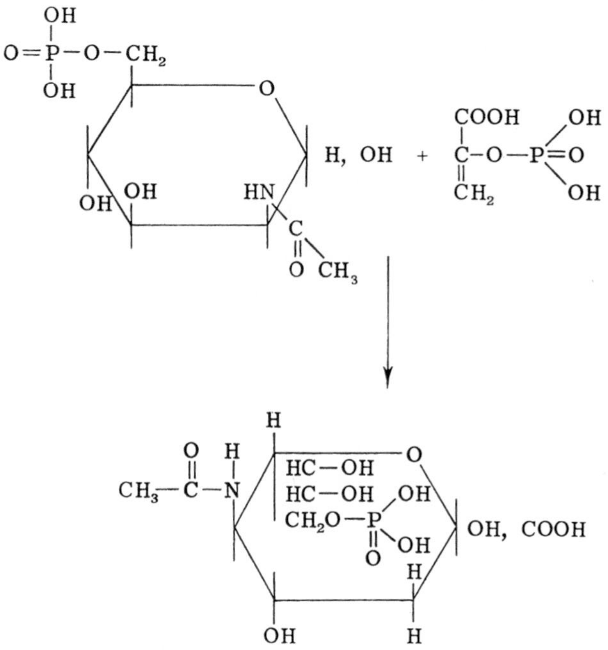

5. *N*-Acetylneuraminic Acid-9-phosphate Phosphatase

The final step in *N*-acetylneuraminic acid synthesis appears to be the dephosphorylation of *N*-acetylneuraminic acid 9-phosphate in a simple hydrolytic cleavage (Warren and Felsenfeld, 1962). The system requires Mg^{++}, but the substrate specificity has not been extensively studied. Whether this enzyme will fall into the class of specific phosphatases and thus exert a metabolic control function is not known at present.

The net synthesis of *N*-acetylneuraminic acid from *N*-acetylmannosamine may be written as follows:

N-acetylmannosamine + ATP → *N*-acetylmannosamine 6-phosphate + ADP (7)

N-acetylmannosamine 6-phosphate + phosphoenolpyruvate + H_2O →
N-acetylneuraminic acid 9-phosphate + pyruvate + phosphate (8)

N-acetylneuraminic acid 9-phosphate + H_2O →
N-acetylneuraminic acid + phosphate (9)

Sum:
N-acetylmannosamine + phosphoenolpyruvate + ATP + $2H_2O$ →
N-acetylneuraminic acid + 2-phosphate + ADP (10)

6. *N*-Acetylmannosamine-phosphoenolpyruvate Aldolase

A reaction similar to the one just mentioned but utilizing the free sugar instead of its phosphorylated derivative is catalyzed by extracts of *Neisseria meningitidis* (Warren and Blacklow, 1962):

N-acetylmannosamine + phosphoenolpyruvate $\xrightarrow{Mn^{++}}$
N-acetylneuraminic acid + inorganic phosphate (11)

The reaction appears to be highly specific for both substrates and was not detectably reversible.

7. Cytidine 5′-phosphoneuraminic Acids

The activation of the neuraminic acid structure prior to its transfer to glycoproteins, complex lipids, and the like is apparently mediated through cytidine monophosphate-*N*-acetylneuraminic acid, a compound first described by Comb, Shimizu, and Roseman (1959). The synthesis of this complex nucleotide has been studied in extracts of porcine submaxillary gland and *Neisseria meningitidis* (Roseman, 1962; Warren and Blacklow, 1962), and the net reaction is as follows:

cytidine triphosphate + *N*-acetylneuraminic acid →
cytidine monophosphate-*N*-acetylneuraminic acid + inorganic pyrophosphate (12)

Studies on the nature of the linkage between the cytidylic acid moiety and the sugar indicate it to be ketosidic (to carbon-2 of the *N*-acetylneuraminic acid), but configuration has not been established. *N*-Glycolylneuraminic acid is active as a substrate for the mammalian enzyme system but inactive with the bacterial preparation. The possibility of separate enzymes for the various forms of neuraminic acid has not been resolved. The bacterial system is stated to be irreversible, and, in fact,

N-acetylneuraminic acid-dependent P^{32}-pyrophosphate exchange into cytidine triphosphate could not be demonstrated. Thus, this reaction appears to differ from the formation of other sugar nucleotides, since they exist as diphospho derivatives and are formed reversibly; analogous monophosphate nucleotide derivatives involving fatty acids or amino acids (Berg and Newton, 1956; Berg, 1958) exhibit characteristic pyrophosphate exchange and have equilibria strongly in favor of the nucleotide triphosphate.

8. Complex Neuraminic Acid Derivatives

The occurrence of neuraminic acid in a wide variety of natural polymers has been well documented. Neuraminic acid-linked oligosaccharides have been obtained from cow colostrum (Heimer and Meyer, 1958), mammary glands of lactating rats (Trucco and Caputto, 1954), and guinea-pig mammary glands and colostrum (Heyworth and Bacon, 1957); in addition, an extracellular bacterial product obtained from *Escherichia coli* K235 has been identified as a polymer of *N*-acetylneuraminic acid (Barry, 1958). A variety of nucleotide-linked neuraminic acid-containing compounds, some with bound peptide fragments, have been isolated from *Escherichia coli* (O'Brien and Zilliken, 1959), and nucleotide-linked sialic acid oligosaccharides have been isolated from sheep colostrum (Jourdian, Shimizu, and Roseman, 1961). Extracts of *Escherichia coli* K235 apparently convert this labile nucleotide to an alcohol-insoluble product which has not been further identified (Comb *et al.*, 1960).

9. *N*-Glycolyl- and *O,N*-Diacetylneuraminic Acids

Neuraminic acid derivatives are known in which either the nitrogen of the amino sugar is substituted by a group other than acetate or one of the hydroxyls in the chain is acetylated. The biosynthesis of *N*-glycolylneuraminic acid or of *O,N*-diacetylneuraminic acid has not been described, although the reversible cleavage of *N*-glycolylneuraminic acid is catalyzed by enzyme preparations which are also able to cleave the *N*-acetyl derivative (Jourdian and Roseman, 1960).

Mannosamine 6-phosphate may be synthesized by direct phosphorylation of mannosamine but does not function as a substrate for the hexosamine phosphate *N*-acetylase system.

G. *Lactobacillus bifidus* Factors

The occurrence in milk of a family of nitrogen-containing reducing substances has been known for a number of years (see Volume I, Chapter 3). The total fraction present represents approximately 0.4% of the weight, which is a considerable percentage of the total solid. These compounds may be separated into a dialyzable fraction which contains several oligosaccharides similar to those already mentioned and a non-dialyzable fraction which contains, in addition to neutral *N*-acetylhexosamine-containing oligosaccharides, neuraminic acid-containing fragments, as well (Zilliken, Braun, and György, 1955, 1956).

These oligosaccharides are not contained to any significant degree in bovine milk, although compounds of similar structure have also been isolated from epithelial secretions (see Chapters 22, 26, 40). Chemical analyses indicated the presence of *N*-acetylneuraminic acid, *N*-acetylglucosamine, glucose, galactose, and fucose.

These complex sugars function as growth factors for *Lactobacillus bifidus,* a normal inhabitant of the intestinal flora of infants which may be partially responsible for the protection of newborns against attack by certain enteric organisms (György, Norris, and Rose, 1954). Growth of the organism in the absence of these oligosaccharides yields cellular structures which demonstrate marked morphological alterations and have bizarre shapes.

There is relatively little information available about the detailed mode of biosynthesis of these compounds. Resting cells of *Lactobacillus bifidus* catalyze the synthesis of *N*-acetyllactosamine in a medium containing lactose and *N*-acetylglucosamine. This reaction is a simple transglycosidation in which the galactose residue is transferred to the amino sugar acceptor. Similar synthetic pathways were demonstrated in cell-free extracts of *Lactobacillus bifidus,* mammary gland, liver, and kidney (Glick *et al.,* 1960). Extracts of *Lactobacillus bifidus* produced a mixture of β-D-1 → 4 and β-D-1 → 6-linked oligosaccharides. Crude preparations of testicular hyaluronidase or of yeast lactase catalyze similar transglycosidase reactions, yielding 3-*O*-β-D-linked and 6-*O*-β-D-linked sugars, respectively. Partial hydrolysis studies on isolated oligosaccharides revealed that cleavage of the *N*-acetylhexosamine moiety from such compounds rendered them completely inactive as growth factors. It could also be demonstrated that relatively simple structures, such as *N*-acetylglucosamine, *N*-acetylgalactosamine, and even ammonium ion were able to provide growth-stimulating activity when present at very high concentrations. The structural specificities involved in growth-factor activity apparently resided in the configuration at the anomeric center of the *N*-acetylhexosamine and the position of linkage of the various sugar components. Thus, 3-*O*-β-D-galactosyl-*N*-acetylglucosamine was inactive as a growth factor for *Lactobacillus bifidus,* whereas the 4-*O*-β-analogue was active. Alkyl β-glycosides (α-glycosides are inactive) of *N*-acetylglucosamine possess growth-factor activity, and it is possible that the ability of such compounds to permeate the cell membrane provides the basis for their biological role. A transport mechanism might facilitate entry of these oligosaccharides into the cell so that they could function as precursors of cell-wall material.

N-Acetylglucosamine functions as a precursor of cell-wall muramic acid, and therefore the organism may be deficient in its ability to synthesize *N*-acetylglucosamine 1-phosphate. The hexosamine is apparently required by the cell in the glycosyl form where the energy required to form glycosidic bonds pre-exists. The cleavage of these alkyl glycosides by a type of displacement yielded *N*-acetylglucosamine 1-phosphate in a reaction which did not require a high-energy source; thus, the conversion of derivatives of *N*-acetylglucosamine to UDP-*N*-acetylglucosamine and, subsequently, to cell-wall muramic acid may be envisioned. No report has appeared on the possible enzymic defect which appears to exist with regard to hexosamine biosynthesis and activation in this organism. Although the gross symptom appears to be an inability of the organism to provide *N*-acetylhexosamine phosphate for muramic acid synthesis, this block may occur at the fructose-phosphate glutamine transamidase level, the hexosamine-phosphate acetylase level, or the *N*-acetylhexosamine-phosphate mutase level. It is also possible that none of these enzymes are defective and that the problem resides in the inability of the cell to concentrate or transport the requisite materials and make them available for subsequent enzymic utilization (Kuhn, Gauhe, and Baer, 1954; Glick *et al.*, 1960).

The ability of hexosamines to act in glycosyl transfer reactions as donors or acceptors is not limited to the system just discussed, but is also exhibited by hyaluronidase (Weissmann, 1955) and levan sucrase (Hestrin and Avigad, 1958; Srinivasan and Quastel, 1958). Levan sucrase is able to transfer the fructose moiety of sucrose to *N*-acetylhexosamine and to incorporate the resulting structure into polymeric material. The role of this pathway is unknown at the present. Transfer reactions of this type are also catalyzed by several galactosidases obtained from yeast and from a trichomonad, resulting in the synthesis of *N*-acetylgalactosamine-containing oligosaccharides. These reactions may be significant for the biosynthesis of growth factors for *Lactobacillus bifidus* but probably have little relation to the mechanism of heteropolysaccharide synthesis.

H. Amino Sugars Other than Glucosamine or Galactosamine

A large number of naturally occurring amino sugars in addition to glucosamine and galactosamine have been reported as constituents of antibiotics, cell-wall materials, lipopolysaccharides, and the like (Davies,

1960) (see Volume I, Chapters 5, 9, 15). Whereas the majority of these compounds has been isolated from bacteria and fungi, corresponding mammalian sources, such as cell-wall and epidermal or keratinous structures, have not been sufficiently investigated to eliminate the possibility of finding such sugars in these loci, as well.

In one or two instances, the carbon chain of the amino sugars has been demonstrated to arise directly from glucose, but the details of the biosynthetic pathways are generally unknown at the present time (Hunter and Hockenhull, 1955). Synthesis of methylpentosamines, such as D-fucosamine, probably follows a pathway similar to that involved in D-fucose synthesis; in general, inversions of the carbon chain are quite unlikely. Attention should be called to the recent report of the occurrence of talosamine in preparations of chondroitin sulfate obtained from cartilage (Heyworth, Perkins, and Walker, 1961). The isolation of this sugar followed prior treatment of the chondroitin sulfate with hot alkali, and the confirmation of this isolation requires procedures in which such drastic conditions have been avoided. It is probably conservative to anticipate that still additional compounds which have the general structure of 2-amino-2-deoxy aldoses will be found in natural sources. The number and variation of other amino sugar structures is very large, especially when methylpentose dideoxy and trideoxy sugar backbones can be utilized to provide the basic structure. These might be characterized as cationic reducing compounds giving no color in the Elson–Morgan hexosamine reaction (Wheat and Rollins, 1962).

I. Summary of Anabolic Pathways of Amino Sugar Metabolism

The general summary of the anabolic pathways involved in amino sugar metabolism is presented in Fig. 2. There has been considerable emphasis in recent years on the operation of control mechanisms for the establishment of enzyme activities in both reconstructed and *in vivo* systems, but no such experimentation has been carried out with the hexosamine-metabolizing enzyme systems. Two reactions may serve as control points: the first would be the irreversible amination of fructose phosphate to yield glucosamine phosphate, with the hexose no longer available for conventional glycolytic pathways; and the second would be the formation of UDP-*N*-acetylglucosamine, a reaction which, although theoretically reversible, is pulled in the synthetic direction by the ever-present inorganic pyrophosphatase. Since the synthetic reactions involved in heteropolymer synthesis have not been completely elucidated, it is impossible at present to identify the level at which controls are operative.

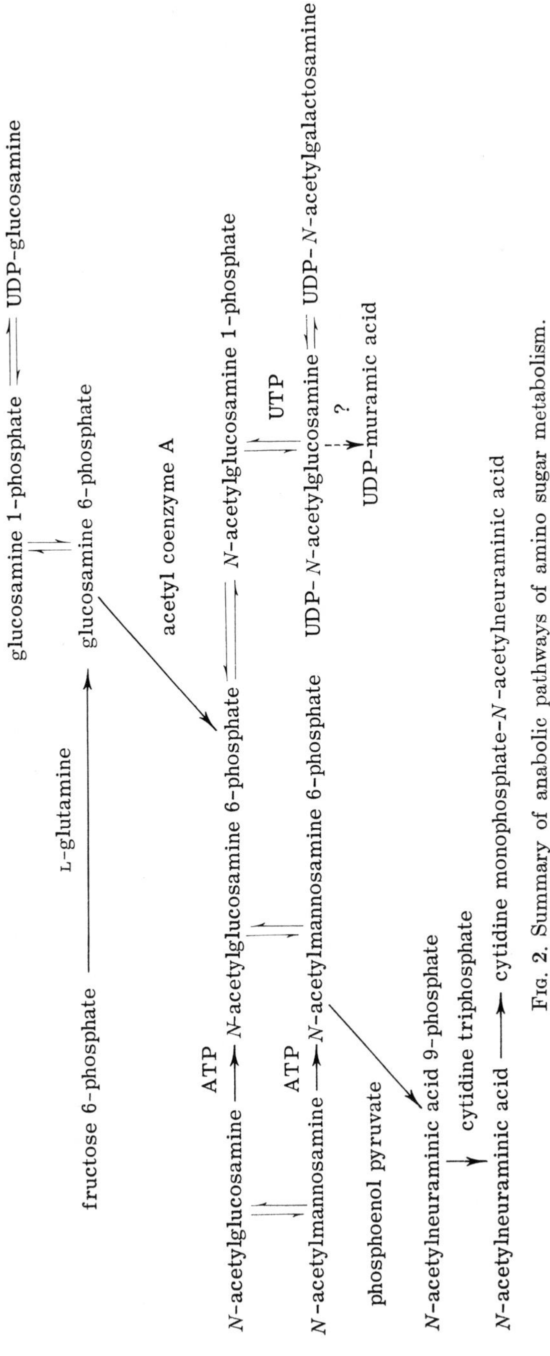

FIG. 2. Summary of anabolic pathways of amino sugar metabolism.

II. Pathways of Degradation

A. *In Vivo* Effects and Reactions

The clarification of the structure of glucosamine as that of an amino aldose led biologists to assume that this material occupied a position intermediate between carbohydrates and proteins. Experimentation was carried out to ascertain whether ingested amino sugar could function as a glycogenetic substance, but the weight of liver glycogen was not significantly increased (Fabian, 1899; Cathcart, 1903). Glucosamine ingestion did not give rise to an increased glucose output in the urine of diabetics. However, a considerable amount of the amino sugar could be recovered from the urine of animals fed glucosamine, and normal humans were able to utilize a significant amount of the amino sugar without the appearance of any in the urine (Meyer, 1907). These early studies indicated that the mode of utilization of glucosamine was likely to be different from that of glucose, the two sugars were probably not in equilibrium in the mammalian organisms, and there did not seem to be an active pathway for the active reabsorption of glucosamine in the renal tubules.

Biological effects of ingested amino sugar were described as early as 1932 (Zummo, 1932). The feeding of glucosamine to pigeons resulted in a rather unusual hypometabolic state with subsequent recovery (Zummo, 1932a). The reason for this was not understood and has not been clarified to date. The ability of glucosamine to function as a precursor of ammonia in brain has been described (Walshe, DeCarli and Davidson, 1958), however, and it is possible that the quantities fed to the animals under study in the early experiments were sufficient to cause either hepatic or cerebral coma.

Studies on the fate of glucosamine in whole animals revealed that there was some possibility for conversion to glucose and that glucosamine did have a marked effect on insulin hypoglycemia (Moschini, 1924). These results were extended and confirmed in a series of papers in which the fate and distribution of glucosamine among various tissues and its possible role as a glycogen precursor were examined (Kawabe, 1934,a,b; Yositake, 1939,a).

Rose and Fierke, in their systematic study of the nitrogen requirements of man, demonstrated that glucosamine was a nonessential dietary component (1942). Quantitative balance studies on the excretion and the absorption of glucosamine indicated that approximately 15% of ingested amino sugar is excreted directly, with absorption from the intestine being very incomplete. The hexosamine was compared with amino acids for its ability to function as a carbon and nitrogen source for protein and was found to be inferior to most of the amino acids studied, although there was some utilization of the amino sugar (Bergfeld and Kapfhammer, 1944). The effect of glucosamine present in synthetic liquid diets on the growth of laboratory animals has been studied (Winitz, Birnbaum, and Greenstein, 1957). Surprisingly enough, it was found that high levels of glucosamine inhibited dietary intake by these animals so that there was an apparent cessation of growth. The reason for the refusal of the animals to ingest the diet is not known, but may be related to the high level of ammonia production that resulted.

B. Effects of Amino Sugars in Tissue Cultures

Studies on the *in vitro* action of glucosamine on the nutrition and mitotic activity of cell cultures have been carried out. Glucosamine reduced the mitotic index in cultures of embryonic chicken-heart cells but was far less effective in this capacity than was 2-deoxyglucose (Ely, Tull, and Schanen, 1953). A similar study on the effect of glucosamine on epidermal mitotic activity revealed that in the presence of glucose there was a slight inhibition of mitosis, but, in the absence of glucose, glucosamine exerted a stimulatory effect. In these latter studies, the inhibition could be overcome by the addition of adenosine triphosphate to the culture medium (Katayama, 1957). Apparently, the amino sugar is competing for hexokinase that would normally phosphorylate glucose, and the resulting inhibition can be released by sufficient levels of glucose. Since the hexosamine is not nearly so effective as 2-deoxyglucose, it may be concluded that the resulting hexosamine phosphate is subsequently metabolized, and thus the cell can utilize the amino sugar, whereas it is unable to utilize 2-deoxyglucose 6-phosphate. Adenosine triphosphate may cause extracellular phosphorylation of the hexosamine to yield a product which could not permeate the cell, or it may form a salt with the cationic sugar which would also not be permeable to the cellular membrane.

A summary of the physiological and nutritional studies indicates that glucosamine is: (i) incompletely absorbed from the intestine; (ii) may be utilized without substantial increases in glycogen; (iii) is readily cleared by the kidney; (iv) does not function as a good source of protein nitrogen; and (v) is a dispensable dietary constituent, and is rejected when present in high concentrations in synthetic diets. Comparable studies have not been carried out with galactosamine.

C. Microbial Degradations

The metabolic behavior of glucosamine in animals was studied before comparable experimentation on the ability of microorganisms to utilize the amino sugar. Although it was known that yeast was able to ferment glucosamine, and this was, in fact, one of the early tools for distinguishing glucosamine from galactosamine, detailed reports on the ability of various other microorganisms to degrade glucosamine did not appear prior to 1920.

The microbial degradation of glucosamine was reported by several workers (Takao, 1923; Noble and Knacke, 1928; Lieben and Löwe, 1932). The amino sugar could be utilized by microorganisms, but no details were given as to either the nature of the fermentation products or the possible fate of the amino group. The ability of several strains of pathogenic staphylococci to utilize glucosamine as a nutrient was studied, and the suggestion was made that growth on glucosamine increased the virulence of these strains (Kuroya and Kurose, 1940).

The products of glucosamine fermentation have been examined and appear to resemble those which are obtained from the comparable fermentation of glucose (Matsushima, 1948, 1951; Matsushima and Shimazu, 1952; Antonio *et al.*, 1954; Oka and Murachi, 1954).

Several strains of hemolytic streptococcus which produce capsular hyaluronic acid metabolize the amino sugar in a manner analogous to the metabolism of glucose, forming both polymer and lactate (Hayano and Tobimatsu, 1956). In general, the metabolism of glucosamine by whole cells has followed classic pathways, with the early liberation of ammonia and the absorption of oxygen (Rosenberg, 1948).

A significant contribution to isotopic degradation methods was provided by Jourdian, Koffler, and Garner (1958), who demonstrated that *Leuconostoc mesenteroides* ferments D-glucosamine to ammonia and products with distribution identical to those obtained from D-glucose: CO_2 from carbon 1, ethanol from carbons 2 and 3, and lactic acid from carbons 4, 5, and 6. Thus, after suitable degradative procedures, each of the carbon atoms in glucosamine can be isolated, and complete analysis of isotopically labeled material may be carried out.

The effect of glucosamine on the metabolic behavior of various microorganisms has been examined, and several interesting reports have appeared. *Hemophilus pertussis* is able to oxidize glucosamine with concomitant oxygen consumption, but a wide variety of aldoses and ketoses were unable to increase oxygen utilization (Abe, 1953). *Serratia marcescens* is unable to utilize glucosamine as a nitrogen donor for amino acid synthesis and lacks either a deaminase or a transaminase (Payne *et al.*, 1955).

Endamoeba histolytica requires either associated streptobacillus, which produces bound glucosamine, or some other form of glucosamine in order to maintain growth (Greenberg, Taylor, and Bond, 1956; Loran, Kerner, and Anderson, 1956).

Microorganisms, in addition to having fermentative actions on the amino sugars directly, can give rise to products which degrade hexosamine-containing polymers. This general phenomenon was described as early as 1934, when the ability of *Bacillus pyocyaneus* and pyocyanine to degrade chondroitin sulfuric acid was described (Miyazaki, 1934). It is interesting to note that this phenomenon, which is probably nonenzymic, has recently been rediscovered (Bonde and Jensen, 1956). The decomposition of chitin by a wide variety of microorganisms has been reported; enzyme fractions obtained include oligosaccharases, as well as simple hexosaminidases (Hackman, 1954; Reynolds, 1954; Veldkamp, 1955; Jeuniaux, 1959a). The presence of both glucosamine and galactosamine in soil has been described (Bremner, 1958), and it is reasonable to assume that these sugars are end products of chitin and galactosaminan or cell-wall degradation. The ability of microorganisms to utilize galactosamine as a substrate for energy-yielding or synthetic pathways has not been examined.

D. Degradation of Amino Sugars by Tissue Slices and Homogenates

The *in vivo* ability of several systems to utilize the hexosamines was indicated in very early studies. Approaches toward the *in vitro* definition of the pathways involved, however, were not attempted until relatively recently. As early as 1934, a report appeared which indicated that crude homogenates of several tissues were able to cause the disappearance of glucosamine (Kawabe, 1934a; Kawakami, 1934, 1936).

These studies remained virtually unnoticed until Lutwak-Mann (1941) carried out a rather extensive investigation of the ability of a variety of tissue preparations and microorganisms to decompose glucosamine, *N*-acetylglucosamine, and galactosamine. Her procedures and results may be summarized as follows: Slices of liver, lung, kidney, and pancreas were incubated with the various substrates, and the production of lactate, ammonia, and urea was measured, as was oxygen consumption. Glucosamine was found to be the most efficient ammonia producer, *N*-acetylglucosamine the next most efficient, and galactosamine the least efficient. All of the amino sugars were able to stimulate oxygen uptake by slices of kidney, testis, and brain at pH 7.4–7.8. Similar preparations of liver, muscle, and cartilage gave relatively low oxygen uptakes, and it was suggested that an oxidative step was necessarily involved in hexosamine utilization. The ability of glucosamine and *N*-acetylglucosamine to give rise to glycolytic intermediates is now recognized. Metabolism of the amino sugars by liver preparations yielded increased urea; the ammonia formation, however, was insufficient to account for the amount of glucosamine that disappeared. This disappearance of glucosamine was not explained, but it is likely that some of the hexosamine would be utilized to yield products not assayed by the methods employed. The formation of ammonia from the *N*-acetylhexosamine substrate was a clear indication that some pathway existed for the cleavage of the *N*-acyl bond, and, although such enzymes have been reported from microbial systems, the specificity and properties of the mammalian deacetylase have not as yet been described.

The ability of muscle to yield ammonia from the hexosamine substrates was quite limited, suggesting relatively low levels of deaminase activity, whereas yeast was able to catalyze rapid degradation of the hexosamine, with production of ammonia. The requirement of kidney extracts for a high-energy source (such as ATP) and a glucokinase preparation for ammonia production was noted. The ability of glucose to inhibit ammonia production from glucosamine and of galactose to inhibit ammonia production from galactosamine was also reported, a forerunner of subsequent cell-free experiments with hexokinases. Although several tissues exhibited oxygen uptake in the presence of glucosamine, no formation or further metabolism of glucosaminic acid could be detected. Glucosaminic acid was not a substrate for D-amino acid oxidase, and glucosamine was not a substrate for amine oxidase. Liver homogenates were unable to form lactate, acetate, or succinate from glucosamine, although the initial product of degradation (presumably, hexose phosphate in this system) could be converted to lactate by a muscle extract and a pyridine nucleotide coenzyme.

It is extremely interesting to note that these studies by Lutwak-Mann (1941) provided a clear preview of the precise enzymic reactions involved in hexosamine catabolism, including the requirement of a high-energy source, the early liberation of ammonia, and the formation of a product which is a substrate for the glycolytic enzymes of muscle. The other point of interest is that *N*-acetylglucosamine was virtually inert in the presence of brain extracts or homogenates, implying either the inability of this tissue to phosphorylate the *N*-acetylhexosamine or the absence of a deacylase. Similar experiments were not performed with *N*-acetylgalactosamine as a substrate. The ability of brain extracts to catalyze the deamination of glucosamine under anaerobic conditions was described by Faulkner and Quastel (1956).

E. Cell-Free Systems

The marked developments in the biochemistry of amino sugars with regard both to their role as structural components of connective tissue and to their gross metabolic behavior preceded studies in cell-free systems. Investigations carried out by earlier workers clearly indicated the ability of microorganisms and mammalian systems to catalyze the degradation of amino sugars, and some clues as to the nature of the metabolic steps involved had already been provided.

1. Glucosamine-6-Phosphate Deaminase

Reports appeared from several laboratories which indicated that *Escherichia coli* grown on glucosamine as a sole carbon and nitrogen source produced an enzyme system which was capable of converting glucosamine 6-phosphate into ammonia and a hexose phosphate (Comb and Roseman, 1956; Imanaga, 1957; Wolfe, Britton, and Nakada, 1957). This enzyme appeared to be partially inductive, since cells grown on glucose still had detectable deaminase (Soodak, 1955), but the hexosamine-grown cells had much greater activity. The stoichiometry of the reaction indicated that a mole of ammonia was formed for each mole of hexosamine phosphate that disappeared; the other product of the deamination was identified as a hexose phosphate capable of reacting with glucose-6-phosphate dehydrogenase and triphosphopyridine nucleotide. Enzyme fractionation revealed that the initial product formed in this reaction was fructose 6-phosphate, with no glucose 6-phosphate being formed (Imanaga, 1957a). This is, in some sense, analogous to the synthetic pathway, and, although the reactions are distinctly different with regard to their equilibrium position, there are probably some mechanistic features in common.

Leloir and Cardini (1956) reported on a similar reaction catalyzed by crude extracts of rat brain and by partially purified preparations obtained from pig kidney. The hexose phosphate formed was not definitively identified, although it was presumed to be fructose 6-phosphate on the basis of colorimetric analysis. There was, however, a striking discrepancy in the apparent properties and mechanism of action of the kidney enzyme as compared with the bacterial enzyme. Leloir and Cardini studied preparations that catalyzed the conversion of *N*-acetylglucosamine 6-phosphate to fructose phosphate, acetate, and ammonia, and they reported that glucosamine 6-phosphate was inactive in their system unless *N*-acetylglucosamine 6-phosphate was present. The following reaction scheme was postulated:

$$N\text{-acetylglucosamine 6-phosphate} \rightarrow \text{X} \tag{13}$$

$$\text{glucosamine 6-phosphate} + \text{X} \rightleftharpoons N\text{-acetylglucosamine 6-phosphate} + \text{fructose 6-phosphate} + NH_3 \tag{14}$$

$$\text{X} \rightarrow \text{fructose 6-phosphate} + NH_3 + \text{acetate} \tag{15}$$

Compound X was thought to be *N*-acetylfructosylamine phosphate, arising by an Amadori type of rearrangement. According to the postulation just cited, glucosamine 6-phosphate deamination proceeds in stoichiometric amounts via *N*-acetylglucosamine 6-phosphate, although the latter compound is only required at catalytic levels. The actual participation of the *N*-acetylhexosamine phosphate was not demonstrated, nor was satisfactory stoichiometry reported. Studies on the bacterial enzyme system indicated that *N*-acetylglucosamine phosphate was not required as a cofactor for the reaction, nor did it function as a substrate. Thus, the bacterial and mammalian enzyme systems acting on hexosamine phosphate as a substrate apparently proceeded to the same end products but by substantially different mechanisms.

The apparent discrepancy between the results reported for the two systems was resolved by means of sufficient purification of the kidney enzyme system so that extraneous activities were removed (Comb and Roseman, 1958b). These conclusions were based on kinetic studies, the use of isotopically labeled substrates both for product formation and as potential trapping agents, isolation and identification of the products of the reaction, and comparison of several potential activators, such as *N*-acetylgalactosamine 6-phosphate. It was demonstrated that *N*-acetylglucosamine phosphate did not participate as a substrate or as intermediate in the conversion of hexosamine phosphate to fructose phosphate and ammonia by the kidney extracts; therefore, the deamination of glucosamine 6-phosphate by bacterial or kidney enzyme preparations proceeded in an identical fashion. *N*-Acetylglucosamine 6-phosphate was able to markedly stimulate the activity of both preparations, and the enzymes involved were found to be extremely sensitive to the type of buffers employed. It was postulated that the *N*-acetylhexosamine phosphate served to stabilize the substrate on the enzyme, protecting the enzyme against inactivation or against inhibition by products of the reaction. Suggestions that there was participation of *N*-acetylhexosamine phosphate as an enzyme-bound intermediate in the reaction were effectively ruled out (Comb and Roseman, 1958).

During the purification of the kidney enzyme preparations, it was noted that *N*-acetylglucosamine phosphate acted as a substrate throughout a very extensive purification; it was suggested that an enzyme was present which carried out the deacetylation of *N*-acetylglucosamine phosphate to form glucosamine phosphate which would then be active in the deaminase reaction. Thus, the formation of fructose phosphate and ammonia from *N*-acetylhexosamine phosphate could be explained by a combination of the activities of the deacetylase and the deaminase enzyme, although a separate pathway similar to that proposed by Leloir was not completely ruled out.

Comb and Roseman (1958) also reported that the equilibrium constant for the deamination reaction lies primarily in the direction of ketose phosphate formation, in contrast with the opposite equilibrium position of the hexosamine synthetase reaction which utilizes L-glutamine as a substrate rather than ammonia. However, the deaminase reaction can be reversed in the direction of hexosamine phosphate formation if an appropriate trap is employed. Comb and Roseman (1958b) were able to demonstrate that coupling of the deaminase reaction with the hexosamine-phosphate *N*-acetylase system allowed a net free-energy change which was sufficiently large to permit synthesis of acetylhexosamine phosphate in a manner which was linear with time. This is illustrated by the following reaction sequence:

$$\text{fructose 6-phosphate} + \text{ammonia} \rightleftharpoons \text{glucosamine 6-phosphate} \quad (16)$$

$$\text{glucosamine 6-phosphate} + \text{acetyl coenzyme A} \rightarrow N\text{-acetylglucosamine 6-phosphate} + \text{coenzyme ASH} \quad (17)$$

In the pathway just cited, it is possible both to fix ammonia and to arrive at the level of *N*-acetylhexosamine phosphate with the net utilization of one less ATP than is required by the glutamine pathway. A calculation of the levels of hexosamine phosphate deaminase and *N*-acetylase indicated that these substances are present in sufficient quantity for it to be postulated that this pathway is responsible for a considerable proportion of hexosamine synthesis in the organism. This postulation, however, seems extremely unlikely, since analogous pseudoreversible systems, such as fatty-acid synthesis and breakdown, glycogen synthesis and breakdown, and the like, clearly do not follow the same sequence in the synthetic and degradative pathways. The additional utilization of high-energy phosphate is apparently the price paid to ensure the irreversibility of the reaction under consideration at the synthetic locus.

A similar enzyme catalyzing the formation of tagatose 6-phosphate and ammonia from galactosamine 6-phosphate was recently reported (Shiota *et al.*, 1962).

2. DEACYLASES

The deacetylation of the *N*-acetylglucosamine was clearly indicated by the gross metabolic behavior of this sugar and was similarly suggested by enzymic studies carried out in several laboratories. The properties and specificity of the mammalian enzyme have not been described, but the reaction involved is probably identical to that reported for several bacterial systems. The deacylase reaction may be written in one of two ways:

$$N\text{-acetylhexosamine} \rightarrow \text{hexosamine} + \text{acetate} \quad (18)$$

$$N\text{-acetylhexosamine phosphate} \rightarrow \text{hexosamine phosphate} + \text{acetate} \quad (19)$$

The first of the two reactions was demonstrated to occur in extracts of several microorganisms grown on *N*-acetylglucosamine (Roseman, 1957).

N-Acetylglucosamine and *N*-acetylgalactosamine were both able to serve as substrates, although the rate of deacylation of the former was approximately ten times that of the latter. The enzyme system described was very labile, and the loss of activity on dialysis and purification attempts suggests that the initial reaction may have been phosphorylation of the acetylamino sugar by a kinase, followed by cleavage of the phosphorylated substrate and subsequent phosphatase hydrolysis to liberate the free hexosamine. This enzyme has not been purified.

A preliminary report by Soodak (1955) indicated that extracts of *Escherichia coli* 26 grown on glucose were able to convert *N*-acetylhexosamine phosphate to hexose phosphate, and it was suggested that the initial step was the deacetylation of the acetylamino sugar. This enzyme, a deacetylase, has not been purified, nor has the specificity been examined in any detail. The most active preparations were probably those obtained as a by-product of studies on the kidney hexosamine-phosphate deaminase. These deacylase activities are probably constitutive in the majority of cells, with the most likely substrate being *N*-acetylglucosamine 6-phosphate.

3. Phosphatases

The role of phosphatases in the liberation of free hexosamines has not been extensively investigated. A recent report described a phosphatase preparation from extracts of *Neurospora crassa* which exhibits highest activity with glucosamine 6-phosphate as a substrate, with considerably lower activities against other hexose phosphates (Kuo and Blumenthal, 1961). There is at present no knowledge or description of the possible existence of specific phosphatases involved in hexosamine catabolism.

4. Direct Oxidative Pathway

A direct oxidative pathway was described for glucosamine; the subsequent catabolic reactions were different from those occurring in mammalian systems but analogous to reactions carried out by a number of microorganisms acting on glucose. The oxidation of glucosamine to glucosaminic acid by a glucose oxidase-like enzyme was described in extracts of several microorganisms (Imanaga, 1957b). This enzyme is also present in extracts of oranges, and was described as a nonspecific flavin aerobic dehydrogenase (Bean, Porter, and Steinberg, 1961). Galactosamine is oxidized at the terminal hydroxymethyl group by a galactose oxidase obtained from *Polyporus circinatus* (Asensio and Amaral, 1961). The nature of the product has not been described, although galactose gives rise to a dialdehyde.

5. Glucosaminic Acid Catabolism

D-Glucosaminic acid formed is not a substrate for amino acid oxidase preparations, but is rapidly catabolized by cell-free systems obtained from bacteria adapted to grow on this substrate as the sole carbon and nitrogen source (Imanaga, 1958; Merrick and Roseman, 1960). Cells which have been adapted in this manner are unable to oxidize glucose to any significant extent; extracts obtained from such organisms appear to contain most of the enzymes involved in the normal glycolytic pathways, but apparently are deficient in glucokinase activity. The initial reaction involved in the catabolism of glucosaminic acid is the elimination of ammonia to form 2-keto-3-deoxy-D-gluconic acid.

The glucosaminic acid dehydrase is analogous to serine and threonine dehydrases and requires pyridoxal phosphate as a cofactor (Merrick and Roseman, 1960). Specificity studies indicated that this dehydrase was distinct from those acting on serine and threonine, and the reaction was found to be not detectably reversible. The inability to detect comparable enzymic activities in extracts of *Neurospora crassa* grown on conventional substrates or on preparations from rat liver and *Escherichia coli* which possessed serine and threonine dehydrases suggests that this enzyme system was largely adaptive. The resulting ketodeoxygluconic acid serves as substrate for a phosphorylating enzyme with subsequent metabolism of the gluconic acid phosphate occurring via aldolase cleavage through a Doudoroff type of pathway similar to that present in *Pseudomonas saccharophila* (Entner and Doudoroff, 1952).

The ability of microorganisms to catalyze these reactions suggests that a similar, although quantitatively smaller, pathway may be distributed elsewhere. It should be noted that animals fed glucosaminic acid yielded increased amounts of lactate, oxalate, and acetate in their urine; the detailed relationships involved in these conversions have not been established (Imaizumi, 1937).

The comparable ability of microorganisms to utilize galactose via a pathway involving 2-keto-3-deoxy-D-galactonic acid suggests that a similar pathway may operate for galactosamine catabolism, but studies of this type do not seem to have been done.

6. Degradation of Neuraminic Acid Derivatives

Extracts of *Vibrio cholerae* cleaved *N*-acetylneuraminic acid between carbons 3 and 4 to yield pyruvate and an acetylhexosamine identified by chromatographic methods as *N*-acetylglucosamine (Heimer and Meyer, 1956).

Enzymic studies carried out by several authors indicated that the initial product of enzymic cleavage of *N*-acetylneuraminic acid was not *N*-acetylglucosamine but, rather, *N*-acetylmannosamine (Comb and Roseman, 1958a; Kuhn and Brossmer, 1958; Brug, Esser, and Paerels, 1959; Comb and Roseman, 1960). Comb and Roseman carried out their studies with a highly purified enzyme preparation, and they were able to demonstrate unequivocally that the initial product of cleavage of the neuraminic acid derivative was *N*-acetylmannosamine rather than *N*-acetylglucosamine. Two other derivatives of neuraminic acid were investigated; the *N*-glycolylneuraminic acid was cleaved at approximately two thirds the rate of the *N*-acetyl analogue, and the *N,O*-diacetyl compound was inactive in this system. The cleavage product of the *N*-glycolyl compound was also identified as *N*-glycolylmannosamine.

Studies of the equilibrium constant of the *N*-acetylneuraminic acid aldolase reaction showed cleavage to be favored by about 10 to 1; however, starting with pyruvate and the acetylamino sugar, the formation of acetylneuraminic acid could be demonstrated. Although it was suggested by Comb and Roseman that this pathway was operative for *N*-acetylneuraminic acid synthesis and that subsequent activation prior to conversion to various nucleotide derivatives took place, the operative pathway for neuraminic acid synthesis is that involving the irreversible condensation of *N*-acetylmannosamine phosphate and phosphoenolpyruvate.

The presence of neuraminic acid in the receptor sites of red blood cells and viral systems has prompted numerous studies of its metabolic behavior. It has been demonstrated that the production of the receptor-destroying enzyme (preparations which will cleave neuraminic acid from more complex substrates) of *Vibrio cholerae* can be substantially stimulated if the organism is allowed to grow in the presence of neuraminic acid derivatives (Ada and French, 1957). The existence of this neuraminidase is not restricted to *Vibrio cholerae;* it also is present in influenza virus, and it is considered to be essential to the hemagglutination phenomenon characteristic of these particular organisms (Gottschalk, 1957 (see also Chapter 50).

7. Lysozyme and Cell Wall

The presence of muramic acid in cell-wall structures has led recently to extensive investigation regarding the mechanism of the action of lysozyme. The similarity among the action of lysozyme on cell-wall structures, the lytic ability of phage, and the inhibition of bacterial cell-wall synthesis by antibiotics should be noted (Weidel and Primosigh, 1957). Muramidase and hexosaminidase activities have been claimed for lysozyme, and, although lysozyme is able to cleave chitodextrin preparations, it is clear that its action and that of the lytic principle in phage are exerted at a muramic acid-containing site (see Chapters 43 and 44). The structure cleaved appears to be essential for maintenance of the integrity of the bacterial cell.

The accumulation of uridine diphosphomuramic acid peptide derivatives, demonstrated by Park (1952,a), apparently arises from a situation in which the cell-wall precursors cannot be completed or linked together, and thus continuing metabolic activity results in disruption of the bacteria. This may be termed lysis from within. The use of a sufficiently high ratio of phage to host cell results in a lysis-from-without phenomenon, wherein the cell is disrupted before phage infection and multiplication have taken place. This is presumably a result of the cleavage by the phage enzyme of a sufficient number of muramic acid-containing structures to render the cell unable to maintain a proper envelope.

Addendum

The major recent emphasis in studies of hexosamine metabolism has been on synthesis of macromolecules; isolation, identification, and synthesis of new amino sugars; and some preliminary work on physiological control of hexosamine metabolism.

The incorporation of glucose-1-C^{14} into glycoprotein hexosamine was studied in a perfused liver preparation and shown to proceed, as expected, without randomization of the carbon chain (Sarcione, 1963). A similar study of the synthesis of *N*-acetylneuraminic acid from radioactively labeled carbohydrate precursors was carried out in slices of ovine submaxillary gland (Eichberg and Karnovsky, 1963). The labeling pattern found in the isolated *N*-acetylneuraminic acid was in agreement with the pathway elucidated previously in studies carried out with cell-free systems. The labeling found in the pyruvate portion of the molecule could be accounted for on the basis of conventional glycolytic enzymes. A certain amount of radioactive *N*-acetylneuraminic acid was still in bound form but was dialyzable; the suggestion was made that a pool of nucleotide or similar derivatives may be present in such tissues. Further identification of this fraction was not carried out.

A study of hormonal effects on bone-marrow cells revealed that the uptake of glucosamine by these cells was stimulated by erythropoietin (Dukes, Takaku, and Goldwasser, 1963). The specificity of this stimulation is not restricted to the amino sugar, but is extended to other small molecular weight metabolites, as well. This effect, as with so many other hormonal effects recently reported, may be on the transport of metabolites through the cell membrane.

A further study on the fructose-6-phosphate L-glutamine transamidase indicated that the action of this enzyme is inhibited by salicylate (Jacobson and Boström, 1963). Whether this inhibition is at all related to the apparent therapeutic role of salicylates in rheumatic diseases is unknown.

The transfer of *N*-acetylneuraminic acid from cytidine monophosphate-*N*-acetylneuraminic acid (CMP-NAN) to acceptor substrates has been reported in two separate studies. The formation of sialyllactose in a reverse action between CMP-NAN and lactose was described by Jourdian and co-workers (Jourdian, Carlson, and Roseman, 1963), and appears to involve a glycosyl transfer reaction analogous to those demonstrated in the synthesis of other simple oligosaccharides. The conversion of CMP-NAN to colominic acid was reported and is another example of the synthesis of homopolysaccharides from activated sugar nucleotide derivatives (Aminoff, Dodyk, and Roseman, 1963).

A wide variety of new amino sugars has been reported recently, and it is certain that the list is far from complete. The isolation of D-fucosamine from a *Bacillus* species was reported by Leatherwood *et al.*, and this sugar appears to be fairly widespread in microorganisms, although it has not been found in higher animals as of this time (Leatherwood *et al.*, 1963). In addition to the new amino sugars, amino uronic acids of both the *gluco* and *manno* configuration have been added to the *galacto* isomer previously found in Vi antigen. 2-Amino-2-deoxy-D-mannuronic acid is a constituent of *Micrococcus lysodeikticus* cell wall (Perkins, 1963), and 2-amino-2-deoxy-D-glucuronic acid was reported as a constituent of the capsular substance of *Haemophilus influenzae* type A (Williamson and Zamenhof, 1963a). 3-Amino sugars have been reported (Volk and Ashwell, 1963), and the identification of a previously reported 4-amino sugar has been completed (Stevens *et al.*, 1963). The latter sugar, viosamine, was identified as 4,6-dideoxy-4-amino-D-glucose by synthetic, degradative, and spectroscopic methods. The biosynthesis of this class of compounds was reported to involve amination of a thymidine diphospho-4-keto-6-deoxyglucose intermediate (Matsuhashi, 1963). This type of compound was previously described by workers in several laboratories as an intermediate in the synthesis of 6-deoxy sugars, such as fucose or rhamnose.

It is expected that the major emphasis in hexosamine metabolism will continue to be on the formation of macromolecules containing hexosamine moieties and on the distribution and occurrence of amino sugars other than glucosamine and galactosamine, both in microorganisms and in higher animals.

Chapter 39

METABOLISM OF GLYCOSAMINOGLYCANS

Harry Boström and Lennart Rodén

Knowledge of the chemistry of the glycosaminoglycans has developed gradually since the nineteenth century, and a surprisingly correct picture of the composition of chondroitin sulfate from cartilage—the first substance in this group to be isolated—had been obtained by the early pioneers in this field: Krukenberg (1884), Mörner (1889), and Schmiedeberg (1891). On the other hand, our present concepts of the metabolism of the acid glycosaminoglycans have emerged largely from the work of the past decade, as a result of the introduction of radioactive carbon, sulfur, and hydrogen into this field of investigation. The search into the metabolic pathways of the acid glycosaminoglycans and their constituents has also benefited from simultaneous advances in the adjacent field of detoxication, from which present knowledge of uronic acid biosynthesis and sulfate activation is largely derived.

Thus, we now have a fairly good conception of the pathways along which the constituents of the carbon chains of the glycosaminoglycans are formed from glucose. The pioneer work of Leloir on uridine coenzymes has been of particular importance in elucidating the mechanisms of saccharide synthesis (see Chapter 38 of this volume and reviews: Kalckar and Maxwell, 1958; Leloir, Cardini, and Cabib, 1960; Strominger, 1960). After the isolation of UDP-*N*-acetylglucosamine (Cabib, Leloir, and Cardini, 1953) and UDP-D-glucuronic acid (Dutton and Storey, 1953; Smith and Mills, 1954; Storey and Dutton, 1955), it was obvious that these substances could be regarded as potential precursors of the carbon skeleton of the glycosaminoglycans. This assumption was proved subsequently by the demonstration that uridine nucleotide-bound sugars are incorporated into a number of different microbial polysaccharides, including chitin (Glaser and Brown, 1957), cellulose (Glaser, 1958), hyaluronic acid of streptococci (Markovitz, Cifonelli, and Dorfman, 1959), and Type III-pneumococcus polysaccharide (Smith *et al.*, 1960).

Progress in the study of the biosynthesis of animal glycosaminoglycans has been slower, and only in the case of hyaluronic acid has it been possible to obtain synthesis in a cell-free system of mammalian origin (Altshuler, Kinsman, and Bareta, 1961; Schiller, Slover, and Dorfman, 1961). Nothing is known, however, about the immediate precursors of the carbon skeleton in the sulfated glycosaminoglycans (see *Addendum*).

The problem of the origin and pathway of incorporation of the sulfate has recently received much attention. As a result of these studies, the mechanism of sulfate activation is now known in great detail, and some information is also available concerning the pathway of sulfate incorporation into the polysaccharide molecules. A large number of reviews on the metabolism of the acid glycosaminoglycans has been published during the past years (Asboe-Hansen, 1954; Dorfman, 1955; Kent and Whitehouse, 1955; Kent, 1957; Bazin and Delaunay, 1959; Gibian, 1959; Roseman, 1959; Springer, 1959; Dorfman, 1960; Boström and Rodén, 1961).

I. Metabolism of Moieties

A. Monosaccharide Moieties

1. Hexosamines

The biosynthesis of hexosamines is discussed in detail in Chapter 38 of this book.

2. Uronic Acids

Uronic acid metabolism has recently been the subject of several reviews (Utter, 1958; Holzer, 1959; Roseman, 1959; Hollmann, 1960). Our presentation will therefore be limited to those reactions which at present seem to be pertinent in a discussion of glycosaminoglycan synthesis (Fig. 1).

Of the several uronic acids now known to occur in nature, only two are relevant in this review: D-glucuronic acid and L-iduronic acid. D-Glucuronic acid is present in hyaluronic acid, chondroitin, chondroitin 4-sulfate, chondroitin 6-sulfate, heparin, and heparan sulfate, whereas L-iduronic acid is found in dermatan sulfate and—together with D-glucuronic acid—in heparin and heparan sulfate (see Volume I, Chapter 7).

a. D-*Glucuronic Acid.* The formation of conjugates of glucuronic acid has been studied since the days of Fischer, who was the first to propose a theory for the *in vivo* synthesis of the glucuronic acid skeleton. According to Fischer and Piloty (1891), the conjugated glucuronic acid was probably formed in a two-step reaction, involving (*i*) coupling of an acceptor with glucose to a glucoside, and (*ii*) oxidation of the glucoside to a glucuronide. From later work with tissue slices (Lipschitz and Bueding, 1939), it seemed more likely that three-carbon intermediates were involved in the glucuronide formation, and *in vivo* experiments with C^{14}-labeled precursors (lactate, pyruvate, glycerol, and glucose), which were administered together with glucuronidogenic substances, lent

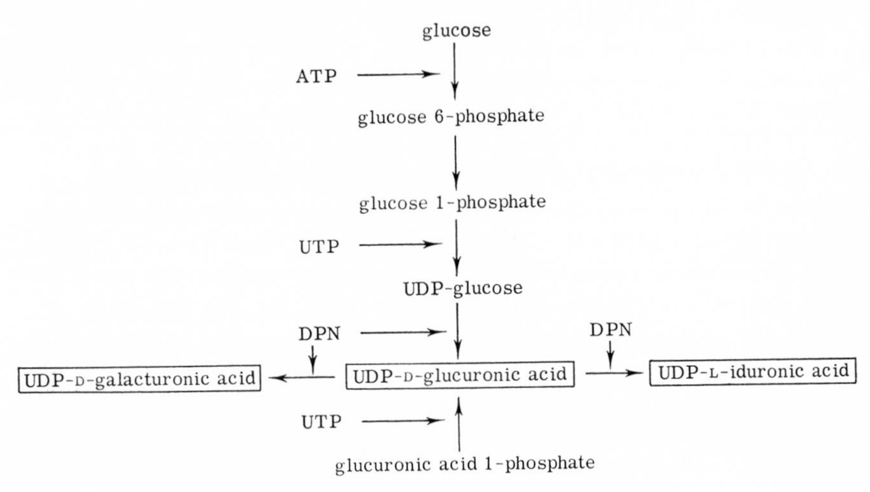

FIG. 1. Biosynthesis of UDP-uronic acids.

further support to this view (Packham and Butler, 1952; Doerschuk, 1952). These results could not be confirmed in other experiments, in which the incorporation of glucose-1-C^{14} and glucose-6-C^{14} into glucuronides was studied (Mosbach and King, 1950; Eisenberg and Gurin, 1952; Douglas and King, 1953). The radioactivity of the glucuronic acid was still located in positions 1 and 6, respectively, indicating that the transformation had occurred without cleavage of the carbon chain.

The problem of glucuronide synthesis was finally solved by the isolation of UDP-D-glucuronic acid and the demonstration that this compound is essential for the formation of phenyl glucuronides in cell-free liver suspensions (Dutton and Storey, 1953, 1954; Smith and Mills, 1954; Storey and Dutton, 1955). The glucuronic acid moiety is linked to the terminal phosphate group of UDP in an α-uronidic linkage and can be transferred to various acceptors, as reviewed in detail by Williams (1959). UDP-D-glucuronic acid was shown to originate from UDP-D-glucose by a diphosphopyridine nucleotide–dependent oxidation catalyzed by a liver enzyme, UDP-D-glucose dehydrogenase (Strominger *et al.*, 1954; Maxwell *et al.*, 1956; Strominger *et al.*, 1957). Although it seems reasonable to assume that the oxidation of the primary alcohol group of

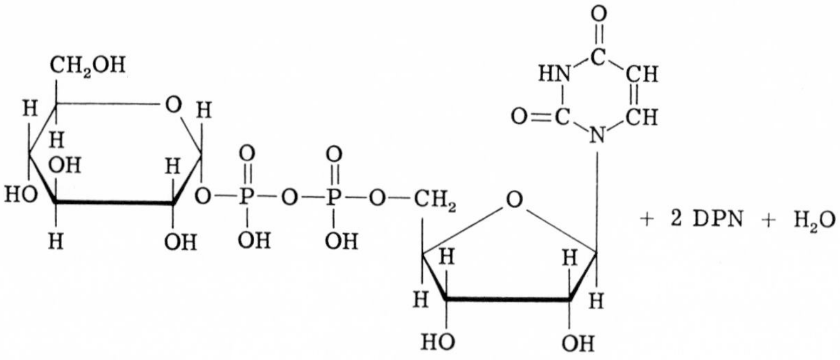

$+ 2\ DPN + H_2O$

Uridine-5-(D-glucosyl dihydrogen pyrophosphate) (UDP-D-glucose)

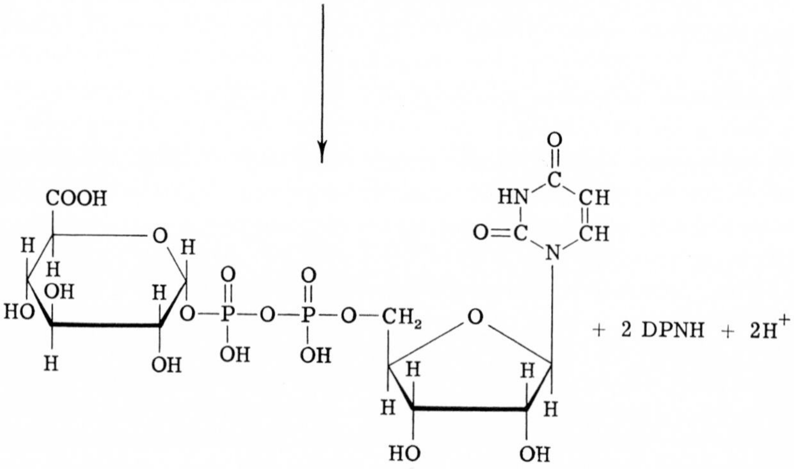

$+ 2\ DPNH + 2H^+$

Uridine-5-(D-glucosyluronic acid dihydrogen pyrophosphate)
(UDP-D-glucuronic acid)

glucose to a carboxyl group passes through the intermediate formation of an aldehyde group, all attempts to trap such an intermediate have been fruitless. UDP-D-glucose dehydrogenase has also been detected in pea seedlings (Strominger and Mapson, 1957), cartilage (Castellani, de Bernard, and Zambotti, 1957), pneumococcus (Smith *et al.*, 1958,a), mast-cell tumors (Hambraeus, Rodén, and Boström, 1959), group-A streptococcus (Markovitz, Cifonelli, and Dorfman, 1959), and skin (Jacobson and Davidson, 1962).

Prior to the discovery of UDP-D-glucose dehydrogenase, the close resemblance of UDP-D-glucuronic acid to other UDP-glycosyl compounds suggested that its formation could take place by a mechanism analogous to the uridyl transferase reactions catalyzing the synthesis of the UDP derivatives of glucose (Munch-Petersen *et al.*, 1953; Ganguli, 1958; Ginsburg, 1958; Turner and Turner, 1958), galactose (Kalckar, Braganca, and Munch-Petersen, 1953; Isselbacher, 1958), *N*-acetylglucosamine (Smith, Munch-Petersen, and Mills, 1953), and glucosamine (Maley, Maley, and Lardy, 1956), as indicated below:

$$\text{glycosyl 1-phosphate} + \text{UTP} \rightleftarrows \text{UDP-glycosyl} + \text{pyrophosphate} \quad (1)$$

The analogous reaction involving D-glucuronic acid 1-phosphate

$$\text{D-glucuronic acid 1-phosphate} + \text{UTP} \rightleftarrows \text{UDP-D-glucuronic acid} + \text{pyrophosphate} \quad (2)$$

has been sought in vain in mammalian tissues, but has been detected in plants (Ginsburg, Neufeld, and Hassid, 1956). The reverse reaction is catalyzed by particulate fractions from rat kidney (Ginsburg, Weissbach, and Maxwell, 1958) and liver (Evans *et al.*, 1959). As UDP-D-glucose dehydrogenase is present also in plants, it is possible that Reaction 2 is not used as an alternate pathway for the synthesis of UDP-D-glucuronic acid but rather operates in the reverse direction, yielding D-glucuronic acid 1-phosphate which, after dephosphorylation to D-glucuronic acid, can be utilized for pentose or ascorbic acid formation.

It is obvious that UDP-D-glucuronic acid is a likely precursor of the glucuronic acid moiety of acid glycosaminoglycans, as well as of phenolic and other low molecular weight glucuronides. Isotopic data similar to those described earlier for phenyl glucuronides have provided evidence in agreement with this concept. Thus, C-6 of glucose is transformed into C-6 of D-glucuronic acid in streptococcal (Roseman *et al.*, 1954), as well as in rat skin, hyaluronic acid (Rodén and Dorfman, 1958). Furthermore, UDP-D-glucuronic acid is utilized for a cell-free net synthesis of hyaluronic acid in an ultrasonicate of streptococci (Markovitz, Cifonelli, and Dorfman, 1959). It was recently shown that UDP-D-glucuronic acid is also a precursor of mammalian hyaluronic acid (Altshuler, Kinsman, and Bareta, 1961; Schiller, Slover, and Dorfman, 1961). As far as the sulfated glycosaminoglycans are concerned, isotopic evidence has been obtained for the conversion of glucose, without splitting, into the D-glucuronic acid moiety of the hyaluronidase-sensitive chondroitin sulfate fraction of rat skin (Rodén and Dorfman, 1958).

b. L-*Iduronic Acid.* The origin of L-iduronic acid from glucose without scission of the chain was established by Rodén and Dorfman (1958). Of the radioactivity of dermatan sulfate isolated from rat skin after the administration of glucose-6-C^{14}, 43% was recovered from C-6 of the L-iduronic acid moiety, indicating a conversion without cleavage. The epimerization was recently shown by Jacobson and Davidson (1962a) to occur on the uridine nucleotide level, with UDP-D-glucuronic acid being converted to UDP-L-iduronic acid. The enzyme, UDP-D-glucuronic acid 5′-epimerase, was isolated from rabbit skin. The reaction required catalytic amounts of diphosphopyridine nucleotide, and reduced diphosphopyridine nucleotide inhibited the reaction—properties which are similar to those reported for UDP-D-galactose 4′-epimerase (Maxwell, 1957).

Another UDP-D-glucuronic acid epimerase has been found in pneumococci (Smith *et al.*, 1958a) that catalyzes the epimerization of UDP-D-glucuronic acid to UDP-D-galacturonic acid.

B. Sulfate

It has long been known that sulfate is a component of the body fluids, and the early work of Baumann (1876,a) indicated that inorganic sulfate is the precursor of the various ester sulfates produced in the mammalian body, although direct proof of this fact had to await the availability of radioactive-tracer methods.

In the first study utilizing radioactive sulfate, the isotope was administered orally to a human subject, and the excretion of radioactivity in the urine was followed for 48 hr (Borsook *et al.*, 1937). Forty-seven per cent of the administered isotope could be accounted for in the urine collected during the first 24 hr. Similar studies on rats demonstrated a high rate of excretion, with 95% of the sulfate being eliminated in urine and feces during the first 120 hr after intraperitoneal administration of the isotope (Dziewiatkowski, 1949).

The close agreement among the specific activities of the various sulfur-containing fractions of urine—inorganic sulfate, total sulfate, and ester sulfate—clearly indicated that the exogenous inorganic sulfate was the source of ester-bound sulfate (Laidlaw and Young, 1948; Dziewiatkowski, 1949a). Thus, earlier work on whole animals (Baumann, 1876a; Hele, 1924, 1931) and liver tissue slices (Bernheim and Bernheim, 1943) could be confirmed and extended with the new technique.

The fate of the sulfate retained in the body was first investigated by measurement of the S^{35} uptake by a number of different tissues. Singher and Marinelli (1945) reported a very high *in vivo* incorporation into bone marrow, whereas other tissues, such as liver and skeletal muscle, showed only a moderate uptake. Further studies on the S^{35} uptake of various tissues and organs *in vitro* were made by Layton (1950), who found the highest uptake in cartilage, blood vessels, skin, and other mesenchymal tissues.

It seemed plausible to assume that inorganic sulfate could be incorporated into sulfated glycosaminoglycans. Support for this hypothesis was first provided by the classic work of Dziewiatkowski, Benesch, and Benesch, in 1949, demonstrating that the S^{35} activity was incorporated into the knee-joint cartilage of suckling rats. Further work by Dziewiatkowski (1951) showed that S^{35}-labeled chondroitin sulfate could be prepared from articular cartilage, after the addition of nonradioactive carrier chondroitin sulfate. The work of Boström (1952, 1953) provided additional evidence in favor of the view that inorganic sulfate is the precursor of the sulfate group of chondroitin sulfate. Boström demonstrated that radioactive chondroitin sulfate could be isolated—without using carrier—from rib cartilage of rats to which S^{35}-sulfate had been administered.

From this time on, progress in the field of glycosaminoglycan biosynthesis followed several parallel lines: (*i*) studies on the incorporation of S^{35}-sulfate and C^{14}-labeled precursors into glycosaminoglycans *in vivo* and *in vitro* in tissue fragments; (*ii*) autoradiographic studies of S^{35} uptake in various tissues; (*iii*) enzymic work on the formation of hexosamines, glucuronides, and sulfate esters; and (*iv*) studies on cell-free systems from various microbial and animal sources incorporating radioactive S^{35}-sulfate or C^{14}-labeled or tritiated precursors into glycosaminoglycans.

It has been shown that, *in vivo,* nearly all connective tissues take up S^{35}-sulfate. In most cases, the compounds containing the sulfate groups have not been isolated, and the assumption that the S^{35} is part of a sulfated polysaccharide is based on the fact that the radioactivity is nondialyzable or follows a carrier polysaccharide in the course of the isolation procedure. A number of tissues which incorporate S^{35}-sulfate are listed in Tables I and II. Since many studies of this type have now been reported, the list is by no means complete.

A vast literature on autoradiographic studies on S^{35}-sulfate incorporation has also appeared (Table III; and for more extensive reviews, see Boström, 1953, and Dziewiatkowski, 1958).

In most cases it can safely be inferred that the autoradiographic picture truly reflects an incorporation of S^{35} activity into sulfated polysaccharides. It has thus been demonstrated in the case of several tissues that incorporation of S^{35}-sulfate into compounds other than glycosaminoglycans is absent or insignificant (Boström and Åqvist, 1952; Rodén, 1956; Dohlman, 1957). It is nevertheless evident that, in some instances, an appreciable S^{35} incorporation must also have occurred into substances other than sulfated polysaccharides. Cremer and Dittmann (1956) reported a comparatively high S^{35} incorporation *in vivo* into methionine and cystine, which were isolated from rat cartilage after administration of S^{35}-sulfate. Similarly, Dohlman found (1957a) that a

TABLE I

PAPERS DEALING WITH *in Vivo* STUDIES ON S^{35}-LABELED SULFATE INCORPORATION IN VARIOUS TISSUES

Organ or tissue	References
Skeleton	
Cartilage	Singher and Marinelli (1945), Dziewiatkowski (1949), Dziewiatkowski, Benesch, and Benesch (1949), Dziewiatkowski (1951), Layton (1951), Boström (1952, 1953), Ellis, Hublé, and Simpson (1953), Denko and Bergenstal (1955), Denko and Priest (1957), Dziewiatkowski *et al.* (1957), Friberg (1958a), Boni *et al.* (1960), Hauss, Junge-Hülsing, and Schulze (1960), Priest, Koplitz, and Benditt (1960), Castellani *et al.* (1961), Hirschman (1961), Hjertquist (1961), Takemitsu (1961)
Bone and periosteum	Singher and Marinelli (1945), Dziewiatkowski (1949), Layton (1951), Dziewiatkowski (1954), Engfeldt, Engström, and Boström (1954), Kent *et al.* (1956), Cremer and Dittmann (1956), Kowalewski and Gouws (1957), Denko and Priest (1957), Friberg (1958a), Picard (1959), Bronner (1960), Hirschman (1961), Hjertquist (1961), Takemitsu (1961)
Bone marrow	Singher and Marinelli (1945), Dziewiatkowski (1949), Layton (1951), Hauss, Junge-Hülsing, and Schulze (1960)
Alimentary tract	Layton (1951), Kent *et al.* (1956a), Denko and Priest (1957), Denko (1958), Friberg (1958a), Kowalewski and Williams (1958), Hauss, Junge-Hülsing, and Schulze (1960), Häkkinen (1960)
Cardiovascular system	Layton (1951), Denko and Priest (1957), Buck and Heagy (1958), Kowalewski (1959), Hauss, Junge-Hülsing, and Schulze (1960), Priest, Koplitz, and Benditt (1960), Crane (1962), Hauss, Junge-Hülsing, and Holländer (1962)
Nervous system	Layton (1951), Holmgård (1955), Ringertz (1955), Radin, Martin, and Brown (1957), Denko and Priest (1957), Friberg (1958a), Green and Robinson (1959, 1960)
Urogenital system	Singher and Marinelli (1945), Layton (1951), Denko and Priest (1957), Westin, Allgén, and Odeblad (1959), Hauss, Junge-Hülsing, and Schulze (1960)
Skin	Boström and Gardell (1953), Schiller *et al.* (1956), Denko and Priest (1957), Denko and Stoughton (1958), Friberg (1958a), Junge-Hülsing and Hauss (1960)
Teeth	Cremer and Dittmann (1956), Denko and Priest (1957), Friberg (1958a)
Eye	Layton (1951), Dohlman and Boström (1955), Dohlman (1956), Denko and Priest (1957), Smelser (1959)
Mast cells	Magnusson and Larsson (1955), Monkhouse (1956), Eiber and Danishefsky (1957), Ringertz (1960)
Platelets	Odell and Anderson (1957), Robinson, Bier, and McCarter (1961)
Embryonic tissues	Layton, Frankel, and Scapa (1950), Dziewiatkowski (1953), Larsson (1960)
Granulation tissue	Kodicek and Loewi (1955), Junge-Hülsing (1959)

TABLE II
PAPERS DEALING WITH *in Vitro* STUDIES ON S^{35}-LABELED SULFATE INCORPORATION IN VARIOUS TISSUES

Organ or tissue	References
Skeleton	
Cartilage	Layton (1949), Boström and Månsson (1952, 1953), Boström *et al.* (1955), Rodén (1956,b,c), Friberg (1958), Collins and Meachim (1961), Whitehouse and Boström (1962)
Bone	Layton (1949, 1950)
Nucleus pulposus	Rodén (1956a)
Alimentary tract	Sato *et al.* (1956), Pasternak, Kent, and Davies (1958), Pasternak and Kent (1958)
Cardiovascular system	Layton (1950), Bellman *et al.* (1956), Dyrbye (1959), Crane (1962), Boström, Moretti, and Whitehouse (1963)
Skin	Lawrence and Ricketts (1957), Pelc and Fell (1960)
Eye	Aurell, Dohlman, and Rodén (1956), Wortman and Strominger (1957), Strömberg and Dohlman (1959), Whitehouse and Boström (1962)
Embryonic tissues	Layton (1950), Boström and Månsson (1953), Ito, Takamura, and Endo (1960), Lash, Holtzer, and Whitehouse (1960)
Granulation tissue	Layton, Frankel, and Scapa (1950a), Kodicek and Loewi (1955), Loewi and Kent (1957)

considerable amount of S^{35}-sulfate was incorporated into sulfur-containing amino acids in some ocular tissues. In an autoradiographic study of the S^{35} uptake in mouse brain, Ringertz (1955) showed that the use of lipid solvents in the histologic treatment of the sections gave a predominance of activity in the gray matter, whereas the reverse situation applied when lipid solvents were omitted. This effect is most likely due to the existence of fat-soluble sulfatides in the white matter.

The work of De Meio and his collaborators (1955), Bernstein and McGilvery (1952a), and Lipmann and co-workers (for reviews see Lipmann, 1958; Gregory and Robbins, 1960) has shown that sulfate conjugation is at least a two-step process which involves the activation of sulfate and the subsequent transfer of the sulfate group from the "active sulfate" to the receptor molecule. The first indications of this mechanism originated in the work of De Meio and Tkacz (1950), who demonstrated that adenylic acid and α-ketoglutarate are required in the formation of phenyl sulfate by a liver homogenate. The adenosine triphosphate (ATP) dependence of the reaction sequence was later established by Bernstein and McGilvery (1952), who also showed the presence of an activating step (1952a) by demonstrating the increased rate of phenyl sulfate formation, when the sulfate-containing medium

TABLE III
PAPERS DEALING WITH AUTORADIOGRAPHIC STUDIES ON S^{35}-LABELED SULFATE INCORPORATION IN VARIOUS TISSUES

Organ or tissue	References
Skeleton	
Cartilage	Dziewiatkowski (1951a), Campbell and Persson (1951), Boström, Odeblad, and Friberg (1952), Dziewiatkowski (1952), Odeblad and Boström (1952), Gottschalk and Allen (1952), Bélanger (1954), Engfeldt and Hjertquist (1954), Pelc and Glücksman (1955), Curran and Kennedy (1955), Amprino (1955), Dziewiatkowski *et al.* (1957), Bélanger (1958a), Engfeldt and Westerborn (1960), Gottschalk (1960), Campo and Dziewiatkowski (1961), Takemitsu (1961), Hjertquist (1962), Hjertquist and Westerborn (1962)
Bone and periosteum	Dziewiatkowski (1952), Bélanger (1954), Engfeldt, Engström, and Boström (1954), Vincent (1954), Amprino (1955), Vincent (1955), Duthie and Barker (1955), Amprino (1956), Lacroix (1956), Vincent (1957), Bélanger (1958), Tonna and Cronkite (1959), Tonna and Cronkite (1960)
Bone marrow	Dziewiatkowski (1951a), Lajtha, Ellis, and Oliver (1953), Bélanger (1954), Odell, Tausche, and Gude (1955), Greulich (1956)
Alimentary tract	Odeblad and Boström (1952), Holt and Warren (1953), Bélanger (1953, 1954a), Boström and Odeblad (1954), Davies and Young (1954), Curran and Kennedy (1955), Dziewiatkowski (1956), Jennings and Florey (1956), Voronin (1959)
Respiratory system	Odeblad and Boström (1952, 1953), Bélanger (1954a), Curran and Kennedy (1955)
Cardiovascular system	Odeblad and Boström (1952, 1953a), Bélanger (1954a), Buck (1955), Curran and Kennedy (1955), Copenhaver (1958), Crane (1962)
Nervous system	Boström and Odeblad (1953), Curran and Kennedy (1955), Ringertz (1955)
Urogenital system	Boström and Odeblad (1952), Odeblad (1952), Holt and Warren (1953), Odeblad and Boström (1953), Drenckhahn and Meissner (1956), Norhagen and Odeblad (1955), Verne *et al.* (1956), Moricard and Giro (1957), Moricard, Gothié, and Rodriguez-Galindo (1959), Westin and Odeblad (1959), Gothié (1961)
Skin	Boström, Odeblad, and Friberg (1953), Jorpes, Odeblad, and Boström (1953), Bélanger (1954), Curran and Kennedy (1955), Montagna and Hill (1957), Mancini *et al.* (1961)
Teeth	Verne *et al.* (1952), Bélanger (1954, 1955), Engfeldt, Bergman, and Hammarlund-Essler (1954), Curran and Ken-

TABLE III (*Continued*)

Organ or tissue	References
	nedy (1955), Engfeldt and Hammarlund-Essler (1956), Greulich and Friberg (1957), Kennedy and Kennedy (1959)
Eye	Odeblad and Boström (1952), Smelser and Ozanics (1957), Dohlman (1957a), Larsen (1959), Smelser (1959)
Ear	Bélanger (1953a), Friberg and Ringertz (1956)
Mast cells	Jorpes, Odeblad, and Boström (1953), Asboe-Hansen (1953, 1954a), Bélanger (1954a), Larsson (1956), Guidotti (1957), Wegelius and Lamberg (1960)
Embryonic tissues	Boström and Odeblad (1953a), Dziewiatkowski (1953), Mancini and de Lustig (1954), Amprino (1955), Friberg and Ringertz (1956), Johnston and Comar (1957), Smelser and Ozanics (1957), Copenhaver (1958), Larsson, Boström, and Carlsöö (1959), Walker (1961), Larsson (1962)

had been incubated with ATP prior to the addition of phenol. The enzyme activity responsible for sulfate activation was later separated from the transferring activity by De Meio, Wizerkaniuk, and Schreibman (1955).

Starting from the level of knowledge reached by the pioneer work just mentioned, Lipmann and co-workers extended their general interest in enzymic group activation and transfer to the field of sulfate conjugation. At that time, little was known about the exact nature of the "active sulfate" which arose during incubation of a liver supernatant with ATP; consequently, in order to clarify this question, Hilz and Lipmann (1955) undertook isolation of the "active sulfate" from a reaction mixture in which an extract of rat liver or *Neurospora siderophila* had been used as a source of enzyme. Initially, the "active sulfate" was tentatively identified as adenosine-5′-phosphosulfate (APS) but, after

3′-Phosphoadenosine 5′-phosphosulfate (PAPS)

further work, it was characterized as 3′-phosphoadenosine-5′-phosphosulfate (PAPS) (Robbins and Lipmann, 1957). Adenosine-5′-phosphosulfate is formed, however, as an intermediate in the synthesis of 3′-phosphoadenosine-5′-phosphosulfate (Wilson and Bandurski, 1956; Robbins and Lipmann, 1956; Lipmann, 1958; Robbins and Lipmann, 1958). Hence, sulfate activation is the result of a two-step sequence catalyzed by ATP-sulfurylase which carries out Reaction 3 and by APS-kinase which is responsible for the phosphorylation of APS (Reaction 4) in the scheme presented as follows:

$$\text{inorganic sulfate} + \text{ATP} \xrightarrow[\text{Mg}^{++}]{\text{ATP-sulfurylase}} \text{APS} + \text{pyrophosphate} \tag{3}$$

$$\text{APS} + \text{ATP} \xrightarrow[\text{Mg}^{++}]{\text{APS-kinase}} \text{PAPS} + \text{ADP} \tag{4}$$

The first phase in sulfate conjugation, the activating process, has been essentially clarified by this work. Our knowledge of the second phase—the transfer of the sulfate group to various acceptors—is less complete. In this case, the situation is considerably more complex, since several transferring enzymes apparently exist which carry out the conjugation with acceptors of several different types. For instance, the separation of phenol sulfokinase from two different steroid sulfokinases was reported (Gregory and Nose, 1957; Nose and Lipmann, 1958), and indications were obtained of the existence of a whole family of sulfokinases which catalyze the conjugation of various steroids. In connective tissue, sulfokinases participating in the formation of sulfated glycosaminoglycans are present, as will be discussed elsewhere.

C. Acetate

In the mammalian glycosaminoglycans, the amino groups are generally fully acetylated, even if small amounts of free amino groups may sometimes be found. The question of whether this is due to incomplete acetylation during the biosynthesis or to partial deacetylation during the isolation procedure has not yet been satisfactorily answered.

Heparin, however, constitutes an exception to the aforementioned generalization, in that it contains no acetyl groups. Instead, the amino groups are linked to sulfate groups in a sulfamic linkage, which is considerably more labile than the usual *O*-ester sulfate bonds (Jorpes, Boström, and Mutt, 1950; Foster, Martlew, and Stacey, 1954). The closely related heparan sulfate contains amino groups which are partially sulfated, but also partially acetylated (Jorpes and Gardell, 1948; Brown, 1957; Linker *et al.*, 1958; Cifonelli and Dorfman, 1960) (see Volume I, Chapter 7).

The introduction of the acetyl group into a glycosaminoglycan molecule probably takes place at the glucosamine 6-phosphate stage, through the action of a hexosamine-specific acetylase. The existence of this enzyme had been indicated by Leloir and Cardini (1953), who observed acetylation of glucosamine 6-phosphate in the same extract of *Neurospora crassa* that catalyzed the formation of glucosamine 6-phosphate from glucose 6-phosphate and glutamine. The acetylation was not, however, studied in detail by these workers. A more thorough study of this enzyme, including a tenfold purification from yeast, was subsequently undertaken by Brown (1955), and its presence in several animal tissues has since been reported by Davidson, Blumenthal, and Roseman (1957).

Hence, acetylation seems to proceed via the conventional pathway, the acetyl group of acetyl coenzyme A being transferred by the hexosamine-specific acetylase to glucosamine 6-phosphate.

Alternative pathways for the introduction of the acetyl group into the glycosaminoglycans can be envisaged. According to Chou and Soodak (1952), glucosamine can be acetylated by an enzyme of pigeon liver which may be identical to the nonspecific arylamine acetylase (Tabor, Mehler, and Stadtman, 1953). The specific activity of the enzyme was low in comparison with the more specific enzyme isolated by Brown (1955) and Davidson, Blumenthal, and Roseman (1957). Moreover, the product, *N*-acetylglucosamine, is not readily utilized for the biosynthesis of glycosaminoglycans, and most likely is not on the main pathway in glycosaminoglycan formation.

II. Formation of Macromolecules

A. General Discussion

It would seem that the *in vitro* formation of a polysaccharide, whether it is of the homopolysaccharide type—like glycogen—or belongs to the group of heteropolysaccharides—like the glycosaminoglycans—represents a simpler problem than the synthesis of a nucleic acid or a protein, in which a complicated array of constituents has to be lined up in a specific order. Nevertheless, although the past 20 years have witnessed an enormous development in the general area of saccharide synthesis (Leloir, Cardini, and Cabib, 1960), we are still very much in the dark concerning the macromolecular aspects of the biosynthesis of the heteropolysaccharides. It is true that a vast number of data indicate that the glycosaminoglycans are formed from UDP derivatives of the different characteristic monosaccharide units. Despite this, it does not seem possible at present—on the basis of available data—to give a general, distinct picture of the enzymic polymerization processes leading to the formation of the macromolecules. Some progress has been made in recent years with respect to the synthesis of hyaluronic acid, as will be discussed later (Section III), but the closest precursors of the carbon chains of the sulfated glycosaminoglycans are still unknown, and, so far, no single example has been presented of a cell-free synthesis of the carbon chain of a sulfated glycosaminoglycan (see *Addendum*).

It is not intended in this chapter to discuss the general problems of polysaccharide formation, as this subject has been covered in several recent reviews (Barker and Bourne, 1953; Stacey, 1957; Roseman, 1959; Leloir, Cardini, and Cabib, 1960; Dedonder, 1961), but a few pertinent points will be briefly mentioned. According to our present concepts, the formation of a polysaccharide chain, once initiated, proceeds by successive transfers of glycosyl units from the appropriate donor. The uridine nucleotides seem to be more efficient as glycosyl donors than are the simple sugar phosphates; e.g., the glucose transfer potential decreases in the following order: UDP-glucose, sucrose, glucose 1-phosphate (Leloir, Cardini, and Cabib, 1960).

As group-transfer reactions involving optically active compounds may lead to an inversion of configuration (see Koshland, 1954, 1959), it is of interest to compare the configuration of the uridine-bound sugars with that of the polysaccharides. In the uridine nucleotides, which have hitherto been studied, the configuration at the anomeric carbon atom in the sugar is α, whereas most glycosaminoglycans have β linkages. These facts are thus compatible with a synthetic mechanism involving one transfer process. It should be noted, however, that a change in configuration does not always occur, as, for example, in formation of the α-linked glycogen from UDP-α-glucose (Fig. 2).

Like glycogen, heparin and heparan sulfate seem to be exceptions to the rule that β-linked polysaccharide constituents arise from α-linked uridine-bound sugars. Any theory on glycosaminoglycan synthesis will have to account for the formation of the α-uronidic linkages in heparin, and at least two possibilities can be suggested at present: (*i*) an even number of group transfers from UDP-D-glucuronic acid resulting in no configurational change at the anomeric carbon atom; and (*ii*) the existence of UDP-D-glucuronic acid with a β linkage, from which the uronic acid moiety can be transferred by a single transfer reaction (or another odd number of transfers) to the appropriate acceptor, thus producing an inversion of the configuration to α.

Because the reactions initiating the chain formation in glycosaminoglycan synthesis are not even known in the case of hyaluronic acid, which has been studied so extensively, it is at present futile to make any speculations on this topic. In connection with the studies on hyaluronic

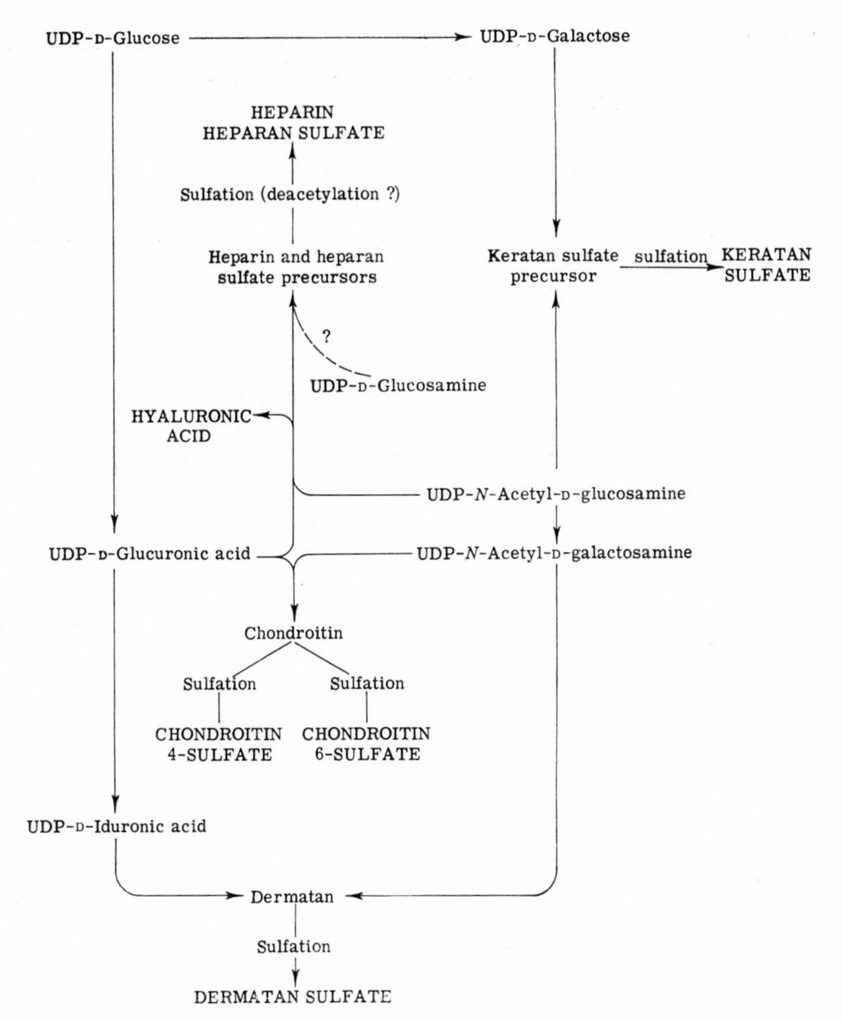

FIG. 2. Possible pathways of glycosaminoglycan biosynthesis.

acid synthesis (Markovitz, Cifonelli, and Dorfman, 1959), some different possibilities were suggested, but no definite conclusions could be drawn.

The instances of homopolysaccharide synthesis, which have so far been shown to involve uridine nucleotides (chitin, cellulose, and glycogen), generally exhibit a need for a primer, preferably in low molecular weight form (Glaser and Brown, 1957; Leloir and Cardini, 1957; Glaser, 1958; Hauk and Brown, 1959; Leloir *et al.*, 1959; Leloir and Goldemberg, 1960). Hyaluronic acid formation, on the other hand, did not need the addition of primer, but, since the particulate enzyme preparation still contained uronic acid, the existence of a tightly bound hyaluronic acid acting as primer could not be excluded (Markovitz, Cifonelli, and Dorfman, 1959).

In the native state, several of the acid glycosaminoglycans are apparently covalently linked to protein (see Volume I, Chapter 7). It has not yet been possible to study the biosynthesis of the carbohydrate–protein linkages, and this remains a major problem in the field of glycosaminoglycan metabolism.

B. Sulfate Acceptors

The formation of the sulfated glycosaminoglycans raises the special problem of the nature of the sulfate acceptors. Sulfation can be envisaged to take place either on the monosaccharide level or after some or all of the polymerization has occurred. When the isolation of a sulfate-containing uridine nucleotide, UDP-*N*-acetylgalactosamine sulfate, was reported by Strominger (1955), it was naturally believed that this substance was the immediate precursor of polysaccharide sulfate. Strangely enough, however, all attempts to demonstrate a role for this compound in glycosaminoglycan synthesis have failed (Suzuki and Strominger, 1960), and its function, as well as its own biosynthesis, is still completely unknown.

On the other hand, the work of Davidson and Meyer (1954) on corneal glycosaminoglycans lent support to the view that polymerization precedes sulfation. They observed that cornea contains polysaccharide fractions, which are only partially sulfated, with a sulfate content varying between zero and one sulfate group per disaccharide unit. As these fractions were not likely to be mixtures of nonsulfated and completely sulfated substances, it was suggested that the polysaccharide, rather than a monosaccharide, is the sulfate acceptor.

The possibilities of a more direct study of the problem of the sulfate acceptor were opened up by the work of D'Abramo and Lipmann (1957, 1958), who showed that S^{35}-labeled inorganic sulfate and sulfate from PAPS could be incorporated into chondroitin sulfate in a cell-free extract of embryonic cartilage. Continued work on this and other systems has provided much evidence to support the view that sulfation occurs on the polymer stage. It was preliminarily reported by Delbrück and Lipmann (1959, 1960) that a purified enzyme preparation from embryonic cartilage, obviously devoid of carbohydrate precursors, could transfer sulfate from PAPS to chondroitin 4-sulfate, dermatan sulfate, and chondroitin 6-sulfate or to the corresponding desulfated compounds, but not to hyaluronic acid, heparin, or keratan sulfate. Essentially the same results were obtained by Adams (1959, 1960), who studied the incorporation of radioactivity from S^{35}-labeled sulfate and PAPS into chondroitin 4-sulfate in the embryonic cartilage system. An uptake two to three times higher occurred in the presence of a chondroitin 6-sulfate–protein complex prepared from umbilical cord, and the stimulating activity was demonstrated to be due entirely to the chondroitin 6-sulfate component. Chondroitin 4-sulfate also stimulated the S^{35} incorporation, but to a lesser degree. After removal of the acid glycosaminoglycans from the original extract by precipitation with protamine, however, chondroitin 4-sulfate and chondroitin 6-sulfate possessed equal stimulating power. The results of Adams differed from those of Delbrück and Lipmann in one important respect, i.e., in the failure to obtain an increase in sulfate incorporation on addition of chondroitin (see also Adams, 1959a). The reason for this discrepancy is not clear.

Independent observations on various other tissue systems have now been reported from several laboratories. Greiling and Bauditz (1959) demonstrated sulfate incorporation into chondroitin and chondroitin 4-sulfate in a particle-free rat-liver extract. The sulfation of heparin in homogenates and particle-free extracts of mast-cell tumors was studied by Spolter and Marx (1959), Korn (1959a), and Ringertz (1960,a). Evidence was obtained for PAPS as the sulfate donor, and, again, the data pointed toward sulfation at the polymer level.

In an extensive study, Suzuki and Strominger (1959, 1960,a,b) found that a soluble extract of oviduct catalyzed the incorporation of radioactivity from S^{35}-labeled 3′-phosphoadenosine-5′-phosphosulfate into a number of glycosaminoglycans, including chondroitin 4-sulfate, dermatan sulfate, chondroitin 6-sulfate, chondroitin sulfate from shark cartilage, chondroitin from bovine cornea, chondroitin prepared by chemical desulfation of chondroitin 4-sulfate, and a heparan sulfate-like heptasaccharide. Hyaluronic acid, heparin, keratan sulfate, and charonin sulfate were inert. It is of interest to note that the naturally occurring chondroitin was a much better sulfate acceptor than the chemically desulfated compound was. In the same system, sulfate transfer could also be demonstrated to a large number of model acceptors, i.e., *N*-acetylgalactosamine, *N*-acetylgalactosamine monosulfate, and a series of nonsulfated and sulfated oligosaccharides prepared from chondroitin and chondroitin sulfate by digestion with hyaluronidase and β-glucuronidase. A relationship between chain length and velocity of sulfate transfer was established, the larger molecules generally being sulfated more rapidly than the smaller ones, with the notable exception of the nonsulfated trisaccharide and pentasaccharide, which were sulfated at the same rate as chondroitin 4-sulfate was. The fact that the sulfate content of the acceptor is important for the rate of sulfation was also observed by Ringertz (1960,a), who found that heparin fractions with a low sulfate content were most readily sulfated.

On a quantitative basis, the sulfate incorporation obtained in most of the studies mentioned above has been very low. Recently, however, Davidson and Riley (1960) isolated a sulfokinase from rabbit skin with a considerable specific activity, the incorporation of sulfate averaging one group per five to six disaccharide units. This enzyme was specific for dermatan as compared with chondroitin, chondroitin 4-sulfate, dermatan sulfate, chondroitin 6-sulfate, hyaluronic acid, and keratan sulfate. The particular problem of the specificity of the sulfokinases has also been studied by Suzuki, Threnn, and Strominger (1961). With the preparation from hen oviduct, the apparent Michaelis constant and maximum velocity differed for each acceptor, suggesting that several different sulfokinases might be present. Through chromatography on diethylaminoethylcellulose, a partial separation of three different sulfokinases was obtained, which catalyzed the sulfation of heparan sulfate, chondroitin 4-sulfate, and chondroitin 6-sulfate, respectively. Because only the heparan sulfokinase was stable during storage, it could be obtained completely free of other sulfokinases.

In summation, it now seems evident that a large number of glycosaminoglycan sulfokinases occur in various tissues which generally exhibit a high degree of substrate specificity. As most studies have been concerned with the *in vitro* sulfation of highly polymerized molecules, the degree of polymerization at which the sulfation occurs under physiological conditions still remains an open question. It seems reasonable to assume, however, that sulfation *in vivo* goes hand in hand with the chain elongation of the polysaccharide through the addition of further mono- or oligosaccharide units.

III. Formation of Individual Glycosaminoglycans

A. Hyaluronic Acid

1. Formation in Tissue Culture

Hyaluronic acid is the member of the group of acid glycosaminoglycans, the enzymic synthesis of which has been most successfully studied. In contrast to the sulfated glycosaminoglycans, hyaluronic acid is produced by both mammalian tissues and bacteria, and the large metabolic activity of the latter has been of great help in the elucidation of the biosynthetic pathways along which hyaluronic acid is formed.

The first experimental study of the production of hyaluronic acid seems to be that of Vaubel (1933), who studied the formation of synovial mucin, which is now known to be made up largely of hyaluronic acid. Using the mucin-clot technique, in which the mucin was precipitated with acetic acid, he could show the production of mucin in cultures of synovial tissue from rabbits. In experiments with other tissues, the results were either negative or indicative of only a slight mucin formation. The production of mucin continued over a long period in those cultures where the cells continued to grow as typical synovial cells—"synovioblasts"—whereas a dedifferentiation in the direction of typical fibroblasts was accompanied by a decrease in mucin synthesis.

Little progress was made in the study of glycosaminoglycan production in tissue culture until 1955, when experiments with human synovia and other tissues were reported from two different laboratories (Grossfeld, Meyer, and Godman, 1955; Kling, Levine, and Wise, 1955). Grossfeld, Meyer, and Godman (1955) demonstrated the formation of glycosaminoglycans in a variety of different tissues, including human synovia, rat subcutaneous tissue, and skin, bone, tendon, epiphysis, aorta, and pericardium from embryos. The nature of the product was indicated by the inhibition of mucin-clot production by testicular, as well as by bacterial, hyaluronidase. The correlation between the morphology of the cells and the mucin formation, which was found by Vaubel, could not be confirmed by Grossfeld, Meyer, and Godman, and mucin-clot production was observed for several different cell forms. In a similar study, Kling, Levine, and Wise (1955) showed the presence, in tissue-culture supernatants, of hyaluronic acid, which was characterized by the precipitation reaction with acetic acid, hyaluronidase digestibility, viscosity determination, tests for metachromasia, and electrophoretic patterns. Control cultures of periarticular tissues were negative with respect to hyaluronic acid production. In a subsequent study by Hedberg and Moritz (1958), both synovial and periarticular tissues were found to synthesize hyaluronic acid.

Continued work by Grossfeld *et al.* (1957) on various tissues showed that the fibroblasts in all cases produced more than one acid glycosaminoglycan. In addition to hyaluronic acid, a chondroitin sulfate with low sulfate content was also formed. The chondroitin sulfate fraction was also observed in the studies of Berenson, Lumpkin, and Shipp (1958), and the fact that it was only partially attacked by testicular hyaluronidase indicated the presence of dermatan sulfate in addition to chondroitin 4-sulfate or chondroitin 6-sulfate, or both.

Castor (1957), using a simplified culture medium, studied the production of hyaluronic acid in explants from synovial membranes from donors of different age. The amount of hyaluronic acid was determined by either hexosamine analysis or a turbidimetric method. The first method gave values ranging from 9 to 48 μg of hyaluronic acid per milliliter of medium, whereas the turbidimetric method gave considerably higher figures, varying from 72 to 264 μg of hyaluronic acid per milliliter. No explanation for the discrepancy between the two methods could be obtained. In a subsequent study, Castor (1959) refined the culture technique by using a suspension of trypsinized cells for subcultures in order to make possible a more quantitative approach to the study of hyaluronic acid metabolism in normal and pathologic conditions. He also investigated the influence of serum concentration in the medium and found a considerable increase in hyaluronic acid formation in the complete absence of serum.

In 1960, Morris reported a quantitative study on the formation of acid glycosaminoglycans in fibroblast cultures from calvaria of newborn rats (Morris, 1960; Morris and Godman, 1960). A correlation could be established between the rate of glycosaminoglycan production and the growth rate of the cells, with the more rapidly growing cells having a larger specific production over a given period of time. (Specific production was defined as micrograms of polysaccharide-bound uronic acid produced per microgram of mean deoxyribonucleic acid over the entire period studied.) From experiments with S^{35}-sulfate, Morris concluded that a sulfated component was produced to the extent of 5 to 10% of the total glycosaminoglycan formation. No attempts at further characterization were made.

2. Biosynthesis of Moieties

Although tissue-culture studies are able to give important information about many aspects of glycosaminoglycan production, such as, for instance, the influence of different environmental factors, they have, so far, been of very limited value in the elucidation of biosynthetic pathways. Knowledge about the biosynthesis of hyaluronic acid has come, in particular, from work on bacterial systems, which will later be described in detail, and also from *in vivo* and *in vitro* studies on various mammalian tissues.

The first indications of hyaluronic acid synthesis in bacteria were obtained in the studies of Kendall, Heidelberger, and Dawson (1937) on the production of capsular material from *Streptococcus hemolyticus*. Since then, several bacterial strains have been shown to produce hyaluronic acid (see Volume I, Chapter 7), although *Streptococcus hemolyticus* A has been most extensively used for the biosynthetic work.

Through work with radioactive glucose, it was established that the glucosamine, as well as the glucuronic acid, moieties of hyaluronic acid originated from glucose by direct conversion of the carbon chain. This conclusion was based on the fact that hyaluronic acid produced by streptococci grown on a medium containing unsymmetrically labeled glucose contained the major part of the radioactivity in the same position as the glucose. This was shown for the glucosamine moiety by the use of glucose-1-C^{14} (Roseman *et al.*, 1953; Topper and Lipton, 1953), and for the glucuronic acid moiety by the use of glucose-6-C^{14} (Roseman *et al.*, 1954). The pathways of incorporation are shown in Fig. 2 of Chapter 38 and Fig. 1 of this chapter.

Dilution experiments with unlabeled glucosamine and *N*-acetylglucosamine (Topper and Lipton, 1953) indicated that these substances could be utilized for the formation of the glucosamine moiety of hyaluronic acid. In similar studies (Dorfman *et al.*, 1955a), it was demonstrated that doubly labeled glucosamine (C^{14}, N^{15}) was actually incorporated into hyaluronic acid without appreciable change of isotopic ratio. Also, radioactivity from carboxyl-labeled *N*-acetylglucosamine was found in hyaluronic acid grown on an *N*-acetylglucosamine-containing medium. The incorporated radioactivity was, however, considerably decreased in the presence of nonradioactive acetate, indicating that the acetyl group was split off prior to incorporation into the hyaluronic acid. This is consistent with the previous finding of Rogers (1949) that streptococci contain a strong deacetylase activity. The utilization of *N*-acetylglucosamine, therefore, most likely proceeded via deacetylation and subsequent incorporation of the glucosamine by phosphorylation to yield glucosamine 6-phosphate, which can be acetylated and transformed into UDP-*N*-acetylglucosamine, as shown in Fig. 2 of Chapter 38.

Several mammalian tissues have also been used to study the formation of hyaluronic acid from C^{14}-labeled precursors. Incorporation of uniformly labeled glucose C^{14} was obtained *in vitro* with slices of synovia (Yielding, Tomkins, and Bunim, 1957), cells from the vitreous body, and sections or homogenates of the mucoid layer of the rooster comb (Balazs, Sundblad, and Toth, 1958) (see also Chapters 37 and 41); *in vivo* studies have been performed on rooster comb (Balazs, Mars, and Szirmai, 1955; Balazs, Szirmai, and Bergendahl, 1959) and on rat skin (Schiller *et al.*, 1956) (see Chapter 24). An experiment with glucose-6-C^{14} provided evidence for the direct conversion of glucose to the glucuronic acid moiety of rat-skin hyaluronic acid without rearrangement of the carbon chain (Rodén and Dorfman, 1958).

3. Role of Glutamine

The utilization of glucosamine for the formation of hyaluronic acid most likely represents a biosynthetic sidetrack which is only rarely used. The normal route seems to involve the enzyme system described by

Leloir and Cardini (1953), which catalyzes the formation of glucosamine 6-phosphate from glucose 6-phosphate and glutamine. (As described more extensively in Chapter 38, the substrate of amination is fructose 6-phosphate rather than glucose 6-phosphate.) In the formation of streptococcal hyaluronic acid in a resting-cells suspension, glutamine plays an essential role as a nitrogen donor (Lowther and Rogers, 1955a, 1956). In fresh cells, glutamine could be replaced by ammonium ions, which, presumably, formed glutamine together with intracellular glutamic acid. The synthesis of hyaluronic acid in aged cells required the addition of either glutamine or ammonium ions and glutamic acid, as the cells were evidently deprived of their intracellular glutamic acid during storage. Both fresh and aged cells could utilize serine and asparagine as nitrogen sources instead of ammonium ions. It was finally demonstrated that the formation of hexosamine in cell-free extracts could only occur from glutamine and not from ammonium glutamate. These studies, therefore, showed that glutamine can be regarded as an essential intermediate in the formation of hyaluronic acid in streptococci.

In the tissue-culture work of Morris (1960), the effect of glutamine on hyaluronic acid production was also investigated. Under most of the experimental conditions tried, glutamine either had no effect at all on the rate of hyaluronic acid synthesis or else produced a slight inhibition. If the cells had been preadapted to excess glutamine, however, there was a dependence on glutamine for growth (deoxyribonucleic acid synthesis), with a direct proportionality between glutamine concentration and growth rate. The total production of acid glycosaminoglycans was almost constant, irrespective of the glutamine concentration and the growth rate. In conclusion, therefore, no evidence was obtained to indicate a role for glutamine as a nitrogen donor in the fibroblast system.

4. Synthesis from Uridine Nucleotides

Once the basic features of hexosamine and uronic acid metabolism had been established, including the discoveries of the uridine-linked hexosamine and uronic acid derivatives, it was natural to postulate that the synthesis of glycosaminoglycans takes place from these "activated" compounds.

The first study concerned with the role of uridine nucleotides in the synthesis of hyaluronic acid was reported by Glaser and Brown (1955). Cell-free homogenates of the Rous chicken sarcoma were found to synthesize hyaluronate oligosaccharide chains from C^{14}-labeled UDP-*N*-acetylglucosamine. The product of the reaction was evidently not high molecular weight hyaluronic acid, as the recovery of radioactivity on reprecipitation was considerably less than the recovery of the hyaluronic acid, which had been added as carrier. Practically all the radioactivity was removed by electrodialysis in Visking casings, also indicating that the isotope was present in comparatively small molecules, although paper chromatographic examination of the incorporated radioactivity indicated that the product was larger than an octasaccharide. Evidence that the label had been incorporated into hyaluronic acid oligosaccharides was obtained by hyaluronidase digestion, after which C^{14}-labeled tetrasaccharide and small amounts of labeled disaccharide (*N*-acetylhyalobiuronic acid) could be isolated.

Incorporation of radioactivity was obtained not only from uridine diphosphate *N*-acetylglucosamine, but also from *N*-acetylglucosamine 6-phosphate. The latter compound was incorporated, however, via UDP-*N*-acetylglucosamine, and this was, therefore, considered to be an obligatory intermediate.

Similar experiments were also performed in order to establish a role for UDP-D-glucuronic acid in the Rous sarcoma system (Glaser, 1956). It was expected that a stimulation of the incorporation of UDP-*N*-acetylglucosamine would occur on the addition of UDP-D-glucuronic acid to the reaction mixture. Crude homogenate, ammonium sulfate–fractionated preparations, and homogenates treated with Dowex 1 in order to remove nucleotides were used as sources of enzymes, but in none of these cases could a dependence on UDP-D-glucuronic acid be established. C^{14}-labeled UDP-D-glucuronic acid was also used as a precursor, but in none of the systems mentioned could any incorporation be obtained. It was suggested (Glaser, 1956) that the UDP-D-glucuronic acid could not be utilized by the system because of rapid degradation to glucuronic acid 1-phosphate, and C^{14}-labeled UDP-D-glucose was therefore used as a continuously generating source of UDP-D-glucuronic acid. In this case, incorporation was observed, UDP-D-glucose being approximately half as efficient a precursor as UDP-*N*-acetylglucosamine. In view of the lack of incorporation of labeled UDP-D-glucuronic acid, however, it was considered possible that the reaction studied was a partial synthesis of hyaluronic acid involving the addition of single amino sugar residues to the ends of pre-existing chains.

Continued work on the streptococcal system has provided definite evidence for the participation of both UDP-*N*-acetylglucosamine and UDP-D-glucuronic acid in the synthesis of hyaluronic acid (Markovitz, Cifonelli, and Dorfman, 1959). By use of a preparation obtained by sonic disruption of streptococci and uridine nucleotides labeled with tritium according to the Wilzbach method (1957), synthesis of apparently high molecular weight hyaluronic acid could be demonstrated. In contrast to the system studied by Glaser and Brown (1955), the streptococcal system showed an absolute requirement for both UDP-*N*-acetylglucosamine and UDP-D-glucuronic acid, and, in addition, it also required Mg^{++}, Mn^{++}, or Co^{++}. UTP, UDP, and pyrophosphate inhibited the reaction. As UDP is one of the products of the synthetic reaction, its inhibiting effect could be of possible significance as a mechanism regulating the rate of synthesis. In a large-scale experiment, net synthesis of hyaluronic acid was obtained, with the amount of hyaluronate synthesized being at least ten times as large as that present from the beginning in the washed particles.

Markovitz, Cifonelli, and Dorfman suggested a possible mechanism for the hyaluronic acid formation, which explains (*i*) the formation of β linkages from the α-linked nucleotides, and (*ii*) the alternating addition of acetylglucosamine and glucuronic acid units to the hyaluronic acid chain. It is postulated that a single enzyme with three active sites is involved. Their attractive hypothesis is still, however, completely without experimental support, and further work with the streptococcal system can be expected to yield important information about the mechanism of synthesis of not only hyaluronic acid, but also of other heteropolysaccharides.

Recently, a study of the site of synthesis of hyaluronic acid within the streptococcal cell was reported by Markovitz and Dorfman (1962). It was found that practically all the synthesizing activity resided in the protoplast membrane. Attempts at solubilization invariably failed; phospholipase A, ribonuclease, and deoxyribonuclease neither solubilized nor inactivated the system, whereas inactivation resulted from the treatment with cold acetone or butanol, a filtrate from *Streptomyces albus*, and trypsin.

A preliminary report has appeared on the synthesis of hyaluronic acid in cell-free extracts of human synovia or fibroblasts of different origins (Altshuler, Kinsman, and Bareta, 1961). Tritium-labeled UDP-*N*-acetylglucosamine or C^{14}-labeled UDP-D-glucuronic acid was used as precursor. In another report, Schiller, Slover, and Dorfman (1961) showed that incorporation of radioactivity from tritium-labeled UDP-*N*-acetylglucosamine into hyaluronic acid could be obtained in a cell-free extract of skin from rat fetuses. The reaction required the presence of UDP-D-glucuronic acid and magnesium, and the enzymic activity was sedimentable at $20{,}000 \times g$.

B. Chondroitin

In contrast to the progress made in the study of the biosynthesis of hyaluronic acid, the knowledge of the metabolism of the closely related chondroitin is extremely limited.

In addition to the ability of chondroitin to serve as sulfate acceptor in various connective tissue systems, which has been discussed previously (see Section II,B) (Greiling and Bauditz, 1959; Suzuki and Strominger, 1959; Delbrück and Lipmann, 1960; Suzuki and Strominger, 1960), no information is as yet available on its biosynthesis or its possible role as an intermediate in the chondroitin sulfate synthesis *in vivo*. It seems, however, reasonable to assume that the formation of chondroitin follows the same scheme which is suggested for the carbon skeleton of the chondroitin sulfates (see *Addendum*).

C. Chondroitin 4-Sulfate

Although chondroitin sulfate, in contrast to hyaluronic acid, is absent in primitive organisms such as bacteria, important information with possible bearing even on chondroitin sulfate synthesis derives from studies on the synthesis of hyaluronic acid and other polysaccharides in microorganisms. Most studies on the chondroitin sulfate metabolism *per se* have, however, been made on mammalian or avian tissues by various *in vivo* or *in vitro* techniques.

1. Sulfation

Isotope-labeled sulfate has been an often-used tool in metabolic studies on sulfated glycosaminoglycans. Applied *in vivo,* this tracer technique has been of particular value in establishing the fact that the sulfate group of chondroitin sulfate and other sulfated glycosaminoglycans (Dziewiatkowski, 1951; Boström, 1952; Magnusson and Larsson, 1955; Rodén, 1956a; Schiller *et al.*, 1956), as well as ester sulfates in general (Laidlaw and Young, 1948; Dziewiatkowski, 1949a), actually derive from inorganic sulfate. The technique has also been extensively used in studies on the turnover rates of sulfated acid glycosaminoglycans, as will be discussed later (see Section IV).

Applied *in vitro* in various whole-tissue systems which synthesize chondroitin 4-sulfate, S^{35}-labeled sulfate has been of value in proving the enzymic nature of the sulfation process, its dependence on energy supply, and the influence of various agents on the rate of synthesis (see, for instance, Layton, 1951; Boström and Månsson, 1952, 1953,a; Boyd and Neuman, 1954; Rodén, 1956d; Whitehouse and Boström, 1961).

As previously discussed, additional and very detailed information on the sulfation process in the synthesis of the different sulfated acid glycosaminoglycans has been obtained recently from studies on cell-free systems of embryonic cartilage, hen oviduct, and other tissues. On the basis of these data, it seems to be well established that the sulfate group can be transferred from PAPS by means of specific sulfokinases to acceptors which are more-or-less high molecular weight compounds.

2. Biosynthesis of Moieties

Compared with the extensive studies on the formation of hyaluronic acid in various systems, very few observations with bearing on the formation of the carbon skeleton of chondroitin 4-sulfate have been reported. Whole tissue experiments *in vitro* have shown, however, that C^{14}-labeled acetate and glucose are introduced into the chondroitin 4-sulfate.

In experiments with cartilage slices, Boström and Månsson (1952a) showed that radioactive acetate was incorporated into the acetyl group of chondroitin 4-sulfate. Incorporation of C^{14}-glucose was obtained in the same system (Rodén, 1956c), with the major part of the radioactivity residing in the uronic acid and galactosamine moieties of the chondroitin 4-sulfate molecule with only slight labeling of the acetyl group. The specific activity of the glucuronic acid was four times larger than that of the galactosamine. Essentially, the same relation between uronic acid and hexosamine labeling was found by Friberg (1958a) in *in vivo* experiments on guinea-pig cartilage, whereas other *in vivo* studies on rat skin showed an equal distribution between the two moieties in hyaluronic acid, as well as in dermatan sulfate (Schiller *et al.*, 1956; Rodén and Dorfman, 1958). Several explanations for these differences can be suggested, but the complexity of the systems involved does not permit any specific conclusions at this point.

Although no experiments on chondroitin 4-sulfate synthesis with unsymmetrically labeled glucose have been reported, it might be concluded, in analogy with results obtained from such experiments on the synthesis of hyaluronic acid in streptococci (Topper and Lipton, 1953; Roseman *et al.*, 1953, 1954) and of hyaluronic acid and dermatan sulfate in rat skin (Rodén and Dorfman, 1958), that the introduction of glucose into the galactosamine and glucuronic acid moiety most likely takes place without cleavage of the carbon chain of glucose.

Some observations have been reported on the presence in cartilage and other glycosaminoglycan-forming tissues of enzymes which might be directly involved in the synthesis of chondroitin 4-sulfate. The enzyme system catalyzing the formation of glucosamine 6-phosphate from glucose 6-phosphate and glutamine (phosphohexoisomerase and fructose-6-phosphate L-glutamine transamidase) has been found in cartilage (Castellani and Zambotti, 1956) and cornea (Pogell and Koenig, 1959). UDP-D-glucose dehydrogenase, the key enzyme of uronic acid biosynthesis, is also present in cartilage (Zambotti, Castellani, and De Bernard, 1957), and, in addition, several nucleotides which presumably participate in the synthesis of chondroitin 4-sulfate: UTP, ATP, UDP-D-glucose, and UDP-*N*-acetylglucosamine (Bianco *et al.*, 1957, 1958).

3. Role of Glutamine

The effect of glutamine on the synthesis of chondroitin 4-sulfate has now been demonstrated by several authors. It was first observed by Boström and Månsson (1953a) that the uptake of S^{35}-sulfate into chondroitin 4-sulfate of cartilage *in vitro* was greatly enhanced by the addition of a liver homogenate to the medium. The compound responsible for this effect was subsequently isolated and identified as L-glutamine (Boström, Rodén, and Vestermark, 1955; Rodén, 1956). In view of the function of glutamine as nitrogen donor in hexosamine synthesis, it seemed most likely that the effect on S^{35} incorporation did not primarily involve the process of sulfate esterification. Rather, it could be assumed that the increased S^{35} uptake was concomitant with an increased hexosamine formation. This assumption received support by the demonstration that the incorporation of C^{14}-glucose and C^{14}-acetate was also enhanced by glutamine (Rodén, 1956c). Furthermore, replacement of glutamine with glucosamine produced an increase in S^{35} uptake of the same order of magnitude as that caused by glutamine (Rodén, 1956b), and, as the effects of the two substances were not additive, it is most likely that they both increased the amount of glucosamine 6-phosphate available for chondroitin 4-sulfate synthesis. Galactosamine stimulated the S^{35} incorporation only slightly—to the extent of a few per cent of the effect of glucosamine—which is in keeping with the fact that no pathway is known by which galactosamine can readily be converted into any of the presumptive galactosaminoglycan precursors.

The effect of glutamine on C^{14}-glucose incorporation into the hexosamines of cornea was studied by Pogell and Koenig (1959). Both in galactosamine, representing mainly chondroitin and chondroitin 4-sulfate, and in glucosamine, representing mainly keratan sulfate, an increase in label occurred in the presence of glutamine.

4. Synthesis from Uridine Nucleotides

Chondroitin and chondroitin 4-sulfate are assumed to be formed from UDP-D-glucuronic acid and UDP-*N*-acetylgalactosamine, but no experimental proof for this reaction has yet been obtained (see *Addendum*).

D. Chondroitin 6-Sulfate

The theories on the formation of the carbon skeleton of chondroitin 4-sulfate, which have been discussed above, might be valid even for the biosynthesis of chondroitin 6-sulfate, since the only known difference between these two compounds is the location of the sulfate group. In most metabolic studies made on chondroitin sulfate-containing tissues and tissue extracts, there has also been very little effort made to study separately these two sulfated galactosaminoglycans which, in fact, occur together in most tissues. Chondroitin, chondroitin 4-sulfate, and chondroitin 6-sulfate can all serve as sulfate acceptors in various systems. Although so far not established by actual isolation, the existence of a chondroitin 6-sulfokinase, in addition to a chondroitin 4-sulfokinase, seems to be very likely. Strongly supporting this view is the fact that a sulfokinase present in a human chondrosarcoma extract which contained only chondroitin 6-sulfate showed a specificity for chondroitin 6-sulfate, but practically no activity with chondroitin 4-sulfate or dermatan sulfate (Hasegawa, Delbrück, and Lipmann, 1961).

E. Dermatan Sulfate

Most information on the biosynthesis of dermatan sulfate available so far has been obtained from *in vivo* and *in vitro* investigations on skin of mammalian origin, the easiest available source of this compound.

The first metabolic studies showed that isotope-labeled sulfate, acetate, and glucose (Boström and Gardell, 1953; Schiller *et al.*, 1955, 1956) could be incorporated into the chondroitin sulfate fraction of rat skin, which is now known to consist mainly of dermatan sulfate. Information about the turnover of the skin glycosaminoglycans was also obtained in these studies, as will be discussed elsewhere (see Section IV).

1. Sulfation

Despite the fact that the sulfate group is located in the C-4 position of the galactosamine residue in both dermatan sulfate and chondroitin 4-sulfate, different sulfokinases are obviously responsible for the sulfation of these compounds. Thus, Davidson and Riley (1960,a) were able to purify partially a sulfokinase from extracts of rabbit skin which exhibited an acceptor specificity for dermatan. Sulfation of dermatan by this system was very strongly stimulated by UTP, but not by the triphosphates of guanosine, cytosine, and adenosine. The latter finding, which is not fully understood, is probably an indication of the close relationship between the sulfation and the polymerization process. The specificity of dermatan sulfokinase was also demonstrated when, in a recent study on the specificity of sulfate transfer to galactosaminoglycans, a sulfokinase specific for dermatan sulfate was demonstrated in a leiomyosarcoma (Adams and Meaney, 1961).

2. Formation of Moieties

The formation of L-iduronic acid constitutes a particular and interesting problem in the biosynthesis of dermatan sulfate, which has been discussed in Section III,E. Through the work of Jacobson and Davidson (1962a), UDP-L-iduronic acid has been implicated as a precursor of dermatan sulfate. The mechanism of formation of this nucleotide from UDP-D-glucuronic acid, however, still remains obscure.

The rabbit-skin extracts which form UDP-L-iduronic acid also contain an epimerase which converts UDP-*N*-acetylglucosamine to UDP-*N*-acetylgalactosamine in the presence of catalytic amounts of diphosphopyridine nucleotide (Jacobson and Davidson, 1963).

It would seem reasonable to suggest that the latter compound and UDP-L-iduronic acid are the direct precursors of dermatan sulfate.

F. Heparan Sulfate

The structure of heparan sulfate seems to be considerably more complicated than that of any of the glycosaminoglycans dealt with previously. It contains glucosamine residues, which are partly *N*-acetylated and partly *N*-sulfated. Furthermore, it apparently has a branched structure with great differences between different parts of the molecules. It has been claimed that the outer branches contain mainly disaccharide units with *N*-acetylglucosamine and no sulfate, whereas the inner branches contain *N*- and *O*-sulfated (disulfated) disaccharide units (Linker and Sampson, 1960). The uronic acid of heparan sulfate seems to be mainly glucuronic acid, but the presence of L-iduronic acid has also been demonstrated (Cifonelli and Dorfman, 1962) (see Volume I, Chapter 7).

The complicated and partly unknown structure of heparan sulfate, in addition to its sparse occurrence in normal tissues, has delayed elucidation of its biosynthesis, and, as yet, no reports have appeared on the formation of its carbon skeleton.

With regard to sulfation of heparan sulfate, Suzuki, Threnn, and Strominger (1961) recently reported on the separation of heparan sulfokinase from other sulfokinases present in an extract of hen oviduct. It was, however, not established by this study which type of sulfate residues was introduced into the heparan sulfate molecule by this enzyme, i.e., whether *O*-sulfation, *N*-sulfation, or both, occurred.

G. Heparin

1. Sulfation

It was known in the 1930's (Holmgren and Wilander, 1937; Jorpes, Holmgren, and Wilander, 1937) that heparin occurs in the mast cells of Ehrlich (see Chapter 27). Although these cells have been intensively studied with various cytological and histochemical methods, no information on the biosynthesis of heparin was obtained until recently. Isotope studies with S^{35}-labeled sulfate showed the introduction of this precursor into the mast cells of normal tissues (Asboe-Hansen, 1953; Jorpes, Odeblad, and Boström, 1953), spontaneous mastocytomas in dogs and mice (Asboe-Hansen, 1954a; Magnusson and Larsson, 1955; Larsson, 1956), dog-liver heparin *in vivo* (Eiber and Danishefsky, 1957), and heparin from slices and homogenates of rat liver (Sato *et al.*, 1958), but the possibilities of obtaining a suitable source of heparin-producing tissues were limited until the introduction of two transplantable mouse mast-cell tumors, the ascites type of Dunn and Potter (1957), and the solid type of Furth, Hagen, and Hirsch (1957). Since then, these tools have been used by several authors, mainly with the purpose of studying the introduction of the sulfate group into the heparin molecule. Some reports with bearing on the carbohydrate components of the molecule have also appeared.

It was shown by Day and Green (1959) and Korn (1959) that S^{35}-sulfate can be incorporated into heparin in slices of mast-cell tumors of the Dunn–Potter type. The *in vitro* sulfation of heparin in tumor homogenates was first reported by Spolter and Marx (1958, 1959), who demonstrated that labeling of heparin could be obtained when inorganic S^{35}-labeled sulfate or S^{35}-labeled PAPS was present in the incubation mixture. In more detailed studies on particle-free preparations of ascitic mast-cell tumors (Korn, 1959a; Pasternak, 1960), as well as tumors of the solid type (Pasternak, 1960; Ringertz, 1960,a), the findings were confirmed and extended. The formation of PAPS in these systems (Korn, 1959a; Pasternak, 1960; Ringertz, 1960,a), as well as of APS (Ringertz, 1960,a), was also demonstrated. In Chapter 27 of this volume the separation of various polysaccharide fractions of the mast-cell tumors is reviewed. When heparin or heparinlike fractions with different degrees of sulfation were tested as sulfate acceptors in the particle-free mast-cell tumor extract, it was noted that those fractions with lower sulfate content accepted sulfate more easily than did fractions with high sulfate content (Ringertz, 1960a). The sulfokinase activity found in the particle-free supernatant represents only a small fraction of the total activity of the homogenate (Ringertz, 1963). The largest activity was found in the granular matter which sediments at $11{,}000 \times g$. Ammonium sulfate fractionation of the $100{,}000 \times g$ supernatant indicated the existence of different sulfokinases, possibly specific for *N*- and *O*-sulfation.

Despite the interesting findings just mentioned, which seem to indicate that sulfation of heparin precursors takes place on the polysaccharide level, many problems concerning the sulfation process still remain to be elucidated. Among these are the possible specificity of *N*- and *O*-sulfokinases, the exact localization and distribution of the sulfate groups introduced in the molecules of the various members of the heparin family, and the relationship between the heparan sulfokinase isolated from the hen oviduct by Suzuki, Threnn, and Strominger (1961) and the sulfokinase activities demonstrated in mast-cell tumor.

2. Formation of Carbohydrate Moieties

Very little is known so far about the formation of the carbohydrate skeleton of heparin. It has been shown that C^{14}-glucose is incorporated into heparin in slices of mast-cell tumor (Korn, 1959). The existence in mast-cell tumors of an enzyme which catalyzes the formation of UDP-glucosamine from UTP and glucosamine 1-phosphate (Silbert and Brown, 1961) is of particular interest, since the glucosamine residues of heparin are sulfated rather than acetylated. It is, therefore, possible that heparin is formed from this nucleotide and UDP-glucuronic acid, which can also be synthesized by mast cells (Hambraeus, Rodén, and Boström, 1959). The sulfation would then occur after some degree of polymerization has taken place.

It was recently demonstrated (Spolter and Marx, 1961) that L-glutamine stimulates the sulfate incorporation into heparin in homogenates of mast-cell tumor. This observation, which is analogous to those made in studies on chondroitin 4-sulfate and keratan sulfate synthesis, most likely indicates that glutamine serves as the nitrogen donor in the synthesis of the glucosamine moiety of heparin, as well. Stimulation of the sulfate uptake was also obtained by the addition of glucosamine and glucuronic acid (Ringertz, 1963). The effect of glucosamine is in keeping with the results found in chondroitin 4-sulfate synthesis and is most easily explained by the assumption that glucosamine can be used as a substrate for the synthesis of the hexosamine moiety of the polysaccharide. The effect of glucuronic acid, on the other hand, is more difficult to understand at the present time.

H. Keratan Sulfate

The sparse occurrence of keratan sulfate and difficulties in its isolation have precluded more detailed studies on its biosynthesis. Labeled keratan sulfate could be isolated from nucleus pulposus after incubation with S^{35}-sulfate or C^{14}-glucose (Rodén, 1956a), and L-glutamine stimulated the uptake of isotope into the keratan sulfate, as well as into the chondroitin sulfate fraction (presumably mostly chondroitin 6-sulfate). In a study on cornea, Wortman (1961) demonstrated transfer of sulfate from PAPS to an unresolved mixture of corneal polysaccharides which probably contained keratan sulfate as its major component.

I. Chitin

Chitin is present in many lower animals as the major organic constituent of the skeleton. In particular, the exoskeleton of crabs and lobsters has often been used as a source of chitin (see Whistler and Smart, 1953). It is also a frequent constituent of the mycelia and spores of fungi. Practically nothing is known about the metabolism of chitin in animals, although the fact that the shells of crabs and lobsters become very thin during periods of starvation (Le Goffe, 1939) seems to indicate that, in addition to its more obvious function of providing mechanical support, chitin can be utilized as a carbohydrate and nitrogen reserve. Chitin always seems to occur together with protein, and the difficulties in isolating pure chitin without harsh treatment make it impossible to decide at present whether the protein is part of the native molecule.

It was first suggested by Leloir and Cardini (1953) that UDP-*N*-acetylglucosamine might be involved in chitin biosynthesis. The hypothesis has been substantiated by the work of Glaser and Brown (1957), who showed that chitin could be synthesized from C^{14}-labeled UDP-*N*-acetylglucosamine by a particulate enzyme from *Neurospora crassa.* Net synthesis of insoluble chitin was obtained, and the enzyme also synthesized soluble chitodextrins. In order to characterize the reaction product, it was subjected to partial acid hydrolysis followed by digestion with chitinase, which liberated C^{14}-*N*-acetylglucosamine in amounts large enough to account for all of the radioactivity of the partial acid digest. Further evidence that the reaction product was identical with chitin was obtained from the isolation of a series of C^{14}-oligosaccharides, including *N,N'*-diacetylchitobiose, after partial acid hydrolysis of the synthesized chitin.

Soluble chitodextrins stimulated the reaction, apparently functioning as primers, and were converted into insoluble chitin during the course of the reaction. Chitodextrins with a high average molecular weight showed the highest activity per unit weight. A stimulation of another kind was obtained with *N*-acetylglucosamine, which strongly stimulated the synthesis of chitin with the particulate enzyme, whereas no effect was obtained with a solubilized preparation of the synthetase.

A uridine nucleotide with possible significance in the metabolism of chitin has been isolated from the hypodermis of the shore crab, *Carcinus maenas* (Kent and Lunt, 1958). Although its composition indicated that it was closely related to UDP-*N*-acetylglucosamine, chromatographic analysis demonstrated that it differed from this substance, and the authors suggested that the hexosamine moiety might contain some labile substituent.

IV. Catabolism

Although various enzymes from bacterial, as well as mammalian, sources are able to split the acid glycosaminoglycans, our knowledge of their physiological breakdown in mammalian tissues is very limited so far. Davidson and Riley (1960a) reported, however, in a recent paper that extracts of young rabbit and chick embryo skin catalyzed the breakdown of S^{35}-labeled dermatan sulfate. The presence of UTP seemed to prevent the breakdown. This finding might indicate that this nucleotide is involved in the resynthesis of the polysaccharide from breakdown products formed by catabolic enzymes within the tissues. Different indirect approaches with bearing on the catabolism of glycosaminoglycans have also been made—e.g., studies on the turnover rates of glycosaminoglycans, on the excretion of glycosaminoglycans or their breakdown products in the urine, or on the fate of glycosaminoglycans after administration of these compounds to human beings or experimental animals. Since investigations of the latter type are discussed in Chapter 21, the present review will be limited to turnover studies on glycosaminoglycans.

Turnover Rates

A considerable amount of data collected during the past decade on the turnover rates of sulfated glycosaminoglycans has been obtained by S^{35}-sulfate experiments *in vivo*. The impetus for most of this work was derived from the short paper by Dziewiatkowski, Benesch, and Benesch, published in 1949, reporting a high uptake of S^{35}-labeled sulfate in articular cartilage of suckling rats which received injections of this isotope. An incorporation of S^{35} in the chondroitin sulfate of the cartilage was suggested and was later confirmed by actual isolation of labeled chondroitin sulfate from the cartilage of rats treated in a similar way (Dziewiatkowski, 1951; Boström, 1952).

This type of isotope labeling was used in the first turnover studies on sulfated glycosaminoglycans, the chondroitin sulfates of costal cartilage, and the dermatan sulfate of skin of adult rats, the half-life times of which were estimated at 16 days and 9 to 10 days, respectively (Boström, 1952; Boström and Gardell, 1953). Subsequent turnover studies on dermatan sulfate of rabbit skin by means of simultaneous labeling with C^{14}-labeled glucose and acetate and S^{35}-labeled sulfate gave essentially the same results (Schiller *et al.*, 1956).

The first studies on the turnover of hyaluronic acid were performed on rabbit skin in 1955 and 1956 by Schiller *et al.*, using C^{14}-labeled acetate and glucose as precursors. They found that the half-life time of hyaluronic acid amounted to 2 to 4 days, indicating a much more rapid turnover than that of sulfated glycosaminoglycans in the same type of tissue.

Extended and more recent studies on the turnover of hyaluronic acid and sulfated glycosaminoglycans have stressed the influence of age and various hormonal and environmental factors on the metabolic activity of glycosaminoglycans (see Chapter 24). To some extent, these studies have revealed very complicated and hitherto not fully understood conditions. Thus, the work of Davidson and Small (1963,a,b) showed a marked age dependence in the metabolic activity of the various glycosaminoglycans in rabbit skin, cartilage, and nucleus pulposus. Moreover, some of the glycosaminoglycans in the older animals did not show any appreciable turnover during the experimental period.

Although it has been known for a long time that chondroitin sulfate occurs in cartilage as a complex with protein (Mörner, 1889; Schmiedeberg, 1891; Shatton and Schubert, 1954), the metabolic studies have, until recently, been confined to the chondroitin sulfate moiety of the molecule. The problem of the turnover of the whole complex was recently approached by the labeling of the chondroitin sulfate moiety with S^{35}-sulfate and the protein moiety with lysine-1-C^{14}. The turnover rates (Gross, Mathews, and Dorfman, 1960) of the two moieties were found to be identical, indicating that the complex was metabolized as a unit. In the same study, it was also shown that the chondroitin sulfate which could be extracted with water had a turnover different from that of the residual chondroitin sulfate which could only be extracted with alkali, suggesting that the metabolic pool of complex is not homogeneous.

In addition to the just-mentioned studies on the glycosaminoglycans of cartilage, nucleus pulposus, and skin, which involved isolation of the compounds studied in reasonably pure form, some additional data obtained by more crude methods with bearing on the turnover rates of some other sulfated glycosaminoglycans in other tissues have been reported.

Thus, in studies of the sulfated glycosaminoglycans of the cornea and sclera of the rat eye, a marked difference was found between the elimination of ester sulfate from these two tissues (Dohlman and Boström, 1955). Although the half-value of the scleral curve was reached in about 10 days, the corneal curve showed a much slower decrease. Whether this difference indicates that the turnover rate of keratan sulfate is slower than that of the chondroitin 4-sulfate or is secondary to differences between the two tissues with respect to fluid and electrolyte exchange is unknown.

Studies on the turnover of sulfated glycosaminoglycans in the rat intestinal mucosa revealed a fairly rapid turnover (half-life, 1 to 2 days) of the labeled material of the mucus present in the goblet cells, whereas the S^{35}-labeled material diffusely distributed over the epithelial lining showed a much slower exchange of sulfate (Boström and Odeblad, 1954; Dziewiatkowski, 1956). In the absence of analytical data on the labeled compounds studied in these experiments on intestinal mucosa, no definite conclusions on the chemical nature of the actual compounds showing these metabolic activities can, however, be drawn. The same is true for the studies on the sulfate exchange demonstrated in the mast cells of subcutaneous tissues (Jorpes, Odeblad, and Boström, 1953), suggested to indicate the synthesis and breakdown of heparin or heparin precursors in the mast cells. Combined with the more detailed chemical studies on the glycosaminoglycans of cartilage and skin, they seem, however, to indicate that formation and disappearance of various glycosaminoglycans are steadily going on in various tissues.

The intricate problem of whether the metabolic activity demonstrated with the isotope methods does, in fact, represent a continuous synthesis and breakdown of the glycosaminoglycan molecules *in situ* or merely reflects the restoration of the amounts of material lost from the tissues by, for instance, physiological wear and tear, excretion to the body fluids, or mechanical damage of the tissues has not been established so far. The failure in the attempts to demonstrate the presence of hyaluronidases or chondroitinases in the mesenchymal tissues and to elucidate the physiological role of heparinase, in addition to the fact that the glycosaminoglycans (with the exception of heparin) are mainly deposited outside the cells, seems to favor the second possibility mentioned.

It might also be pointed out that many of the turnover studies on glycosaminoglycans discussed above, like similar studies performed on other polydisperse macromolecular compounds, are open to criticism from a theoretical point of view (Bergner, 1962). Thus, essentially nothing is known concerning the homogeneity of the compartments to which the tracer has been supplied in most of these experiments. Certain studies (Gross, Mathews, and Dorfman, 1960; Anderson and Odell, 1960; Hirschman, 1961) have revealed great variation in the turnover rates of various subfractions of the same type of glycosaminoglycan. It is entirely possible that the turnover rates demonstrated previously with the tracer methods apply only to a small fraction of the total glycosaminoglycan pool, and a more detailed understanding of these problems will have to await further methodological progress within this field.

Addendum

The incorporation of uridine nucleotides into chondroitin sulfate has recently been demonstrated (Perlman, 1963). A particulate fraction from a homogenate of embryonic chick cartilage catalyzed the incorporation of tritium-labeled UDP-*N*-acetylglucosamine into chondroitin sulfate, presumably via UDP-*N*-acetylgalactosamine, as the system contained UDP-*N*-acetylglucosamine 4′-epimerase. With particles from which the epimerase had largely been removed by repeated washing, UDP-*N*-acetylgalactosamine was a much more efficient precursor than UDP-*N*-acetylglucosamine.

The behavior of the newly synthesized polysaccharide on chromatography and paper electrophoresis indicated that a large part was low in sulfate. Since the sulfating activity was localized in the supernatant fraction of the homogenate, it was suggested that polymerization precedes sulfation.

Further support for the idea that polymer formation precedes sulfation was obtained by Silbert (1963), who studied polysaccharide synthesis in a cell-free system from mast-cell tumors. Incorporation of UDP-*N*-acetylglucosamine and UDP-D-glucuronic acid into a glucosamine-containing polysaccharide which behaved like hyaluronic acid in ion exchange chromatography was demonstrated. The polysaccharide was different from hyaluronic acid, however, as it was not digested by testicular hyaluronidase. UDP-Glucosamine could not be substituted for UDP-*N*-acetylglucosamine, and it was suggested that the acetylated polysaccharide could be transformed into heparin by exchange of the acetyl groups with sulfate at the polymer stage.

The fact that sulfation may occur at an early stage of polymerization is indicated by the work of Spolter, Rice, and Marx (1963). A large portion of the radioactive sulfate incorporated in a high-speed supernatant from mast-cell tumors was present in a fraction which was assumed to contain dialyzable heparin precursors of low molecular weight.

NOTE: The following papers of interest have been published since the preparation of this addendum and are also included in the reference list:

Boström, H., Gustafsson, B. B., and Wengle, B. (1963). Studies on ester sulphates. 18. Ester sulphate formation in the germfree rat.

Di Ferrante, N., Meyers, A. L., and Miller, L. L. (1964). Incorporation of sulphate-S^{35} and glucosamine-1-C^{14} into heparin during perfusion of isolated rat liver.

Larsson, K. S., and Boström, H. (1965). Teratogenic action of salicylates related to the inhibition of mucopolysaccharide synthesis.

Perlman, R. L., Telser, A., and Dorfman, A. (1964). The biosynthesis of chondroitin sulfate by a cell-free preparation.

Searls, R. L. (1965). An autoradiographic study of the uptake of S^{35}-sulfate during the differentiation of limb bud cartilage.

Silbert, J. E. (1964). Incorporation of ^{14}C and ^{3}H from labeled nucleotide sugars into a polysaccharide in the presence of a cell-free preparation from cartilage.

White, B. N., Shetlar, M. R., Shurley, H. M., and Schilling, J. A. (1965). Incorporation of [I-^{14}C] glucosamine into mucopolysaccharides of rat connective tissue.

Chapter 40

METABOLISM OF GLYCOPROTEINS, GLYCOPEPTIDES, AND GLYCOLIPIDS

Ikuo Yamashina

I. Metabolism of Glycoproteins

In this chapter, an attempt will be made to review the more recent work on the breakdown and the biosynthesis of glycoproteins. Although the description should be focused on the amino sugars in glycoproteins, the review will be extended to include their whole molecules, because at the present stage of investigation very little is known about the specific behavior of amino sugars in relation to other parts of the glycoproteins. Most of the studies have been made on the metabolic fate of the entire glycoprotein molecule.

A. General Features

1. Biosynthesis

The carbohydrate constituents of glycoproteins of various origins are generally various types of amino sugar, hexose, pentose, deoxyhexose, neuraminic acid, and, in a few cases, hexuronic acid, and sugar alcohol. Usually, several of these monosaccharides make up the polysaccharide moiety of each individual glycoprotein. Consequently, metabolic studies on glycoproteins certainly must deal with the breakdown and biosynthesis of these constituent sugars.

The metabolism of compounds of low molecular weight will be described in other chapters (see Chapter 38).

The pathways of the biosynthesis of glycoproteins are quite obscure. No direct evidence on the incorporation of the sugar moiety of the intermediary sugar derivatives into the glycoproteins appears to have been presented. The successful demonstrations that the nucleotide derivatives of sugars are utilized for the biosynthesis of various types of polysaccharides as direct precursors would lead us to postulate the occurrence of a similar mechanism in the case of glycoprotein biosynthesis, too. This postulation is especially supported by the presence in nature of the guanosine diphosphate derivatives of glucose, galactose, mannose, and fucose (Ginsburg, 1958a; Ginsburg and Kirkman, 1958; Denamur, Fauconneau, and Guntz, 1958; Foster and Ginsburg, 1961; Ginsburg, 1961), of the thymidine diphosphate derivatives of glucose, mannose, fucose, rhamnose, and hexosamines (Okazaki, Okazaki, and Kuriki, 1960; Baddiley *et al.*, 1961; Blumsom and Baddiley, 1961; Glaser, 1961; Pazur and Shuey, 1961; Kornfeld and Glaser, 1962), and of cytidine monophosphate-neuraminic acid (Roseman, 1962) and cytidine diphosphate ribitol (Baddiley, Buchanan, and Carss, 1957; Strominger, 1959) since these derivatives, as well as other uridine diphosphate derivatives, such as those of hexosamines and hexoses (Hassid, Neufeld, and Feingold, 1959), carry sugars specific for glycoproteins.

Nucleotide derivatives of oligosaccharides and sugar–amino acid conjugates have also been isolated from various sources. Thus, the isolation of uridine diphosphate-*N*-acetylglucosamine-galactose-*N*-acetylneuraminic acid, uridine diphosphate-*N*-acetylglucosamine-galactose-*N*-glycolylneuraminic acid, both from sheep milk (Jourdian, Shimizu, and Roseman, 1961), uridine diphosphate-*N*-acetylglucosamine-galactose-fucose from human milk (Kobata, 1962), uridine diphosphate-neuraminic acid peptides from *Escherichia coli* (O'Brien and Zilliken, 1959), and uridine diphosphate derivatives of *N*-acetylmuramic acid and its peptide conjugates from bacteria (Section I,E,1) have been reported. Since the oligosaccharide and the glycopeptide moieties of these nucleotides correspond to parts of the glycoproteins existing in the sources from which these nucleotides were isolated, these nucleotides are considered to be intermediates for biosynthesis of the glycoproteins.

There are, however, possibilities that these nucleotides may be the catabolic products of the glycoproteins. Much is to be expected in the exploration of the metabolic behavior of these nucleotides.

Besides the supposed participation of sugar nucleotides in glycoprotein synthesis, the possibility of transglycosylation reactions must be considered; for instance, Zilliken *et al.* (1954) and Alessandrini *et al.* (1956) succeeded in showing the enzymic synthesis of oligosaccharides containing *N*-acetylglucosamine by the action of enzyme preparations of *Lactobacillus bifidus* and mammalian tissues on lactose and *N*-acetylglucosamine, and Srinivasan and Quastel (1958) reported the enzymic synthesis of glucosamine-containing oligosaccharides and polysaccharides by the action of preparations of yeast and *Aerobacter aerogenes* on sucrose and glucosamine or *N*-acetylglucosamine.

Since the most characteristic feature in the chemical structure of glycoprotein is the combination of amino acid and carbohydrate, the biosynthetic formation of this combination would certainly characterize the glycoprotein synthesis.

Recent findings suggest that carbohydrates can be linked to the carboxyl or amide groups of aspartic acid or asparagine (Jevons, 1958; Johansen, Marshall, and Neuberger, 1961; Neunke and Cunningham, 1961; Rosevear and Smith, 1961; Izumi, Makino, and Yamashina, 1961; Yamashina and Makino, 1962), to the amino group of glycine (Konno and Altman, 1958), and to the hydroxyl group of serine (Masamune, 1956; Muir, 1958; Tsugita and Akabori, 1959). These suggested linkages indicate the existence of a mechanism by which these amino acids effect the combination of the polypeptide chain with the carbohydrate moiety in some specific ways.

It was shown that, in glycoproteins of bacterial cell wall, muramic acid combined with L-alanine through amide linkage, and enzymes participating in the biosynthesis of this amide linkage were extracted (Section I,E,1).

The asparagine–glucosamine linkage in ovalbumin has been well established in several laboratories (Yamashina, Ban-I, and Makino, 1963; Bogdanov, Kaverzneva, and Andreyeva, 1964; Tsukamoto, Yamamoto, and Miyashita, 1964; Neuberger, 1964). The same type of linkage seems to be implicated in ovomucoid (Montgomery and Wu, 1963; Montreuil, Biserte, and Chosson, 1963; Montreuil *et al.*, 1962), pancreatic ribonuclease B (Plummer and Hirs, 1964), α_1-acid glycoprotein from human plasma (Kamiyama and Schmid, 1962a; Eylar, 1962; Bourrillon, Got, and Meyer, 1964; Izumi, Makino, and Yamashina, 1962), γ-globulin (Nolan and Smith, 1962,a; Rothfus, 1961; Rothfus and Smith, 1963), and also in blood-group substance A from hog-stomach linings (Kochetkov *et al.*, 1964). The second type of linkage—a glycosidic one between sugar and hydroxyl groups of serine or threonine of proteins—has also become rather evident, although the evidence is so far still indirect. The existence of the linkage was postulated in glycoproteins of submaxillary gland (Tanaka, Bertolini, and Pigman, 1964; Bhavanandan *et al.*, 1964; Herman *et al.*, 1964) and in glycosaminoglycan–protein complexes (Anderson, Hoffman, and Meyer, 1963; Anderson *et al.*, 1964; Rodén, Gregory, and Laurent, 1964). In the former, *N*-acetylgalactosamine links to proteins, but, in the latter, the sugar concerned in the linkage is unknown. Rodén, Gregory, and Laurent (1964) claimed, however, that the residue galactosylgalactosylxylosylserine represents the terminal structure of chondroitin sulfate from bovine nasal septa. The third type of linkage, a glycosidic ester, as proposed by Gottschalk, Murphy, and Graham (1962) for glycoproteins of submaxillary gland glycoprotein, seems to possess minor importance, whereas the glycosidic linkage (the second type, previously mentioned) may be dominant in the same glycoprotein.

The linkage of serine to neutral sugar in Taka-amylase, as claimed by Tsugita and Akabori (1959), has been found to be erroneous. The linkage between aspartic acid and glucosamine seems to occur in this case, too (Anai, Ikenaka, and Matsushima, 1963).

Isolation of uridine diphosphate *N*-acetylglucosamine-6-fucose from hen oviduct was reported by Takahashi and Suzuki (1962). Adenosine diphosphate-glucose was as effective as uridine diphosphate-glucose as a glucose donor in polysaccharide synthesis in wheat germ (Trivelloni, Recondo, and Cardini, 1962; Dankert *et al.*, 1964a) and also in sweet corn (Frydman and Cardini, 1964). Adenosine diphosphate derivatives of mannose, galactose, and *N*-acetylglucosamine were isolated from corn grains (Dankert *et al.*, 1964), and guanosine diphosphate-D-mannuronic acid was isolated from a marine brown alga (Lin and Hassid, 1964). Enzymic formation of guanosine diphosphate-D-rhamnose and guanosine diphosphate-D-talomethylose from guanosine diphosphate-D-mannose was reported in a system extracted from a gram-negative, motile bacillus of soil, strain GS (Markovitz, 1964). Likewise, enzymic synthesis of cytidine diphosphate ascarylose (3,6-dideoxy-L-mannose) from cytidine diphosphate-4-keto-6-deoxy-D-glucose (Matsuhashi *et al.*, 1964) and that of thymidine diphosphate-4-acetamido-4,6-dideoxyhexoses (glucose and galactose) was demonstrated (Matsuhashi and Strominger, 1964). Formation of inosine 5′-diphosphate glucose and inosine 5′-diphosphate mannose in rat mammary gland, rat liver, and calf liver from inosine 5′-triphosphate and C-1 phosphates of the corresponding sugars was found to be catalyzed by enzymes which are different from those concerned with uridine diphosphate or thymidine diphosphate derivatives of glucose and mannose (Verachtert, Bass, and Hansen, 1964). Enzymic transfer of the sugar moieties to cell-wall lipopolysaccharides of *Escherichia coli* from guanosine diphosphate colitose (3,6-dideoxy-L-xylohexose) and cytidine monophosphate 3-deoxyoctulosonate was demonstrated (Edstrom and Heath, 1964).

2. Enzymic Breakdown

a. Proteolytic Breakdown. Proteolytic digestion of the glycoproteins of low carbohydrate content by gastrointestinal proteases seems to be a rather general phenomenon, since carbohydrates as minor constituents do not significantly alter the protein character of the glycoproteins. The presence of proteases specific for some glycoproteins has been reported. For instance, rennin acting on casein (Nitschmann and Beeby, 1960; Alais and Jollès, 1961; Jollès, Alais, and Jollès, 1961; Gibbons and Cheeseman, 1962), "collagen glycoproteinase" splitting off glycoprotein from collagen (Banga, Baló, and Szabó, 1961), and "ovomucinase" acting on glycoproteins of egg white (Lowenthal and Berman, 1959) belong to this category.

Proteolytic enzymes have been purified from *Streptococcus albus* that are able to lyse a variety of organisms, including staphylococci, and to dissolve cell walls prepared from the bacteria (Salton and Ghuysen, 1957). Since the cell-wall substances contain amino acids of the D series, and the streptococcal lytic enzymes were shown to liberate small dialyzable peptides and amino acids during the action on cell walls, at least one of these lytic enzymes seems to be specific for glycoproteins containing D-amino acid.

Utilization of glycoprotein of α_1-globulin fraction of human plasma by *Diplococcus pneumoniae* might be ascribed also to a specific protease of this organism, but the mode of the action has not yet been investigated (Li and Shetlar, 1961).

Digestion of a few glycoproteins of high carbohydrate content by gastrointestinal and plant proteases has also been reported. Bourrillon and Michon (1960) succeeded in effecting the digestion of α_1-acid glycoprotein of pleural fluid successively by pepsin, chymotrypsin, trypsin, and papain, and in obtaining glycopeptides of 88% carbohydrate content.

A similar glycoprotein, α_1-acid glycoprotein of human plasma, appears to be cleaved into at least two fragments by pepsin (Weinfeld and Tunis, 1960). There have been reports of digestion by papain or ficin of mucinous substances in the course of the preparation of glycoproteins with blood-group activity and of further digestion of these glycoproteins, which caused partial loss of their biological activities (Lawton, McLoughlin and Morgan, 1956; Morgan and Pusztai, 1961; Pusztai and Morgan, 1961a). Likewise, fetuin, a glycoprotein of fetal calf serum, was shown to be digested by papain (Spiro, 1962). Loss of the biological activities of gonadotropic hormones or of erythropoietic-stimulating factor by treating them with pancreatic proteases can be attributed to proteolysis (Li, Simpson, and Evans, 1949; Got and Bourrillon, 1960; Winkert and Gordon, 1960).

In general, however, glycoproteins of high carbohydrate content (30 to 40%) are rather resistant to gastrointestinal proteases, probably because of steric hindrance caused by the carbohydrate moiety to the accessibility to the enzymes of the susceptible bonds, as pointed out by Gottschalk and Fazekas de St. Groth (1960). The steric hindrance caused by the carbohydrate moiety seems to be partly due to the presence of neuraminic acid at the terminal position.

Gottschalk and Fazekas de St. Groth (1960), Gottschalk and Murphy (1961), and Gottschalk and Thomas (1961) showed that tryptic digestion of ovine submaxillary-gland glycoprotein was accelerated by enzymic removal of neuraminic acid, and Yamashina (1956) and Schmid *et al.* (1959) also showed that the α_1-acid glycoprotein of human plasma could be digested by trypsin, carboxypeptidase, or papain after acid treatment, which causes the splitting off of neuraminic acid and, at the same time, the denaturation of the residual part of the glycoprotein. The glycoprotein is otherwise quite resistant to the enzymes just mentioned.

In contrast to the difficult processes of effecting the digestion of the carbohydrate-rich glycoproteins, it appears to be a rather easy task to split amino acids further from the partially digested products (glycopeptides) of the glycoproteins. Digestion of a carbohydrate-enriched fraction of ovalbumin (Johansen, Marshall, and Neuberger, 1958; Nuenke and Cunningham, 1961) or of γ-globulin (Rosevear and Smith, 1958) by a mold protease (Crawther and Lennox, 1953) or by pancreatic proteases and papain was reported. Carboxypeptidase or leucineaminopeptidase has also been used for digestion of glycopeptides in connection with structural studies (Jevons, 1958; Johansen, Marshall, and Neuberger, 1958; Rosevear and Smith, 1958; Johansen, Marshall, and Neuberger, 1961; Rosevear and Smith, 1961; Yamashina and Izumi, 1962).

It is worthy of note that a protease of *Streptomyces griseus* (Pronase) was found to be extremely effective in digesting even the intact carbohydrate-rich glycoproteins, which illustrates the broad specificity of this enzyme. By this enzyme, polysaccharides to which only a single amino acid is linked were prepared (Yamashina and Makino, 1962; Izumi, Makino, and Yamashina, 1961, 1962; Kamiyama and Schmid, 1962).

Pronase is now the most widely used proteolytic reagent for preparing glycopeptides in the structural studies of a number of glycoproteins. It has often been experienced, however, that a few amino acids other than the one linking to carbohydrate still remain in glycopeptides, even after prolonged and repeated pronase digestion. The hindrance exerted by the carbohydrate may be conceivable as the explanation of the incompleteness of pronase digestion, but one has to pay attention to the fact that pronase is not quite a nonspecific protease. Actually, peptide linkages involving glycine and proline were found to be resistant to pronase when attempts to effect a complete digestion of pancreatic ribonuclease A by pronase were made by Kesner, Muntwyler, and Griffin (1964).

Kochetkov *et al.* (1964) found that a proteolytic enzyme of Asian influenza virus, strain Krasnodar 101-59, was able to digest blood-group substance A from hog-stomach linings releasing, among other components, a glycopeptide possessing aspartic acid as the only amino acid. Likewise, Bhavanandan *et al.* (1964) succeeded in effecting the digestion of submaxillary gland glycoprotein by pronase and a peptidase from bovine spleen, successively yielding *O*-seryl- or *O*-threonyl-*N*-acetylgalactosaminides.

b. Glycosidic Breakdown. Glycosidic digestion of the glycoproteins is still more difficult to effect. Specific splitting off of neuraminic acid is an exceptional case, and will be discussed in other chapters (see Chapter 43).

Lysozyme seems to be a β-*N*-acetylhexosaminidase, splitting the substances of the bacterial cell wall into soluble fragments (Schütte and Krisch, 1958) and has a slight activity toward chitin (Berger and Weiser, 1957) and its depolymerization products (Lenk, Wenzel, and Schütte, 1960) (and see Chapter 44). A markedly enhanced activity was observed when glycolylated chitin was used as a substrate (Hamaguchi and Funatsu, 1959).

Since the soluble fragments of the cell-wall substances produced by the action of lysozyme possess *N*-acetylmuramic acid as their reducing component, substitution of a hydroxyl group of C-3 of hexosamine by a lactyl group, as in muramic acid, or by a glycolyl group, as in glycol chitin, seems to accelerate the action of lysozyme.

Action of lysozyme on bacterial cells is generally affected very much by cell-wall structure (Salton and Pavlik, 1960). For instance, *Staphylococcus aureus* was found to be ten times less sensitive than *Micrococcus lysodeikticus* to the action of lysozyme when the enzyme action was followed by means of turbidity measurement. This difference might be due to differences in the glycosidic linkages of the glycoprotein on which lysozyme acts. Some of the constituents of cell wall other than the glycoprotein seem to affect the action of lysozyme. Thus, the removal of teichoic acid (Section I,E,1) from *Lactobacillus arabinosus* increased the sensitivity of the bacterium to lysozyme (Salton and Pavlik, 1960). Various strains of *Micrococcus lysodeikticus* differ in sensitivity to lysozyme action, depending on the content of carotenoid pigments in the cells. A yellow strain rich in carotenoid was sensitive, whereas a white strain of low carotenoid content was fairly resistant (Prasad and Litwack, 1961).

Many enzymes which are able to lyse living cells or to dissolve the isolated cell walls have been reported. An enzyme obtained from the autolyzate of *Bacillus subtilis* and an extracellular enzyme of the same bacterium are able to dissolve cell walls of various bacteria, and their action appears to resemble that of lysozyme (Kaufmann and Bauer, 1958; Nomura and Hosoda, 1956; Richmond, 1959,a; Satomura, Okada, and Fukumoto, 1957). *Bacillus cereus, Bacillus megatherium,* and *Bacillus anthracis* spores contain enzymelike substances which are able to lyse vegetative cells of both the same and other species. The mode of the action has not been fully investigated, although the release of glycopeptides from the cells was observed (Strange and Dark, 1957).

Similarly, the presence of a potent extracellular enzyme in *Staphylococcus aureus* was reported that is able to lyse cell walls of *M. lysodeikticus,* but not the living cells (Richmond, 1959,a). Many strains of actinomycetes produce various lytic enzymes. One of them, called actinomycetin (Welsch, 1947, 1958), is able to lyse many heat-killed gram-negative organisms, resulting in the release of soluble substances. An autolytic enzyme of a marine pseudomonad has also been found (Brown, 1961). Although the mode of the action of the lytic principles of enzyme nature just mentioned is not well known, enzymes of *Streptomyces albus* have been investigated fairly well as to their mode of action. Salton and Ghuysen (1960) and Ghuysen (1960) demonstrated that one of the lytic enzymes of this organism, called F_1, resembles lysozyme in its specificity of the action toward the cell-wall substances of *M. lysodeikticus.* Another enzyme from the same origin, called F_2B, seems to possess amidase activity hydrolyzing the linkage between muramic acid and amino acids or peptides. Welsch and Ghuysen (1953) and Ghuysen (1954) also described the presence of other enzymes in some streptomyces cultures which are able to lyse streptococci or pneumococci, but are unable to lyse *M. lysodeikticus.* In these respects, these enzymes resemble those found by McCarty (1952,a) and Mori *et al.* (1960). Nothing is known yet, however, about their mode of action.

A lytic enzyme seems to be present in bacteriophage. When *Escherichia coli* was infected by T_2 phage, glycopeptides were released which showed a pattern in chemical composition similar to those glycopeptides released by the action of lysozyme (Weidel and Primosigh, 1958; Primosigh *et al.,* 1961). A similar observation was made by McQuillen (1955) and Salton and Milhaud (1959) on *B. megatherium,* but it is not known whether the lytic enzymes and bacteriophage-tail enzymes are identical.

Enzymes acting on glycoproteins with blood-group activity, with the liberation of carbohydrates, have been recorded by numerous workers and are discussed in Chapter 49.

There have been also extensive enzymological studies on mammalian *N*-acetylhexosaminidase (Woollen, Walker, and Heyworth, 1961) and fucosidase (Levvy and McAllan, 1961)—enzymes which might play a role in the catabolism of glycoproteins; so far, studies have only been made with synthetic, low molecular weight substrates. Many glycosidases of microbial and plant origins have been investigated well, and some of them are active toward glycoproteins and the oligosaccharides derived from them, although activities of these enzymes on the intact glycoproteins are generally very poor. A crude extract of *Diplococcus pneumoniae* exhibiting β-galactosidase and *N*-acetylglucosaminidase activities is able to liberate the corresponding monosaccharides from the oligosaccharides prepared from α_1-acid glycoprotein of human plasma by partial acid hydrolysis (Eylar and Jeanloz, 1962). β-Galactosidase of *Escherichia coli* (Hu, Wolfe, and Reithel, 1959) and the crude preparations of β-glucosidase (almond) and those of testicular hyaluronidase have activities toward fetuin, a glycoprotein of fetal calf serum. The activity was, however, higher toward the glycopeptides derived from the glycoprotein by proteolytic digestion than it was toward the parent glycoprotein (Spiro, 1962).

Very extensive, stepwise glycosidic degradation of a carbohydrate moiety of α_1-acid glycoprotein of human urine was recorded by Barker *et al.* (1963). The principle was based on sequential enzyme induction in *Klebsiella aerogenes* (Barker *et al.*, 1964).

During the studies on the mechanism of the enzymic transformation of fibrin to insoluble fibrin, Loewy *et al.* (1964) and Chandrasekhar, Osbahr, and Laki (1964) observed that about 20% of the carbohydrate in fibrin was lost during the transformation. Based on the further findings of the concomitant reactions—the release of ammonia and the blocking of the α-amino group of the polypeptide chain—they presumed that the enzyme, fibrinase or fibrin-stabilizing factor, responsible for this transformation is a kind of transamidase, splitting off the linkage between ω-carboxyl groups of the protein and carbohydrate, which is probably of glycosylamine type, such as that found in ovalbumin and other glycoproteins, and forming a new amide linkage between the terminal amino groups and the ω-carboxyl groups of the protein. Thus, the carbohydrate is released, and ammonia is split off easily from C-1 of the reducing end of the carbohydrate. Enzymes exhibiting a similar type of reaction appear to be widely distributed in tissues (Tyler and Lack, 1964). This type of reaction is extremely interesting and important in structural and biological studies of glycoproteins, and further studies are awaited.

The asparaginyl–polysaccharide prepared by extensive pronase digestion of ovalbumin could be hydrolyzed by a prolonged action of emulsin, releasing aspartic acid and a mixture of tri-, tetra-, and higher oligosaccharides (Lee, Wu, and Montgomery, 1964). Blocking of the α-amino group of the asparagine residue made the glycopeptide resistant to the action of emulsin. Bhavanandan *et al.* (1964) found β-*N*-acetylgalactosaminidase in bovine spleen that was able to hydrolyze *O*-seryl- or *O*-threonyl-*N*-acetylgalactosaminides to the amino acids and *N*-acetylgalactosamine.

β-*N*-Acetylglucosaminidase was extracted from *E. coli* cells by sonication and then purified. It was found to act upon cell-wall glycopeptides (Maass, Pelzer, and Weidel, 1964).

Five glycopeptidases were identified in the dried acetone precipitate of a suspension of *E. coli* B on the basis of their action on purified glycopeptides from the same bacteria. By examining the reaction products, the enzymes were defined as D-alanine carboxypeptidase, *N*-acetylglucosaminidase, muramidase, mucoendopeptidase, and *E. coli* lysozyme, respectively (Pelzer, 1963).

Sharon and Seifter (1964) were able to show that lysozyme of egg white was capable of transglycosylation reaction when the tetrasaccharide, *N*-acetylglucosaminyl-*N*-acetylmuramyl-*N*-acetylglucosaminyl-*N*-acetylmuramic acid was used as a substrate. After the reaction, tri-, tetra-, and penta-oligomers of the disaccharide, *N*-acetylglucosaminyl-*N*-acetylmuramic acid, were detected, whereas neither free *N*-acetylglucosamine nor *N*-acetylmuramic acid was detectable.

Identity of T_2 phage enzyme and egg-white lysozyme in their actions on cell walls was proved by Maass and Weidel (1963).

The presence of a lytic factor in the cell wall of *Streptococcus faecalis* was reported by Montague (1963). Novaes and Villanueva (1963) reported the presence of enzyme activity in culture medium of *Streptomyces* GM that was able to lyse *Candida subtilis,* resulting in the formation of protoplast. From the lysate, glycopeptides were isolated and analyzed. The spore coat of *Aspergillus oryzae* was found to be partially hydrolyzed by a lytic factor from *Bacillus circulans* (Horikoshi and Iida, 1964).

Sequential action of the enzyme of *Bacillus subtilis* and lysozyme caused the liberation of muramic acid from the cell-wall polysaccharide of *Micrococcus lysodeikticus* (Okada and Fukumoto, 1960,a). A lytic factor from *Bacillus subtilis* was further characterized, and its production was discussed in relation to growth, sporulation, phage multiplication, and transformation (Young and Spizizen, 1963). One of the lytic enzymes from *Streptomyces albus* (strain G) was purified and named "32 enzyme," and the amidase from the same strain was further characterized (Ghuysen, Leyh-Bouille, and Dierckx, 1962). The two enzymes were used successively in degrading the cell wall of *Staphylococcus aureus,* strain Copenhagen (Ghuysen and Strominger, 1963). The lytic principle of phage K was attributed to the sensitization of staphylococcal lysin caused by the phage infection (Ralston, 1963).

β-*N*-Acetylglucosaminidase from pig epididymis and α-*N*-acetylglucosaminidase from testis were able to liberate *N*-acetylglucosamine from teichoic acids (Nathenson and Strominger, 1962). The localization of *N*-acetyl-β-glucosaminidase in rat tissues was investigated, and the enzyme activities were found to be rich in the tissues which related to the metabolism of glycoproteins (Pugh and Walker, 1961). β-*N*-Acetyl-D-glucosaminidase has been extensively purified from acetone powder of beef liver, and it was found that relative activities of the enzyme toward the trisaccharide prepared from hyaluronic acid and phenylglycoside were constant throughout the purification stages (Weissmann, Hadjiioannou, and Tornheim, 1964). The localization of β-galactosidase, β-*N*-acetylglucosaminidase, and α-L-fucosidase in tissues and in subcellular particles has been investigated (Conchie and Hay, 1963). Levvy and McAllan (1963,a) reported the presence of β-D-fucosidase in the limpet and further studied mammalian β-D-fucosidase and β-D-galactosidase.

B. Plasma Glycoproteins

As the many review articles indicate (Winzler, 1955; Jorpes and Yamashina, 1956; Winzler, 1960), there are so many proteins carrying various amounts of carbohydrate of different types that the phrase "metabolism of plasma glycoproteins" may almost be replaced by the phrase "metabolism of plasma proteins."

Specific features of the metabolism of plasma glycoproteins have very often been discussed, since the concentration of the glycoproteins in plasma has very frequently been considered to indicate many physiological and pathological conditions. Many experiments have actually been performed by the estimation of protein-bound carbohydrate on whole plasma or serum or on each individual glycoprotein isolated by electrophoresis (mostly by paper) or by various fractionation methods.

It is beyond the scope of this chapter to describe these endeavors limited to the measurements of glycoprotein levels in plasma, since the details are discussed in Chapter 34. In contrast to the abundance of these rather clinical studies, there are very few studies on the site and the pathways of biosynthesis and on the breakdown of the plasma glycoproteins.

Werner (1949) claimed that the liver may be an organ where the plasma glycoproteins are synthesized; he showed that the level of glycoproteins in plasma was significantly lowered when the liver was injured by a chemical reagent, such as benzol or phosphorus. This view, although based on indirect evidence, is also compatible with results obtained by others, for instance by Greenspan (1954), who demonstrated that the glycoprotein (α_1-acid) level was subnormal in patients with parenchymatous liver disease. Plasma proteins, in general, are considered to be synthesized mainly in the liver (Miller and Bale, 1954; Tarver, 1954; Peters, 1957).

When labeled amino acids are administered to animals orally or by injection, marked labeling of proteins occurs in various tissues, such as the intestinal mucosa, liver, kidney, spleen, pancreas, and bone marrow. The incorporation into the plasma proteins is usually somewhat delayed. When intact mice were used as recipients, the maximum rates of the incorporation into the plasma proteins occurred 20 to 30 min after the intravenous injection of the amino acids, whereas the rates of the incorporation into the tissues occurred 10 to 20 min after the injection, as demonstrated by Borsook *et al.* (1950). It appears reasonable that the administered amino acids are transported to the site where protein synthesis takes place, and that the synthesized proteins are delivered into the circulating blood stream. The existence of a dynamic equilibrium among plasma proteins, tissue proteins, and the intermediates in the pool of the synthesis site and the effect of this equilibrium on the breakdown and the synthesis should be taken into account, however.

Estimation of the turnover of plasma proteins was attempted by calculations on the descending part of the curves of isotope concentration in proteins versus time.

As long as the curve follows the first order of kinetics, it is possible to estimate half-life time, turnover rate, or other related constants. This principle has most widely been applied to other metabolites in various biological systems. In the use of this type of method, however, it is usual not to obtain a first-order decay curve because of the complexity of the metabolism, and, consequently, only an approximate estimation of half-life value may be obtained.

Another method which was devised to estimate the turnover of plasma proteins involves the labeling of the protein in a donor animal, removal of the protein from the donor, and transference of it to the recipient animals. Lysine-C^{14} or -N^{15}, methionine-S^{35}, and other amino acids are used as labeling reagents. Numerous investigations have also been made by use of proteins labeled *in vitro* with I^{131}. General surveys of these investigations were given by Tarver (1954) and Anker (1960).

In summary, it may be said that the half-life time of the total plasma proteins was estimated to be 2.6 to 4.4 days in rats, 5.2 to 6.6 days in dogs, and 7 to 10 days in humans by the use of the method of calculation of the isotope concentration versus time. More accurate results—that is, 3 days in rats and 5.0 to 5.4 days in dogs—were obtained by use of labeled proteins. Studies on a single protein fraction of plasma were also carried out.

Recently, Jeffay and Winzler (1958) made rather accurate measurements on the turnover rates of rat plasma proteins. S^{35}-Yeast protein was given to rats, blood was taken and submitted to paper electrophoresis, and the separated protein bands were eluted and injected into recipient rats. At various time intervals, blood samples were taken, and the plasma was again subjected to paper electrophoresis. A comparison was also made with the results obtained from similar experiments in which L-methionine-S^{35} was given orally. Although first-order decay curves were obtained on albumin and γ-globulin, in clear contrast to those obtained with oral-administration experiments in which no accurate calculation was possible, the decay curves for other proteins were of different types, and many different conclusions were drawn. In these experiments, it was evident that reutilization of orally administered S^{35}-methionine is so great as to preclude accurate estimates of metabolic activity of plasma proteins; the use of a labeled protein circumvents this difficulty and leads to more accurate values for turnover rates. In agreement with observations by previous investigators (Niklas and Maurer, 1952), it was concluded by Jeffay and Winzler (1958) that γ-globulins turn over more slowly than any other plasma proteins. The deviation of curves for β-globulins from those expected could be explained mostly by heterogeneity of the β-globulin fraction. Catabolism of the β-globulins, followed by the re-entering of labeled amino acids into newly formed β-globulins, could be neglected, since such reutilization did not appear important in the turnover of albumin or γ-globulin. The α_1-globulins have a rapid rate of turnover, but Niklas and Maurer claim that the calculations of pool size and replacement rate were less satisfactory than those obtained in albumin or γ-globulin studies, apparently because of the difficulties in the isolating of α_1-globulin free from albumin by paper electrophoresis. α_2-Globulins behave in a quite different way. The rapid disappearance of the radioactivity suggests that a sequestration of components of the α_2-globulins in some body compartment may occur.

Besides these observations, it was further demonstrated that radioactivity from intravenously administered S^{35}-labeled rat albumin was later incorporated into the various globulin fractions, an observation in agreement with the report of Maurer and Müller (1955). It was also stated that the injection of any radioactive globulin leads to the labeling of the other globulin fractions, as well as of the albumin fraction. Since the isotope reutilization, if it occurs at all, is minimal under the conditions employed, Jeffay and Winzler (1958,a) claimed that rather direct conversion of one plasma protein into another, with only partial hydrolysis to free amino acids, may be considered to occur. Conversion of serum albumin to α-globulin was claimed to occur also in the liver of rats *in vitro* (Roberts and Kelley, 1956).

In other experiments performed by Jeffay and Winzler (1958a), interesting observations were made which indicated that the turnover of albumin is increased when the dietary protein content is high. The half-life of rat plasma albumin when the dietary protein content was normal (3.7 days) was found to be elevated up to 1.5 days when the dietary protein content was three times as high as the normal. The turnover of albumin when the dietary protein content is low had a rather clear trend toward a decreased rate, although the differences were not so great as when there was a high dietary protein content. On the contrary, the turnover rate of α_1, α_2-, β- and γ-globulins showed no obvious tendency to increase or decrease according to the dietary protein content. A similar observation was made also on the effect of dietary proteins on the serum proteins of chickens (Leveille, Fisher, and Feigenbaum, 1961). These observations may lead to a hypothesis that serum albumin serves as the useful source for the synthesis of other body proteins, probably by contributing to the tissue pools of the intermediates.

In this connection, Walter *et al.* (1957) studied the rate and the extent of incorporation of radioactive residues from the homologous plasma protein, which had been injected, into proteins of various tissues. They found that the rate of incorporation of S^{35} into the proteins of liver, lung, spleen, and other tissues after injection of S^{35}-serum albumin was approximately the same as it was after injection of a mixed acid hydrolyzate of S^{35}-yeast protein and S^{35}-serum albumin or pepsin digest of the S^{35}-serum albumin. From these experiments, it may be assumed that plasma protein, especially albumin, is converted to other plasma proteins and tissue proteins—probably through breakdown to amino acids or small peptides. The assumption may be compatible with the previous reports of failure of attempts to prevent, by injections of nonradioactive methionine, the appearance of S^{35} in the tissue proteins of rabbits or rats which had received injection of homologous serum proteins containing S^{35}-methionine (Loftfield and Harris, 1956). It is likely, therefore, that the intracellular amino acids are not in an immediate equilibrium with the free amino acids of the blood plasma.

The observations just reviewed involve the fate of the protein moiety of the glycoproteins, although no measurements were made on the carbohydrate moieties of the glycoproteins.

Metabolic studies on plasma proteins with labeled carbohydrate were performed rather recently. Becker and Day, in 1953, were the first to report that administered radioactive isotopes were incorporated into plasma glycoproteins. These authors investigated the route of glucosamine biosynthesis from glucose and glucosone, the latter being supposed to be a direct intermediate of glucosamine biosynthesis. Glucosone was oxidized to carbon dioxide by a much slower rate than was glucose, but both are utilized for liver glycogen synthesis to a nearly equal extent. The C^{14} from the glucosone-1-C^{14} that was fed, however, was recovered in the protein-bound serum glucosamine in an amount much greater than when the glucose-1-C^{14} was fed. Although Becker and Day supposed that glucosone formation from glucose may be a step in glucosamine biosynthesis, a further investigation into this subject made by Dorfman *et al.* (1955a) was not able to support this hypothesis. These latter authors showed, using glucosone-1-C^{14} and uniformly labeled glucosone-C^{14}, that glucosone could be utilized for not only glucosamine but also glucuronic acid in hyaluronic acid produced by group-A streptococcus, as well as for acetate and lactate in the culture medium. At least in this organism, it seems possible that equal labeling of the glucuronic acid and glucosamine moieties may result from the conversion of glucosone to glucose before it is transformed into direct intermediates (see Chapter 38).

Südhof and Abraham (1957) observed that glucose and fructose carbons administered intravenously were incorporated into serum protein-bound galactose, mannose, and glucosamine by normal rats, rabbits, and dogs. C^{14} was detected in the serum protein-bound hexoses as early as 1 hour after the injection, and the specific activities of galactose and mannose in any animal and at all intervals studied were of the same magnitude. It made no difference whether glucose or fructose was used as C^{14} source, so long as the same counts of radioactivity were injected per unit weight of animals. Galactose and mannose may well be synthesized from the common intermediate derived equally from glucose or fructose, possibly without scission of the carbon chain. On the other hand, incorporation of uniformly labeled glucose-C^{14} into protein-bound glucosamine proceeded more slowly than it did into hexoses, reaching its peak 8 to 10 hr after the injection, and the specific activities of glucosamine were also always lower than those of hexoses.

Spiro (1959) studied the incorporation of C^{14} of uniformly labeled glucose-C^{14} into protein-bound glucosamine in tissues and plasma. After a single intraperitoneal injection of uniformly labeled glucose-C^{14} given to rats, the specific activity and, consequently, total activity of liver protein-bound glucosamine reached its maximum in 1½ hr. Glucosamine in the serum, on the other hand, was at first much less active than that in the liver, had about equal activity at 3.75 hr when it reached a peak, and was more active than that in the liver at all times thereafter. Incorporation of C^{14} from uniformly labeled fructose-C^{14} into the liver and the serum glucosamine was similar in manner to that of C^{14} from uniformly labeled glucose-C^{14}. From the curves from which the specific activities of serum glucosamine and liver glucosamine were plotted versus various times after the injection of the tracer dose, it became apparent that the liver and serum glucosamines meet the criteria for the precursor–product relationship as formulated by Zilversmit, Entenman, and Chaikoff (1948). This relationship suggested that liver is the main site of the serum glucosamine synthesis. Half-life times calculated from the decay curve were 8.9 hr for liver glucosamine and 14.0 hr for serum glucosamine. The value for serum glucosamine may be comparable with the results obtained by Jeffay and Winzler (1958) if consideration is given to the fact that the proteins containing glucosamine in plasma are heterogeneous and belong mainly to α_1- and α_2-globulins.

Instead of an investigation into the mixture of glycoproteins, an incorporation study on a separated glycoprotein was made by Boström, Rodén, and Yamashina (1958). In their study, C^{14}-labeled α_1-acid glycoprotein was isolated in a fairly homogeneous state, as judged by paper electrophoresis, from the plasma of guinea pigs after intraperitoneal injection of uniformly labeled glucose-C^{14}. A degree of incorporation of C^{14} into the glycoprotein that was higher than that into the other plasma proteins was observed. Activity was rather concentrated in the neutral sugar moiety and less concentrated in glucosamine and neuraminic acids, indicating very low radioactivity in the peptide moiety of the glycoprotein. The maximal labeling was observed at about 24 hr after the injection, except in the case of glucosamine, for which the maximal labeling was observed at 12 hr or earlier after the injection. The approximate half-life time of the glycoprotein was calculated to be 1 to 2 days. It is apparent, even from these few experiments, that the metabolic behavior of the various glycoproteins of plasma is different for each one.

We may conclude from the information available that glycoproteins belonging to α_1- and α_2-globulins turn over more rapidly than do other plasma proteins. It is supposed, furthermore, that at least a considerable part of the peptide moiety of these globulins may be derived from serum albumin through a breakdown to amino acids or small peptides. In this connection, it may be worthwhile to notice that plasma proteins are not independent, but interrelated to each other—that is, in all the protein fractions of plasma, the molar ratios of a number of pairs of amino acids remained constant although their absolute quantities per unit of nitrogen varied markedly (Block, 1961).

On the other hand, the carbohydrate moiety of the globulins may be derived from another carbohydrate pool in which the intermediates are formed from monosaccharides, such as glucose, fructose, or glucosamine, although these monosaccharides are interconvertible in tissues via the common intermediates.

In very recent studies on biosynthesis of plasma glycoproteins, glucosamine-1-C^{14} was found to be most useful. Shetlar *et al.* (1961) found that glucosamine-1-C^{14} injected intraperitoneally into rats and rabbits was rapidly and effectively incorporated into liver protein-bound glucosamine and into various serum fractions. Maximum incorporation of the radioactivities into serum proteins was observed 2 or 3 hr and 6 to 8 hr after the injection of the glucosamine into rats and rabbits, respectively, when 25 to 28% of the injected radioactivities appeared in serum proteins. The α_1-acid glycoprotein gained the highest concentration of the radioactivity, but α_1- and α_2-globulins were also considerably radioactive. It is of particular interest that the neutral hexoses (mannose and galactose) had very little radioactivity (Shetlar, 1961). Kohn, Winzler, and Hoffmann (1962) also investigated the metabolism of glucosamine-1-C^{14} and *N*-acetylglucosamine-1-C^{14} in liver of rats. They showed that the injected glucosamine was an excellent precursor of glucosamine and neuraminic acid of high molecular weight substances, most probably glycoproteins, in liver, whereas *N*-acetylglucosamine-1-C^{14} was much less effective, and glucose-1-C^{14} was very poor. Based on the earlier observations that glucosamine is phosphorylated much more rapidly than *N*-acetylglucosamine by hexokinase preparation of liver and other organs, Kohn, Winzler, and Hoffmann (1962) suggested the presence of a route of the utilization of glucosamine for glycoprotein synthesis via glucosamine 6-phosphate, glucosamine 1-phosphate, and uridine diphosphate glucosamine. This pathway was also recently shown to be involved in heparin biosynthesis in mouse mast-cell tumor (Silbert and Brown, 1961).

Of course, a pathway which involves *N*-acetylglucosamine, *N*-acetylglucosamine 6-phosphate, *N*-acetylglucosamine 1-phosphate, and uridine diphosphate *N*-acetylglucosamine as the intermediates for the biosynthesis of glycoproteins or other bound glucosamines has generally been agreed on as existing (see Fig. 1). It appears, however, from the results of Shetlar (1961) and Kohn, Winzler, and Hoffmann (1962) that the conversion of glucosamine to fructose 6-phosphate is not a favored pathway for glucosamine metabolism, and *N*-acetylglucosamine is deaminated and oxidized to carbon dioxide much more rapidly than glucosamine, either directly or through *N*-acetylglucosamine 6-phosphate, but not through glucosamine 6-phosphate. Even if the deamination and the oxidation of *N*-acetylglucosamine occurs via glucosamine 6-phos-

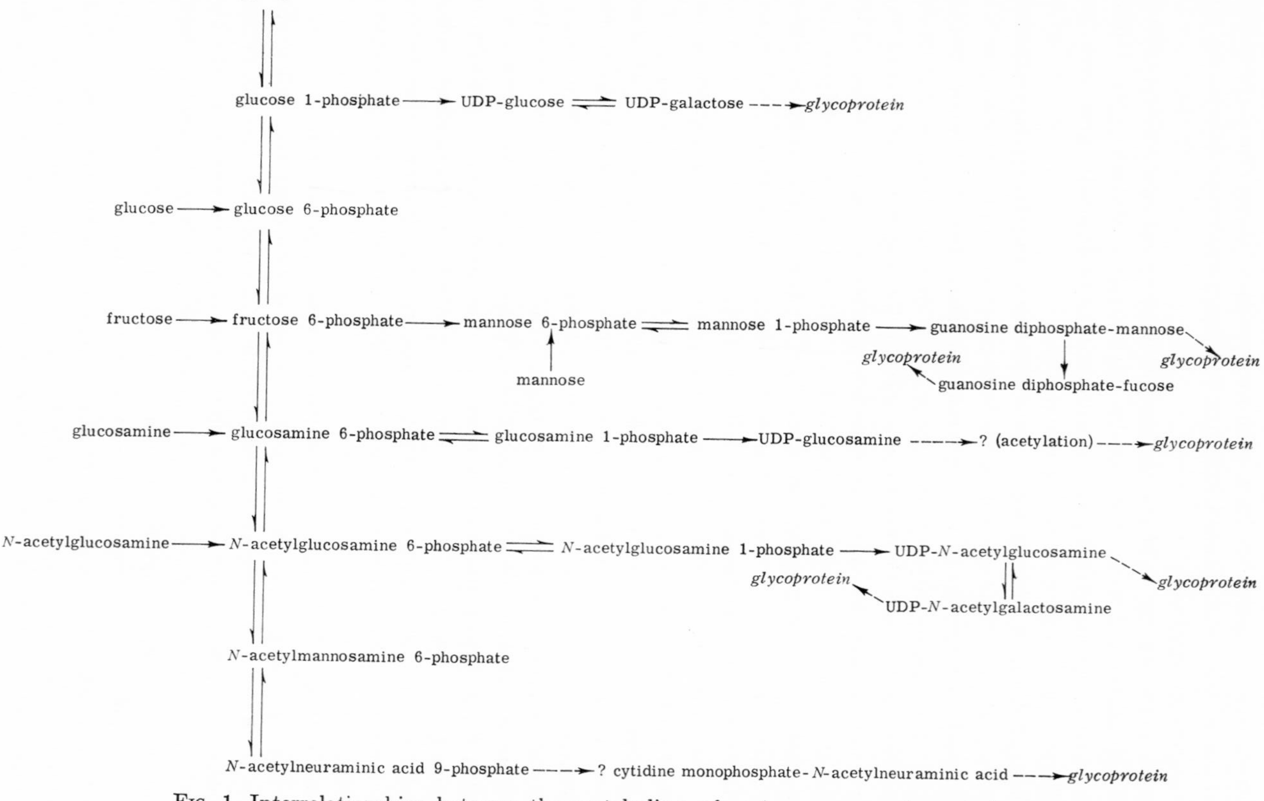

FIG. 1. Interrelationships between the metabolism of amino sugars and neutral sugars.

phate, this glucosamine 6-phosphate may not be mixed with the glucosamine 6-phosphate that is formed from glucosamine, probably because of the localization of the enzyme systems. Thus, insofar as the use of intact animals is concerned, it appears reasonable that glucose is a poor precursor for labeling the amino sugars and neuraminic acid of glycoproteins because of the variety of the metabolic routes, and glucosamine is the most effective precursor. *N*-Acetylglucosamine is intermediate between glucose and glucosamine.

In preliminary studies made by Yamashina and Izumi (unpublished data), uniformly labeled glucose-C^{14} was not an effective precursor for glycoprotein synthesis of rat liver *in vitro*. No measurable incorporation of C^{14} into glucosamine of high molecular weight substances could be observed in systems containing uniformly labeled glucose-C^{14} and the microsome, mitochondria, or supernatant fractions of liver, supplemented with the necessary cofactors and amino acids. It is to be hoped that localization of the enzymes working in the biosynthesis of glycoprotein and, especially, the incorporation of the labeled glucosamine into glycoproteins at the subcellular level will be studied.

The catabolic features of plasma glycoprotein are even less clear. No specific studies have been made on the route of glycoprotein catabolism, which is supposed to be similar to that of other plasma proteins. Catabolism of serum albumin has rather often been discussed. Liver seems to contribute in a rather small part to the catabolism of serum albumin, amounting to not more than 25% of the catabolism (Katz, Sellers, and Golden, 1960; Gordon, 1961; Tarver *et al.*, 1961), whereas a large part of the catabolism may be accounted for by loss and breakdown in the gastrointestinal tract (Tarver *et al.*, 1961). In these experiments, the breakdown was followed by the appearance of the fragments which are soluble in 5% trichloroacetic acid. A breakdown of serum albumin was also noted by Hawkins (1961) in spleen, kidneys, lungs, and lymph nodes of rats, although at a much slower rate than in liver.

Secretion of serum proteins into milk cannot be dismissed. Montreuil *et al.* (1960) investigated the glycoproteins of human milk and found that some of the glycoproteins (β-globulins) are quite similar, probably identical, to those of serum proteins. Dixon, Weigle, and Vasquez (1961) also showed the appearance of serum proteins in cow's milk.

Normal human urinary proteins have been investigated by immunoelectrophoresis (Grant and Everall, 1957). α-Globulins could be demonstrated in the urine in a concentration similar to that of serum relative to other components. In the normal urine, several proteins, like the mucoprotein of Tamm–Horsfall (1952) or of Bourrillon, Got, and Michon

(1961), are present which do not occur in serum. The origin of these proteins is not known.

The pattern of urinary proteins under pathological conditions has been investigated very frequently, but in this review it suffices to note that, in proteinuria, α_1-acid glycoprotein was detected and found to be identical with that in plasma (Popenoe, 1955). This glycoprotein comprises 4 to 20% of the total urinary protein in proteinuria.

Synthesis of plasma glycoproteins in liver was directly shown by Sarcione (1962, 1963), who demonstrated that glucose-C^{14} was incorporated into the glycoproteins of only the blood that circulates into the liver. Kukral *et al.* (1963) also showed that incorporation of glucosamine-1-C^{14} into plasma glycoproteins, with the exception of γ-globulins, did not occur in liverless dogs. With the use of partial hepatectomy, Derache and Mariel (1962) showed the parallel decrease of glycoproteins and albumin levels in plasma. Incorporation of glucosamine-1-C^{14} into α_1-acid glycoprotein of canine plasma was demonstrated by Athineos, Kukral, and Winzler (1964), and this incorporation did not occur in liverless dogs. All these findings have now given convincing proof for glycoprotein biosynthesis in liver.

Miller *et al.* (1964) also reached the conclusion that the liver is the site of biosynthesis of plasma albumin, α-globulins, and β-globulins, including fibrinogen and ceruloplasmin.

Reutilization of albumin seems to involve the breakdown of albumin to the amino acid stage, according to observations with doubly labeled albumin (Haurowitz *et al.*, 1958–1959). In rabbits, reutilization of γ-globulins was observed with γ-globulins labeled with S^{35}. Newly formed serum proteins which appeared after 4 days were different from the parent γ-globulins in immunological properties (Bednarik, Rejnek, and Knesslova, 1962; Rejnek, Bednarik, and Knesslova, 1962).

Using labeled amino acids and glucosamine-1-C^{14}, Richmond (1963) showed that α_1-acid glycoprotein of plasma of calf, rat, and rabbit turned over three to four times more rapidly than albumin, and puromycin did not inhibit the carbohydrate labeling of the glycoprotein, although it inhibited the general protein synthesis. The results of Richmond (1963) are compatible with those of Sarcione (1963), who showed that the incorporation of leucine-C^{14} into the α_1-acid glycoprotein was as fast as that into serum albumin.

Shetlar, Capps, and Hern (1964) compared the incorporation of glucosamine-1-C^{14} into plasma glycoproteins in rats and rabbits and found that there was a difference in sialic acid labeling in the two species.

Robinson, Molnar, and Winzler (1964) followed the incorporation of glucosamine-1-C^{14} into glycoproteins of tissues and plasma. Ten to fifteen minutes after injection of the labeled sugar into rats, 90% of the acid-soluble radioactivity was found to be present in the liver as uridine diphosphate *N*-acetylglucosamine. This radioactivity rather rapidly disappeared with a concurrent appearance of the activity in the particulate fractions of the liver and, subsequently, in plasma. The bound radioactivity in the liver supernatant fraction was consistently low, and this suggests that the glycoproteins produced in cytoplasmic structures are directly transferred to the blood with no or very little accumulation in the cells. These findings are like those of Peters (1962) for plasma albumin biosynthesis.

Although catabolism of serum albumin *in vitro* by mitochondria was reported (Beeken and Imredy, 1962), catabolism of albumin still seems to be obscure. Inasmuch as complete enterectomy of rabbit did not reduce the albumin catabolism to less than 50%, this was considered to be the total contribution of the gut (Franks, Mosser, and Anstadt, 1963; Franks *et al.*, 1963).

C. Glycoproteins in Various Organs

Although the wide distribution of the various glycoproteins has been reported, metabolic studies are few. Numerous studies have been made on the metabolism of glycosaminoglycan in connective tissues, and these studies are reviewed in Chapter 39 of this volume.

Chondroitin sulfate, one of the glycosaminoglycans present in connective tissues, is associated with a protein in the cartilage (see Chapter 31) and this protein seems to metabolize parallelly with the polysaccharide. Gross, Mathews, and Dorfman (1960) found that, in the compound containing chondroitin sulfate and protein, the polysaccharide part labeled with $S^{35}O_4^{--}$ and the protein part labeled with lysine-1-C^{14} have the same turnover rate, indicating that both parts metabolize parallelly or evenly as a unit. In the studies on the biosynthesis of collagen in pig skin, Schultz-Haudt and Eeg-Larsen (1961,a) found that proline-C^{14} could be incorporated as radioactive proline and hydroxyproline in a ratio of close to 1, as in true collagen, into a water-soluble compound containing a heteropolysaccharide and protein. The polysaccharide of this complex was quite different from chondroitin sulfate. Although it has not been definitely stated that the complex is a true glycoprotein, Schultz-Haudt and Eeg-Larsen (1961,a) suggested that this complex might be a precursor to the collagen fibers.

Biggers *et al.* (1961) and Lucy, Webb, and Biggers (1961) investigated the chemical composition of cartilage from the embryonic chick and the biosynthesis of amino sugars in the cartilage cultivated in a chemically defined medium. The presence of the glycoproteinlike substances containing hexosamine in the cartilage and the incorporation of glucose-1-C^{14} or uniformly labeled glucose-C^{14} into glucosamine and galactosamine without any rearrangement of the carbon chain have been found, but the studies are at present quite preliminary. In this connection, an unknown nucleotide was extracted from spinal cords and notochords of chick embryo somite and had a chondrogenic activity (Hommes, Van Leeuwen, and Zilliken, 1962). This nucleotide appeared to be quite complex in its composition, producing cytidine monophosphate, aspartic acid, threonine, serine, glutamic acid, glycine, alanine, valine, an unknown form of guanosine nucleotide, and amino sugar on hydrolysis. It would be of particular interest to see if this nucleotide is really composed of these constituents and plays a role in the biosynthesis of glycoproteins.

In diaphragm of rats, uniformly labeled glucose-C^{14} was found to be rapidly incorporated into a glucan–peptide complex. This complex, however, does not contain amino sugar or hexoses other than glucose and seems to participate in membrane transport of glucose in the diaphragm (Walaas *et al.*, 1960).

Although the pattern of the proteins of the spinal fluid is rather similar to that of the serum proteins, there may also be other constituents specific for the cerebrospinal fluid (Gavrilesco *et al.*, 1955). Albumin and γ-globulin appear to be in rapid equilibrium with the corresponding fractions of serum, but others migrate very slowly from blood. A cerebrogenesis of the proteins was suggested by Frick and Scheid-Seydel (1960).

The glycoproteins of synovial fluid are discussed in Chapter **29** of this volume.

In the study on the biosynthesis of neuraminic acid, Lauenstein and Altman (1956) observed the incorporation of uniformly labeled glucose-C^{14} into hexosamines and neuraminic acid in the whole tissue of rats and found higher radioactivities in galactosamine than in glucosamine or neuraminic acid. Spiro (1959), as described earlier in this chapter, reported the incorporation of uniformly labeled glucose-C^{14} or uniformly labeled fructose-C^{14} into liver glucosamine, which makes up a part of the conjugated substances and is transferred to the serum glycoproteins subsequently. Similarly, Shetlar (1961) and Kohn, Winzler, and Hoffmann (1962) showed that, in rat liver, there was incorporation of glucosamine-1-C^{14} into macromolecular substances of glycoprotein nature.

Rieder and Buchanan (1958a) studied, in ovomucoid, the incorporation of glucose-1-C^{14} into glucosamine. Glucose-1-C^{14} was fed to hens, and the specific activity in respiratory carbon dioxide, blood glucose, liver glycogen, and glucosamine of ovomucoid was measured at various time intervals. The specific activity of the glucosamine increased until it equaled or slightly exceeded that of the blood glucose and glycogen glucose. This indicates that either glucose or some loosely associated metabolic product is the direct precursor of glucosamine. The ratio of the specific activity of carbon-1 in glucosamine to the average specific activity of the entire molecule was found to be 4.5. Thus, it appeared that the major portion of the isotope was incorporated into glucosamine from fed glucose without any skeletal rearrangement of the carbon chain. The remainder of the radioactivity in the carbons other than carbon-1 might be assumed to be derived from glucose in which carbon atoms had been randomized via the metabolic pathway of glucose.

In a quest for the origin of the nitrogen of glucosamine in ovomucoid, Rieder and Buchanan (1958a) studied the incorporation of $N^{15}H_4Cl$ nitrogen into glucosamine, using experimental techniques the same as those for the carbon incorporation. The time curve showed that the incorporation of N^{15} into the glucosamine from fed $N^{15}H_4Cl$ was very rapid and occurred at roughly the same rate as N^{15} incorporation of the uric acid. Whereas the isotopic concentration of the uric acid reflects directly the isotopic concentration of its precursors (as judged from the time curve that showed that the N^{15} concentration of the uric acid dropped precipitously at the cessation of the feeding of $N^{15}H_4Cl$), the N^{15} concentration of the glucosamine isolated from the ovomucoid after the cessation of the feeding of $N^{15}H_4Cl$ dropped off more slowly. The data were interpreted as indicating that the glucosamine used for ovomucoid synthesis is in equilibrium with the general body stores of glucosamine. It was further found that the N^{15} concentration in nitrogen atoms 3 and 9 of uric acid, both of which are known to be derived from amide nitrogen of glutamine, is of the same magnitude as that in the glucosamine nitrogen, suggesting that the amide nitrogen of glutamine is also involved as the direct precursor of the nitrogen atom of glucosamine. This is consistent with the known fact that glutamine in animal tissues is readily synthesized from glutamic acid and ammonia.

Besides the nitrogen of NH_4Cl, the nitrogen of glycine and, possibly, other amino acids was also demonstrated to be utilized for glucosamine synthesis to some extent. The turnover rate of glucosamine in ovomucoid was found to be 1.6 to 2.3 days, the calculation being made from the decay curves obtained after cessation of the feeding of N^{15} and C^{14}.

The subcellular site of hexose incorporation into liver protein was investigated by Sarcione (1964) by using the isolated rat liver *in vitro*. The site of incorporation of hexoses was the deoxycholate-soluble fraction of microsomes. In a double-labeling experiment, the patterns of leucine-H^3 and galactose-C^{14} incorporation were different. Initial incorporation of leucine-H^3 took place into the ribosomal protein, and this was followed by its progressive appearance in the deoxycholate-soluble protein of microsomes. In contrast, initial incorporation of galactose-C^{14} was into the membranous protein of microsomes, and virtually no incorporation was observed into the ribosomal protein. These data were interpreted to indicate that the membranes of the endoplasmic reticulum are the actual site of covalent linkage of hexoses to the completed polypeptide chains, unless a small amount of carbohydrate or glycopeptide of high specific activity could be involved in the ribosomal fraction.

The fate of glucosamine-1-C^{14}, the most potent reagent for labeling plasma glycoproteins, has been investigated rather extensively. Del Giacco and Maley (1964) analyzed the acid-soluble fraction of rat liver that was perfused with glucosamine-1-C^{14}, and found three minor peaks in the chromatogram, in addition to the main peak that is uridine diphosphate-*N*-acetylglucosamine (IV); they were free sialic acid (I), a mixture of phosphorylated *N*-acetylglucosamine and *N*-acetylgalactosamine (II), and a phosphorylated *N*-acetylgalactosamine (III). The structures of these phosphorylated compounds have not been elucidated. The same authors also noticed that the total radioactivity of II, III, and IV and the specific activity of IV was higher in the livers of diabetic animals than in those of normal animals.

In liver, the phosphorylation of glucosamine to glucosamine 6-phosphate seems to be markedly inhibited by naturally present free glucose; thus, the experimentally administered glucosamine is preferentially transformed to *N*-acetylglucosamine 6-phosphate via *N*-acetylglucosamine (McGarrahan and Maley, 1962).

Inhibition of glucose oxidation by glucosamine—that is, hyperglycemic effect—as shown in rat adipose tissue by Silverman (1963)—was supposed to be ascribed to the accumulation of *N*-acetylglucosamine 6-phosphate.

Accumulation of uridine diphosphate-*N*-acetylglucosamine in rat liver caused by administration of puromycin was shown to effect feedback control of formation of glucosamine 6-phosphate from fructose 6-phosphate and glutamine (Kornfeld *et al.*, 1964). Likewise, cytidine-monophosphate-*N*-acetylneuraminic acid inhibits uridine-diphosphate-*N*-acetylglucosamine 2-epimerase. In these experiments, however, puromycin inhibition of glycoprotein biosynthesis is inconsistent with that observed by Richmond (1963).

In the liver of rats with Walker 256 carcinoma, protein-bound hexosamines were elevated during the early stage after the implantation of the carcinoma. This observation, coupled with previous findings on plasma glycoproteins under similar circumstances, was interpreted as proof that the liver was responsible for the increase, at least initially, of the plasma glycoprotein elevation observed in malignant diseases (Macbeth and Bekesi, 1964,a).

In cell-free preparation from mast-cell tumors in mice (Silbert, 1962), the incorporation of C^{14} from uridine diphosphate glucosamine-1-C^{14} into heparin-like polysaccharide did not occur, whereas the incorporation from uridine diphosphate derivatives of *N*-acetylglucosamine-C^{14} and glucuronic acid-C^{14} did occur. Silbert (1963) extended his studies on *in vitro* biosynthesis of glycosaminoglycans of the mast-cell tumor and showed that, under certain conditions, 5% of the radioactivity from uridine diphosphate glucuronic acid and uridine diphosphate *N*-acetylglucosamine could be transferred to a glycosaminoglycan–protein complex. The radioactive glycosaminoglycan could be released from protein by papain, but its precise chemical nature is still unknown.

The role of cytidine monophosphate neuraminic acid in the biosynthesis of glycoproteins and glycopeptides has been well documented, and no contradictory observation has so far been described. Carubelli *et al.* (1964) showed the incorporation of uniformly labeled glucose into neuramin-lactose in slices of rat mammary glands and presented the following reaction diagram:

$$\text{UDP-galactose} + \text{glucose-C}^{14} \rightarrow \text{UDP} + \text{galactosyl } (1 \rightarrow 4) \text{ glucose-C}^{14} \quad (1)$$

$$\text{CMP-sialic acid} + \text{galactosyl } (1 \rightarrow 4) \text{ glucose-C}^{14} \rightarrow \text{CMP} + \text{sialyl } (2 \rightarrow 3) \text{ galactosyl } (1 \rightarrow 4) \text{ glucose-C}^{14} \quad (2)$$

Reaction (2) was postulated to occur much faster than reaction (1) on the basis of the results that showed the equal labeling of lactose and neuramin-lactose throughout the whole reaction.

Using slices of ovine submaxillary gland, Eichberg and Karnovsky (1963) studied the formation of *N*-acetylneuraminic acid and found that 2–6% of the total neuraminic acid was dialyzable and was metabolically active. Warren (1964) discovered a new type of sialic acid, *N*-glycolyl-8-*O*-methylneuraminic acid in a starfish (*Asterias forbesi*) and also found that the extract of this organism was able to synthesize a cytidine monophosphate derivative of this type of sialic acid.

X-Irradiation increased the incorporation of sulfate-S^{35} and uniformly labeled glucose-C^{14} into glycosaminoglycan of collagen (Gerber *et al.*, 1962). The amount of hexosamine contained in granulation tissue of articular surfaces at different stages of regeneration was measured (Olah and Hadhazy, 1962).

Draper and Kent (1963) observed the *in vitro* incorporation of C^{14} from glucose-1-C^{14} into neutral sugars, hexosamines, and sialic acid of glycoproteins in sheep colonic mucosa.

Glucosamine-1-C^{14} was found to be a precursor for glycoprotein in tracheal mucosa of rats, and the incorporation was inhibited by isopropylnoradrenaline, a curative for bronchial dilatation and also for toxic swelling of the mucosa (Formijne, Van der Schoot, and DeNie, 1964).

In the presence of erythropoietin, marrow cells of rats incorporated glucosamine into an insoluble fraction at a significantly increased rate. Thirty per cent of the glucosamine incorporated was recovered in the form of neuraminic acid (Dukes, Takaku, and Goldwasser, 1963).

The carbohydrate composition of glycoprotein of submaxillary gland saliva was found to be altered, depending on the dose of pilocarpine (the stimulant for saliva secretion). The ratio of neuraminic acid to fucose ranged from 0.16 to 2.6. These findings suggest that at least these two sugars are added to the termini of the glycoproteins at the final stage of the biosynthesis of glycoproteins (Dische *et al.*, 1962).

Enzymic degradation of glycopeptides from submaxillary gland glycoprotein to amino acids and monosaccharides by bovine spleen homogenate was presumed to exemplify the events in the catabolism of glycoprotein (Bhavanandan *et al.*, 1964).

The excretion in urine of a number of glycopeptides has been recorded, and the fractionation of these glycopeptides was reported from several laboratories (Hakomori and Ishimoda, 1962; Masamune, Hakomori, and Sugo, 1959; Hakomori, Kawauchi, and Ishimoda, 1962; Brada, 1963; Pechan, 1963; Miettinen, 1963; Miettinen and Huttunen, 1964).

A glycoprotein whose molecular weight was assessed to be around 20,000 was isolated from urine of plasmocytoma patients. This glycoprotein contained 43% carbohydrate and, in immunoelectrophoresis, showed three precipitation lines against antihuman serum (Weicker, Huhnstock, and Grässlin, 1964).

From the urines of patients with acute nephritis, a glycoprotein of the α-globulin type was isolated (Lange and Dubin, 1964).

Herman (1963) investigated the location of the site of production of urinary glycoprotein by using antibody against the Tamm–Horsfall urinary glycoprotein. The antibody tagged with sulforhodamine was found to be fixed in the renal tubule epithelium.

D. Glycoproteins with Blood-Group Activity

The biosynthesis of the specific blood-group substances, such as secretion or nonsecretion of a blood-group substance, has been discussed from the viewpoint of genetics, but, apparently, direct studies on the pathway of the synthesis have not been reported. Likewise, nothing is known about the catabolism, except for breakdown of the substances by microbial enzymes, which has been studied in particular relation to the changes in serological reactions (see Section I,A,2).

Although the chemical structure—i.e., the sequence of the constituent amino acids and monosaccharides—and even the composition of some of the blood-group substances of both water-soluble and water-insoluble types have not been established, it has been suggested that the immunologically determinant groups of the specific substances reside in the proximity of the terminal sugars of the polysaccharide chains (see Volume I, Chapter 13). This suggestion was based on inhibition experiments on specific serological reactions using mono- and oligosaccharides and on changes in the specific substances induced by enzymes.

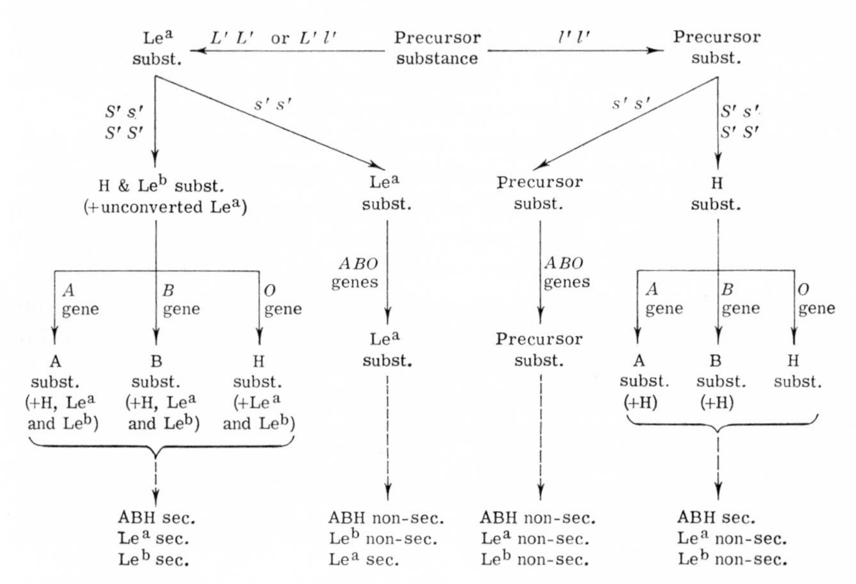

FIG. 2. Possible genetical pathways for the biosynthesis of blood-group substances (from Morgan, 1960).

The enzymic transformation of A- or B-specific substances into O(H) substances and then into the substance serologically specific to anti-pneumococcus-Type-XIV serum (Iseki and Masaki, 1953; Iseki and Ikeda, 1956; Watkins, 1953, 1956) suggests a pathway for the biosynthesis of these specific substances. It is quite significant that the control of genes on the structure of heteropolysaccharides or glycoproteins is so clearly demonstrated in the synthesis of blood-group substances. Therefore, it seems in order to include here a review of some genetically possible pathways of the biosynthesis of blood-group substances.

Figure 2 represents a scheme proposed by Watkins and Morgan (1959) and Morgan (1960), based on current structural and serological information on human blood-group substances in reference to serological observation on family material. In this figure, L′ and l′, S′ and s′, and ABO genes are three independent genes by which the orderly conversion of a precursor substance to the serologically specific product which finally appears in the secretion is controlled. The superscript was added because, earlier, the symbols without the superscript were used by Schiff and Sasaki (1932) and Ceppellini and Siniscalco (1955) for the identification of genes of secretors and nonsecretors. In this scheme, first of all, the formation of the precursor substance is postulated, although the path of the biosynthesis of this precursor substance is, of course, not known. This substance is secreted by a person with a blood-cell phenotype O, Le(a-, b-), and, therefore, this person does not possess specificities associated with the ABO or Lewis systems, but this substance, however, reacts with a Type-XIV-pneumococcus antiserum.

The most specific features of the biosynthesis of blood-group substances may be represented by the specific addition of mono- or oligosaccharides to nonreducing ends of the precursor and also of the intermediary glycoproteins. For instance, the transformation of the precursor substance to Le^a substance involves at least the addition of α-L-fucosyl residues to the nonreducing ends of the polysaccharide chains. Likewise, the formation of O(H), A, B, and Le^b substances may occur by addition of the terminal determinant sugars to each immediate precursor (see Volume I, Chapter 13).

These stepwise syntheses of a macromolecule seem to be different from the biosynthesis of protein, nucleic acid, and some of the polysaccharides possessing repeating units in which, as currently proposed, the macromolecules are built up in one stage directly from individual constituents.

E. Glycoproteins and Glycopeptides in Microorganisms and Other Organisms

1. Bacterial Cell Wall

Data have recently become available which indicate that the bacterial cell walls are composed of carbohydrates, amino acids, and lipids (Work, 1957) (see also Volume I, Chapter 9). Cell walls were isolated as structural, but not as chemical, entities. Physical tests of homogeneity of cell walls are not possible because of the insolubility of the walls, and electron micrographs indicate a highly complex structure. In this chapter, formation and breakdown of the cell walls will be mentioned. Although there have been a number of cytological investigations of the appearance of the cell walls at the time of cell division, there is no precise knowledge of the location and manner of the synthesis of the bacterial cell wall.

Cell-wall synthesis appears to occur at the peripheral extracytoplasmic location. This idea is supported by the observation that *Bacillus megatherium* protoplast, produced by lysozyme, could not form cell walls, although it could divide (McQuillen, 1956). In contrast, however, protoplasts of some of the gram-negative bacteria, for instance *Escherichia coli* or *Proteus vulgaris,* behave in various ways depending on the medium. Protoplasts of these gram-negative species produced by penicillin are able to revert to parent bacteria in a protective hypertonic medium lacking penicillin (Lederberg, 1957). Protoplasts of *Proteus vulgaris* were, furthermore, found to produce L-forms which are stable to osmotic shock and are able to multiply as the parent cells do, although L-forms lack a rigid cell wall (Klieneberger-Nobel, 1960).

If the cell-wall synthesis is an extracytoplasmic process, it would be presumed that the intermediates of low molecular size necessary for the cell-wall synthesis are produced in cytoplasm, transported through the semipermeable cytoplasmic membrane, and supplied for enzymic polymerization at the peripheral location. At present, however, the existence of the enzymes participating in the synthesis of the cell-wall substances has not directly been shown. McQuillen (1955) studied the incorporation of C^{14}-labeled substrates into proteins, lipids, and nucleic acids of protoplasts of *B. megatherium.* One striking difference has been found in comparison with the incorporation into these substances of the whole cell: protoplasts could not incorporate C^{14} of glucose, acetate, aspartic acid, or glycine into diaminopimelic acid, whereas the whole cell could. In *B. megatherium,* diaminopimelic acid did not appear to be detectable in protoplasts, but was clearly demonstrated to be present in the cell wall. It may well be, however, that protoplasts are also able to synthesize diaminopimelic acid; this amino acid, however, is known to be excreted rapidly through the cytoplasmic membrane, although the nature of this excreted diaminopimelic acid has not been investigated.

In summary of the results collected by Hoare and Work (1957), it appears that the free form of diaminopimelic acid is present more or less in the Eubacteriales and Actinomycetales, possibly as the cellular metabolic pool, and its amount and isomer content depend on the metabolic state of the cells at harvesting.

In the more recent studies on the incorporation of the labeled amino acids into cell-wall substances of *B. megatherium,* Brookes, Crathorn, and Hunter (1959) showed that the incorporation of alanine-C^{14} into cytoplasmic-membrane fraction preceded that into cell wall at the shortest times—that is 2 min—and the labeled amino acid afterwards appeared in the cell wall. Since, under the conditions used in these experiments, the synthesis of the cellular proteins is inhibited by chloramphenicol, it could be suggested that the site of synthesis of the cell-wall peptides lies within the cytoplasmic-membrane fraction.

In *Escherichia coli*, a remarkable accumulation of diaminopimelic acid in combined form was observed, provided that a certain amount of lysine was added to the culture medium (Hoare and Work, 1955). When the mode of combination of diaminopimelic acid was examined, Hoare and Work (1957) found this amino acid to be present in the supernatant liquid remaining after 4 hr of centrifuging of the cytoplasmic contents of *E. coli* at $105{,}000 \times g$. This fraction was found to be free from nucleic acid, indicating that diaminopimelic acid combines with cellular substances other than nucleic acid.

The cell-wall synthesis appears to be separated from the protein synthesis of the cells. Hancock and Park (1958) and Crathorn and Hunter (1958) demonstrated that the synthesis of the wall substances of *Staphylococcus aureus* proceeded in the presence of chloramphenicol, whereas ordinary protein synthesis in the cells was nearly completely inhibited. This was the case for gram-positive bacteria and also for gram-negative bacteria, although to a lesser extent.

Trucco and Pardee (1958) claimed that, in the presence of penicillin, *E. coli* did not show any depression of cell-wall formation in relation to cytoplasmic synthesis. No difference was detected in cell-wall composition, either. In this experiment, the incorporation of C^{14} of uniformly labeled glucose-C^{14} into the components of *E. coli* (strain B) was studied in both the absence and the presence of penicillin in both a hypertonic and a hypotonic medium. In the hypotonic medium, there was practically an equal number of cells remaining after 30 min in both conditions, although there were fewer viable cells in the medium containing penicillin. The total amount of cell wall was also practically the same in all cases, and the specific activity of cell components did not show any significant difference. In the hypertonic medium, there were fewer cells in the medium containing penicillin than there were in the controls, but the amount of cell wall relative to other cellular components and the specific activity of cell wall was found to be practically equal in both cases. These results are apparently not consistent with the suggestion of Lederberg (1957) that synthesis of some components of the cell wall is inhibited preferentially by penicillin to such an extent that continued growth of the cytoplasm brings about extrusion of the cell contents as spherical protoplasts instead of the rod-shaped parent cells. McQuillen (1958) showed that the penicillin-induced spherical forms of *E. coli* contain much less diaminopimelic acid than the parent cells do, and Weibull (1958) also reported that L-forms of *Proteus vulgaris* contained only small quantities of hexosamine and diaminopimelic acid. Accordingly, penicillin might inhibit the last stage of cell-wall synthesis—that is, the synthesis of glycopeptides—and these glycopeptides would comprise such a small percentage of the cell wall that they would have been missed in the analysis of Trucco and Pardee (1958).

The property of gram-negative species of forming fairly stable protoplasts is considered to be the result of a low content of glycoprotein and a high content of lipid in the cell wall. The blocking of the synthesis of the glycoprotein in the cell wall by penicillin does not seem to abolish completely the formation of the cell wall.

In contrast with these observations made on gram-negative bacteria, a rapid accumulation of "nucleotide-peptide" in cells of *Staphylococcus aureus* was observed in the presence of penicillin in a culture medium (Park and Strominger, 1957) (see also Volume I, Chapter 4). Three such compounds isolated by Park (1952,a,b) were uridine diphosphate acetylmuramic acid; uridine diphosphate-acetylmuramic acid-L-alanine; and uridine diphosphate-acetylmuramic acid bearing D,L-alanine, D-glutamic acid, and L-lysine (the chemical structures of these nucleotides are discussed in Volume I, Chapter 4). Low concentrations of these nucleotides were found in normal cells, but, after the addition of penicillin, in the short period (45 min) during which the cells remained viable, the nucleotides increased fiftyfold and they accounted for 5% of the total phosphorus used by the cells in that time. They were considered to be intermediary compounds for cell-wall formation, since the amino acids and, especially, muramic acid, that are contained in these nucleotides are also rather specific components of the cell wall of the same bacterial strain (Cummins and Harris, 1956,a). Moreover, the presence of uridine in these nucleotides excludes the possibility that they are derived from the breakdown of existing walls, which are free of pyrimidines. These nucleotides are possibly destined, in conjunction with other subunits containing glucosamine, glycine, and serine, to form basal cell-wall units, but the reactions are inhibited by penicillin. The inhibition of glycopeptide synthesis by penicillin and its analogues (benzylpenicillin, 6-aminopenicillanic acid, etc.) seems to run parallel to the antibiotic potency of these substances (Rogers and Jeljaszewicz, 1961).

Other types of antimetabolites could also cause the accumulation of nucleotides. In *Staphylococcus aureus,* uridine nucleotide accumulation was observed during treatment with bacitracin, novobiocin, gentian violet, oxamycin (Strominger and Threnn, 1959; Strominger, Threnn, and Scott, 1959), and vancomycin (Reynolds, 1961). 6-Azauracil, a uracil analogue, was shown to inhibit the growth of *E. coli* and to cause the accumulation of an ester form of *N*-acetylamino sugar (Otsuji and Takagi, 1959).

The action of 5-fluorouracil on some bacteria is somewhat different from that of other inhibitors (Rogers and Perkins, 1960). During the incubation of a strain of *Staphylococcus aureus* in the presence of 5-fluorouracil, compounds accumulated which contained bound amino sugar. Fractionation of the materials revealed the presence of at least four compounds: one containing fluorouracil, phosphorus, muramic acid, alanine, glutamic acid, and lysine, with the molar proportions of 1:2: 1:3:1:1; one containing fluorouridine, phosphate, and *N*-acetylglucosamine, with molar proportions of 1:2:1; and a mixture of two compounds containing fluorouridine, phosphate, muramic acid, and alanine. These compounds could not be readily utilized by the bacterial cells for glycopeptide synthesis, even after fluorouracil was removed from the medium. A similar observation was made by Tomasz and Borek (1960). Thus, on incubation of a strain of *E. coli*, K_{12}, in the presence of 5-fluorouracil, accumulation of a mixture of at least several nucleotides occurred. One of them contained diaminopimelic acid, glutamic acid, and alanine, besides an ultraviolet-absorbing component (not fluorouracil), but no hexosamine. Another nucleotide contained 5-fluorouracil. The presence of nucleotides containing *N*-acetylhexosamine but no amino acids was also indicated. According to the interpretation of Tomasz and Borek, 5-fluorouracil could be metabolized to some cell-wall precursor, and this product may inhibit the whole enzyme complex of cell-wall synthesis and, at the same time, lead to the accumulation of relatively large amounts of the normal precursors. A phenomenon called "osmotic imbalance" induced by 5-fluorouracil on *E. coli*, as observed earlier by Tomasz and Borek (1959), could be interpreted to mean that this imbalance was initiated by an early injury of the cell-wall synthesizing mechanism by 5-fluorouracil and accompanied by relatively uninhibited cytoplasmic growth.

Ito and Strominger (1960,a) extracted enzymes from *Staphylococcus aureus* which were able to catalyze the stepwise addition of amino acids to uridine diphosphate-muramic acid. The reaction proceeds in the following way:

UDP-*N*-acetylmuramyl-L-alanine-D-glutamine + L-lysine-C^{14} + ATP $\rightleftharpoons$
UDP-*N*-acetylmuramyl-L-alanine-D-glutamine-L-lysine-C^{14} +
ADP + inorganic phosphate

Since exchange of P^{32} between ATP and ADP^{32} did not seem to occur in the absence of the uridine nucleotide, the reaction appears to be quite different from those reactions involved in ordinary protein biosynthesis in which amino acids have to be activated as esters of adenylic acid.

Nucleotides related to those described by Park (1952,a,b) were found also in other organisms. Thus, cytidine diphosphate glycerol (Baddiley *et al.*, 1956) and cytidine diphosphate ribitol (Baddiley, Buchanan, and Carss, 1957) were isolated from a strain of *Lactobacillus arabinosus,* and their biological origin from cytidine triphosphate and L-α-glycerophosphate or D-ribitol-5-phosphate was also established (Shaw, 1957). More recently, Strominger (1959) reported the appearance of cytidine diphosphate ribitol in *Staphylococcus aureus* in treatment with penicillin or gentian violet. Since, in later experiments, Baddiley, Buchanan, and Carss (1958) were not able to show the presence of glycerol in hydrolyzates of the cell wall of *L. arabinosus,* the glycerol-containing nucleotide was considered to possess a minor role in the cell-wall synthesis. This nucleotide may be of some importance in the synthesis of the protoplast membrane, since macromolecular material of uncertain composition, containing glycerophosphate residues, was isolated from *L. arabinosus* by Mitchell and Moyle (1951). Similarly, McQuillen (1955) and Mitchell and Moyle (1956) also found glycerophosphate, probably in a polymerized form, in protoplast membrane of *Micrococcus lysodeikticus.*

More recently, Kelemen and Baddiley (1961) extracted a macromolecule from a strain of *Lactobacillus* which contained glycerol, phosphate, and alanine and was named glycerol teichoic acid.

On the other hand, ribitol-containing polymers, named ribitol teichoic acid, were isolated from the cell wall of *L. arabinosus* (Archibald, Baddiley, and Buchanan, 1961), *B. subtilis* (Armstrong, Baddiley, and Buchanan, 1961), and *S. aureus* (Baddiley *et al.*, 1961a). The teichoic acid from *L. arabinosus* and that from *B. subtilis* are rather similar in composition, containing ribitol, phosphate, D-glucose, and D-alanine, although the type of glycosidic linkage differs with each one. The teichoic acid from *S. aureus* contains, however, *N*-acetylglucosamine in place of glucose. Janczura, Perkins, and Rogers (1961) more recently isolated a polymer containing *N*-acetylgalactosamine and glucuronic acid in equal proportions from vegetative cells of *B. subtilis.* Although structural studies on these interesting substances have been rather extensively developed, metabolic studies have not yet appeared.

In view of the presence of D-amino acids in cell-wall peptides, the effects of D-amino acid or D-amino acid–containing peptide on bacterial growth or cell-wall synthesis have been investigated. D-Alanylglycine, and D-alanyl-L-alanine were more active than D-alanine in promoting the growth of *Streptococcus faecalis,* whereas L-alanyl-D-alanine and D-alanyl-D-alanine were inactive (Kihara, Ikawa, and Snell, 1961). D-

Methionine was found to induce spheroplast formation during cell-wall synthesis of *Alcaligenes faecalis*. This amino acid is not a normal constituent of cell wall, so the incorporation of D-methionine in place of other normal constituents may cause the cell wall to be unusual. The fraction to which D-methionine was incorporated was found to be phenol insoluble, a fraction similar to the "links" fraction of *E. coli* as previously described by Weidel, Frank, and Martin (1960). This incorporation was inhibited by penicillin but not by chloramphenicol. The formation of the unusual "links" fraction of the cell wall may impair the formation of the usual, rigid cell wall (Lark and Lark, 1961).

When microorganisms are allowed to grow under conditions whereby a single nutrient is the growth-limiting factor, the extent of the growth response is a measure of the amount of the particular nutrient. This phenomenon is used for the quantitative determination of the particular nutrient and is known as microbiological assay. It is rather general knowledge that there are differences in the patterns of the growth responses evoked by different growth-limiting nutrients.

Shockman, Kolb, and Toennies (1958) studied the response of a strain of *Streptococcus faecalis* to amino acids and found that termination of the exponential growth phase and termination of the assimilation of amino acids required for cytoplasmic synthesis are normally followed by a phase of metabolism during which a large increase in the amount of cell-wall substances takes place. Thus, it was shown that during the growth after depletion due to nutritional factors, the amount of rhamnose and glucosamine in the whole cell increased about 100%, with these sugars being localized specifically in the cell wall. The content of nitrogen and rhamnose and the weight of the wall increased also about 100%. Thus, the net gain in rhamnose and glucosamine could account for the gain in the cell wall. A certain time after the depletion point, the lysis of cells occurs. If there is a lack of any nutrient which is indispensable for the cell-wall synthesis, the lysis would occur a very short time after the depletion of this particular nutrient. Lysine, the prominent amino acid contained in the cell wall, is one of the amino acids which is directly utilized for the cell-wall synthesis. In this connection, Strominger and Threnn (1959) showed the accumulation of uridine diphosphate-muramylalanine in *Staphylococcus aureus* under the condition of lysine deprivation.

In some bacteria which form spores, high molecular weight compounds composed of certain amino acids and sugars are found in spore coats. These compounds are insoluble, as in the cell wall, but, on some occasions, disintegrate into soluble form when the spore coats are suspended in an aqueous medium. The liberation of the soluble substances occurs from the coats of resting or germinated spores or from intact germinated spores. In the case of *Bacillus megatherium* (Strange and Dark, 1956), a peptide containing glutamic acid, alanine, diaminopimelic acid, hexosamine, and muramic acid, with an average molecular weight of 15,300, was released out of the spore coat. In this bacterium, the release of the hexosamine-containing peptide was found to be an enzymic reaction, with the action being similar to that of lysozyme. This last-mentioned enzyme could accelerate the release of the peptide, although the peptide liberated might be of a different type.

It appeared possible, at least with *Bacillus megatherium* and *Bacillus subtilis,* that the hexosamine-containing peptide was associated with the spore coat. The breakdown of an insoluble peptide complex by either depolymerization or detachment from some other constituents of the spore coat may well be one of the first steps of the germination process, preceded, perhaps, by activation of an enzyme system which is able to release the hexosamine-containing peptide. It is interesting to note that there was no liberation of the peptide from the whole resting spore, and also no liberation by the action of lysozyme on it. This means, therefore, that either the peptide was not present at the surface or that it was present in some resistant form which became susceptible to attack during germination or disintegration.

The spore peptide is quite similar in its composition to that of the cell wall. The functions of both the cell-wall substance and the spore-coat substance have not yet been clarified. They might be "dead inert substances," as has often been asserted. It is of interest that the spore can be synthesized from the protoplast, whereas the cell wall cannot be, insofar as *B. megatherium* is concerned (Salton, 1955).

Some bacteria are known to produce capsules surrounding the cell wall. The structures of the capsules were investigated, and polyglutamic acid and polysaccharide were found in *Bacillus megatherium.* The polysaccharide part was analyzed for chemical composition and antigenicity and found to be identical with that isolated from a noncapsulated strain (Tomcsik, 1956). The extensive work, however, carried out with the capsular substances of *Diplococcus pneumoniae, Streptococcus, Klebsiella, Bacillus anthracis,* and *Pasteurella pestis* indicates the great probability that the capsular substances of those organisms, in contrast to *B. megatherium,* are not identical with those which form part of the cell wall proper. These capsular substances might be produced from the cytoplasmic membrane, although no biochemical evidence has been presented (Tomcsik, 1956).

Edwards and Panos (1962) compared the pattern of acid-soluble nucleotide of a group A streptococcus and the derived L-form and found that the L-form contained a large concentration of uridine diphosphate muramylpeptides and a significant increase of uridine diphosphate-*N*-acetylglucosamine, whereas the parent streptococcus contained uridylic acid as a major nucleotide, together with some unidentified uridine nucleotides.

Ristocetin A, ristocetin B, and the products of the partial acid hydrolysis were also able to effect the accumulation of uridine diphosphate muramylpeptides in *Staphylococcus aureus* (Wallas and Strominger, 1963). Vancomycin inhibits growth and glycopeptide synthesis in *Bacillus subtilis* strain W 23. These effects in this organism could be minimized by the addition of magnesium ions (Best and Durham, 1964).

The time for the accumulation of uridine diphosphate-*N*-acetylamino sugar derivatives was measured by Ito and Saito (1963) in *Staphylococcus aureus*.

Addition of sodium laurylsulfate to the incubation medium caused an increase in accumulation of *N*-acetylamino sugar esters by *Staphylococcus aureus* (Berti and Trocca, 1964).

Studies on the biosynthesis of cell wall in *in vitro* systems have become rather abundant. Zeleznick *et al.* (1963) demonstrated the incorporation of rhamnosyl residue from thymidine diphosphate-rhamnose into the protoplast membrane of *Streptococcus pyogenes*, and, likewise, Pazur and Anderson (1963) showed enzymic transfer of rhamnosyl units from the same nucleotide into the cell-wall fragments of *Streptococcus faecalis*. Chatterjee and Park (1964) investigated the enzymic transfer of radioactive lysine from uridine-diphosphate-muramyl(C^{14}-lysine) peptide (Ala-Glu-Lys-Ala-Ala) to the insoluble membrane material of *Staphylococcus aureus*. The highest activity was found in a particulate fraction which was composed of membrane material and ribosome, but the latter seems not to be essential for the transfer reaction. The activity was dependent on ATP, Mg^{++}, and uridine diphosphate-*N*-acetylglucosamine. Free lysine could also be utilized, but the rate of the incorporation was only one-eighth of that from the nucleotide peptide. Free glycine was also shown to be incorporated into the insoluble membrane fraction, but this reaction depended on the presence of UDP-muramyllysine peptide, UDP-*N*-acetylglucosamine, and ribosome. It seems, therefore, that the biosynthesis of the polyglycine part of the cell-wall glycoprotein requires factors of protein biosynthesis, and the addition of the polyglycine to the glycopeptide would then be a single reaction requiring newly formed glycopeptide backbone (i.e., glycopeptide lacking glycine) as acceptor. It was, however, very peculiar that the same authors observed that the antibiotics penicillin, vancomycin, and bacitracin had no effect on the transfer of the polyglycine to the glycopeptide when added directly to the cell-free system, whereas the particulate enzyme obtained from cells which had grown in the presence of antibiotics for 20 min showed specific damage. Thus, the particulate enzymes were inhibited about 90% in their ability to utilize UDP-muramyl(C^{14}-lysine) peptide, whereas they could utilize glycine normally.

Ito and Strominger (1964) extended their work on the enzymic synthesis of the glycopeptide of *Staphylococcus aureus* and found that γ-glutamyl-lysine linkage in the glycopeptide could be formed in a system similar to that previously reported by them.

A particulate system obtained from *Staphylococcus aureus* strain H was capable of forming a polymer utilizing UDP-acetylmuramyl-L-Ala-D-Glu-L-Lys-D-Ala-D-Ala and UDP-acetylglucosamine. The polymer formed, like cell-wall glycopeptide, could be hydrolyzed by lysozyme. This formation was inhibited by penicillin, bacitracin, novobiocin, vancomycin, and ristocetin, whereas cycloserine and chloramphenicol exhibited very low inhibitory effect (Meadow, Anderson, and Strominger, 1964).

Enzymes were discovered by Nathenson and Strominger (1962) that were able to synthesize the linkage between α- and β-*N*-acetylglucosamine and polyribitolphosphate (the product of the action of β-*N*-acetylglucosaminidase on teichoic acids).

The glycopeptide layer of the cell wall of *Bacillus megaterium* is broken down into components during growth of the cells. The rate of the turnover was a function of the rate of growth of the culture. About 15–20% of the rigid layer of the cell wall is degraded during one cell division. The resistance of the cell wall to lysozyme also increased during the stationary phase. The smaller portion of the degraded glycopeptide was released into the medium in the form of nonutilized fragments. The rigid component of the cell wall may also be broken down during growth of *B. cereus* and *E. coli* cultures (Chaloupka, Ríhová, and Křečková, 1964).

In the experiments with a lysine-requiring mutant of *E. coli*, Municio, Diaz, and Martinez (1963) observed the accumulation of glycopeptides in the lysine-limited culture. The glycopeptides had a positive precipitin test against antisera obtained from rabbits immunized with purified cell wall of the organism, indicating that the structure of the glycopeptides was closely related to that of the cell wall.

Incorporation of D-methionine into the rough layer of the cell walls of *Alcaligenes faecalis* was recorded, but the high concentration of the amino acid in the culture medium led the bacteria to form spheroplast by the consequence of inhibition of the rough-layer synthesis (Lark, Bradley, and Lark, 1963).

Vinter (1963) found that the incorporation of diaminopimelic acid-C^{14} into the cells of *Bacillus cereus* during sporogenesis was markedly inhibited by chloramphenicol, but was stimulated by penicillin. This indicates that the mechanism of the formation of spore is different from that of the cell wall.

The action of cycloserine on certain microorganisms was ascribed to its inhibition of cell-wall synthesis, and Neuhaus and Lynch (1964) observed that cycloserine had an inhibitory action on D-alanyl-D-alanine synthesis by enzymes from *Streptococcus faecalis* strain R8043.

Cells of *Micrococcus lysodeikticus* grown in the presence of D-serine incorporated D-serine into the glycopeptide in amounts almost equal to the amount of lysine or glutamic acid. The effect of serine incorporation appeared to be a replacement of approximately 50% of the glycine and extension of the wall peptide length (Whitney and Grula, 1964).

Cell walls and spore coats of various microorganisms were analyzed, and glycoproteins or glycopeptide fragments therefrom were isolated. A particle was separated by sonication from the cell wall of *Staphylococcus aureus* which possessed capacities of attachment to and inactivation of the bacteriophage (Rosato and Cameron, 1964). In the cell wall of *Nitrosomonas europaea,* galactose, galactosamine, and galacturonic acid were detected, whereas the whole cells contain ribose, rhamnose, and xylose (Lewis, 1964). Horikoshi and Iida (1964) isolated the spore coats of *Aspergillus oryzae* and found that they contained mannose, glucose, galactose, and glucosamine, the pattern of which was similar to the cell wall. A polymer containing glucose and aminohexuronic acid was isolated from the cell walls of *Micrococcus lysodeikticus* (Perkins, 1963).

The serologically active C polysaccharide (noncapsular) of pneumococcus was isolated and found, interestingly enough, to contain a uridine nucleotide composed of uridine diphosphate, muramic acid, and a peptide in addition to a polysaccharide moiety. The nucleotide was responsible for the serologic activity of the C polysaccharide and probably also for the complexing with human C reactive protein (Hornung and Berenson, 1963).

2. Higher Plants

Glucosamine was found to occur in bound form as a glycoprotein and a polysaccharide in the seeds of fourteen kinds of plants (Pusztai, 1964).

Linko (1958) reported the presence of a conjugated amino sugar compound, possibly a derivative of glutamic acid and glucosamine. This compound was detected in the acid hydrolyzate of the leaves of *Phlox decussats* and *Asplenium septentrionale* (a kind of fern) after infiltration of radioactive pyruvate.

II. Metabolism of Glycolipids

After the pioneering studies of Thudichum (1884), a number of the sugar-containing lipids—glycolipids—were described, and they are discussed in detail in Volume I, Chapters 14 and 15. Although most of them were discovered originally as components of nerve tissue, now they appear to be present in a wide variety of living organisms (see Volume I, Chapter 15). The studies of the metabolism of these lipids have been undertaken within only the last few years.

Meltzer (1955) and Weiss (1955) showed that the sphingolipid fraction became labeled during perfusion of monkey brains with either acetate-1-C^{14} or octanoate-1-C^{14}. Weiss (1956) further discovered by chromatography on silicic acid that C^{14} activity was involved in at least three fractions. One of them was considered to be a mixture of phosphorus-containing and carbohydrate-containing components. The second fraction was considered to be the ganglioside, and the third fraction contained two species of phosphosphingoside, entirely free from hexose reaction. Since no radioactivity was found in the choline, fatty acids, and sphingosine under these experimental conditions, it was suggested that the C^{14} resides in the carbohydrate moiety of the sphingolipid.

Radin, Martin, and Brown (1957) found that galactose-1-C^{14} and sulfate-S^{35} are incorporated into galactolipids of rat brain and they investigated the turnover of each fraction of galactolipids. They used fractional extraction for the separation of each lipid fraction. The rapid appearance of radioactivity and its slower disappearance were found in a "water-extractable, nondialyzable lipid fraction." This fraction contained strandin, strandin peptide (Folch, Meath, and Bogoch, 1956)—which contributed little to the total activity—gangliosides, and various nonlipid materials. Glucose was also detected in this fraction. Less, although significant, radioactivity was also found in the lipoidal fraction, soluble in chloroform and obtained from the cerebroside hydrolyzates. The lipoidal fraction includes cholesterol, sphingosine, and cerebroside acids. Thus, galactose enters a large and varied metabolic pool; its total activity in sulfatide rises more slowly than it does in cerebroside and strandin. The half-life times was calculated to be around 8 days for the strandin fraction and around 13 days for cerebrosides. By means of polystyrene-spheres chromatography, a cerebroside fraction was found which contained two moles of hexose and accounted for a small percentage of the total cerebrosides but no detectable radioactivity. The accumulation of sulfatides was also demonstrated by labeling with sulfate-

S^{35}. The radioactivity, however, was found to be abundant in the lipids which are not extracted with the strandin or cerebroside fractions but are bound by Florisil (Radin, Lavin, and Brown, 1955). Roughly, 20% of the total lipid galactose occurred in the Florisil-bound fraction, and in one experiment where analyses were made 6 hr after injection of galactose-1-C^{14}, 88% of the lipid radioactivity was found to be present in galactose, whereas 70% of the lipid activity was bound by Florisil. The Florisil-bound lipid was supposed to be a polycerebroside (Uzman, 1953), but the calculated radioactivity plotted against time showed that this lipid has a higher turnover rate than does the strandin. Slight radioactivity was also found in the protein-bound galactolipid (Folch and LeBaron, 1953).

The cerebroside sulfate of various organs of rats differs in its metabolic behavior (Green and Robinson, 1960). In contrast to the slow turnover in brain, this sulfatide turns over very rapidly in kidney, liver, spleen, heart, and mastocytoma (mast-cell tumor), and the half-life time varies between 10 and 96 hr. This half-life time is more similar to that of phosphatides than to that of other neutral glycolipids.

From these observations, no conclusive ideas on the metabolic route of galactolipids were drawn, except that the cerebroside sulfate may be synthesized from cerebrosides. The unknown rapidly metabolizing Florisil-bound glycolipids might play an important role.

Moser and Karnovsky (1959) studied the *in vivo* incorporation of C^{14} glucose and galactose, labeled at various positions, into glycolipids of mouse brain. By measurement at 1 hr after the injection of glucose-6-C^{14} or uniformly labeled glucose-C^{14}, it was found that the specific activity of cerebroside galactose exceeded that of any of the strandin carbohydrate components. It was further found that the specific activity of cerebroside galactose was 5.4 times that of strandin glucose, and that of the strandin galactose was 3.2 times that of glucose, and that of the strandin galactosamine was 1.4 times that of glucose. When glucose-6-C^{14} was administered, almost all of the activity of the cerebroside galactose and strandin glucose was found in the carbon-6. In strandin galactose and galactosamine, on the other hand, there was a significant amount of radioactivity in carbons other than carbon-6. Strandin galactose and galactosamine might be derived in part from glucose by a mechanism other than that which only involves Walden inversion of the uridine diphosphate-glucose, a possible intermediate, as will be mentioned later. It was further found by Moser and Karnovsky (1959) that glucose was a better precursor of cerebroside galactose than was galactose itself, but, for total strandin, galactose was the better precursor.

Burton, Sodd, and Brady (1958) studied the metabolism of *N*-cerebronyl-*O*-galactosylsphingosine (kerasin), which was purified with the aid of an ion-exchange resin and Florisil. After intraperitoneal injection of uniformly labeled glucose-C^{14} and galactose-1-C^{14}, a considerable amount of C^{14} was found in the neutral glycolipid fraction of brain tissue, but a negligible amount of radioactivity was detected in the glycolipid fraction of liver. From experiments on rats 14 days post partum, the maximal labeling of the neutral glycolipid of the brain was determined to occur at 8 hr after the injection, and the activity fell to one-third of the maximal level at 24 hr, indicating that this fraction turns over rapidly. The incorporation was found to be deeply dependent on the age of the rats, since the count was measurable in rats 8 days old, was maximal in rats between 11 and 18 days old, and dropped as the rat got older. The fact that the degree of incorporation is dependent on age is also reflected by histological observations. Myelinization was first discernible in the mouse at about the age of 8 days and was complete by the age of 50 days (Folch-Pi, 1955). In the investigation of Burton, Sodd, and Brady (1958), kerasin and phrenosin were the only neutral glycolipids in the cerebroside fraction which bore the radioactivity in *in vivo* experiments. On the other hand, in *in vitro* experiments, phrenosin was found to be the only radioactive neutral glycolipid. Although radioactivity was detected in the fractions soluble in water, in acetone, and in chloroform–methanol (2:1), as well as in the purified neutral glycolipid fraction, turnover studies were not made on these fractions. The rapid turnover of kerasin and phrenosin, in contrast to the results obtained by Radin, Martin, and Brown (1957), would indicate that these neutral glycolipids may serve as intermediates for the biosynthesis of other glycolipids. This idea is supported by the fact that the radioactivity of the fraction soluble in chloroform–methanol increased with time, whereas the radioactivity of the neutral glycolipid remained constant, at least until 8 hr after injection.

In further studies made by Burton, Sodd, and Brady (1958) on the biosynthesis of the neutral glycolipid, it was found that glucose or galactose is incorporated into the glycolipids directly. It appeared that, in the brain cell, the microsomal fraction is a main site for hexose incorporation into glycolipid. In this fraction were found most of the gangliosides, too (Wolfe, 1961). Uridine nucleotides are very frequently involved in glycosyl transfer reactions, and uridine diphosphate-galactose was found to be a galactose donor in the glycolipid synthesis. Thus, the microsomal fraction with galactose-1-C^{14}, adenosine triphosphate, and UDP-glucose or with galactose-1-C^{14}-1-phosphate and UDP-glucose, as well as with UDP-galactose-1-C^{14}, resulted in the incorporation of a significant amount of radioactivity into the glycolipid. Cleland and

Kennedy (1958) also showed the incorporation of radioactivity into the lipid fraction when galactose-1-C^{14}-phosphate or UDP-galactose-1-C^{14} was incubated with homogenates of guinea-pig brain. Hexokinase, phosphoglucomutase, UDP-glucose pyrophosphorylase, UDP-galactose 4-epimerase (Shapiro and Wertheimer, 1943; Slein, Cori, and Cori, 1950; Maxwell, Kalckar, and Burton, 1955), galactokinase (Leloir, 1953), and galactose-1-phosphate-uridyl transferase (Kurahashi, unpublished data) were found to be present in brain tissue. Based on these findings, Burton, Sodd, and Brady (1958) suggested the following pathways for the incorporation of glucose and galactose into the neutral glycolipid:

Glucose pathway:
glucose + ATP $\rightleftharpoons$ glucose 6-phosphate + ADP
glucose 6-phosphate $\rightleftharpoons$ glucose 1-phosphate
glucose 1-phosphate + UTP $\rightleftharpoons$ UDP-glucose + pyrophosphate
UDP-glucose $\rightleftharpoons$ UDP-galactose
UDP-galactose + acceptor $\rightleftharpoons$ neutral glycolipid + UDP

Galactose pathway:
galactose + ATP $\rightleftharpoons$ galactose 1-phosphate + ADP
galactose 1-phosphate + UDP-glucose $\rightleftharpoons$ UDP-galactose + glucose 1-phosphate
UDP-galactose + acceptor $\rightleftharpoons$ neutral glycolipid + UDP

The nature of the acceptor has not been investigated, but it may well be that *N*-acylsphingosine (ceramide) is the acceptor, as it is in sphingomyelin biosynthesis (Sribney and Kennedy, 1958). In this case, cytidine diphosphate-choline would be replaced by UDP-galactose.

Although nothing is known concerning the pathways of biosynthesis of other glycolipids like strandin and the gangliosides, the presence of UDP-*N*-acetylglucosamine (Koransky, 1958) suggests that the ganglioside may be synthesized from glucocerebrosides by lengthening of the carbohydrate chain.

Recent structural studies on brain gangliosides and strandin revealed that the basic constituent is a cerebroside composed of stearic acid, sphingosine, and glucose (glucostearocerebroside) (Bogoch, 1957). Thus, a reaction between the ceramide (*N*-stearylsphingosine) and UDP-glucose, or transferring reactions between phrenosine and UDP-glucose and stearylcoenzyme A, might be involved in the biosynthesis of ganglioside and strandin.

Occurrence of behenyl glucocerebroside (Rosenberg and Chargaff, 1958) in spleen affected by Gaucher's disease also indicates that glycolipid metabolism is related to carbohydrate and lipid metabolism in many ways. In this connection, a galactose oxidase preparation was utilized to demonstrate the accumulation of cerebroside in Gaucher's disease (Agranoff, Radin, and Suomi, 1962). This enzyme was extracted from the fungus *Polyporus circinatus* and is able to oxidize the cerebroside, producing an aldehyde group at carbon-6 of the galactose.

The metabolism of plant glycolipids (phytoglycolipids) (Carter *et al.*, 1958) has not been studied.

Rhamnolipid biosynthesis by *Pseudomonas aeruginosa* was studied by Hauser and Karnovsky (1957), and glycerol was found to furnish all of the carbon of rhamnolipid, whereas acetate carbon supplies only the β-hydroxydecanoic acid carbons. In the recent studies on rhamnolipid biosynthesis, Burger, Glaser, and Burton (1962) were able to demonstrate that the incubation of thymidine diphosphate-rhamnose-C^{14} and β-hydroxydecanoyl-coenzyme A with a sonic extract of *Pseudomonas aeruginosa* could produce radioactive rhamnolipid.

Benson *et al.* (1958) found that galactolipids are labeled very rapidly with C^{14}; this was indicated by radioautographs of deacylated products obtained after photosynthesis in $C^{14}O_2$ by *Chlorella*. These glycolipids include the *O*-β-D-galactosyl- and the *O*-α-D-galactosyl-(1 → 6)-β-D-galactosyl monoglyceride and the 3′-*O*-oleyl-glycerol-1′-β-D-galactopyranoside-6-sulfate. Glycerol phosphatides and small amounts of a galactotriosyl monoglyceride were also detected. Uridine diphosphate-galactose has been detected in *Chlorella* and is supposed to be a precursor of the biosynthesis of these glycolipids (Ginsburg, Stumpf, and Hassid, 1956).

Stepwise transfer of glycosyl residues from nucleotide sugars in cell-free systems to glycolipids (or, rather, lipopolysaccharides) of cell walls has been investigated very thoroughly, and the results afford extremely valuable information on chemical structure and biosynthesis of glycolipids.

From a wild strain of *E. coli*, a lipopolysaccharide composed of at least fatty acid, phosphate, glucosamine, 3-deoxyoctulosonate, heptose (L-glycero-D-mannoheptose), glucose, galactose, colitose, and ethanolamine was isolated (Osborn, 1963), and, similarly, from a wild strain of *Salmonella typhimurium*, a lipopolysaccharide composed of rhamnose, abequose, and tyvelose, in addition to heptose, glucose, galactose, and mannose. Stepwise syntheses of these polysaccharides were then conducted by using, as the substrates, the incomplete lipopolysaccharides which lack one or two or more sugar components at the side chains of the complete lipopolysaccharides. These incomplete lipopolysaccharides were found in the cell walls of the mutant strains which are not able to synthesize the complete lipopolysaccharides because of defects in formation of appropriate nucleotide sugars, the sugars which are found in the side chains (Nikaido, 1961, 1962,a; Fukasawa and Nikaido, 1961).

Thus, using a cell-free system from a mutant strain of *Salmonella typhimurium* which lacks UDP-galactose 4-epimerase and enzymes for

UDPG formation, but is not deficient in UDP-sugar transferases, Osborn and D'Ari (1964) were able to demonstrate the following stepwise synthesis of lipopolysaccharide (LPS: lipopolysaccharides containing only heptose, phosphate, ethanolamine, and 3-deoxyoctulosonate).

$$\text{UDPG} + \text{LPS} \rightarrow \text{G-LPS} + \text{UDP} \quad (3)$$

$$\text{UDP-Gal} + \text{G-LPS} \rightarrow \alpha\text{-Gal}(1 \rightarrow 3)\text{-G-LPS} + \text{UDP} \quad (4)$$

$$\text{UDPG} + \alpha\text{-Gal}(1 \rightarrow 3)\text{-G-LPS} \rightarrow \text{G-}\alpha\text{-Gal}(1 \rightarrow 3)\text{-G-LPS} \quad (5)$$

$$\text{UDP-GNAc} + \text{G-}\alpha\text{-Gal}(1 \rightarrow 3)\text{-G-LPS} \rightarrow \text{GNAc-G-}\alpha\text{-Gal}(1 \rightarrow 3)\text{-G-LPS} \quad (6)$$

A similar type of reaction was studied in *E. coli* by Edstrom and Heath (1964). In this reaction, transfer of GDP-colitose and cytidine monophosphate 3-deoxyoctulosonate to acceptor lipopolysaccharides was also demonstrated.

Cytidine diphosphate derivatives of tyvelose and abequose were found to occur in the culture medium of mutant strains of *Salmonella* which were unable to produce the cell wall containing these 3,6-dideoxyhexoses (Nikaido, 1962a).

In the experiments carried out by Distler and Roseman (1964) on polysaccharide biosynthesis of Type XIV pneumococcus, reactions seem to be more complicated. The labeled glucose and galactose from the uridine diphosphate derivatives were found to be significantly transferred to acceptors of lipid nature when UDP-*N*-acetylglucosamine was absent in the incubation mixture. Upon incubation of all these nucleotides together, incorporation of the sugars took place into the polysaccharide rather than into the lipid fraction. These findings would suggest that the primarily synthesized glycolipids might be intermediates for complete polysaccharide synthesis. In these experiments, however, the kind of synthesis that occurred remains to be solved, since the radioactive polysaccharides thus synthesized were, in gel diffusion, different from the Type XIV polysaccharide which was endogenously present in the enzyme system employed, although the newly synthesized polysaccharides were reactive to the antibody against Type XIV polysaccharide.

After all these experiments, it is now clear that nucleotide sugars are really precursors for lipopolysaccharide synthesis and that there are transferases which function in transferring sugars from the nucleotides to proper positions in the polysaccharide chains. These incorporations, however, do by no means imply that net syntheses of polysaccharide could be demonstrated in the cell-free systems. Regulatory mechanisms other than specificity of the transferases must certainly exist for the synthesis of the whole polysaccharide to be accomplished.

Other types of lipopolysaccharides from cell wall of *E. coli* were sought, and a tentative structure for one of them was presented by Burton and Carter (1964), in which glucosamine was placed as a major sugar in the backbone structure.

Sussman and Osborn (1964) investigated the appearance and the disappearance of UDP-galactose-polysaccharide transferase during cell differentiation of a slime mold, *Dictyostelium discoideum,* and found that the activity was absent in the vegetative cells and appeared during the period when the synthesis of a galactose-containing polysaccharide occurred. The activity disappeared again after the end of fruiting-body construction. One of the polysaccharides synthesized by this organism was serologically reactive to the anti-*D. discoideum* spore area and anti-pneumococcal (Type XIV) serum, and its main sugar components were galactose, galactosamine, and galacturonic acid, of which galactose appeared to be located at the terminal position.

Sulfatide seems to be a lipid typical of membranous structure, being abundant in myelin and mitochondria. Metabolism of sulfatide may be parallel, in general, to that of other constituents of myelin sheath (Davison and Gregson, 1962). The biosynthesis of sulfatide was slow in fully developed animals. The rate of turnover of sulfatides in brain is slow, but it is comparable to that of cerebrosides in organs other than brain (Davison, 1964).

Whereas Radin, Martin, and Brown (1957) drew the conclusion, based on galactose incorporation experiments, that cerebrosides are precursors of sulfatides in brain, a contrary idea was postulated by Jatzkewitz (1960), who showed that sulfatides appeared to be precursors of cerebrosides in a disease, named metachromatic leukodystrophy, characterized by abnormally high sulfatide concentrations in brain and kidney. The results of Hauser (1964), however, were rather in accord with the postulate of Radin, Martin, and Brown, 1957. Hauser used glucose-6-C^{14} as a precursor and measured the incorporation of C^{14} into galactose in these two glycolipids at different times. In his experiments, these glycolipids were purified carefully.

In kitten brain, the amount of galactose contained in lipid, ganglioside, and cerebroside was independent of the dietary galactose level (Varma, Schwarz, and Simpson, 1962).

With labeled acetate and glucose, studies were made on the conversion of blood glucose or acetate to lipids in mouse brain and peripheral nerve. Cerebroside galactose formation showed a pattern with age very different from that of cholesterol or other lipid components, in that, with age, there was an enormous distribution in the specific activity achieved by cerebroside galactose after administration of glucose-C^{14} (Karnovsky, Moser, and Majno, 1959).

Acetate was also found to be an effective precursor of ganglioside and cerebroside of rat brain (Prokhorova and Taranova, 1962). In rat brain lipid, C^{14} of acetate was abundantly incorporated primarily into palmitic acid of cerebrosides, and fatty acids other than palmitic acid were labeled later (Bernhard *et al.*, 1962; Hajra and Radin, 1963).

With glucose-1-C^{14} and galactose-1-C^{14}, all of the sugar components of rat brain glycolipids were labeled, whereas with glucosamine-1-C^{14} only galactosamine and *N*-acetylneuraminic acid were labeled. This pattern resembles that of the metabolism of glycoproteins in liver and plasma (Burton *et al.*, 1963).

Svennerholm (1962) analyzed gangliosides of normal human brain and gangliosides from patients with Tay–Sachs disease and found that the latter contained 1 mole less of galactose. These findings indicate that, in the biosynthesis of normal brain gangliosides, galactose may be attached to the termini of the sugar chain of gangliosides, whereas, in Tay–Sachs disease, this final stage is lacking.

Enzymic synthesis of gangliosides was demonstrated in kidney homogenate by Kanfer *et al.* (1964). In a system similar to that used by Jourdian, Carlson, and Roseman (1963), Kanfer and associates were able to show a stepwise synthesis of galactosyl(2-acetamido-2-deoxygalactosyl) galactosylglucosylceramide, in which *N*-acetylneuraminic acid is attached to the inner galactose, by incubating, with the homogenate, galactosyl (2-acetamido-2-deoxygalactosyl)galactosylglucosylceramide and cytidine monophosphate-neuraminic acid at the first stage and then incubating the glycolipid formed and uridine diphosphate galactose at the second stage.

Suzuki and Korey (1963) separated gangliosides of rat brain into four fractions by means of thin-layer chromatography and compared the incorporation of uniformly labeled glucose-C^{14} into these fractions. The differences of the incorporation rate among these gangliosides were small, but the radioactivities were lower in neuraminic acids which could be split off by neuraminidase than in those resistant to the enzyme.

A cell-free system containing rat brain microsomes and soluble fraction was capable of incorporating D-glucose-C^{14} into the ganglioside fraction. Some of the glucose was converted to *N*-acetylneuraminic acid. The rate of incorporation of glucose into each of the four gangliosides was similar, with the initial rate of incorporation being very rapid (Suzuki, 1964).

Contents of gangliosides and cerebrosides in chicken brain during embryonic development were measured by Garrigan and Chargaff (1963). Noteworthy features of their study were the observations that the quantity of cerebrosides in the early embryonic brain was not negligible, although the highest rate of cerebroside accumulation did coincide with the time of most rapid myelin formation, and the rate of formation of mucolipids (gangliosides, strandin, etc.) was faster than that of cerebrosides. In view of the finding (Stanacev and Chargaff, 1962) that, in ox brain, the mucolipids were distinct from the cerebrosides in the type of base and fatty acid that they contain, the authors presumed that mucolipids and cerebrosides contain a certain degree of anabolic autonomy.

On the basis of a different pattern of splenic glycolipids in Gaucher's disease, Philippart and Menkes (1964) presumed that the metabolic defect in Gaucher's disease may be in the degradative pathway of the red-cell glycolipids.

Burger, Glaser, and Burton (1963) further investigated the mechanism of the rhamnolipid biosynthesis; the enzymic synthesis of each of the following steps was demonstrated by them as follows:

2-β-hydroxydecanoyl-coenzyme A → β-hydroxydecanoyl-β-hydroxydecanoate (7)

TDP-L-rhamnose + β-hydroxydecanoyl-β-hydroxydecanoate → TDP
+ L-rhamnosyl-β-hydroxydecanoyl-β-hydroxydecanoate (8)

TDP-rhamnose + L-rhamnosyl-β-hydroxydecanoyl-β-hydroxydecanoate → TDP
+ L-rhamnosyl-L-rhamnosyl-β-hydroxydecanoyl-β-hydroxydecanoate (9)

III. General Comments

Structural studies have revealed that glycoproteins are usually composed of four or five types of monosaccharide, and these monosaccharides make up a heteropolysaccharide unit without forming simple repeating units. In glycolipids also, at least two or more types of monosaccharide are involved.

In view of this, the synthesis of the heteropolysaccharide moiety of a glycoprotein or glycolipid may require a preformed template similar to that involved in the biosynthesis of proteins. The template will control the transfer of the glycosyl residues of the activated sugars (most probably sugar nucleotides) to a proper position within the macromolecule at the site of synthesis.

It is evident that one can think of four ways in which the synthesis of glycoproteins may proceed: (*i*) the polysaccharide and the protein may be synthesized separately and then conjugated in one macromolecule; (*ii*) the protein synthesis may occur first, and then a single monosaccharide (probably amino sugar) may become attached to the protein, and then the lengthening of the carbohydrate moiety proceeds; (*iii*) the carbohydrate moiety may be synthesized first, and then a single amino acid (most probably asparagine) may become attached to it, and then the protein synthesis proceeds; and (*iv*) the amino acids and monosaccharides may be attached at random for the synthesis of a whole macromolecule, in which process one should consider the intermediate stage of peptide, oligosaccharide, or amino acid–monosaccharide-complex formations.

Study of the subcellular systems would be one of the most important ways to solve these problems of biosynthesis of glycoproteins and glycolipids.

According to the recent studies on intracellular distribution of amino sugars and sialic acid (Wallach and Eylar, 1961; Wolfe, 1961; Patterson and Touster, 1962; Yamashina, Izumi, and Naka, 1964; Izumi *et al.*, 1963), glycoproteinlike or glycolipidlike substances containing hexosamine and neuraminic acid appear to be distributed in microsome and mitochondria, as well as in the soluble fraction of liver cells of rats and rabbits. Thus, it may be suspected that glycoproteins and glycolipids are building blocks of living cells in general, as are glycopeptides in bacterial cell wall.

The correlation of the biosynthesis of glycoproteins with that of other macromolecules and with cell growth or cell proliferation, in general, would also be a fruitful area to be explored.

Addendum

The following papers of interest have been published since the preparation of this chapter and are also included in the reference list:

Kornfeld, S., Kornfeld, R., and Ginsburg, V. (1965). Intracellular site of synthesis of soluble blood group substance.

Molnar, J., Robinson, G. B., and Winzler, R. J. (1965). Biosynthesis of glycoproteins. IV. The subcellular sites of incorporation of glucosamine-1-^{14}C into glycoprotein in rat liver.

Zeleznick, L. D., Rosen, S. M., Saltmarsh-Andrew, M. J., Osborn, J. J., and Horecker, B. L. (1965). Biosynthesis of bacterial lipopolysaccharide, IV. Enzymatic incorporation of mannose, rhamnose, and galactose in a mutant strain of *Salmonella typhimurium*.

Chapter 41

EFFECT OF STEROID HORMONES ON THE GLYCOSAMINOGLYCANS OF TARGET CONNECTIVE TISSUES

J. A. Szirmai

The composition of the intercelluar substance of various connective tissues is known to be influenced by many factors, such as age, sex, and numerous endogenous and exogenous agents. Certain steroid hormones occupy in this respect a peculiar position: in addition to generalized effects on connective tissues of the whole body, their action is often restricted to anatomically distinct target sites. Such "steroid-sensitive connective tissues" (Szirmai, 1954) are mostly parts of organs designated as "secondary sex characters," "sexual organs," "end organs," and the like. Since these tissue reactions appear to have no direct relationship to the sex of the individual, preference is given to the term "target tissue." It is used to emphasize the anatomical demarcation of the reactive structures and their relatively high degree of sensitivity to hormones (Szirmai, 1962).

The action of steroid hormones in these instances results in the formation of what has often been termed "mucoid connective tissue" (*Schleimgewebe, Gallertgewebe, tissu muqueux, connettivo turgescente,* etc.). Morphologically, these tissues are characterized by a relatively large amount of intercellular substance, a loose organization of the fibrillar components, and a relative scantiness of cells. In chemical terms, the most prominent feature of the hormone response is an increased content of glycosaminoglycans, together with a marked increase of the water content.

I. Rooster Comb

The comb and other head appendices, such as wattles and earlobes, in fowl (Fig. 1) are modified skin formations. In the single comb common to the Leghorn breed, the subcutaneous tissue has developed into a central core with a symmetrical, dense fibrous partition containing blood

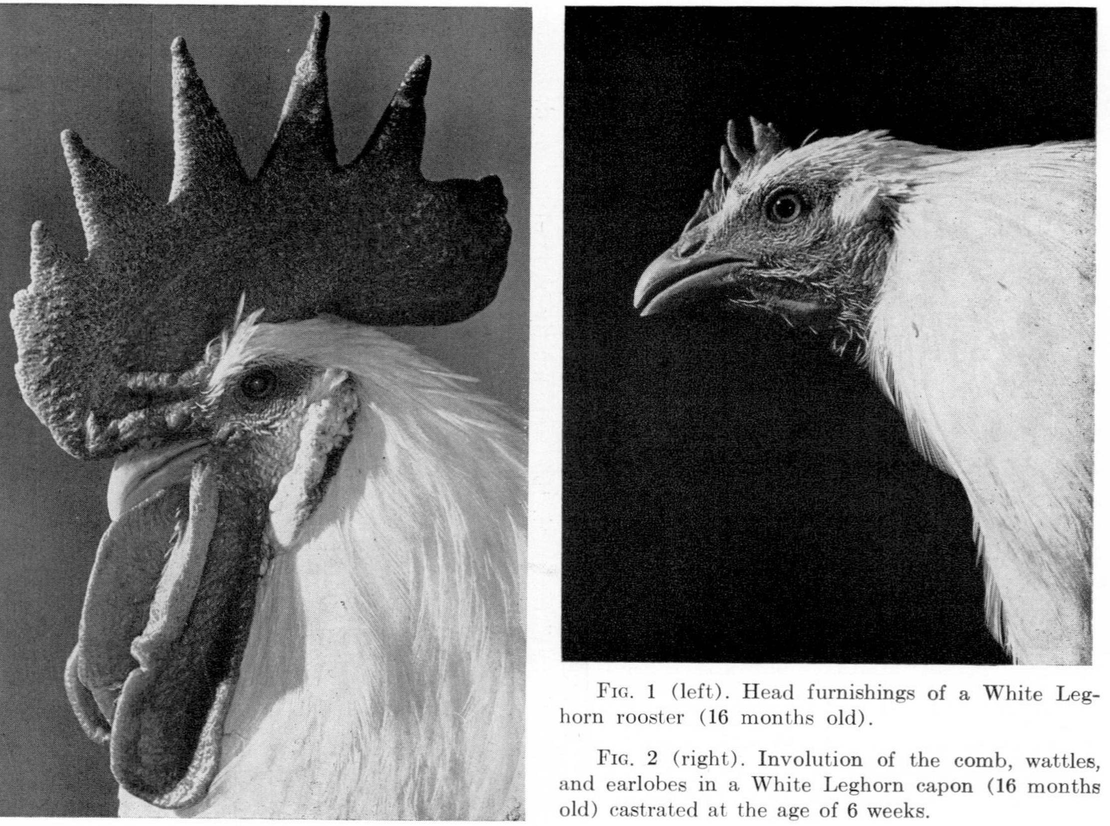

FIG. 1 (left). Head furnishings of a White Leghorn rooster (16 months old).

FIG. 2 (right). Involution of the comb, wattles, and earlobes in a White Leghorn capon (16 months old) castrated at the age of 6 weeks.

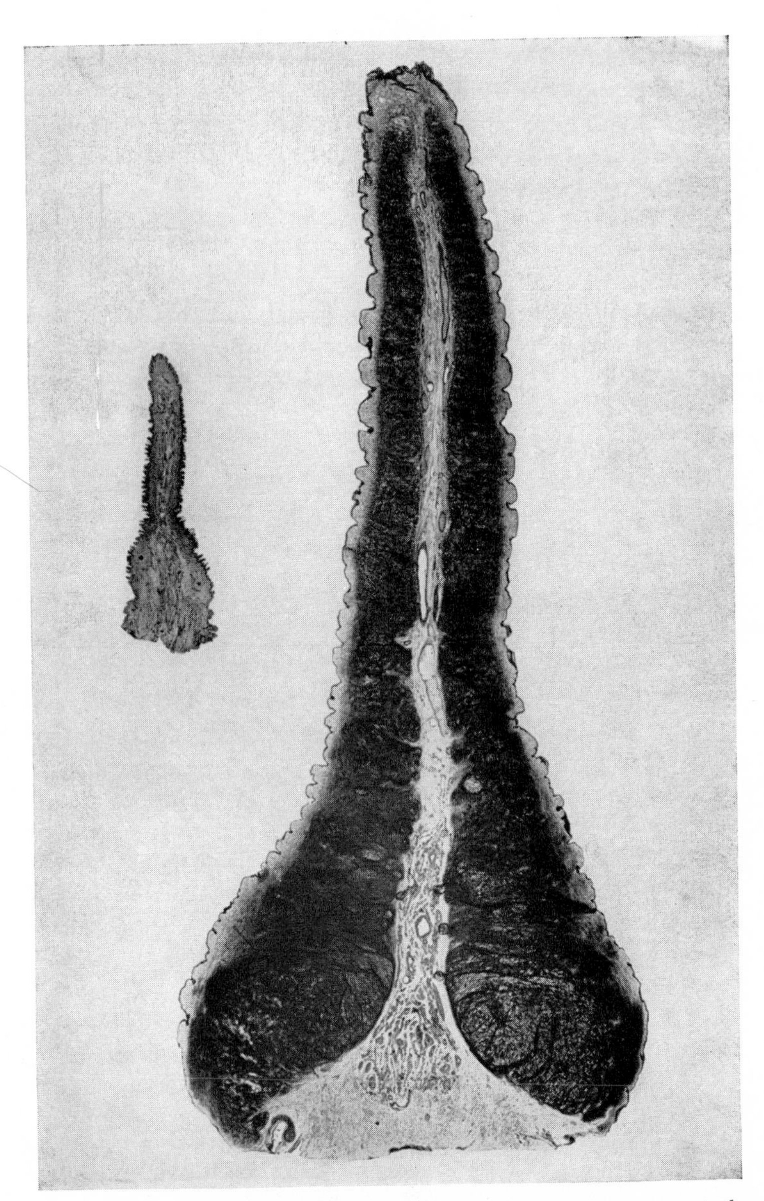

Fig. 3. Cross section of the comb of a White Leghorn rooster (20 months old), stained with azure A (2×10^{-4} M), without previous fixation, photographed in green light (558 mμ). Dark area: mucoid layer. Insert left: cross section of the comb of a White Leghorn capon of the same age by use of the same technique. Final magnification of both sections approximately 2×.

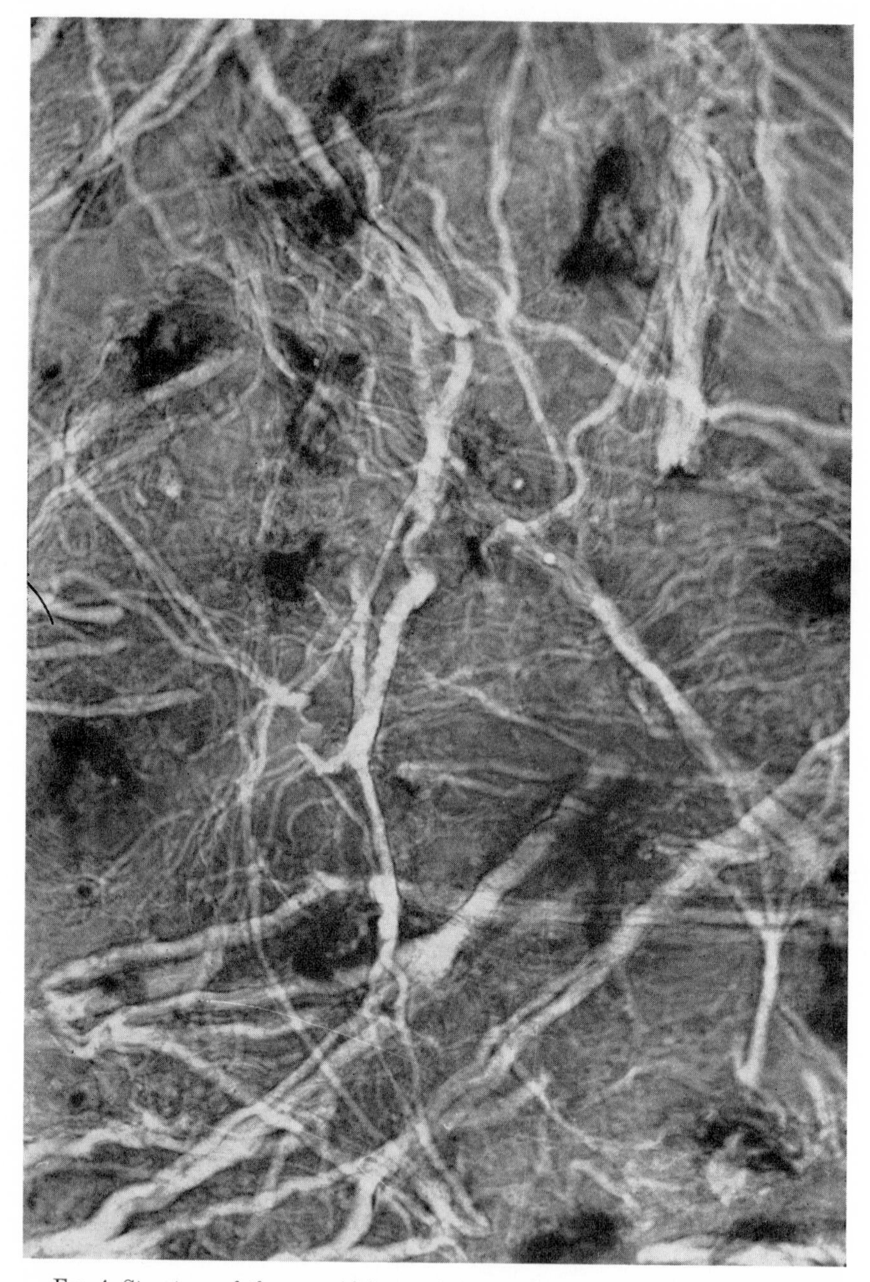

FIG. 4. Structure of the mucoid layer of the rooster comb. Same preparation and technique as in Fig. 3. Dark background: metachromatic intercellular substance. Final magnification approximately 650×.

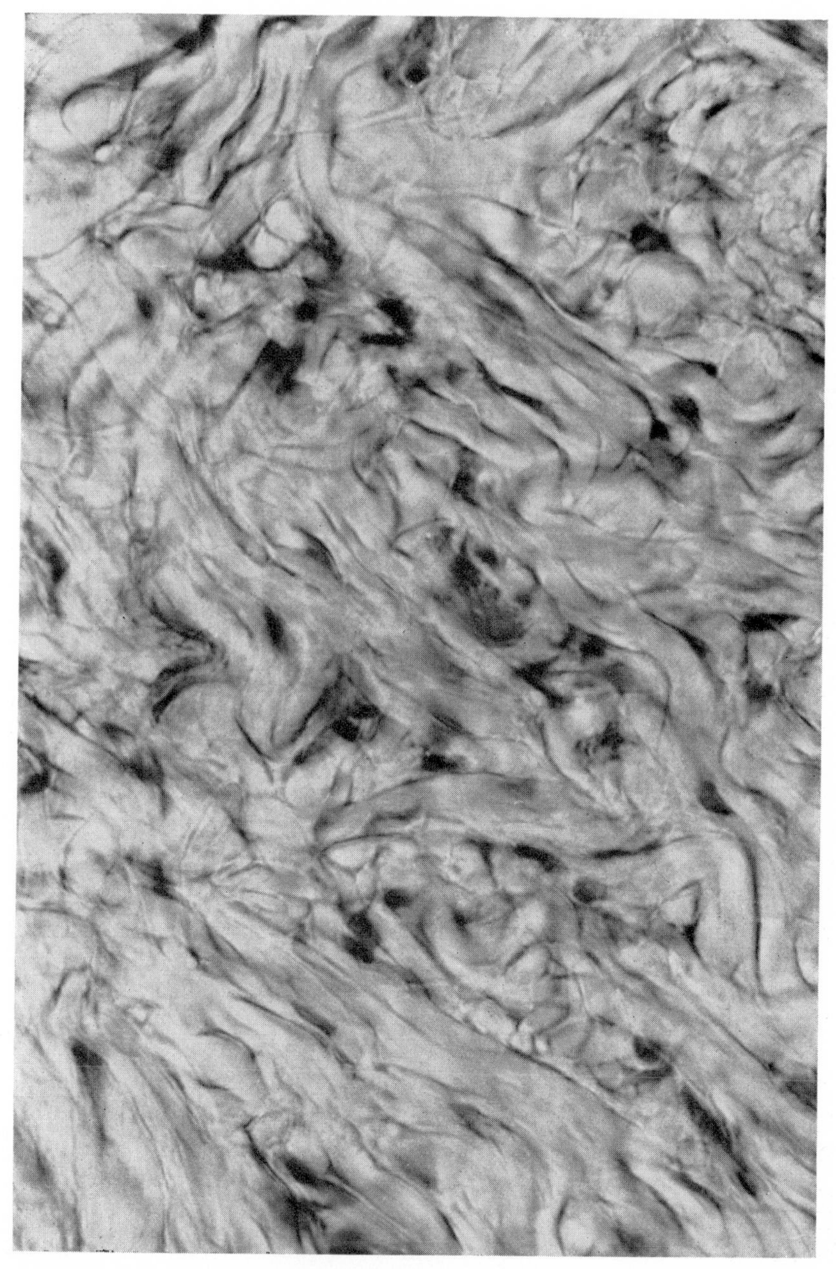

FIG. 5. Structure of the intermediate layer of the capon comb. Preparation and technique as in insert of Fig. 3. Final magnification approximately 650×.

and lymph vessels and fat tissue. The modified dermis of the normal adult rooster comb has been described as the mucoid or intermediate layer and is the main site of the polysaccharide-containing interfibrillar material (Figs. 3 and 4); the subepithelial part contains a large number of wide capillaries, giving the comb its bright-red color. Virchow (1851) casually mentioned that the connective tissue of the comb belongs to the group of "Schleimgewebe," but in so doing he did not seem to pay attention to the observation of Berthold (1849), who was the first to show that the full development of the comb, which regresses and shrinks upon castration (Fig. 2), can be restored and maintained by the presence of implanted testicles. This latter observation—in fact, the first scientific demonstration of the endocrine function of an organ—has also become the basis for the use of the capon or chick comb for the bioassay of androgens (for review see Dorfman and Shipley, 1956; Dorfman, 1962). The variations in the gross appearance of the comb and other "sex characters" in fowls and their dependence on hormonal conditions have been reviewed elsewhere (Pézard, 1928; Parkes and Emmens, 1944; Burrows, 1949).

A. Composition of the Normal Comb

Champy and his co-workers have shown that the intermediate layer of the comb is characterized by metachromatic staining of the interfibrillar material, suggesting the presence of polysaccharides (Champy and Kritch, 1925; Champy, 1926; Champy, Kritch, and Llombart, 1929). These observations have been confirmed, and the development of this substance in growing chicks has been described (Hardesty, 1931; Garrault, 1934; Rommeney, 1934; Szirmai, 1956). It has been pointed out that the metachromatic staining is confined to the interfibrillar substance, whereas the fibrils remain unstained (Fig. 4); the reverse situation is true for the periodic acid–Schiff reaction, which is negative in the interfibrillar space but positive in the fibrils, especially in the subepithelial tissue, the vessel walls, and the collagen of the central core (Szirmai, 1956). As judged by the metachromatic staining, the interfibrillar material is removed by testicular (Szirmai, 1949; Rizzoli and Rondinini, 1950) and by streptococcal (Ludwig and Boas, 1950) hyaluronidase. Detailed studies have been made on the metachromasia and the quantitative determination of the cationic dyebinding of the comb (Szirmai, 1956; Balazs and Szirmai, 1958,a; Szirmai and Balazs, 1958). These investigations have shown that previous water extraction of unfixed frozen sections of the mucoid layer of the comb completely abolishes the metachromasia and considerably reduces the dyebinding.

In early chemical studies of the comb by Berdnikoff and Champy

(1931, 1932, 1934), the substance which was extracted with 12 to 15% sodium chloride was apparently contaminated by phosphate-containing compounds. Garrault (1933, 1934), using the method of Levene (1925), isolated, from the fresh rooster comb (White Leghorn), a substance in a yield of approximately 1.5%. She considered this to be "mucoitin or chondroitin sulfuric acid," although the sulfur values were less than expected for the supposed chemical structure of these compounds.

Boas (1949), using the extraction method of Meyer and Palmer (1936), isolated hyaluronic acid from comb tissue (in assorted breeds). The yield of the substance, after purification with chloroform–amyl alcohol, was approximately 0.6% of the defatted dry tissue weight. Determination of total hexosamine of acetone-extracted comb tissue gave values of 2.8% (Boas, 1953). An average hexosamine content of 4% was found in New Hampshire × Barred Plymouth Rock roosters (Anastassiadis, Maw, and Common, 1955) and of 4.2% in adult White Leghorn roosters (Szirmai, 1956), expressed in defatted dry weight of the comb. Schiller and Dorfman (1956), using NaOH extraction followed by trypsin digestion, found glycosaminoglycans in a concentration of 4.7% of the defatted, epithelium-free comb tissue (in assorted breeds); hyaluronic acid and a galactosaminoglycan have been isolated quantitatively in a ratio of 15:1, the latter substance being, probably, dermatan sulfate ($[\alpha]_D = -56°$). Laurent (1957) prepared hyaluronic acid from comb tissue by papain digestion and cetylpyridinium chloride precipitation (yield: 0.2% of wet weight); the total hexosamine content of the potassium salt was 43.3%, of which 0.4% was galactosamine. From the isolated mucoid layer, obtained by dissection of combs of adult White Leghorn roosters, hyaluronic acid was prepared by pepsin and trypsin digestion in a yield of 11 to 15% on dry weight. The galactosamine content was less than 0.1% of the total hexosamine in the tissue (Balazs and Szirmai, 1958a). In a later study by Doyle and Szirmai (1961), White Leghorn rooster combs were dissected into three main anatomical parts—namely, the epithelium with the reticular layer, the mucoid layer, and the central core. Glucosamine: galactosamine ratios of 22.0:1, 55.4:1, and 16.0:1, respectively, were found for these three layers in the crude polysaccharide preparations obtained by NaOH extraction. In the water homogenate of whole combs, the glucosamine:galactosamine ratio was about 10:1, but, after water extraction for 24 hr followed by high-speed centrifugation, the supernatant of this homogenate was entirely free of galactosamine. Galactosamine was present in the hydrolyzate of the acetone-dried sediment, together with uronic acid and sulfate, indicating that the compound is a chondroitin sulfate. These findings, as well as the constancy of the galactosamine: hydroxyproline ratio found in whole-comb homogenates in a series of regressing combs of capons (see I,C), suggest a close association between a galactosaminoglycan, possibly dermatan sulfate, and the collagen fibers. Blood vessels, occurring mainly in the subepithelial part and the central core, may be another source of galactosaminoglycans. Mast cells, quite numerous in the comb (Szirmai, 1957), may be an additional source of small amounts of sulfated glycosaminoglycans.

Studies of the normal development of the comb in cockerels (White Leghorn) show the presence of dense fibrous tissue in the dermis, with absence of metachromatic staining during the first few weeks after

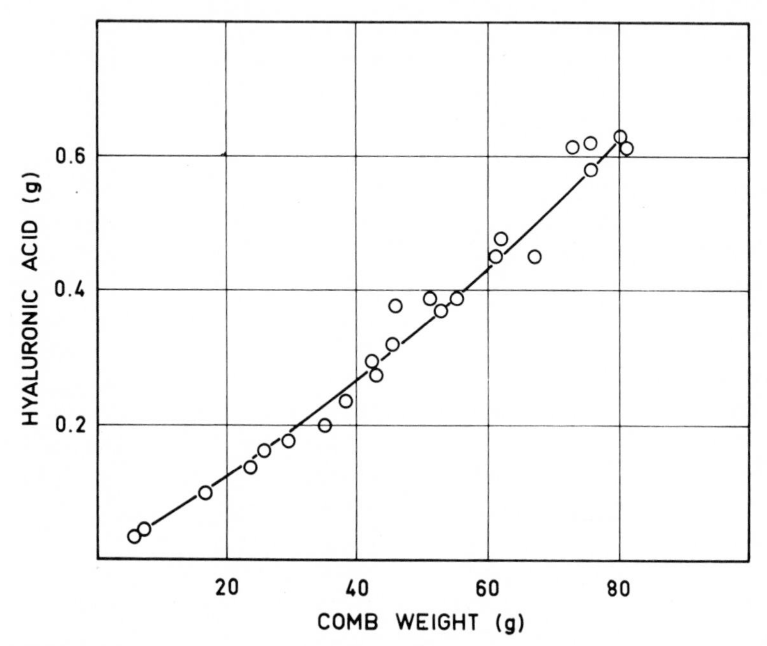

FIG. 6. Relationship between hyaluronic acid content and comb weight in White Leghorn roosters ranging in age from 1 to 7 months (Balazs, Mars, and Szirmai, unpublished).

hatching; metachromasia then gradually develops, and the total hexosamine content increases from about 1% of the defatted dry tissue weight at the age of 1 to 4 weeks to 3 to 4% at the age of 15 weeks (Szirmai, 1956a). The total amount of hyaluronic acid in the comb of growing White Leghorn cockerels from 1 to 7 months of age was determined after quantitative preparation, using pepsin and trypsin digestion (Balazs, Mars, and Szirmai, unpublished); the hyaluronic acid content increased from about 20 mg in the 1-month-old animal to more than 500 mg in the 7-months-old animal. This increase of the amount of hyaluronic acid is proportional to the increasing weight of the comb (Fig. 6).

The metabolism of glycosaminoglycans in the rooster comb has been studied by Balazs, Mars, and Szirmai (1955 and unpublished). The biological half-life time of hyaluronic acid in the comb of adult (7½ months old) White Leghorn roosters, determined after administration of glucose-C^{14} and quantitative preparation of the hyaluronic acid by pepsin and trypsin digestion, was found to be about 4 days. Studies by the same authors have also shown that the rate of incorporation of C^{14} from glucose into the hyaluronic acid of the comb is dependent on age; for instance, maximal values of the specific activity of hyaluronic acid have been found in the combs of cockerels at the age of 3 to 4 months, which is the period of maximal growth rate of the combs. Mancini and Brandes (1956) and Mancini *et al.* (1960) administered S^{35}-sodium sulfate to White Leghorn cockerels 5 to 60 days of age; radioautograms showed, in the comb tissue, the presence of S^{35}, which was eliminated within 15 to 18 days after administration of the isotope. In view of the low content of sulfated glycosaminoglycans in the mucoid layer, the significance of these studies is not clear.

B. Capon Comb and the Mechanism of Hormone Response

In the castrated animal, the comb (Fig. 2) is greatly reduced in size and presents a shrunken, colorless appearance; it shows hyperkeratinization, constriction of the subepithelial blood vessels, and disappearance of the metachromatic material from the intermediate (mucoid) layer, with the latter being gradually transformed (Figs. 2, 3, and 5) into a dense fibrillar tissue (Champy and Kritch, 1925; Hardesty, 1931; Szirmai, 1949). The total hexosamine content of the capon comb (adult White Leghorn) was found to be approximately 0.5% of the defatted dry weight (Szirmai, 1956). On administration of androgens to the capon or baby chick, the changes are reversed, resulting in the appearance of the metachromatic substance in the intercellular space of the mucoid layer. The topography of this reaction (Szirmai, 1956a) and the accompanying histochemical changes have been studied by several authors (Champy, 1926; Hardesty, 1931; Ludwig and Boas, 1950; Schiller, Benditt, and Dorfman, 1952; Szirmai, 1956a).

Parallel with the development of the metachromatic intercellular material, there is a significant increase of the total hexosamine content of the comb in testosterone-treated cockerels or capons (Schiller, Benditt, and Dorfman, 1952; Szirmai, 1956a; Balazs and Szirmai, 1958a). The total amount of hyaluronic acid in the comb, prepared quantitatively by pepsin and trypsin digestion, is proportional to the comb weight in both testosterone-treated cockerels and capons (Balazs, Mars, and Szirmai, unpublished). In studies of the incorporation of glucose-C^{14} into the hyaluronic acid of the comb, it was shown that testosterone treatment increases the rate of incorporation and the specific activity of C^{14} of the hyaluronic acid (Balazs, Mars, and Szirmai, 1955, and also unpublished). Combined microchemical and radioautographic studies using glucose-C^{14} suggest that C^{14} is, in fact, located in the mucoid layer (Balazs, Szirmai, and Bergendahl, 1959). S^{35} has been utilized for radioautographic studies in testosterone-treated White Leghorn cockerels and capons (Mancini, Izquierdo, and Kirschbaum, 1957; Mancini *et al.*, 1960); the identity of the "sulfated mucopolysaccharide," claimed to be present in the mucoid layer on the basis of histochemical and radioautographic studies, was not established by chemical methods.

Regression of the comb occurs immediately upon cessation of androgen treatment in capons, and the changes are similar to those occurring on castration. The metachromatic intercellular material disappears from the mucoid layer (Szirmai, 1949), and the total hexosamine content of the comb is reduced (Szirmai, 1954). In a study of the comb regression, after a 15-day period of testosterone treatment of White Leghorn capons, the hyaluronic acid content of the comb, estimated from the uronic acid and hexosamine contents of the aqueous extract, was found to decrease rapidly to practically zero within 24 days (Doyle, Szirmai, and de Tyssonsk, 1964). A correlation between hyaluronic acid content and comb weight was observed in this series, similar to the results obtained on normal growing roosters and testosterone-treated capons (Balazs, Mars, and Szirmai, unpublished). Whereas the aqueous extracts have been shown to be free of galactosamine, it has been found in the whole comb that the glucosamine:galactosamine ratio changes in the course of regression from about 12:1 to 5:1. The galactosamine-containing material was found to resist 24-hr water extraction and to be entirely associated with the water-insoluble particulate matter, probably with collagen, as indicated by a constant galactosamine:hydroxyproline ratio (Doyle and Szirmai, 1961).

The high hyaluronic acid content of the normal rooster comb is associated with a high water content (approximately 90%, based on defatted dry weight) (Szirmai, 1956; Boas, 1959). In the capon, this amounts to only about 75%, but increases on testosterone treatment up to about 92% (Szirmai, 1954, 1956,a). Similarly, in baby chicks, in the course of testosterone treatment, the water content of the comb increases from about 75 to 85% in White Leghorns and from about 72 to 81% in Barred Plymouth Rocks (Kosin and Munro, 1942). A linear correlation was found between the increasing total hexosamine and water content in the combs of testosterone-treated White Leghorn capons and growing cockerels (Szirmai, 1956a), and a linear correlation was also found between the decreasing hyaluronic acid and the water content in the regressing capon comb (Doyle, Szirmai, and de Tyssonsk, 1964). These results suggest that changes in water content are a most sensitive indication of the response of the comb to both administration and withdrawal of androgens. This applies especially to the mucoid layer, where the water content is found to be highest (91.5%) when compared with that of the epithelium and reticular layer (77.8%) and the central core (15.0%), as determined on dissected adult White Leghorn comb (Szirmai and Balazs, 1958). The comb tissue also readily takes up water, as demonstrated in swelling experiments with dried (Heringa and Weidinger, 1940) and fresh combs (Szirmai, 1949).

Although the appearance of interfibrillar substance, containing mainly hyaluronic acid, is the most dramatic feature of the comb response to androgens, other tissue components undergo concomitant changes. During the hormone reaction, the dense collagen fibrils split up into elementary fibrils and become argyrophilic (Garrault, 1934; Heringa, 1948), but in the stretched state there is no difference in the X-ray diffraction pattern of capon or rooster comb collagen (Szirmai, 1949). As mentioned before, the periodic acid–Schiff reaction is restricted to these fibrils, indicating the presence of glycoproteins. A clue to the formation of these components, on treatment with androgen, is suggested by the significant incorporation of glucose-C^{14}, as shown by radioautography (Balazs, Szirmai, and Bergendahl, 1959). The collagen content, based on hydroxyproline determinations of the hydrolyzed total tissue, suggests that, simultaneously with the formation of hyaluronic acid, collagen synthesis must take place in the combs of testosterone-treated capons (Szirmai, 1954, 1956a). The newly formed collagen is apparently broken down in the course of the regression of the comb on cessation of hormone treatment, as indicated by changes in the hydroxyproline content determined at various time intervals; however, although changes in water and hyaluronic acid content set in immediately during the first few days of regression, a decrease of collagen is not apparent before the twelfth day (Doyle, Szirmai, and de Tyssonsk, 1964). In the same studies it was shown that serum proteins are present in the connective tissue of the comb; on regression, their amount decreases proportionally with the comb weight. The elastic fibrils in the mucoid layers are less numerous than was suggested earlier (Champy and Kritch, 1925), and they play no part in the reaction (Elkner and Slonimski, 1927; Szirmai, 1949). The fibroblasts show changes in shape during the transformation from the capon to the rooster stage, but no mitotic divisions have been observed during the formation of the metachromatic material, except in young cockerels (Szirmai, 1949, 1956a). Increased cytoplasmic basophilia, as well as a positive alkaline phosphatase reaction, has been reported in the fibroblasts in testosterone-treated cockerels (Ludwig and Boas, 1950). In the testosterone-treated capon, histochemical and chemical determinations of alkaline phosphatase gave negative results (Szirmai, 1949). The mast cells in the comb are located mainly in the central core and in the reticular tissue, in both the rooster and the capon; they are scarce in the mucoid layer and apparently do not bear any relationship to the development of the interfibrillar substance (Szirmai, 1957). Vasodilatation of the subepithelial capillary network has been observed as a sign of androgen action (Champy, 1926), but this was also thought to be a passive result of the compression of the venous system from the swelling of the mucoid layer (Hardesty, 1931).

C. Factors Influencing the Comb Response to Androgens

Since the comb weight and the comb size are proportionally related to the hexosamine (Szirmai, 1956a) and the hyaluronic acid content of the comb (Balazs, Mars, and Szirmai, unpublished; Doyle, Szirmai, and de Tyssonsk, 1964), obviously, then, comb measurements, as practiced in endocrinological studies, reflect changes in hyaluronic acid content. Consequently, many factors examined in such investigations may indicate influences on the metabolism of glycosaminoglycans. The degree of the comb response differs with the various androgenic steroids; various breeds of chickens have a different sensitivity, with White or Brown Leghorns being more responsive than, for example, Barred Plymouth Rocks or Rhode Island Reds. The response also depends on the route of application, since local inunction is more effective than intramuscular injection (Dorfman and Shipley, 1956). In studies of the distribution of testosterone-4-C^{14} in 5-day-old White Leghorn chickens it was found that the comb showed markedly higher specific activity than did other organs (Butenandt, Günther, and Turba, 1960). Recent studies indicate that testosterone-4-C^{14} is actively metabolized by comb tissue (of newly hatched White Leghorn chickens) both *in vitro* and *in vivo* (Baggett, 1962). Transplantation experiments demonstrated that the sensitivity of the comb to hormones is localized to the tissue itself. Autotransplanted combs or parts of the comb react as at the original site: they increase in size during development and show regression on castration (Caridroit and Pézard, 1926; Kozelka, 1929). Similar results have been obtained by Hardesty (1931) with subcutaneous autografts of the comb; she observed regression of the graft on castration and restoration of its size on treatment with extract from testicle.

The vast amount of literature concerning the various factors influencing the androgen response of the comb cannot be extensively reviewed here. Variations in the reactivity of the comb have been found in the study of the effect of various other hormones, but, in most cases, the effect is mediated through the complicated channels of endocrine interrelations. An exception might be the antagonistic action of estrogens, observed in androgen-treated capons (Mühlbock, 1938,a) and in young growing cockerels (Breneman, 1942; Kosin and Munro, 1942) and confirmed by findings of decreased metachromasia (Boas and Ludwig, 1950) and a decreased hexosamine content in the comb (Anastassiadis, Maw, and Common, 1955). Experimental evidence suggests that this antagonism might be the result of a direct estrogenic action at the target site (Morató-Manaro and Albrieux, 1939; Martin, Graves, and Dohan, 1955), rather than an intermediate effect of suppressed pituitary activity (Boas and Ludwig, 1950). Results obtained with some antiandrogenic steroids would also favor the possibility of a direct local antagonism (Lerner *et al.*, 1962). Studies on the effects of hypophysectomy and pituitary extracts would suggest that intact pituitary function is necessary for the normal androgen response of the comb (Breneman, 1942; Marlow, 1950; Nalbandov, Meyer, and McShan, 1951). ACTH appears to have no influence on the capon comb (Nalbandov, Meyer, and McShan, 1951); also, no effect on comb growth or metachromasia and hexosamine content of the comb was found in cortisone-treated young chicks (Schiller, Benditt, and Dorfman, 1952). Adrenalectomy of cockerels leads to caponization, with reduced comb size (Herrick and Torstveit, 1938); similar results were also obtained in the hen (Hewitt, 1947). Thyroidectomy results in a reduction in the comb size of capons and roosters (Caridroit and Régnier, 1941; Morris, 1951) and hens (Blivaiss, 1951), whereas administration of thyroxine increases the comb size and increases synergistically the effect of simultaneously administered androgen.

In addition to the endocrine factors just mentioned, many other influences on the comb response have been observed. Restricted food intake reduces the comb weight and its androgen response in growing cockerels (Breneman, 1942; Morris, 1951). Deficiencies of vitamin E (Caridroit, 1942) and vitamin D (Buckner *et al.*, 1951) seem to decrease the reactivity of the comb; administration of these vitamins results in an increased response and increased comb weight in cockerels. These results may be general metabolic effects similar to those occasioned by some other influences, such as the decreased androgen response in capons after prolonged muscular exercise (Wong, Lavenda, and Hawthorne, 1954) or its seasonal variations (up to 100% higher response during the winter) (David, 1938). Such influences might reflect changes in thyroid activity or variations based on the lighting conditions, since it has been shown that the comb response increases when capons are kept in darkness (Caridroit and Régnier, 1944), whereas exposure to sunlight reduces the comb weight in growing cockerels (Wong and Hawthorne, 1954).

Caridroit and Moszkowska (1947, 1948) reported interesting immunological experiments in which the comb response to androgens was suppressed by simultaneous administration of a rabbit "anticomb" serum. Retardation of comb growth in cockerels was observed after subcutaneous application of homologous spinal-cord extract in Freund's adjuvants (Ranzenhofer, Steigman, and Lipton, 1958).

Regressive changes in the wattle and comb, with reduction of the metachromatic intercellular substance, were observed on local application of a carcinogenic tar preparation (Zurhelle, 1937). Local application of methylcholanthrene (Hertz and Tullner, 1947) and benzpyrene (Dorfman and Shipley, 1956) results in inhibition of the androgen response of the comb in chicks.

II. Sexual Skin

The term "sexual skin" was first introduced by Langley and Sherrington in 1891 and "is used to denote any region of skin which responds, either by coloration or by swelling, to oestrogenic stimulation" (Zuckerman, van Wagenen, and Gardiner, 1938). This applies to several genera of primates (baboon—*Papio,* mandril—*Mandrillus,* mangabey—*Cercocebus,* macaque—*Macaca,* chimpanzee—*Pan*) in which the skin area around the external genitals of the female undergoes swelling and reddening on sexual maturation. There are considerable differences in the anatomy, location, and cyclic fluctuations of this phenomenon, but a common feature is the causative effect of estrogens (Allen, 1927; Zuckerman, 1930). In the most typical form, the skin changes parallel the menstrual cycle, in that gradual swelling takes place in the follicular phase (Fig. 7) and these changes subside in the luteal phase (Fig. 8). The phenomenon is suppressed by antagonistic hormones (progesterone, testosterone), by castration (Gillman and Gilbert, 1946), and by hypophysectomy (Gilbert and Gillman, 1953); a transient inhibition was observed after thyroidectomy (Gillman and Gilbert, 1953). The cyclic swelling occurs equally as well in autotransplanted (Bachman, Collip, and Selye, 1936; Zuckerman, van Wagenen, and Gardiner, 1938) and denervated (Zuckerman, 1935; Bachman, Collip, and Selye, 1936) sexual skin. Similar skin changes can be induced in the male by administration

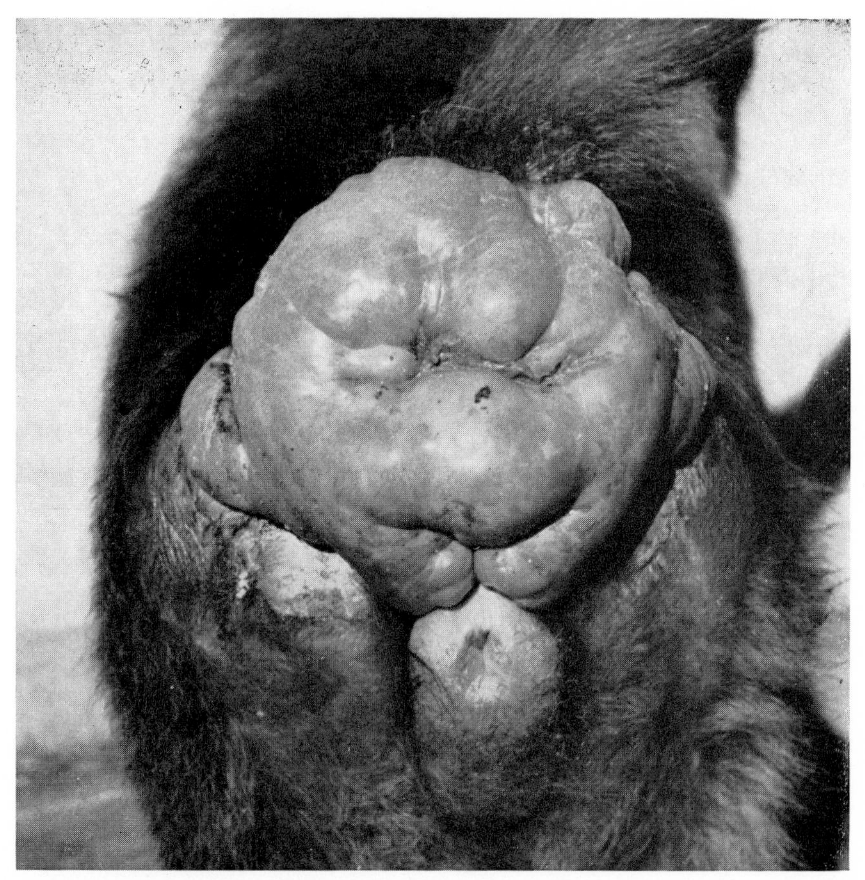

FIG. 7. Sexual skin of a female chacma baboon (*Papio ursinus*) in the phase of maximal swelling.

of estrogens (Bachman, Collip, and Selye, 1935; Zuckerman, van Wagenen, and Gardiner, 1938; Gilbert, 1944), although species differences have been noted (Clark, 1946). The expansion of the sexual skin can show great individual differences and may affect large areas of the back, legs, and tail, as well as the face (Bachman, Collip, and Selye, 1935; Zuckerman, van Wagenen, and Gardiner, 1938; Duran-Reynals, Bunting, and van Wagenen, 1950). Detailed studies have been made of the structural variations and the reproductive physiology of the sexual skin in various genera (Corner, 1923; Allen, 1927; Zuckerman, 1930; Hartman, 1932; Zuckerman, van Wagenen, and Gardiner, 1938; Gillman and Gilbert, 1946; Eckstein and Zuckerman, 1956).

Histologically, the active sexual skin is characterized by the loose fibrillar meshwork in the dermal layer and the excessively rich vascu-

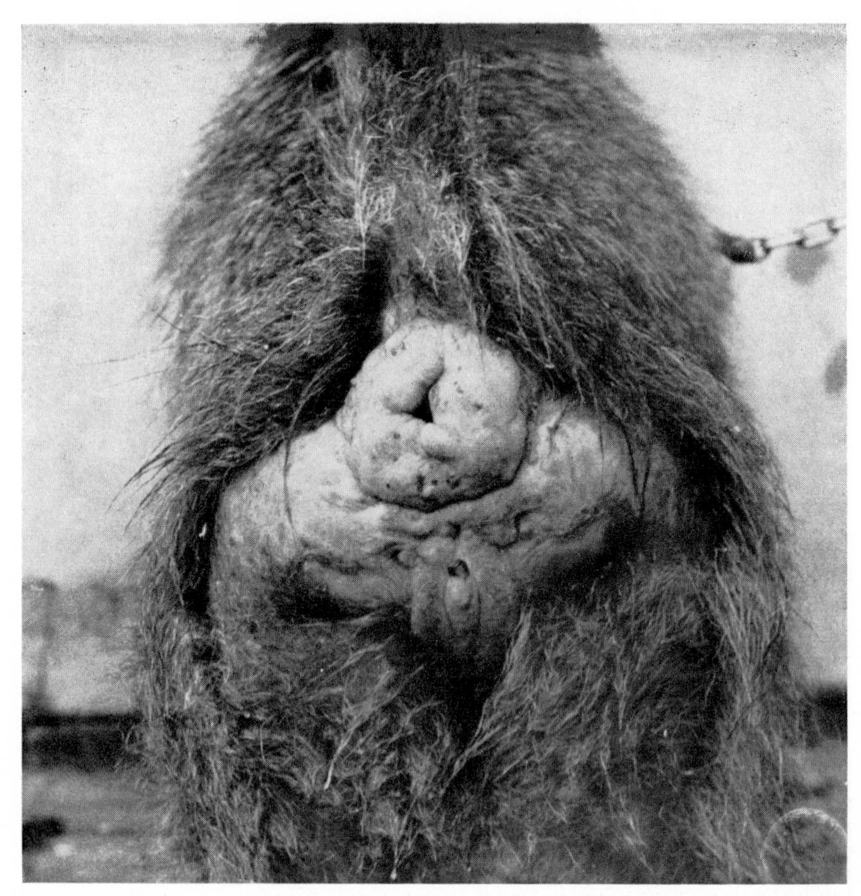

Fig. 8. Involution of the sexual skin at the end of the cycle in same animal as in Fig. 7. Original photographs reproduced through the courtesy of Professor J. Gillman (Gillman and Gilbert, 1946).

larization of the papillary layer (Collings, 1926). Zuckerman and Parkes (1932) suggested that the swelling results from interstitial edema. Enlargement of the fibroblasts has been observed to occur during the swelling phase (Bachman, Collip, and Selye, 1935; Aykroyd and Zuckerman, 1938). The similarity between the sexual skin and the rooster comb was noted by Aykroyd and Zuckerman (1938), who were able to observe metachromatic staining of the interfibrillar substance in the sexual skin; they also noted the presence of metachromatically granulated mast cells and suggested that these cells "discharge mucoprotein into the intercellular spaces." An increased percentage of enlarged fibroblasts with a low mast-cell count was observed during the turgescence phase; a relative increase of both fibroblasts and mast cells was found to occur during deturgescence (Klenerman, 1955). Histochemical studies were reported by Duran-Reynals, Bunting, and van Wagenen (1950), who found that the collagen bundles of the dermis were separated by strongly metachromatic material, which completely disappeared on treatment with either testicular or streptococcal hyaluronidase; they also observed increased cytoplasmic basophilia of the fibroblasts during the swelling phase. The same authors injected testicular hyaluronidase into the maximally swollen sexual skin *in vivo* and noted a collapse within 15 min, which persisted until the end of the cycle. The presence of a metachromatic, but periodic acid–Schiff-negative, intercellular material in the swollen sexual skin was also observed by Preto Parvis and Ugo (1960).

The swollen sexual skin is highly edematous; when it is cut, fluid drips from the surface, and, when it is chopped and squeezed, a viscous fluid can be obtained from it. The use of the term "exudate" for this fluid is misleading, since it has no relationship to the exudates known in pathology. The pressed-tissue fluid obtained from the sexual skin of the rhesus monkey (*Macaca mulatta*) was found to form a precipitate with acetic acid (Krohn and Zuckerman, 1937). This material contained 12.3% of nitrogen, 3.7% of carbohydrate, and 2 to 3% of hexosamine (Ogston, Philpot, and Zuckerman, 1939). The fresh pressed-tissue fluid was also examined in the ultracentrifuge, and three main boundaries were found, one of them very sharp and "representing presumably the mucoprotein component"; the material obtained by squeezing of the chopped rooster comb and umbilical cord showed a similar sharp boundary on the sedimentation diagram (Ogston, Philpot, and Zuckerman, 1939). Chain and Duthie (1940) investigated the effect of testicular hyaluronidase on the redissolved mucin sample that had been studied by Ogston, Philpot, and Zuckerman. Chain and Duthie observed an immediate drop in viscosity, loss of precipitability with acetic acid, and liberation of reducing substance and they also identified hexosamine and hexuronic acid qualitatively among the degradation products. Rienits (1951) found that the "exudate" from sexual skin of the rhesus monkey showed complete loss of turbidity and clot formation on acidification to pH 3 to 4 after incubation with streptococcal hyaluronidase. The material contained no detectable sulfate. With the use of paper chromatography, glucuronic acid and glucosamine were identified; no galactosamine could be detected. Rienits reported later (1960) a more detailed study on the glycosaminoglycans in the various phases of the sexual skin of the baboon (*Papio papio*) and in the estrogen-stimulated sexual skin of the rhesus monkey (*Macaca mulatta*) and the pig-tailed monkey (*Macaca nemestrina*). Both the sexual skin and the pressed fluid obtained from it have been used to prepare glycosaminoglycans, which contained considerable amounts of proteins. When the pressed-tissue fluid was used, no galactosamine could be identified. In the case of whole sexual skin, both glucosamine and galactosamine were present; digestibility with streptococcal hyaluronidase was the criterion for identification of hyaluronic acid. As in the case of the rooster comb, a correlation was found between hyaluronic acid and water content. The data also show that the concentration of glycosaminoglycans, mainly of hyaluronic acid, increases during the swelling of the sexual skin.

In the inactive sexual skin, the dermis consists of a dense fibrillar meshwork, the capillary congestion subsides, and there is a relative increase of cells per unit area (Collings, 1926; Aykroyd and Zuckerman, 1938; Klenerman, 1955). The amount of interfibrillar metachromatic material is greatly reduced (Duran-Reynals, Bunting, and van Wagenen, 1950; Preto Parvis and Ugo, 1960), and no "exudate" can be obtained from the chopped skin (Ogston, Philpot, and Zuckerman, 1939). The phase of deturgescence is, in general, of shorter duration than that of swelling, and the resorption of the bulk of the perineal swelling takes only a few days (Krohn and Zuckerman, 1937; Gillman and Gilbert, 1946).

Parallel with the formation and disappearance of glycosaminoglycans, mainly hyaluronic acid, during the periodical fluctuation of the sexual skin, changes occur in the water and protein content. Studies of the water metabolism during the menstrual cycle of the pig-tailed monkey (*Macaca nemestrina*) showed a fluctuation in the body weight up to 17%; water retention paralleled the increase of the body weight and the sexual-skin turgescence, and a sharp rise in the amount of urine excreted occurred within 24 hr after the beginning of sexual-skin subsidence (Krohn and Zuckerman, 1937). It was assumed that these phenomena are connected "with the accumulation of intercellular fluid in the sexual skin." The fluid pressed from the swollen sexual skin of the rhesus monkey (*Macaca mulatta*) has a protein content of 2.5%, compared with that of the serum (6.3%) (Fisher and Zuckerman, 1937; Aykroyd and Zuckerman, 1938); in the baboon, the corresponding protein values were 3.4 to 4.4%, compared with a 2.2-times higher concentration in the blood (Shall, 1955). On ultracentrifuge diagrams of the pressed-tissue fluid from rhesus monkeys (*Macaca mulatta*), Ogston, Philpot, and Zuckerman (1939) observed a sharp boundary which was interpreted as a glycosaminoglycan-containing fraction.

Considerable fluctuations occur in the plasma volume and protein mass in rhythm with the menstrual cycle of the baboon (*Papio ursinus*). During the swelling of the sexual skin there is a drop in the mass of circulating albumin and globulin which can be prevented by surgical ablation of the sexual skin; in the deturgescence phase, the circulating protein mass increases abruptly (Cohen, 1955). Cohen suggested "that plasma albumin and globulin are lodged in the intercellular fluid of perineal connective tissue during the follicular phase of the cycle," whereas "the simultaneous occurrence of an increase in plasma protein and loss in perineal protein suggests a direct passage of protein from perineum to plasma." Ultracentrifugal and electrophoretic studies support the assumption that the proteins in sexual-skin fluid and in plasma are identical. Turnover studies with iodinated proteins showed that "the extravascular plasma protein of the perineum continues to exchange with circulating protein growth of the perineal swelling" (Cohen, 1956). From the same studies it appears that the protein synthesis exceeds catabolism in the follicular (turgescence) phase, whereas during the luteal phase (perineal involution) there is a reduced rate of synthesis of plasma protein. The relation of the perineal proteins to glycosaminoglycans is not clear from these studies, since no analytical effort was made to identify the carbohydrate components. Gillman, Pillay, and Naidoo (1960) observed elevated levels of both serum glycoproteins, as determined by a turbidimetric method, and plasma fibrin during the turgescence phase of the sexual skin in the baboon (*Papio ursinus*); both values fell rapidly in the phase of deturgescence. The authors discussed the possible relationship of the serum glycoproteins to the changes in the perineal connective tissue.

III. Other Target Connective Tissues

A. Integument

Besides the comb of fowl and the sexual skin of monkeys there are many other specific skin areas with similar hormone reactivity in various species. This applies to many skin formations in birds (Freund, 1926), such as the wattles and earlobes of roosters (Champy, 1926; Champy *et al.*, 1931; Szirmai, 1949), periorbital swelling in pheasants, and wattles in guinea fowl (Champy, Kritch, and Llombart, 1929). All these tissues show the presence of metachromatic interfibrillar material during the active state—that is, while under the permanent or cyclic influence of androgens. Increase of the hexosamine and hyaluronic acid content of the wattle of testosterone-treated capons has been described (Szirmai, 1956a; Balazs, Mars, and Szirmai, unpublished). The "brood patches" of the abdominal skin in one or both sexes of many birds may be a similar structure (Lange, 1928), controlled, probably, by estrogens and prolactin (Bailey, 1952). In several amphibia, the dorsal crest and the cloacal papilla show cyclic variations, and, in active state, contain metachromatic substance in the dermis (Champy and Kritch, 1926; Nakamura, 1927; Champy, Kritch, and Llombart, 1929; Beaune and Falk, 1936; Galgano, 1950). The skin of the external genitals (scrotum, vulva, and labia) and surrounding areas in various mammals shows hormonal sensitivity similar to the sexual skin, as judged from anatomical and histological criteria (Hamilton, 1936; Hall, 1938; Burrows, 1949); data on chemical or histochemical properties are lacking.

B. Accessory Reproductive Organs

Another group of steroid-sensitive connective tissues occurs as a part of the female and male accessory reproductive organs. In the newborn rat, the oviduct shows, on administration of testosterone, the presence of a "gelatinous connective tissue" (Selye, 1940). In the rabbit and rat oviduct, moderate incorporation of S^{35} into the mucosa was observed by radioautography (Boström and Odeblad, 1952). In the laying hen, hypertrophy of the oviduct is caused by estrogenic hormones (Parkes and Emmens, 1944; Bolton, 1953). Hexosamine, hydroxyproline, and dry-weight values were determined in the oviduct of immature pullets treated with estradiol, testosterone, and progesterone and found to be comparable to those obtained for the oviduct of the mature laying hen (Anastassiadis, Maw, and Common, 1955; Anastassiadis, 1959). The presence of sulfated glycosaminoglycans in the isthmus of the hen oviduct has been reported (Suzuki and Strominger, 1959). The nature of these compounds in estrogen-treated chick oviduct was further studied by Schiller (1959). Using NaOH extraction and zone electrophoresis, she isolated glycosaminoglycans in a yield of 0.5% of the defatted dry weight; hyaluronic acid was found to be the main component, with smaller amounts of chondroitin 4-sulfate, dermatan sulfate, and heparan sulfate. High concentrations of various uridine nucleotides and enzymes involved in the biosynthesis and sulfation mechanism of glycosaminoglycans or their building units have been described in the hen oviduct (Strominger, 1955; Suzuki and Strominger, 1959, 1960,a,b; Strominger, 1962). It should be noted that the hypertrophy of hen oviduct by estrogens involves both the connective tissue and epithelial elements, with the latter secreting the egg-shell membranes. Chemical compounds or their precursors, identified in extracts of whole oviduct, might therefore be related to either the glycosaminoglycans of the connective-tissue stroma or the complex polysaccharides of the epithelial secretion, or both.

Abundant intercellular metachromatic material was found in the hypertrophic ovipositor of the skate (*Raja batis*) during the laying period. The isolated substance (method of Levene, 1925) had the elementary composition required for "mucoitin or chondroitin sulfuric acid" (Garrault, 1933a, 1934).

The uterine mucosa in the human and in various mammals contains metachromatic intercellular material, deposited under the influence of estrogens (Holmgren, 1940; Sylvén, 1946; Burrows, 1949; McKay, 1950; Zachariae, 1958; Likar, Likar, and Taylor, 1961), with a parallel increase of water content (Greene and Harris, 1940; Carroll, 1945; Hawk *et al.,* 1961). Gelatinous connective tissue with much intercellular substance is also characteristic of the so-called endometrial moles, produced by various steroids or their combination (Selye, Harlow, and McKeown, 1935; Selye and Friedman, 1940). Incorporation of S^{35} into the endometrial stroma of the rat, rabbit, and guinea pig was observed by use of radioautography by Boström and Odeblad (1952) and Zachariae (1958), and found to be augmented by estrogenic treatment (Gothié, 1961). In the course of uterine growth during pregnancy in the rat, an increased amount of metachromatic intercellular material was observed (Paraventi, da Silva Sasso, and Mastroianni, 1960), and the total hexosamine was found to reach over ten times the initial values toward the end of the pregnancy (Montfort and Pérez-Tamayo, 1961). Iversen (1960) and Iversen and Marcker (1961) isolated, by use of pancreatin digestion, glycosaminoglycans from the myometrium of human uterine cervix in a yield of about 1.5% of defatted dry weight. The glycosaminoglycan mixture was partially digestible with both bacterial and testicular hyaluronidase; on paper electrophoresis, fractions corresponding to hyaluronic acid and chondroitin sulfate were observed. Buckingham, Selden, and Danforth (1962) estimated the total hexosamine content of human cervix in the nonpregnant state and in various phases of pregnancy; the values ranged from 0.4 to 0.7% of dry weight, with no significant difference among the various samples. Loewi and Consden (1962) isolated glycosaminoglycans from human uteri (including cervix) by use of papain digestion and fractional precipitation of the calcium salts by ethanol. The yields were from 0.2 to 0.3% of defatted dry weight. A large portion of the glycosaminoglycan mixture—about 40 to 45%—was found to be dermatan sulfate; 10 to 12% was suggested to consist of heparan sulfate, with the remainder consisting of chondroitin 4- or 6-sulfate, with only small amounts of hyaluronic acid. No significant differences were found between premenopausal or postmenopausal uteri, postpartum uteri, or cases of fibromyoma.

Edematous changes and metachromatic interfibrillar substance have been produced by estrogens in the vas deferens of castrated male mice (Figs. 9 and 10) (Heringa and de Jongh, 1934; Burrows, 1935). The penis of the guinea pig contains a connective tissue that is similar to

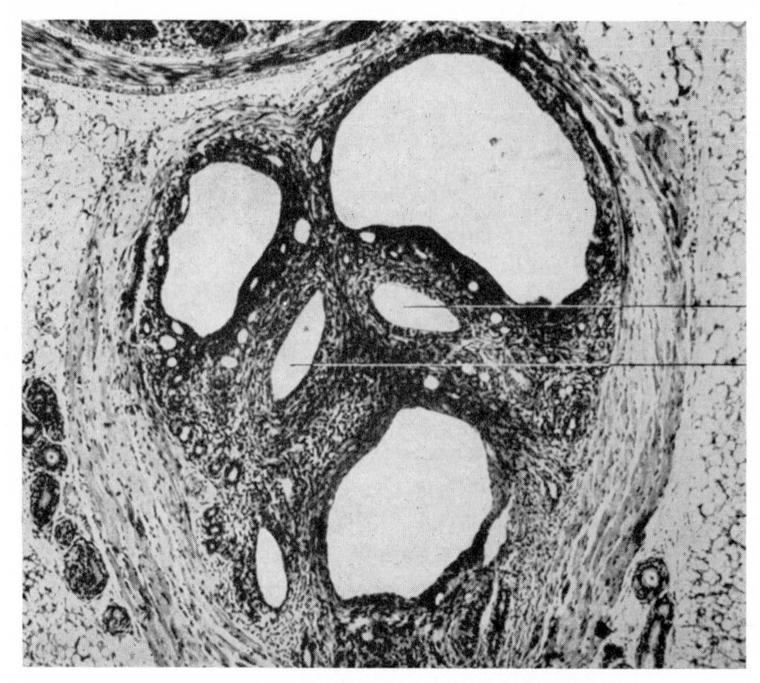

Fig. 9. Dense fibrillar connective tissue of the vas deferens in castrated mouse. Staining according to Dominici, final magnification approximately 90×.

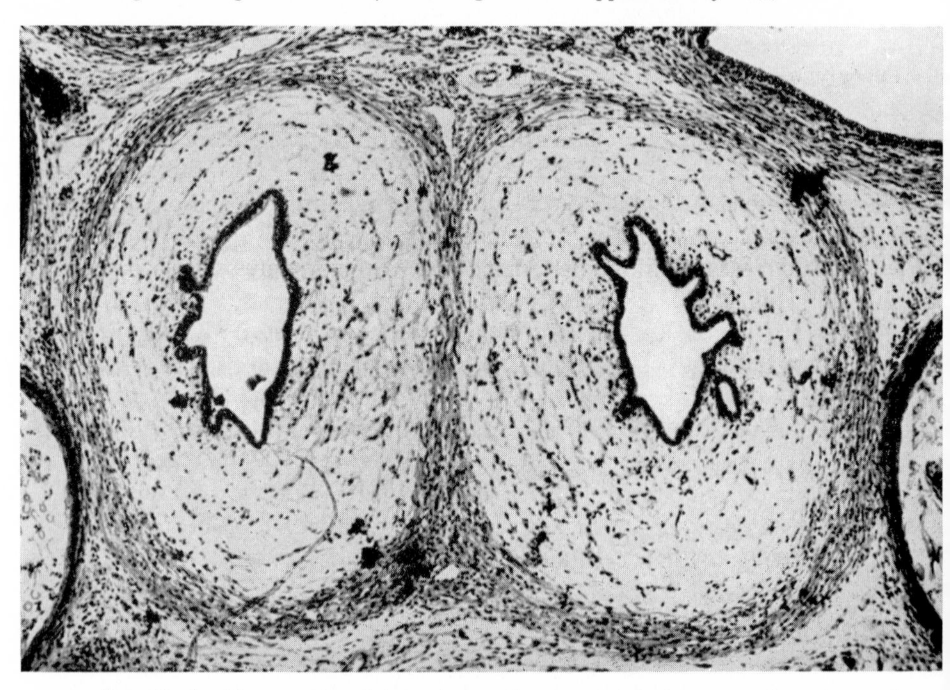

Fig. 10. Swelling, produced by estrogen treatment, of the connective tissue of the vas deferens in a castrated mouse. Staining and magnification as in Fig. 9.

Figs. 9 and 10 reproduced from Heringa and de Jongh (1934), with the permission of the authors and Springer Verlag.

that of the rooster comb, and regresses upon castration (Champy, Kritch, and Llombart, 1929); the same connective-tissue structure also occurs in the copulatory organ of the duck (Champy *et al.*, 1931). In the pig and the rabbit, administration of estrogens causes a "gelatinous transformation" of the connective tissue of the bladder and the urethra (Weide, 1952). Edematous transformation of the periurethral connective tissue was observed on young opossums of either sex after estrogenic treatment (Burns, 1961).

Although not directly related to the reproductive organs, relaxation of the symphysis of the pubic bones in rodents should be mentioned in this connection. From studies of Hisaw (1925), Talmage (1947,a,b), Hall (1947, 1950, 1956), Heringa (1948), Frieden and Hisaw (1951), and others, it appears that the interpubic cartilage undergoes a breakdown process in the course of pregnancy and is transformed into a fine-fibrillar, cellular tissue. The edematous swelling taking place rapidly, just before parturition, is accompanied by changes in the metachromasia of the interfibrillar space. The phenomenon is evoked by relaxin, but a priming with steroid hormones is required.

IV. Glycosaminoglycans and the Target Reaction

The rooster comb, the sexual skin, and the other tissues just discussed show common features which seem to justify grouping them together as "steroid-sensitive" or "target" connective tissues (Szirmai, 1954, 1962). In the active state—this being permanent or showing cyclic fluctuation—they are always characterized by swollen, edematous connective tissue. The abundant intercellular substance contains glycosaminoglycans; chemical studies confirmed that, in most cases, hyaluronic acid is the main component, although sulfated glycosaminoglycans are also present. The water content is high, and the proteins are, at least in part, similar to plasma proteins, but of lower concentration. This differentiation depends on the presence of steroid hormones, the withdrawal of which (experimentally or under physiological conditions) leads to the following characteristic structural changes: the fibrillar meshwork becomes coarse, the histochemically demonstrable interfibrillar material disappears, and the glycosaminoglycan content is greatly reduced. The reaction is essentially reversible and can be reproduced by administration of the steroid hormone required. In the cases studied, this peculiar sensitivity of a tissue is localized to a circumscript area and is retained after transplantation. The main features of this tissue reaction are illustrated in a diagram (Fig. 11), which is necessarily oversimplified; it does not account for concomitant changes in adjacent tissues, such as specific differentiation of epithelium, the remarkable absence of hair or feathers in the skin areas

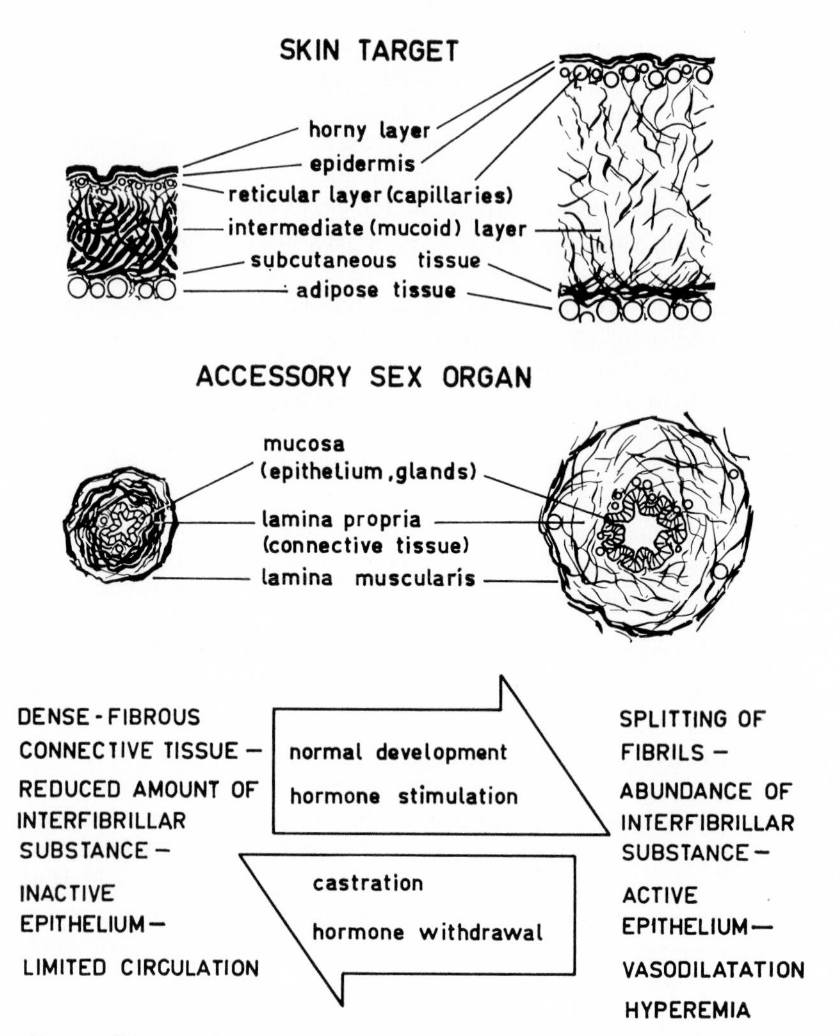

FIG. 11. Diagram illustrating the reversible changes in steroid-sensitive connective tissues.

in question, and the often-complicated vascular differentiation which may, or may not, be dependent on the connective-tissue change itself. The location of the specific steroid-sensitive connective-tissue areas reveals a systemic pattern when various species are compared (Fig. 12). In the skin, the location of these sensitive zones covers two main areas—namely, that of the head and the genital area. In general, the borderlines of sensitivity are sharply demarcated, but, in some cases, can expand in response to hormone overdosage (see studies on sexual skin by Bachman, Collip, and Selye, 1936; Duran-Reynals, Bunting, and van Wagenen,

1950), whereas similar skin reactions can become generalized (estrogen response of the skin in hairless mice—Selye, 1944). Inside the body, these connective tissues seem to be confined to the reproductive organs. This peculiar location of the steroid-sensitive areas may be of interest in the light of some observations during early skin development in the human embryo, in which analogous areas present deviations from the remaining skin in the histological structure of both the dermis and the epidermis (Steiner, 1929, 1931).

The observations brought together in this chapter suggest that stimulation of the biosynthesis of glycosaminoglycans is a prominent feature of the response of certain target connective tissues to various gonadal

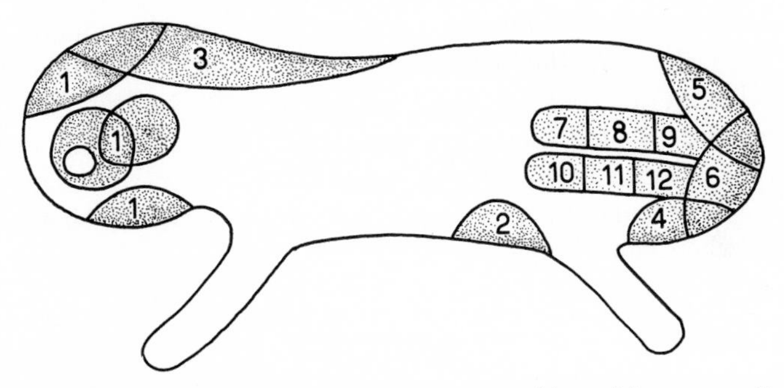

FIG. 12. Diagram illustrating the location of steroid-sensitive connective tissues in various vertebrates.

1. Head furnishings (birds)
2. Brood patches (birds)
3. Dorsal crest (amphibia)
4. Cloacal papilla (amphibia)
5. Sexual skin (monkeys)
6. Scrotum, perineum, vulva (various vertebrates)
7. Oviduct (fish, birds, mammals)
8. Uterus (various mammals)
9. Vagina (various mammals)
10. Vas deferens (various mammals)
11. Urethra (pigs, rabbits)
12. Penis (guinea pigs), copulatory organ (birds)

steroids. In the cases most thoroughly investigated, such as those of the rooster comb or sexual skin, hyaluronic acid appears to be, at least quantitatively, the most important compound. The fact that reactions, morphologically and chemically so similar, are the result of stimulation by androgens in one case and estrogens in others, and the mutual antagonism of these hormones, makes one wonder about the mechanism of the primary effect of these steroids. There is ample experimental evidence that the effect is more pronounced on local application, suggesting that the hormone acts at the target site. However, it cannot yet be decided whether the hormone itself or its metabolites are responsible for the effect produced. Similarly, no information is available on the point of action of the hormone in the biosynthetic pathway of glycosaminoglycans, at least if one assumes that the accumulation of glycosaminoglycans is the result of increased synthesis and not of a blocking of the breakdown process.

The localization of the sensitivity to certain target areas and the relative lack of response in structurally analogous tissues remain at present an unsolved puzzle. The possibility that the sensitivity of target tissues to hormones is determined during the early histogenesis does not explain the phenomenon, even if it might offer some clues for future studies. No satisfactory guess can be made as to the physiological significance of the accumulation of glycosaminoglycans in the target connective tissues. Recognition of a general biological meaning is especially difficult in view of the fact that target connective tissues can be substituted—even in closely related animals—by entirely different tissue structures, such as feather ornaments at the site of the comb in some birds, brilliant fur coat at the location of sexual skin, or epithelial pigmentations, all influenced by gonadal steroids. Target connective tissues thus appear to be only a small group of variants among the "sex characters," and their response to hormones should be interpreted with care when considering the action of steroids on connective tissues in general.

Addendum

The following papers of interest have been published since the receipt of this manuscript and are also included in the reference list:

Donskikh, N. V., and Ivanova, L. N. (1963). On the hyaluronidase activity of the amniotic fluid in normal pregnancy and polyhydramnios.

Likar, I. N., and Likar, L. J. (1964). Acid mucopolysaccharides and mast cells in the bovine uterus at different stages of the sexual cycle.

Likar, I. N., Likar, L. J., and Robinson, R. W. (1964). Mast cells and hyaluronic acid in the bovine endometrium.

Majewski, C., Siwiński, S., and Majewski, H. (1963). Studies on the distribution of acid mucopolysaccharides in the chorion of the mature placenta.

Mèlica, F. (1963). Su alcuni particolari aspetti istochimici dei mucopolisaccaridi nelle iperplasie endometriali.

Vandenbergh, Y. G. (1965). Hormonal basis of sex skin in male Rhesus monkeys.

Chapter 42

HEXOSAMINIDASES

P. G. Walker

Interest in enzymes acting on amino sugar linkages began with the investigation of chitinase (Karrer and Hofmann, 1929; Grassman *et al.*, 1934) and quickened with the growth of understanding of the structure of chondroitin sulfate and hyaluronic acid (Levene, 1925; Meyer and Palmer, 1936a) and the mode of action of hyaluronidase (Rapport, Meyer, and Linker, 1951). Complete degradation of these glycosaminoglycans to their component sugars was known to involve both polysaccharase and oligosaccharase activities, but investigation of the enzymes acting on amino sugar linkages was hampered by the lack of methods for the preparation of suitable substrates. Although phenyl β-*N*-acetylglucosaminide (2-acetamido-2-deoxy-β-D-glucopyranoside) (Helferich and Iloff, 1933) and the α-anomer (Zechmeister and Tóth, 1939) had been prepared by methods which made their suggested structures probable, the configuration of the anomeric glycosides of *N*-acetylglucosamine was not established until the work of Neuberger and Pitt-Rivers (1939). General methods for the preparation of β-glycosides of *N*-acetylglucosamine (Leaback and Walker, 1957) and *N*-acetylgalactosamine (Heyworth, Leaback, and Walker, 1959) are now available, but the range of α-glycosides is much more restricted.

Until recently, glucosamine and galactosamine were the only naturally occurring amino sugars recognized. Many naturally occurring 2-amino-2-deoxy and 3-amino-3-deoxy sugars have been identified recently, especially as components of bacteria and fungi (see Volume I, Chapters 1 and 5), and important advances have been made in methods for the synthesis of amino sugars (see Volume I, Chapter 1), but glycosides of these sugars which might be used for the detection of the corresponding glycosidases have not been prepared.

There is no evidence for the occurrence of a specific β-*N*-acetylglucosaminidase or a specific β-*N*-acetylgalactosaminidase, and much of the evidence concerning the identity of the enzymes which act on β-*N*-acetylglucosaminyl linkages in synthetic substrates, on the one hand, and in oligosaccharides, on the other, is either incomplete or conflicting. These results will, therefore, be discussed as aspects of the specificity of β-*N*-acetylhexosaminidase. Preparations with α-*N*-acetylglucosaminidase and α-*N*-acetylgalactosaminidase activities have been described, but no attempt has been made to decide whether these are due to the same or to different specific enzymes. In the light of these considerations, the terms *N*-acetylglucosaminidase and *N*-acetylgalactosaminidase are indicative only of the nature of the substrate employed, and the available information has been classified under the two main headings: β- and α-*N*-acetylhexosaminidase.

I. β-N-Acetylhexosaminidase

A. Occurrence

The occurrence of β-*N*-acetylglucosaminidase in a wide variety of biological material has been described and is compiled in Table I. β-*N*-Acetylgalactosaminidase was also detected in many of these preparations (Woollen, Walker, and Heyworth, 1961), but the ratios of β-*N*-acetylglucosaminidase to β-*N*-acetylgalactosaminidase activity covered a wide range. In many sources, β-*N*-acetylglucosaminidase occurs in association with chitinase or spreading-factor activity, but the distribution of the enzyme in mammalian tissues (among which testis is the only well-authenticated source of hyaluronindase) indicates a wider biological function.

There are no naturally occurring substrates for β-*N*-acetylglucosaminidase analogous to the heterosidic β-glucosides or β-glucuronides, and none of the amino sugar-containing substances of mammalian origin (epithelial mucins, glycoproteins, glycolipids, blood-group substances, milk oligosaccharides) is known to possess terminal or side-chain β-linked amino sugar. β-*N*-Acetylhexosaminidase may, however, be required for the hydrolysis of terminal amino sugar residues in products formed in the course of the degradation of such materials.

B. Substrates and Methods of Determination

β-*N*-Acetylglucosaminidase is a simple hydrolytic enzyme (Pugh, Leaback, and Walker, 1957); methods of assay may be based on the estimation of either liberated aglycone or liberated amino sugar. Like many other glycosidases, the enzyme shows little specificity toward the aglycone part of the substrate (Borooah, Leaback, and Walker, 1961), and most methods depend on the estimation of a phenolic aglycone.

TABLE I
OCCURRENCE OF β-N-ACETYLGLUCOSAMINIDASE

Biological source	References
Vertebrate	
Rat, mouse, porcine, and bovine tissues (epididymis the richest source)	Watanabe, 1936
	Hahn, 1945
	Conchie, Findlay, and Levvy, 1959
	Findlay and Levvy, 1960
	Pugh and Walker, 1961
Placenta (human)	Walker, Woollen, and Pugh, 1960
Serum (human)	
Semen and male accessory secretions	Conchie and Mann, 1957
Vaginal fluids (human)	Conchie and Levvy, 1957a
Snake (*Crotalus atrox*) venom	East, Madinaveitia, and Todd, 1941
Invertebrate	
Lobster hypodermis	Kuhn and Tiedemann, 1954
Limpet visceral hump	Findlay, Levvy, and Marsh, 1958
Snail (*Helix pomatia*) digestive gland	Zechmeister, Tóth, and Vajda, 1939
Leech (*Hirudo medicinalis*)	Woollen, Walker, and Heyworth, 1961
Locust-crop fluid	Greig, 1960
Microbiological	
Streptomyces griseus	Berger and Reynolds, 1958
Trichomonas foetus	Watkins, 1959
Aspergillus oryzae	Kuhn and Tiedemann, 1954
Lycoperdon pyriforma	Woollen, Walker, and Heyworth, 1961
Clostridium welchii	Humphrey, 1946
Pneumococcus Type II	Roseman and Dorfman, 1951
Lactobacillus bifidus	Rose *et al.*, 1954
Proteus vulgaris	Dodgson, 1959
Plant	
Sweet-almond emulsin	Helferich and Iloff, 1933

Alkyl β-N-acetylhexosaminides are prepared from the appropriate glycosyl halide derivatives by the Koenigs–Knorr procedure, which forms only the β-glycoside (Kuhn and Kirschenlohr, 1953; Tarasiejska and Jeanloz, 1958), or by the direct condensation of alcohol and amino sugar followed by chromatographic separation of the anomeric mixture of glycosides (Zilliken *et al.*, 1955; Watkins, 1959).

A general method for the synthesis of aryl 1,2-*trans* glycosides is the condensation of an alkaline solution of the phenol with an acetone solution of the appropriate 1,2-*cis* glycosyl halide (Glaser and Wulwek, 1924). Acetochloroglucosamine (Baker *et al.*, 1954) is a suitable intermediate and has been used for the synthesis of a wide range of aryl β-N-acetylglucosaminides (Leaback and Walker, 1957; Anderson and Leaback, 1961). Acetochlorogalactosamine has been used similarly for the preparation of β-*N*-acetylgalactosaminides (Heyworth, Leaback, and Walker, 1959). Phenyl (Helferich and Iloff, 1933; Roseman and Dorfman, 1951) and *p*-nitrophenyl (Westphal and Schmidt, 1952; Findlay, Levvy, and Marsh, 1958) β-*N*-acetylglucosaminides have been prepared by fusion of the phenols with glucosamine pentaacetate. Some α-glycoside may be formed in the course of this procedure, and the more drastic conditions limit its applicability to stable phenols of relatively low melting point.

The phenyl, *p*-nitrophenyl, and 4-methyl-7-coumarinyl glycosides are the most generally useful substrates, and details have been given of methods based on the colorimetric estimation of phenol (Neuberger and Pitt-Rivers, 1939; Pugh, Leaback, and Walker, 1957), the spectrophotometric estimation of *p*-nitrophenol (Findlay, Levvy, and Marsh, 1958; Borooah, Leaback, and Walker, 1961; Woollen, Heyworth, and Walker, 1961), and the fluorimetric estimation of 4-methyl-7-hydroxycoumarin (Leaback and Walker, 1961) liberated from them by the enzyme. With the same volumetric technique, the relative sensitivity of methods based on these substrates is approximately 1:10:100.

Addition of NaCl (final concentration, 0.14 *M*) increases the activity of some crude tissue preparations by 10–20% (Pugh, Leaback, and Walker, 1957a). Albumin or Triton X-100 may be required to stabilize partially purified preparations of the enzyme (Findlay and Levvy, 1960; Woollen, Heyworth, and Walker, 1961).

C. Purification

Watanabe (1936a), in his classic work on β-*N*-acetylglucosaminidase, described a preparation obtained from bovine liver by alcohol precipitation and by adsorption onto, and elution from, kaolin. A 24-fold purification was achieved with a yield of 15%.

Findlay and Levvy (1960) obtained a preparation from porcine epididymis by five stages of fractionation with ammonium sulfate and cold acetone. Purification was 70-fold, and recovery was 20%. Albumin caused considerable activation of the purified enzyme and abolished a fall in specific activity on dilution. No indication of the activity of other glycosidases in the preparation was given.

D. Kinetics

The kinetic properties of β-*N*-acetylhexosaminidase are essentially simple. There is no evidence in preparations from bovine liver (Watanabe, 1936b), rat kidney (Pugh, Leaback, and Walker, 1957), ovine testis (Woollen, Heyworth, and Walker, 1961; Leaback and Walker, 1961), and porcine epididymis (Findlay and Levvy, 1960) of more than one active protein; emulsin (Woollen, Walker, and Heyworth, 1961) is a possible exception.

Purified enzyme preparations are partially inactivated in the absence of added albumin (Findlay and Levvy, 1960). The activity in crude preparations may be reduced by adsorption of soluble enzyme onto tissue debris or insoluble protein; this effect is reversed by the addition of various salts (Pugh, Leaback, and Walker, 1957a). No other activators or cofactors have been shown to be necessary.

1. Effect of pH

Citrate buffer has been used in most work, but other carboxylic buffers can be employed. Acetate, which was used in some early work on β-*N*-acetylglucosaminidase, is not satisfactory since it causes pronounced competitive inhibition of the enzyme (Pugh, Leaback, and Walker, 1957). The purified enzyme from porcine epididymis was stable on incubation for 1 hr at 37°C in citrate buffer, pH 3.5–7.5, but was almost completely inactivated beyond these limits (Findlay and Levvy, 1960).

Table II shows the pH optima for β-*N*-acetylglucosaminidase from various sources. A single optimum was obtained in each case, and, with the exception of the enzymes from *Trichomonas foetus* and *Streptomyces griseus,* all the values lay between 3.8 and 5.2.

2. Effect of Substrate Concentration

Typical Michaelis–Menten curves with no inhibition by excess substrate have been obtained with β-*N*-acetylglucosaminidase from various sources. Table III shows that the K_m values of a given substrate cover a tenfold range according to the source of the enzyme. K_m values for galactosaminide were smaller than those for the corresponding glucosaminide. Leaback and Walker (1961) found that the values for 4-methyl-7-coumarinyl β-*N*-acetylglucosaminide varied with the pH of the test, indicating the ionization of a group at the active site of the enzyme.

The relative maximum rates of hydrolysis of ethyl, phenyl, *o*-nitrophenyl, *p*-nitrophenyl, and *p*-acetylphenyl β-*N*-acetylglucosaminides by ovine testis enzyme were 1:10:20:27:25. Similar results were obtained with emulsin (Borooah, Leaback, and Walker, 1961).

3. Inhibitors

The hydrolysis of β-*N*-acetylglucosaminides and of β-*N*-acetylgalactosaminides by β-*N*-acetylhexosaminidase was inhibited competitively by *N*-acetylglucosamine and *N*-acetylgalactosamine (Watanabe, 1936b; Woollen, Heyworth, and Walker, 1961; Walker, Woollen, and

TABLE II

pH Optima for β-*N*-Acetylglucosaminidase from Different Sources

Source of enzyme	Aglycone	pH optimum[a]	References
Porcine epididymis (purified)	Phenol	4.2	Findlay and Levvy, 1960
	p-Nitrophenol	4.2	Findlay and Levvy, 1960
Rat kidney	Phenol	4.3	Pugh, Leaback, and Walker, 1957
	p-Nitrophenol	4.4–4.5	Walker, Woollen, and Heyworth, 1961
Ovine testis	Phenol	4.4	Borooah, Leaback, and Walker, 1961
	p-Nitrophenol	4.5	Borooah, Leaback, and Walker, 1961
	p-Acetylphenol	4.5	Booroah, Leaback, and Walker, 1961
	o-Nitrophenol	4.8	Borooah, Leaback, and Walker, 1961
	Ethanol	4.5	Borooah, Leaback, and Walker, 1961
	4-Methyl-7-hydroxycoumarin	4.6	Leaback and Walker, 1961
Human serum	*p*-Nitrophenol	4.3	Walker, Woollen, and Pugh, 1960
Snail digestive gland	Phenol	4.2	Greig, 1960
Lobster hypodermis	Benzyl alcohol	4.6	Kuhn and Tiedemann, 1954
Trichomonas foetus	*p*-Nitrophenol	7.0–7.2[b]	Watkins, 1959
Lycoperdon pyriforma	Phenol	3.8	Greig, 1960
Streptomyces griseus	Phenol	6.3	Berger and Reynolds, 1958
Aspergillus oryzae	Benzyl alcohol	4.1	Kuhn and Tiedemann, 1954
	Phenol	5.2	Greig, 1960
Clostridium perfringens	*p*-Nitrophenol	5.1	Woollen, Walker, and Heyworth, 1961

[a] Tests carried out in citrate buffer except where indicated.

[b] Phosphate buffer.

TABLE III
K_m VALUES[a] FOR PHENYL AND *p*-NITROPHENYL 2-AMINO-2-DEOXY-β-D-HEXOSIDES

K_m (m*M*) Phenyl	*p*-Nitrophenyl	Source of enzyme	References
β-*N*-Acetylglucosaminide			
1.3	0.7	Rat kidney	Walker, Woollen, and Heyworth, 1961
2.9	1.2	Ovine testis	Woollen, Heyworth, and Walker, 1961
0.7	0.4	Rat epididymis	Findlay, Levvy, and Marsh, 1958
6.4	3.8	Limpet	Findlay, Levvy, and Marsh, 1958
3.6	1.4	Snail	Greig, 1960
1.1	0.4	Emulsin	Borooah, Leaback, and Walker, 1961
β-*N*-Acetylgalactosaminide			
1.0	0.4	Rat kidney	Walker, Woollen, and Heyworth, 1961
1.2	0.3	Ovine testis	Woollen, Heyworth, and Walker, 1961

[a] Values determined by method of Lineweaver and Burk (1934) in tests carried out in citrate buffer, pH 4.3–4.5.

Heyworth, 1961). Findlay, Levvy, and Marsh (1958), in an extension of the important work of Levvy (1952) and Conchie and Levvy (1957) on the inhibition of glycosidases by aldonolactones of corresponding configuration, synthesized *N*-acetylglucosaminonolactone (2-acetamido-2-deoxy-D-gluconolactone) and *N*-acetylgalactosaminonolactone. The former was a mixture of the 1,4-lactone and 1,5-lactone, but the latter, which was obtained in crystalline form, was probably the 1,4-lactone. In aqueous solution, equilibrium mixtures were formed whose composition depended on the pH. Both lactones were powerful competitive inhibitors of β-*N*-acetylglucosaminidase (Findlay, Levvy, and Marsh, 1958) and β-*N*-acetylgalactosaminidase (Woollen, Heyworth, and Walker, 1961;

TABLE IV
K_i VALUES[a] FOR INHIBITORS OF β-*N*-ACETYLGLUCOSAMINIDASE

Enzyme	*N*-Acetylglucosamine (m*M*)	*N*-Acetylgalactosamine (m*M*)	*N*-Acetylglucosaminonolactone (μ*M*)	*N*-Acetylgalactosaminonolactone (μ*M*)
Rat kidney	3.1	0.4	0.7	0.5
Rat epididymis	—	—	0.09	0.4
Ovine testis	5.2	2.5	3.7	1.2
Limpet	—	—	4.0	32

[a] Values determined by method of Lineweaver and Burk (1934); substrate: *p*-nitrophenyl β-*N*-acetylglucosaminide; buffer: citrate, pH 4.3–4.5.

Walker, Woollen, and Heyworth, 1961). Inhibitor constants are shown in Table IV. High concentrations (1 mM) of N-acetylglucosaminonolactone partially inhibited α-N-acetylglucosaminidase.

Pugh, Leaback, and Walker (1957) showed that β-N-acetylglucosaminidase was inhibited by acetate. This was of importance, since acetate had been used as the buffer in some of the early work on the enzyme (East, Madinaveitia, and Todd, 1941). The inhibition was competitive; direct interaction with acetate to form an inactive complex is probably related to the high degree of specificity which the enzyme shows toward the N-acetyl group in a substrate (Neuberger and Pitt-Rivers, 1939; Greig, 1960).

E. Specificity

1. Glycone Specificity

Information concerning the specificity of β-N-acetylglucosaminidase is fragmentary, and many of the observations apply only to enzyme from one source. β-N-Acetylglucosaminidase has an absolute specificity for the β-glycosidic linkage. Preparations from snail (Neuberger and Pitt-Rivers, 1939) and emulsin (Zechmeister and Tóth, 1939) had no action on α-N-acetylglucosaminides. Both activities were present in preparations from mammalian tissues (Roseman and Dorfman, 1951) and limpet (Findlay, Levvy, and Marsh, 1958) but, in each case, evidence of separate stereospecific enzymes was obtained.

β-N-Acetylglucosaminidase and β-glucosidase are different enzymes (Helferich and Iloff, 1933; Roseman and Dorfman, 1951), and no activity toward phenyl β-glucosaminide was detectable in preparations from many sources (Helferich and Iloff, 1933; Neuberger and Pitt-Rivers, 1939; Roseman and Dorfman, 1951; Greig, 1960). The N-acyl group is, therefore, necessary; the effect of variations in the structure of this group was studied by Neuberger and Pitt-Rivers (1939). β-N-Propionyl-, β-N-butyryl-, and β-N-(toluene-p-sulfonyl)-glucosaminides were not attacked, but methyl β-N-formylglucosaminide was rapidly hydrolyzed. Greig (1960) studied the N-acyl specificity of preparations from many sources, using as substrates the phenyl β-glycosides of N-formyl-, N-acetyl-, N-fluoroacetyl-, and N-propionylglucosaminide (Greig, Leaback, and Walker, 1961). Every preparation hydrolyzed phenyl β-N-fluoroacetylglucosaminide; most showed some activity toward the β-N-propionylglucosaminide, but only a few caused detectable hydrolysis of the N-formylglucosaminide. N-Benzoyl- and N-(toluene-p-sulfonyl)-glucosaminonolactones did not inhibit β-N-acetylglucosaminidase (Findlay, Levvy, and Marsh, 1958).

N-Acetylmannosamine (Comb and Roseman, 1958a), *N*-acetylmuramic acid (Strange and Dark, 1956a), gulosamine (Van Tamelen *et al.*, 1956), and, possibly, talosamine (Crumpton, 1957; Heyworth, Perkins, and Walker, 1961) occur naturally, but no glycosides of these amino sugars have been tested as substrates. Evidence has been presented that bacterial Vi antigen is a polymer consisting principally of *N*-acetylaminohexuronic acid units (Clark, McLaughlin, and Webster, 1958). Marsh and Levvy (1957) oxidized phenyl α- and β-*N*-acetylglucosaminide to the corresponding glucosaminouronides, neither of which was hydrolyzed by the appropriate *N*-acetylglucosaminidase or glucuronidase.

The identity of enzymes hydrolyzing β-*N*-acetylglucosaminyl and β-*N*-acetylgalactosaminyl linkages is important in view of the widespread distribution of these amino sugars. In all the preparations examined, the two activities were present together, but they were never additive when both substrates were present simultaneously (Woollen, Walker, and Heyworth, 1961). The ratio of the two activities was unaltered at various stages in the purification procedure of Findlay and Levvy (1960). The activities in extracts of rat testis (Woollen, Heyworth, and Walker, 1961) and rat kidney (Walker, Woollen, and Heyworth, 1961) could not be separated by fractionation procedures or by partial heat inactivation, and a detailed kinetic study of the effects of inhibitors and of mixtures of substrates led to the conclusion that in each preparation the activities were associated with a single site on the same enzyme protein.

2. Aglycone Specificity

β-*N*-Acetylglucosaminidase hydrolyzes both alkyl and aryl β-*N*-acetylglucosaminides; the rate of hydrolysis of aryl glycosides is affected by substitution in the benzene ring (Borooah, Leaback, and Walker, 1961).

The hydrolysis of terminal β-*N*-acetylglucosaminyl linkages in partial degradation products derived from various types of biological material has been studied. Enzyme preparations from a number of sources have been used, all of them known to act on synthetic β-*N*-acetylglucosaminides, but in no case has the identity of the oligosaccharase and the group-specific β-*N*-acetylglucosaminidase been satisfactorily established.

Chitinase preparations from various sources possess phenyl β-*N*-acetylglucosaminidase, *N*,*N*′-diacetylchitobiase, and polysaccharase activities. The two former activities in emulsin were completely separated from the polysaccharase by chromatography on bauxite (Zechmeister and Tóth, 1939). No clear-cut separation of any of the activities was obtained in the case of snail chitinase (Zechmeister, Tóth, and Vajda, 1939). Two polysaccharases, differing only in mobility, were separated by electrophoresis of an extract of *Streptomyces griseus* on starch (Berger and Reynolds, 1958). One of these was only partially separated from a zone containing *N,N'*-diacetylchitobiase and phenyl β-*N*-acetylglucosaminidase. It was suggested that these latter activities might be due to the same enzyme.

It seems probable that lysozyme acts both on 4-*O*-β-(*N*-acetylmuramosyl-*N*-acetylglucosamine linkages in cell wall of *Micrococcus lysodeikticus* (Salton and Ghuysen, 1960) and on 4-*O*-β-(*N*-acetylglucosaminyl)–*N*-acetylglucosamine linkages in oligosaccharides derived from chitin (Berger and Weiser, 1957). With the former substrate, 6-*O*-β-(*N*-acetylglucosaminyl)–*N*-acetylmuramic acid appeared as an end product (Perkins, 1960), but with the latter it was, unfortunately, not established whether the end product was *N,N'*-diacetylchitobiose or *N*-acetylglucosamine. Lysozyme has no action on the terminal β-*N*-acetylglucosaminyl linkage in the mixed disaccharide obtained by Perkins or on phenyl β-*N*-acetylglucosaminide; both of these are split by emulsin (Salton and Ghuysen, 1960). On this evidence, lysozyme appears to be an endo-enzyme which can attack either β-*N*-acetylglucosaminyl or β-*N*-acetylmuramosyl linkages within a polysaccharide chain; its specificity is probably even more restricted, since it does not act on the β-(1 → 4)-*N*-acetylglucosaminylglucuronic acid linkage in hyaluronic acid (Berger and Weiser, 1957).

N-Acetylglucosamine was formed by the action of crude enzyme preparations from testis (Linker, Meyer, and Weissmann, 1955) and *Proteus vulgaris* (Dodgson, 1959) on hyaluronic acid. Both preparations also hydrolyzed aryl β-*N*-acetylglucosaminides. Di-, tri-, and tetrasaccharides with terminal nonreducing β-*N*-acetylglucosaminyl units have been obtained from hyaluronic acid (Linker, Meyer, and Weissmann, 1955; Linker, Meyer, and Hoffman, 1960). *N*-Acetylglucosamine was liberated from all of them by a liver preparation which also acted on phenyl β-*N*-acetylglucosaminide. The trisaccharide, however, was not affected by β-*N*-acetylglucosaminidase from pneumococcus or emulsin. The further degradation of oligosaccharides derived from chondroitin has not been investigated.

McCarty (1958) suggested that the specificity of group-A streptococcal carbohydrate was largely determined by side-chain β-*N*-acetylglucosaminyl residues. Emulsin failed to release detectable *N*-acetylglucosamine from the carbohydrate and caused no loss of serological activity. An induced β-*N*-acetylglucosaminidase was, however, obtained by growth of a soil organism in the presence of either group-A carbohydrate or phenyl β-*N*-acetylglucosaminide. This enzyme resembled emulsin β-*N*-acetylglucosaminidase in its action on synthetic substrates, but was also capable of removing *N*-acetylglucosamine residues from group-A carbohydrate, with concurrent loss of serological activity.

The 3-*O*-β-*N*-acetylglucosaminyl–galactose linkage in lacto-*N*-biose II and lacto-*N*-triose II was split by a preparation from *Aspergillus oryzae* which also acted on synthetic β-*N*-acetylglucosaminides (Kuhn, Gauhe, and Baer, 1956).

The problem of the identity of β-*N*-acetylglucosaminidase with the enzymes which act on these oligosaccharides requires further investigation. The question is important, firstly, in relation to the validity of the conclusions which can be drawn from the use of enzyme preparations as reagents for structural analysis and, second, in relation to the function of the enzyme *in vivo;* for example, in view of the limited distribution of hyaluronidase in mammalian tissues, the combined successive actions of β-glucuronidase and β-*N*-acetylhexosaminidase may play an important role in the degradation of chondroitin and hyaluronic acid.

F. Distribution in Tissues

1. Activity in Tissue Homogenates and Body Fluids

Watanabe (1936) showed that β-*N*-acetylglucosaminidase was widely distributed in bovine tissues. Table V shows representative figures for the activity in adult rat tissues (Conchie, Findlay, and Levvy, 1959;

TABLE V
β-*N*-Acetylglucosaminidase Activity of Rat Tissues[a]

Tissue	Activity on substrates	
	Phenyl glycoside	*p*-Nitrophenyl glycoside
Epididymis	76	291
Submaxillary gland	41	—
Kidney	33	126
Thyroid	25	—
Ileum	17	—
Liver	10	45
Spleen	8	—
Uterus	6	15
Testis	4	18
Ovary	—	26

[a] Substrate: phenyl or *p*-nitrophenyl 2-amino-2-deoxy-β-D-hexosides; activity expressed as microgram of aglycone liberated per milligram of wet weight of tissue per hour.

Pugh and Walker, 1961). The former workers found no significant difference between male and female or between adult and infant rat and mouse tissues, except for epididymis and uterus, in which the values for infant tissues rose to levels for adults at 12–14 days after birth. The level for adults in these secondary sex organs was reduced after castration or ovariectomy, but was restored by injection of testosterone or estrone (Conchie and Findlay, 1959). Activities of porcine tissues were similar to those of the rat, apart from porcine epididymis, which was three to six times more active (Findlay and Levvy, 1960). The activity of malignant mouse and human tissue was similar to that of the corresponding normal tissue (Conchie and Levvy, 1957a).

Serum from human males and females showed similar levels of activity. The activity in serum rose progressively during pregnancy and fell rapidly to normal levels after parturition (Walker, Woollen, and Pugh, 1960).

2. Tissue Fractionation Studies

Sellinger *et al.* (1960) studied the distribution of β-*N*-acetylglucosaminidase by the centrifugal fractionation of isotonic sucrose homogenates of rat liver. The highest specific activity was found in the light mitochondrial fraction, and the enzyme closely resembled acid phosphatase in its distribution, latency, and release from the subcellular particles by various treatments. β-*N*-Acetylglucosaminidase thus forms one of the group of "lysosomal" enzymes.

3. Histochemical Localization

Pugh and Walker (1961) described a method for the localization of β-*N*-acetylglucosaminidase in frozen sections of formalin-fixed tissues based on the substrate 1-naphthyl β-*N*-acetylglucosaminide. Satisfactory localization was achieved, and the relative activity demonstrated in different tissues agreed well with the results of homogenate assays. The principal sites of activity were: epithelium of the respiratory and alimentary tracts, epididymis, renal convoluted tubules, and thyroid; macrophages in spleen and lymphoid tissue; and chondrocytes and synovial cells in cartilage and synovial membrane. The intense activity found in decidual cells of the chorion and placenta probably represents the source of the increased level of the enzyme in pregnancy serum (Walker, Woollen, and Pugh, 1960).

The development of sensitive and reliable methods for the estimation and localization of β-*N*-acetylhexosaminidase and the availability of powerful and specific enzyme inhibitors have provided a foundation for further work on the properties of the enzyme and its significance in physiological and pathological processes.

II. α-N-Acetylhexosaminidase

A. Occurrence

Roseman and Dorfman (1951), in their original survey, found α-*N*-acetylglucosaminidase in many mammalian tissues (e.g., in extracts of liver, spleen, lung, kidney, and testis of rat and rabbit) and in the filtrate from a culture of Type II pneumococci. The enzyme also occurs in snail (Howe and Kabat, 1953) and in limpet (Findlay, Levvy, and Marsh, 1958), which is the richest source. α-*N*-Acetylglucosaminidase and α-*N*-acetylgalactosaminidase activities were detected in extracts of *Trichomonas foetus* (Watkins, 1959).

B. Methods of Determination

Phenyl α-*N*-acetylglucosaminide (2-acetamido-2-deoxy-α-D-glucopyranoside) has been prepared by the fusion of phenol with glucosamine pentaacetate in the presence of $ZnCl_2$ (Zechmeister and Tóth, 1939; Roseman and Dorfman, 1951; Conchie and Levvy, 1957a). Its use as the substrate in colorimetric methods of assay is described by these workers. Alkyl α-*N*-acetylhexosaminides can be obtained by chromatographic separation of the anomeric glycosides formed by the direct acid-catalyzed condensation of alcohols with *N*-acetylglucosamine (Zilliken *et al.,* 1955). Methyl α-*N*-acetylglucosaminide and methyl α-*N*-acetylgalactosaminide have been used as substrates for the estimation of α-*N*-acetylhexosaminidase activities (Watkins, 1959). *N*-Acetylhexosamine liberated by the enzyme was estimated colorimetrically. Attempts to prepare aryl α-*N*-acetylglucosaminides by use of acetochloroglucosamine under a wide range of reaction conditions were not successful (D. H. Leaback, unpublished data; see also Volume IA, Chapter 1, Section IV,A,6). The activity of the enzyme in many sources is low, and more sensitive and specific methods of estimation are desirable.

C. Kinetics

The optimum pH for the hydrolysis of phenyl α-*N*-acetylglucosaminide by an extract of rat testis was 4.5 in citrate buffer and K_m was 0.8 m*M*. Activity was proportional both to time of incubation and to enzyme concentration (Roseman and Dorfman, 1951). The optimum pH for the hydrolysis of methyl α-*N*-acetylgalactosaminide by *Trichomonas foetus* was 6.0 (Watkins, 1959).

D. Specificity

Fractionation studies and heat inactivation showed that α-*N*-acetylglucosaminidase was distinct from β-*N*-acetylglucosaminidase, hyaluronidase, and α- and β-glucosidase (Roseman and Dorfman, 1951). Watkins (1959) found that extracts of *Trichomonas foetus* hydrolyzed methyl α-*N*-acetylgalactosaminide more rapidly than they hydrolyzed methyl α-*N*-acetylglucosaminide. It is not, however, known if these activities were due to the same enzyme. High concentrations of *N*-acetylglucosaminonolactone partially inhibited limpet α-*N*-acetylglucosaminidase. Under similar conditions the *N*-acetylgalactosaminonolactone gave no inhibition.

Agglutination-inhibition and precipitation-inhibition tests suggested that the specificity of blood-group-A substance was largely determined by an α-*N*-acetylgalactosaminyl linkage (Morgan and Watkins, 1953). The destruction of blood-group-A substance by *Trichomonas* enzyme was inhibited by *N*-acetylgalactosamine but not by *N*-acetylglucosamine. Inhibition by *N*-acetylhexosaminides was not investigated (Watkins and Morgan, 1955). It was found, however, that the pH optimum, temperature stability, and inhibition by metal ions of the activity toward blood-group-A substance and methyl α-*N*-acetylgalactosaminide were similar (Watkins, 1959).

α-*N*-Acetylglucosaminyl linkages are probably present in heparan sulfate, and oligosaccharides derived from this material might therefore act as substrates for α-*N*-acetylglucosaminidase.

Addendum

An improved synthesis of the substrate, *p*-nitrophenyl *N*-acetylglucosaminide, has been described (Leaback, 1963).

The uses of β- and α-*N*-acetylhexosaminidase in structural studies are illustrated by recent work on the teichoic acids (Baddiley *et al.*, 1962; Sanderson, Strominger, and Nathenson, 1962). The teichoic acids from various strains of *Staphylococcus aureus* consist of polymers of ribitol phosphate containing glycosidically linked *N*-acetylglucosamine and esterified D-alanine, and they play an important part in determining serological specificity. The acids from different strains contained different proportions of β- and α-*N*-acetylglucosaminyl residues. This was established by the use of crude enzyme preparations containing both β- and α-*N*-acetylglucosaminidase activities and a purified preparation containing only β-activity. β-*N*-Acetylglucosaminidase was also used to establish the nature of the linkage in the disaccharides, β-(1 → 6)-*N*-acetylglucosaminyl-*N*-acetylmuramic acid and β-(1 → 6)-*N*-acetylglucosaminyl-*N*-4-*O*-diacetylmuramic acid, isolated by degradation of a glycopeptide which occurs as a complex with teichoic acid in the cell wall (Ghuysen and Strominger, 1963a).

The intracellular localization of β-*N*-acetylglucosaminidase and other glycosidases has been further investigated by Conchie and Hay (1963).

Uridine diphosphoacetylglucosamine undergoes a hydrolytic cleavage by an enzyme present in sheep brain. This enzyme is present in other tissues of the rat, and ATP, UTP, ADP, and *N*-acetylglucosamine 1-phosphate were found to be inhibitors (Pattabiraman, Sekhara Varma, and Bachhawat, 1964).

Note: The following papers of interest have been published since the preparation of this addendum and are also included in the reference list:

Caygill, J. C., and Jevons, F. R. (1965). Presence of glucosaminidase activity in human synovial fluid and its inhibition by gold compounds.

Hughes, R. C., and Jeanloz, R. W. (1964a). The extracellular glycosidases of *Diplococcus pneumoniae*. II. Purification and properties of a β-*N*-acetylglucosaminidase. Action on a derivative of the α_1-acid glycoprotein of human plasma.

Chapter 43

NEURAMINIDASES

Max E. Rafelson, Jr., Michael Schneir, and Vannie W. Wilson, Jr.

The neuraminidases (sialidases) are an isodynamic group of enzymes which selectively remove a terminal sialic acid from various glycoproteins, glycolipids, and oligosaccharides by catalyzing the hydrolysis of the glycosidic bond between the potential keto group of the sialic acid and an adjacent sugar residue. The enzymes are considered to be α-*O*-glycosidases, although this designated specificity is based on the inferential assignment of the α-configuration to the linkage of a sialyl residue in a single substrate, *N*-acetylneuraminyllactose (sialyllactose) (Gottschalk, 1958a; Kuhn and Brossmer, 1958a).

I. Occurrence

Neuraminidase activity was first observed in the influenza virus (Hirst, 1942a) and subsequently shown to be associated with other viruses of the myxo group: mumps and Newcastle-disease virus (Ada and Stone, 1950); fowl plague virus (Scholtissek, Rott and Schäfer, 1961); and the Sendai strain of parainfluenza virus (Sokol, Blaškovič, and Križanová, 1961). The enzyme has also been demonstrated in the following bacteria: *Vibrio cholerae* (Burnet, McCrea, and Stone, 1946); *Clostridium perfringens* (McCrea, 1947); *Cl. tertium* (Howe *et al.*, 1957); *Pseudomonas fluorescens, P. pyocyaneus* [*pyocyanea*], *P. stuzeri* [*stutzeri*], *Lactobacillus bifidus* (Shilo, 1957), and pneumococcus (Chu, 1948; Heimer and Meyer, 1956). Although neuraminidases had been presumed for some time to be absent from higher organisms, Warren and Spearing (1960) and Ada and Lind (1961) reported, respectively, the presence of the enzyme in commercial preparations of bovine and human glycoproteins and in the chorioallantoic membrane of the chick embryo. This was confirmed later by Schneir, Wilson, and Rafelson (unpublished data). Carubelli, Trucco, and Caputto (1962) reported the presence of neuraminidase activity in several rat organs.

Ada and French (1959) and Schramm and Mohr (1959) first reported, independently, the crystallization of neuraminidase from culture filtrates of *V. cholerae.* The enzymes from several strains of influenza virus were separated by Mayron *et al.* (1961) and Wilson and Rafelson (1962, 1963) and have recently been crystallized (Wilson and Rafelson, 1963, and unpublished data).

II. Isolation, Purification, and Assay

Ada, French, and Lind (1961) utilized methanol fractionation; adsorption to, and elution from, erythrocytes; ammonium sulfate fractionation; and chromatography on hydroxyapatite to obtain a crystalline preparation of the *V. cholerae* enzyme.

Mohr and Schramm's (1960) procedures for obtaining the crystalline enzyme included adsorption to, and elution from, erythrocytes, the specific binding of the enzyme to its substrate in a combined chromatographic step, and ammonium sulfate precipitation.

A method for the preparation of neuraminidase from the Asian and PR8 strains of influenza virus by trypsin treatment was reported by Mayron *et al.* (1961). Although this method yielded highly active enzyme preparations free from demonstrable hemagglutinin, it appeared on occasion not to have general applicability to all strains of influenza virus. Wilson and Rafelson (1962, 1963, and unpublished data) developed, therefore, a second procedure which has allowed the isolation of the enzyme from the Asian, PR8, PR301, Lee, and Great Lakes strains of influenza virus. In this method are used, sequentially, chymotrypsin treatment of butanol-extracted virus, ultracentrifugation, ammonium sulfate fractionation, and column chromatography on Sephadex. Crystallization was obtained from an ethanol solution.

The activity of the enzyme can be accurately measured by determination of the extent of liberation of sialic acid from a suitable substrate. Free sialic acid may be readily determined by the thiobarbituric acid methods (Warren, 1959; Aminoff, 1961). *N*-Acetylneuraminyllactose is an excellent substrate, as it is relatively easy to prepare material of demonstrated analytical purity (Schneir, Winzler, and Rafelson, 1962), and it is cleaved completely into *N*-acetylneuraminic acid and lactose (Mayron *et al.*, 1961). It has been proposed that an enzyme unit be defined as that amount of enzyme which will liberate 1 μmole of *N*-acetylneuraminic acid from an excess of *N*-acetylneuraminyllactose in 1 min. at 37°C at the pH value at which optimum activity of the specific enzyme is shown (Jacobs and Walop, 1960; Mayron *et al.*, 1961; Rafelson, 1963).

III. Properties

A. Enzymic Properties

1. Substrate Specificity

There is, apparently, no enzyme specificity in regard to the chemical structure of the neuraminic acid derivatives in compounds susceptible to neuraminidases. Gottschalk (1960) pointed out that compounds containing *N*-acetyl-, *N*-glycolyl-, *O*,*N*-diacetyl-, or *N*-acetyl-*O*-diacetylneuraminic acids are all substrates for the enzymes. The susceptible linkages so far demonstrated are the $2 \rightarrow 3$ type in *N*-acetylneuraminyllactose (*N*-acetylneuraminyl-($2 \rightarrow 3$)-β-D-galactopyranosyl-($1 \rightarrow 4$)-D-glucopyranose) and the $2 \rightarrow 6$ type in 6-*O*-(*N*-acetylneuraminyl)-*N*-acetylgalactosamine.

The $2 \rightarrow 6$ linkage in *N*-acetylneuraminic acid-galactosamine is of interest because an isomer of *N*-acetylneuraminyllactose in which the linkage is $2 \rightarrow 6$ between the sialic acid and galactose is not cleaved by neuraminidase (Kuhn, 1958).

Other possible types of linkage that might be cleaved by neuraminidase have been suggested by the work of Kathan and Winzler (personal communication). These authors prepared, from human erythrocytes, a glycoprotein inhibitor of viral hemagglutination, in which there appears to be a linkage between C-2 of *N*-acetylneuraminic acid and C-1 of the hexosamine. The suggestion for this linkage is that the treatment of the glycoprotein with neuraminidase removed some 80% of the *N*-acetylneuraminic acid, and subsequent sodium borohydride reduction resulted in a loss of hexosamine equal to the amount of *N*-acetylneuraminic acid enzymically removed. If the conclusions are correct, a linkage of the $2 \rightarrow 1$ type may also be cleaved by neuraminidase.

Colominic acid appears to contain linkages of the $2 \rightarrow 8$ type (McGuire and Binkley, 1962; Rafelson, 1963; Rafelson, Wilson, and Schneir, 1962). This acid was reported by Gottschalk (1960) to be resistant to neuraminidase action. Cassidy, Jourdian, and Roseman (1962), however, reported that the neuraminidase of *V. cholerae* had slight activity with colominic acid, whereas the enzyme from *Cl. perfringens* rapidly liberated more than 50% of the sialic acid of this polymer. The situation is complicated by the probable presence of ester bonds in colominic acid. When these bonds are cleaved, all the sialic acid is liberated by the *Clostridium* enzyme, and the compound appears to be susceptible to the action of the *V. cholerae* and the viral enzymes.

The relative rates of liberation and the total sialic acid liberated from

N-acetylneuraminyllactose and from various glycoproteins by the enzyme prepared from Asian influenza virus are given in Table I (Rafelson, 1963). It is clear that significant differences in rates and in the extent of release of sialic acid exist. Whether the failure to remove all the sialic acid is due to steric factors or to a difference in the linkage of a portion of the sialic acid, or both, is not known. The sialic acid residues

TABLE I
LIBERATION OF SIALIC ACID BY NEURAMINIDASE OF ASIAN INFLUENZA VIRUS

Substrate[a]	Rates[b]	Total sialic acid liberated (%)
N-Acetylneuraminyllactose	100	100
Collocalia glycoprotein	26	85
Haptoglobin 1–1	23	70
Haptoglobin 2–2	22	69
α_1-Acid glycoprotein (orosomucoid)	17	73
Stromal inhibitor	10	58
Urinary glycoprotein	5	76

[a] All substrates were present in concentration to give the same amount of sialic acid in the reaction mixture; the enzyme concentration was also constant.
[b] Rates relative to *N*-acetylneuraminyllactose as 100.

are, presumably, terminal in all compounds. The relative sequence observed may be accurate only for *N*-acetylneuraminyllactose, haptoglobin, and α_1-acid glycoprotein, as these were the only compounds tested at a pH (6.5) known to be optimal for the release of sialic acid by the enzyme of Asian influenza virus. The pH optimum may vary with the substrate used (see Table II and Mohr and Schramm, 1960).

2. KINETICS

It is clear from Table II that there are significant differences in the kinetics of the various enzymes. The pH optimum of the various enzymes for the substrate, *N*-acetylneuraminyllactose, varies from 4.5 to 7.0, and the pH optimum for a specific enzyme may also vary with the substrate used. The Michaelis constants (K_m) vary from enzyme to enzyme, indicating that the enzymes have different affinities for a specific substrate. There is also a significant difference in the inhibitor constants (K_i) for the enzymes of the Asian and PR8 viruses, indicating differences in affinities of the enzymes for a product of the reaction—*N*-acetylneuraminic acid.

Neither the viral enzymes nor the neuraminidase from *Cl. perfringens* is stimulated by the addition of Ca ion, whereas the mammalian and the *V. cholerae* enzymes have increased activity in the presence of calcium.

TABLE II
KINETICS OF NEURAMINIDASES FROM VARIOUS SOURCES

Source of enzyme	K_m[a] (moles/liter)	K_i[b] (moles/liter)	pH optimum	Stimulated by Ca++	Inhibited by ethylenediaminetetraacetate	References
Asian virus	5×10^{-4}	4×10^{-3}	6.5(6.5)[c]	No	Yes	Mayron *et al.* (1961); Wilson and Rafelson (unpublished data)
PR8 virus	1×10^{-3}	2×10^{-2}	7.0(5.4)[c]	No	Yes	Mayron *et al.* (1961); Wilson and Rafelson (unpublished data)
Lee virus	2×10^{-4}	—	—	—	—	Noll, Aoyagi, and Orlando (1961)
Vibrio cholerae	1×10^{-3}	Inhibits	5.6[a]	Yes	Yes	Ada, French, and Lind (1961)
Mammals	—	—	5.5[a]	Yes	Yes	Warren and Spearing (1960)
Chick chorioallantoic membrane	1×10^{-3}	—	4.5[a]	—	No	Ada and Lind (1961)
Clostridium perfringens	—	—	—	No	No	Cassidy, Jourdian, and Roseman (1962)

[a] For *N*-acetylneuraminyllactose as substrate.
[b] For *N*-acetylneuraminic acid as substrate.
[c] For α_1-acid glycoprotein as substrate.

Ethylenediaminetetraacetate inhibits the viral, *V. cholerae,* and mammalian neuraminidases but not the enzymes from *Cl. perfringens* or the chick chorioallantoic membrane. Ethylenediaminetetraacetate inhibits the viral and *Vibrio* enzymes only in the absence of added Ca^{++}. This may indicate that the isolated enzymes contain a metal ion as an essential component.

A large number of substances have been examined for their ability to inhibit the influenza-virus neuraminidases. In Table III are listed the active compounds and the minimal concentration which produced 50% or greater inhibition (Rafelson, Schneir, and Wilson, unpublished data). The mechanism of the inhibition is not clear and requires further study. The following compounds, among others tested, showed no inhibitory activity: methoxyneuraminic acid, methoxy-*N*-acetylneuraminic acid and its methyl ester, periodate-treated and borohydride-reduced α_1-acid glycoprotein and *N*-acetylneuraminyllactose, interferon, α-aminophenylmethanesulfonic acid, phloridzin, glucosamine, *N*-acetylglucosamine, glucosaminic acid, galactosamine, *N*-acetylgalactosamine, and a variety of biguanidine derivatives (Pilcher, Soike, and Trosper, 1961). In addition, neither the viral enzymes nor the *V. cholerae* enzyme (Mohr, 1960) appears to be particularly sensitive to sulfhydryl reagents.

TABLE III

INHIBITORS OF INFLUENZA-VIRUS NEURAMINIDASE

Substance	Concentration (*M*)	Inhibition (%)
Cu^{++}	1×10^{-2}	80
Hg^{++}	1×10^{-3}	100
Fe^{++}	1×10^{-2}	50
Fe^{+++}	1×10^{-2}	50
Merthiolate	1×10^{-3}	100
NaCN	5×10^{-3}	50
Ascorbic acid	5×10^{-2}	100
Glutathione (reduced)	5×10^{-2}	90
Cysteine	5×10^{-2}	90

B. Physical Properties

There are a number of differences reported for the physical properties of the crystalline neuraminidase prepared from *V. cholerae* by Mohr and Schramm (1960) and by Ada, French, and Lind (1961). Pye and Curtain (1961) obtained sedimentation constants of 5.5 S at pH 6.7 and 5.3 S at pH 8.5 for the preparation of Ada, French, and Lind. Mohr and Schramm reported sedimentation constants of 2.3 S at pH 5.5 and 1.3 S at pH 8.5. Molecular weights of 90,000 and 10,000–20,000 were calculated for the preparations of Ada, French, and Lind and of Mohr and Schramm, respectively. In addition to the difference in molecular weight, Mohr and Schramm found that their preparations were relatively unstable unless stored in the presence of chelating agents, cyanide, or various proteins. The differences between the two preparations cannot as yet be explained.

There are practically no data available on the physical properties of other neuraminidases. Preliminary studies suggest a molecular weight in the range of 40,000 to 60,000 for the Asian-virus enzyme (Rafelson, Schneir, and Wilson, unpublished data).

C. Immunologic Properties

Wilson and Rafelson (unpublished data) recently found that influenza-virus neuraminidases can elicit good antibody formation in guinea pigs. The sera from animals immunized with the enzyme isolated from Asian virus react specifically with Asian virus in the hemagglutination-inhibition test and with the enzyme isolated from Asian virus in enzyme-inhibition tests. Antiserum prepared against the enzyme of Asian virus does not react with PR8 virus or B virus or with the enzyme isolated from PR8 virus. Similar results were obtained with antisera prepared against the enzyme isolated from PR8 virus, the reactions being specific for PR8 virus and the enzyme isolated from PR8 virus. The observation that hemagglutinin antibodies are produced is difficult to interpret, since the viral-enzyme preparations are free from demonstrable hemagglutination activity (Mayron *et al.*, 1961; Wilson and Rafelson, 1962). The enzyme preparations used for immunization may have contained fragmented hemagglutinin components which could elicit antibody response and yet not show hemagglutination. On the other hand, the active sites of the virus responsible for the enzymic reaction and for the hemagglutination may be identical or closely related.

Addendum

Romanovska and Watkins (1963) have reported neuraminidase activity in the protozoan, *Trichomonas foetus*. Extracts of this organism could be resolved into four enzymically active fractions by DEAE-Sephadex columns. Fractions II and III, which accounted for 50% of the total activity, were reported to liberate all the sialic acid from the sialomucopolysaccharide from ovarian cyst mucin, the α_1-acid glycoprotein, bovine and ovine submaxillary mucin, and both known isomers of *N*-acetylneuraminyllactose, i.e., $2 \rightarrow 3$ and $2 \rightarrow 6$, and partially to hydrolyze colominic acid. Since there were differences in the relative rates at which sialic acid was liberated from the various substrates, and different pH optima were observed for the sialomucopolysaccharide substrate, it was suggested that the enzyme fractions represent neuraminidases differing in both molecular and enzymic properties.

Further properties of the neuraminidase from *Cl. perfringens* have been described by Burton (1963). The enzyme has a pH optima of 5.1 and a K_m of 4×10^{-4} M for both gangliosides and 3-N-acetylneuraminyllactose. It was stable to freezing and relatively heat-resistant above pH 4.5. The enzyme cleaved both isomers of N-acetylneuraminyllactose, the $2 \rightarrow 6$ isomer being more slowly hydrolyzed.

Ada (1963) has reported further on the purification and properties of the avian neuraminidase. The enzyme was isolated from chick chorioallantoic membranes by extraction with phosphate buffer, heat treatment, precipitation with ammonium sulfate, and chromatography on columns of hydroxyapatite. A 200-fold purification was obtained. The purified enzyme has a sedimentation coefficient of 3.35 and a pH optimum between 4 and 5 for three substrates, N-acetylneuraminyllactose, fetuin, and ovine submaxillary mucin. The K_m values ($\times 10^{-4}$) for these substrates were 6.4, 16.6, and 18.2, respectively. Ada, Lind, and Laver (1963) prepared antisera to several strains of egg-grown influenza virus, to the purified neuraminidase of the chick chorioallantois, and to purified *V. cholerae* neuraminidase. The ability of the antisera to inhibit each enzyme was tested with three substrates of varying molecular weight, sialyllactose (MW 633), fetuin (MW 48,000) and ovine submaxillary mucin (MW 1×10^6). Antiserum to *V. cholerae* and avian neuraminidase inhibited the action of the homologous enzyme on each substrate with fetuin and ovine submaxillary mucin as substrates. With fetuin and ovine submaxillary mucin as substrates, antiserum to the viral neuraminidase inhibited the homologous action almost completely. Only partial inhibition was obtaained with sialyllactose as substrate. With one exception, no serological cross-reactions between any enzyme and heterologous antisera were observed. Antiserum to avian neuraminidase partially inhibited the enzyme from egg-grown Lee virus when fetuin but not sialyllactose was the substrate. No inhibition was obtained when the virus was grown in cultures of calf kidney cells. It was concluded that the viral enzyme is a virus-specific product, but carries some antigenic determinants characteristic of the host.

Rafelson, Schneir, and Wilson (1963) have presented further data on the properties of the soluble enzymes from the Asian (Jap 305) and PR8 strains of influenza virus. The enzymes differ in K_m values, in their K_i values for the competitive inhibitor N-acetylneuraminic acid, in heat stability, and in their pH optima for a number of substrates. The two enzymes are immunologically distinguishable, and the degree of neutralization of enzyme activity is dependent on the substrate employed, the neutralization being greater as the molecular weight of the substrate is increased. No serological cross-reactions between the two enzymes and their antisera were noted, and the antisera contained no detectable hemagglutinin antibodies. Wilson and Rafelson (unpublished data) have detected no serological cross-reactions between the enzymes from the Jap 305, PR8, Great Lakes, and Ann Arbor strains of influenza virus and the appropriate antisera, and were unable to demonstrate the presence of hemagglutinin antibodies. Some serological cross-reactions between the enzymes of Jap 305 and Jap 170 and their antisera were noted.

NOTE: The following paper of interest has been published since the preparation of this addendum and is also included in the reference list:

Hughes, R. C., and Jeanloz, R. W. (1964). The extracellular glycosidases of *Diplococcus pneumoniae*. I. Purification and properties of a neuraminidase and a β-galactosidase. Action on the α_1-acid glycoprotein of human plasma.

Chapter 44

ENZYMES DEGRADING GLYCOSAMINOGLYCANS

Heinz Gibian

In the present chapter, enzymes degrading, or depolymerizing, high molecular weight glycosaminoglycans, but not acting on low molecular weight amino sugar derivatives, will be covered. This includes the following enzymes: chitinases; lysozymes; hyaluronidases acting on hyaluronic acid, chondroitin 4-sulfate, and chondroitin 6-sulfate; enzymes degrading dermatan sulfate; enzymes degrading heparan sulfate and heparin (heparinases); and enzymes degrading keratan sulfate.

Hexosaminidases (see Chapter 42) and sulfatases (see Chapter 45) will therefore be excluded from this chapter. The mode of action of β-glucuronidase will, however, be briefly discussed.

I. Enzymes Degrading Chitin

The glycosidic bonds of chitin are hydrolyzed by chitinases. The activity of these enzymes is shown by the decrease of insoluble chitin, as measured by a turbidity test or by determination of the nonprotein nitrogen (Fischer and Stein, 1960). The hydrolytic nature of the degradation of chitin by these enzymes is also shown by the increase of *N*-acetylglucosamine end groups. The latter test is not, however, unequivocal proof for chitinase activity, since further degradation by oligosaccharidases (chitobiase, β-*N*-acetylglucosaminidase) has to be taken into account. The test becomes specific when no low molecular weight homologues are present in the substrate and when "chitobiase" is added in excess (Devigne and Jeuniaux, 1961).

Chitin-degrading activity has been found in various microorganisms, including *Pseudomonas, Clostridium, Vibrio, Erwinia,* and *Klebsiella* (Benecke, 1905; Waksman *et al.,* 1933; ZoBell and Rittenberg, 1938; Campbell and Williams, 1951; Hock, 1940; Bucherer, 1935; Benton, 1935; Skinner and Dravis, 1937; Stanier, 1947; Veldkamp, 1952; Veldkamp, 1955; Rose and György, 1956; Clarke and Tracey, 1956) (for review see

Dasté, 1956; and Veldkamp, 1955). Chitinase was also described in *Streptomyces* (Bucherer, 1935; Veldkamp, 1955; Schmidt-Lange and Bucherer, 1938; Erickson, 1941; Reynolds, 1954; Jeuniaux, 1955; Jeuniaux, 1957; Berger and Reynolds, 1958), in fungi (Skinner and Dravis, 1937; Veldkamp, 1955; Jeuniaux, 1950,a,b; Karling, 1945; Tracey, 1955a; Cantino, Lovett, and Horenstein, 1957), in mushrooms (Tracey, 1955), and in the intestinal tract of various animal species such as garden snail (*Helix pomatia*) (Karrer and Hofmann, 1929; Zechmeister, Toth, and Vajda, 1939; Hackman, 1954) and earthworm (Devigne and Jeuniaux, 1961), where the source of the enzyme can be bacterial. In the digestive tracts of several vertebrates which can digest insects there is chitin-degrading activity (goldfish, stickleback, lizards, sparrow, pigeon, and bat) (Jeuniaux, 1961,a).

The chitinase of *Streptomyces* cultures was purified by the usual methods and also through adsorption on chitin (Jeuniaux and Armanicu, 1955; Berger and Reynolds, 1958; Jeuniaux, 1959a). In zone electrophoresis at pH 8.2, this preparation could be resolved into those fractions of similar activity. The molecular weights of these basic proteins were found to be approximately 30,000 (Jeuniaux, 1956, 1957). Two chitinases, prepared from *Streptomyces griseus,* degraded chitin to *N*-acetylglucosamine and *N,N*-diacetylchitobiose (Berger and Reynolds, 1958). Chitobiase, a β-*N*-acetylglucosaminidase (see Chapter 42), was separated from various chitinase-containing sources. It was found to hydrolyze the di- and trisaccharides of *N*-acetylglucosamine and phenyl 2-acetamido-2-deoxy-β-D-glucoside (Berger and Reynolds, 1958; Jeuniaux, 1959). It is of interest that lysozyme exhibits chitinase activity. For example, crystalline egg-white lysozyme has been shown to degrade native chitin (Berger and Weiser, 1957) and low molecular weight homologues of chitin (Lenk, Wenzel, and Schütte, 1960; Salton and Ghuysen, 1960; Wenzel, Lenk, and Schütte, 1961), as well as a water-soluble glycol derivative of chitin (Hamaguchi and Funatsu, 1959).

II. The Action of Lysozyme

Lysozymes (Salton, 1957; P. Jollès, 1960; Katz and Weidel, 1961; Weidel and Katz, 1961) bacteriolyze, in particular, Gram-positive saprophytic microorganisms such as *Micrococcus lysodeikticus, Bacillus megaterium,* and *Sarcina flava,* and also some Gram-negative ones. These enzymes are widely distributed in the animal and plant worlds. Lysozymes were prepared from, among other sources, hen egg white (Fleming, 1922; Wolff, 1927; Thompson, 1941; Waksman and Woodruff, 1942), papaya latex (Smith *et al.*, 1955), various strains of *Bacillus subtilis* (Richmond, 1959,b), *Nephthys hombergi* (Annelida) (P. Jollès and Zuili, 1960), rabbit spleen

(G. Jollès and Fromageot, 1953, 1954), rat spleen and kidney (Litwack, 1958), and hen lung (Jollès and Zuili, 1960). The lysozymes, isolated up to the present time, are very similar in their properties and their chemical composition but are not identical. Their stability at acid pH (pH 4.5; 3 min at 100°C) and their instability at alkaline pH are characteristic. The most thoroughly investigated lysozyme, isolated from ovomucoid, was crystallized some time ago (Abraham and Robinson, 1937). It is remarkable that, although the elucidation of the chemical structure of this lysozyme is so advanced (Jollès, Jollès-Thaureaux, and Fromageot, 1958; Jollès-Thaureaux, Jollès, and Fromageot, 1958; Jollès and Ledieu, 1959,a; Jollès, Jollès, and Jauregui, 1959; Jollès and Jollès, 1960), the nature of its substrate has not yet been fully determined.

All lysozymes possess an isoelectric point between pH 10.5 and 11 (Alderton, Ward, and Fevold, 1945), and a molecular weight measured by various authors was found to be between 13,000 and 18,000 (Alderton, Ward, and Fevold, 1945; Abraham, 1939; Passynsky and Plaskeyev, 1945; Palmer, Ballantyne, and Galvin, 1948; Lewis *et al.*, 1950; Halwer, Nutting, and Brice, 1951; Calvin, 1952). The only exceptions are the papaya enzyme, which has a molecular weight of 25,000, and the enzyme that is linked to T_2 phages has a molecular weight of 21,000.

The activity of lysozymes is generally determined by a turbidity test which uses a suspension of acetone-dried *M. lysodeikticus* cells. The success of this test requires, however, a rigid application of the prescription (see for example, Smolelis and Hartsell, 1949; Lobstein and Fogelson, 1951; Dickman and Proctor, 1952; Jollès and Fromageot, 1953; Burghartz and Boosfeld, 1954; Richmond, 1959). Determination of the activity can also be made in following the fall of viscosity of a substrate obtained from the cell walls of the bacteria just mentioned, although the chemical structure of this substrate is not yet completely elucidated (see Volume I, Chapter 9). Since the action of lysozyme is accompanied by the appearance of reducing *N*-acetylhexosamine groups, methods based on reductometry can also be used, but only after extensive purification of the substrate (Colobert and Dirheimer, 1961).

The hydrolysis of chitin and its derivatives by lysozyme has already been mentioned. Based on this observation, lysozyme should be considered a β-*N*-acetylhexosaminidase. Additional proof for this suggestion was provided by the isolation and structure determination of low molecular weight degradation products isolated from lysozyme digests of bacterial cell walls. These products were shown to be *N*-acetyl-β-D-glucosaminyl-(1 → 4)-*N*-acetylmuramic acid [4-*O*-(2-acetamido-2-deoxy-β-D-glucopyranosyl)-2-acetamido-2-deoxy-3-*O*-(D-1′-carboxyethyl)-D-glucose] and its β-(1 → 4) dimer. The latter tetrasaccharide is split by lysozyme to give the disaccharide: N-acetyl-β-D-glucosaminyl-$(1 \rightarrow 6)$-β-N-acetylmuramic acid (Ghuysen, 1960; Salton and Ghuysen, 1960; Perkins, 1960; see Volume I, Chapter 2). Therefore, lysozyme could also be regarded as a "muraminidase."

The influence of the peptide chain, which, in the cell wall, is linked to muramic acid, on the specificity of lysozyme remains to be established. The peptide chain might be responsible for the release of only 50% of dialyzable material during the degradation of isolated cell walls of *M. lysodeikticus* by lysozyme. The nondialyzable portion contains high molecular weight polysaccharides (10,000 to 20,000) linked to amino acids (Salton, 1956; Richmond, 1959,b). The affinity of different lysozymes for substrates of different weights seems to vary (Ghuysen, 1960). Insoluble substrate–enzyme complexes may occur, and be partly responsible for an ambiguous kinetic; this might also explain certain anomalies in the action of lysozymes on whole bacteria (Colobert and Dirheimer, 1961).

The primary structure of lysozyme was recently clarified. It contains 129 amino acids, and only at three points of their sequences are there discrepancies (Jollès, Jauregui-Adell, and Jollès, 1963; Canfield, 1963). The primary structure fully controls the secondary and tertiary structure —namely, after reductive splitting of the S–S bridges, one can recover fully the active crystalline enzyme with reoxidation (Epstein and Goldberger, 1963; Imai, Takagi, and Isemura, 1963). Radiation produces several modified proteins which exhibit enzyme activity (Stevens, Tolbert, and Reese, 1963). The lysozyme of T-even-bacteriophage, with a molecular weight of 16,000, has no S–S bridges; consequently, the tertiary structure was easily determined by altering the immunological characteristics of the enzyme (Merigan and Dreyer, 1963).

Lysozymes isolated from chicken egg white, duck egg white, and human milk differ in their activity when tested on either of two glycopeptide substrates prepared from *Micrococcus lysodeikticus*. The most active of the three enzymes, that prepared from duck egg white, contains a higher percentage of basic amino acid groups than the other enzymes do (Jollès, 1963).

The chemical structure of two glycopeptides liberated by lysozyme from the cell walls of *Escherichia coli* was described as an N-acetylglycosaminyl-N-acetylmuraminyl-L-alanyl-D-glutamyl-meso-α-ϵ-diaminopimelic acid, and N-acetylglucosaminyl-N-acetylmuraminyl-L-alanyl-D-glutamyl-meso-α-ϵ-diaminopimelyl-D-alanine (Pelzer, 1962).

III. Enzymic Degradation of Hyaluronic Acid, Chondroitin, and Chondroitin Sulfates

All enzymes described in this subdivision depolymerize hyaluronic acid and, therefore, they will, for practical purposes, be named hyaluronidases.

Only some of them react also with chondroitin or chondroitin sulfates. Chondroitinases—more accurately named chondroitin sulfate depolymerases—which do not act on hyaluronic acid have not been found up to now. An alleged chondroitinase, "thiomucase" (Castaigne, 1959), was later found to degrade hyaluronic acid, as well (Gibian, unpublished data). Therefore, at present, the continued use of the name hyaluronidase is suggested. The enzyme activities can be classified in three distinct groups (see Table I).

TABLE I
VARIOUS TYPES OF HYALURONIDASES AND THEIR SOURCES

Type	Source	Substrate	Mechanism
IA	Sperm (mammalian testis)	Hyaluronic acid Chondroitin Chondroitin 4-sulfate Chondroitin 6-sulfate	Endo-poly-β-hexosaminidase with transhexosaminylation
IB	Venom of snakes, spiders, scorpions, bees	Hyaluronic acid Chondroitin	Endo-poly-β-hexosaminidase
IC	*Proteus vulgaris* (strain 4636NCTC) *Clostridium perfringens*	Hyaluronic acid Chondroitin sulfate	Poly-β-hexosaminidase
IIA	*Micrococcus pyogenes*, var. *aureus* and var. *albus* *Streptococcus mitis* *Diplococcus pneumoniae* *Clostridium perfringens* *Clostridium septicum* *Clostridium novyi* Adapted strains of *Escherichia coli*	Hyaluronic acid Chondroitin	Endo-poly-β-hexosaminidase with water elimination and formation of $\Delta_{4,5}$ uronides
IIB	Adapted strains of *Flavobacterium heparinum* and *Proteus vulgaris*	Hyaluronic acid Chondroitin Chondroitin 4-sulfate Chondroitin 6-sulfate	—
III	Leech	Hyaluronic acid	Endo-poly-β-glucuronidase

It has been suggested that the enzymes classified in the same group may not necessarily be chemically identical, as shown by the formation of specific antihyaluronidases (Gibian, 1959, page 232). This different comportment, however, could also result from the formation of antibodies by inert accompanying proteins. The inactivation of the enzyme would then be a side effect of such an antigen–antibody reaction.

A. Action of Hyaluronidases *in Vitro*

In vitro, hyaluronidase decreases the viscosity of hyaluronic acid solutions very rapidly, especially at the beginning of the reaction. The ability of the native high molecular weight substrate to form a mucin clot with acidic albumin solutions disappears early, and the release of reducing groups can then be followed with micromethods. As depolymerization progresses, the turbidity resulting from the addition of acid albumin disappears. Only later, when the reducing values have increased noticeably, is it possible to separate chromatographically and identify the degradation products.

All these results can be accounted for by the same mechanism of reaction, and there is no reason to attribute them to the action of a series of enzymes, such as polysaccharidases and oligosaccharidases. There is also no reason to assume that there is a separate enzymic mechanism in the case of "disaggregation" of native hyaluronic acid, in which high molecular weight chains may possibly be linked in micelles. The high molecular weight, as measured by physical methods, can decrease by the scission of a few linkages in the middle of the chain, but this scission, for all practical purposes, cannot be determined chemically.

The methods of qualitative and quantitative determination of hyaluronidases are based on the properties just described. Recent comprehensive reviews which critically evaluate the various assays for hyaluronidase activity were given by Gibian (1959) and Meyer, Hoffman, and Linker (1960). Physicochemical methods alone are not sufficient for the identification of the mode of action of hyaluronidases. It would, for instance, not be possible to distinguish between an oxidative and a hydrolytic (enzyme-specific) degradation. The latter process can be proved only by a specific chemical end-group determination. Final isolation and characterization of the degradation products are, however, necessary. It should be noted that hyaluronidases of the different types can be compared among themselves only in a relative way, even when the same test methods are used (Gibian, 1959, page 188). For instance, absolute values in United States Pharmacopoeia or in international units should not be used for bacterial enzymes, since these enzymes have a reaction mechanism completely different from that of the testis enzymes. Such values are only useful when explicit reference to the method and limitation of the conditions of the determination are given.

The following types of assay methods for hyaluronidase activity have been described.

(*a*) *Mucin-clot-prevention test.* This test is based on the coprecipitation of high molecular weight hyaluronic acid and proteins at acidic pH (pH 4–5) (Robertson, Ropes, and Bauer, 1940; McClean, 1943; Harris and Harris, 1950; McClean, 1941; Di Caprio, Rantz, and Randall, 1952; Burnet, 1948; Evans, Perkins, and Gaisford, 1951; Oakley and Warrack, 1951; Warren and Durso, 1951).

(*b*) *Turbidity-reducing test.* This test is based on the ability of low molecular weight hyaluronic acid to form colloidal suspensions with proteins in acid solutions, and it is in essence a variation of the previous assay (Kass and Seastone, 1944; Dorfman and Ott, 1948; Leonard, Perlman, and Kurzrok, 1946; Schmith and Faber, 1949; Warren, Durso, and Levin, 1948; Alburn and Whitley, 1951; Tolksdorf *et al.*, 1949; Kulonen, 1952; Humphrey, 1957; Glick, Ottoson, and Edmondson, 1958; US Pharmacopoeia, 1955; Gibian, 1952,a; Di Caprio, Rantz, and Randall, 1952; Dorfman, 1948; Bachtold and Gebhardt, 1952; Pearce, 1953; Greif, 1952; Di Ferrante, 1956). Rapport, Meyer, and Linker (1950) estimated that this test is not usable if the hyaluronic acid molecular weight is under the range of 6000 to 8000.

An improved turbidity test which has been accepted by the United States Pharmacopoeia has been developed from the old mucin-clot test. The decrease of turbidity, due to enzymic action, of a purified hyaluronic acid solution, after addition of acid albumin, is measured by nephelometry. The unit is based on the decrease of the starting turbidity to one half its value, often erroneously called "50% degradation."

(*c*) *Colorimetric test with ferric ion.* In this test, the nondegraded hyaluronic acid or chondroitin 4-sulfate is precipitated with Fe^{3+}, and the bound iron is determined colorimetrically (Di Ferrante, 1954).

(*d*) *Viscometric test.* These tests are based on the assumption that the degradation of the long polymer chain is proportional to the decrease of viscosity. The possibility of changes in the molecular interaction and changes in the shape and solvent-drainage characteristics of individual molecules can usually not be excluded, especially in high-concentration solutions of high molecular weight polymers (see Volume I, Chapter 8) (McClean, 1943; Harris and Harris, 1950; Alburn and Whitley, 1954; Kulonen, 1952; Madinaveitia and Quibell, 1940; McClean and Hale, 1941; Glick and Gollan, 1948; Hadidian and Pirie, 1948; Hahn, 1943; Madinaveitia and Quibell, 1941a; Sundblad, 1953).

The decrease of the viscosity of hyaluronic acid solutions can be measured accurately with a simple capillary viscometer. This allows a very early analysis for large numbers of samples (Gibian, 1952a; Harris, Abrams, and Harris, 1950; Werle, Turtur, and Bauereis, 1949; Swyer and Emmens, 1947).

(*e*) *Reducing end-group determination.* Determination of end groups using standard reductometric procedures such as copper, ferricyanide, and hypoiodite methods are necessary for qualitative identification of the type of hyaluronidase tested (Rapport, Meyer, and Linker, 1951; Weissmann *et al.*, 1954; Rapport, Meyer, and Linker, 1950). Unfortunately, all these methods use alkaline conditions, resulting in degradation of the polymer chain and, consequently, in higher analytical values than can be attributed to the enzymic degradation. The determination of well-defined end groups—for instance, of *N*-acetylhexosamine residues by the Morgan–Elson reaction—increases the specificity but does not necessarily give a quantitative account of the degradation (Gibian, 1959).

(*f*) *Spectrophotometric determination of unsaturated oligosaccharides.* Hyaluronidases of Type II can be detected and determined by spectrophotometry, since the appearing double bond formed has a characteristic absorption at about 230 mμ (Greiling, 1957; Greiling, Günther, and Eberhard, 1960; Nakada *et al.*, 1960).

B. Action of Hyaluronidases *in Vivo*

Wherever the presence of hyaluronidase substrates is of biological importance, degrading enzymes cause biological changes (also see Chapter 51). Among them of particular importance are: the increase of spreading, or diffusion, of various substances in tissue and the increase of the permeability of membranes—both effects are not always, in practice, rigorously separable. Spreading is the diffusion in tissues, in two or three dimensions, of any agent, such as dyes, drugs, virus, bacteria, and toxins. In the strictest sense, spreading is only the externally visible two-dimensional diffusion of dye solutions in the skin. This property of the tissue, its diffusibility, depends mostly on the hyaluronidase substrate, which is contained in the intercellular substances, and, therefore, this property can be increased by application of the corresponding enzymes (Bacharach, Chance, and Middleton, 1940,a; Madinaveitia, 1938; McClean and Hale, 1941; Shuman and Finestone, 1950; Koch and Haase, 1952; Málek and Trávníček, 1955, 1957; Lormand, Desbordes, and Bonét-Maury, 1952; Duran-Reynals, 1954; Lenstrup, 1951; Venturi, 1953; Dussaussoy, 1954; Merlen, Cachera, and Dussaussoy, 1954; Valette and Ranson, 1954).

The permeability of membranes (fascial membranes, bladder, and basement membranes) or of certain functional barriers (for instance, capillary beds) accounts for one-dimensional diffusion, permeation, of the same substances as described for the spreading reactions. This permeability also depends, at least partly, on high molecular weight substrates of hyaluronidase, and can also be increased by application of enzymes (see, for instance, Pabst and Auer, 1959; Juhlin, 1960; Földi *et al.*, 1960).

The "spreading" effect is still occasionally used for the detection of hyaluronidases (Jaques, 1953). It is, however, not readily applicable for quantitative determination, and in no case is suitable for identification of hyaluronidase activity, since agents other than hyaluronidases can act similarly.

The enzymic decapsulation of bacteria that possess a capsule containing hyaluronic acid, representing a different "biological" process, should also be mentioned, since a hyaluronidase test is based on it (Fulton, Marcus, and Robinson, 1948; McClean, 1942; Evans, 1953; Lincicome, 1953; Mayer, 1955; Murray and Pearce, 1949; Sherwood *et al.*, 1949; Kaffka, 1957; Mannheim, 1961).

C. The Mode of Action and Sources of Various Types of Hyaluronidases

1. Hyaluronidases Type IA, Type IB, and Type IC

a. Type IA. These enzymes degrade the substrates by hydrolyzing the β-(1 $\rightarrow$ 4)-hexosaminidoglucuronic acid bonds of the polymer chain, presumably by fission of the C-1 $\rightarrow$ O bond, as other glycosidases do. Since the ratio of the analytical values for reducing end groups and *N*-acetylhexosamine end groups remains constant during the entire reaction, it is assumed that only one type of glycosidic linkage is involved (Rapport, Meyer, and Linker, 1951). The enzyme is classified as an endo-poly-β-hexosaminidase, because, at the first part of the reaction, not any dialyzable, low molecular weight degradation products can be observed (Meyer, Linker, and Weissmann, 1952). Gradually, low molecular weight homologues of the substrate appear in the mixture. The main end product (approximately 80–90%) is a tetrasaccharide (Fig. 1, structure 2) and not the disaccharide 3-*O*-(β-D-glucopyranosyluronic acid)-2-acetamido-2-deoxy-D-hexosamine (structure 4) which is present only in an amount of 10–20% after exhaustive digestion with a large amount of enzyme (Weissmann and Meyer, 1953; Weissmann, 1955). The enzyme has transglycosylation activity, which was demonstrated by using a substrate containing both chondroitin sulfate and hyaluronic acid. Hexasaccharides and tetrasaccharides were formed which contained glucosamine, galactosamine, and sulfate (Hoffman, Meyer, and Linker, 1956). The transglycosidase activity may also result in the formation of higher oligosaccharides from hexasaccharides (Weissmann, 1955).

In addition to hyaluronic acid, chondroitin and desulfated chondroitin sulfates are also substrates of this enzyme (Davidson and Meyer, 1954). Chondroitin 4-sulfate and chondroitin 6-sulfate are also degraded by Type IA hyaluronidase, however, with a considerably slower rate. The degradation leads to sulfated oligosaccharides and, after exhaustive digestion, to tetrasaccharides (Fig. 2, structure 7) (Houck and Pearce, 1957,a; Mathews, Roseman, and Dorfman, 1951; Meyer and Rapport, 1950;

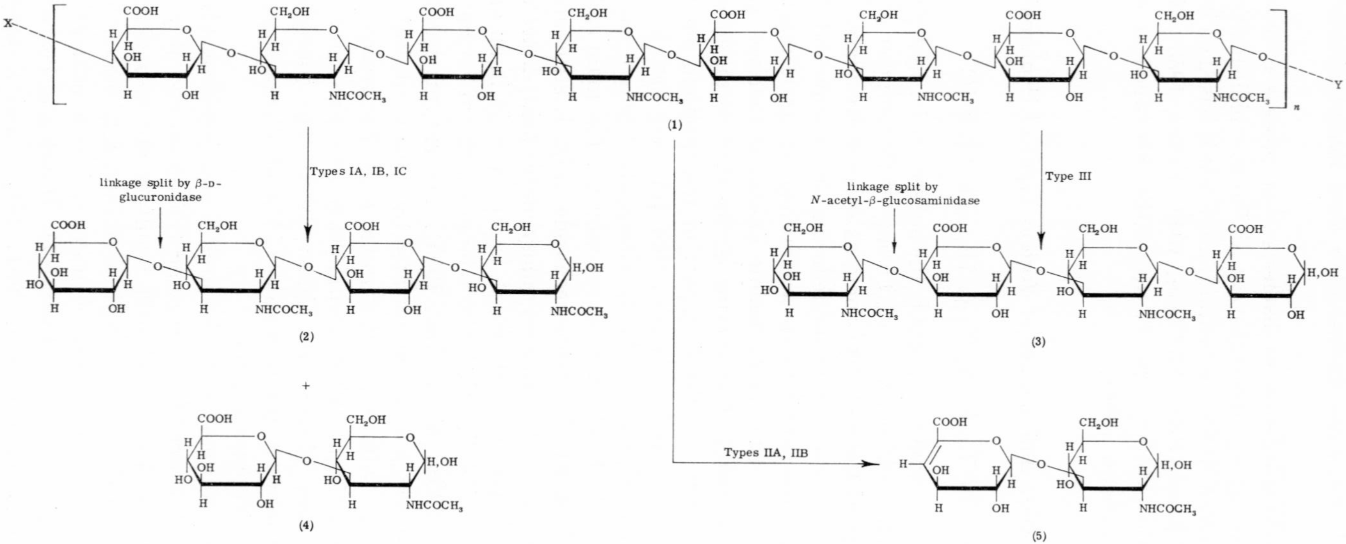

FIG. 1. Action of the three types of hyaluronidase on hyaluronic acid. X is the nonreducing and Y is the reducing end group. It is not definitely established which end group corresponds to the β-D-glucosamine residue and which to the β-D-glucuronic acid residue.

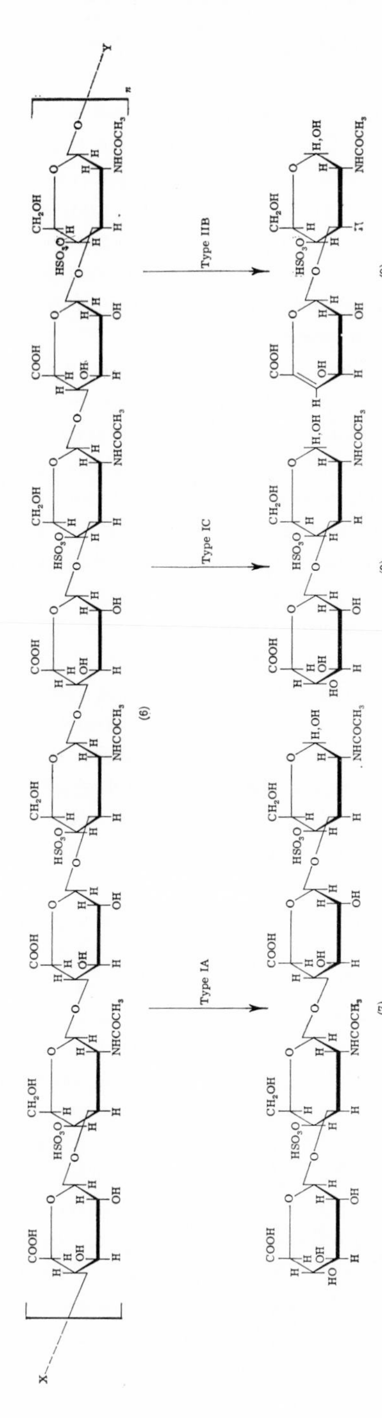

FIG. 2. Action of the three types of hyaluronidase on chondroitin 4-sulfate. X is the nonreducing and Y is the reducing end group. It is not definitely established which end group corresponds to the β-D-galactosamine residue and which to the β-D-glucuronic acid residue.

Mathews and Dorfman, 1954; Emmart and Longley, 1953; Hoffman, Linker, and Meyer, 1958).

The largest amount of Type IA hyaluronidase is found in testes and sperm of various mammals. The spermatozoa are the carriers of the enzyme, which diffuses also into the sperm plasma. There is a correlation between the hyaluronidase content of the testis and the spermatogenesis (Kulonen, 1949). In general, the titer of hyaluronidase is proportional to the number of spermatozoa (Swyer, 1947). Interestingly enough, in the sperm of birds, hyaluronidase activity could not be found (Swyer, 1947,a) (see for review Gibian, 1959, page 132).

Hahn (1945, 1946, 1947,a) first showed the complexity of testicular hyaluronidase and was able to purify the enzyme considerably. Högberg (1954) made a highly purified preparation (500,000 IU per milligram N) which was characterized by sedimentation and diffusion studies. A molecular weight of 11,000–18,000 was calculated, and the isoelectric point was found to be at pH 6.5 (Malmgren, 1953). Setlow and Doyle (1955) estimated the molecular weight of a not-very-pure preparation to be 75,000, based on radiation-inactivation studies. The chemical composition of the enzyme was studied by Malmgren (1953).

The testis enzyme has a temperature optimum of 50°C and a pH optimum of 5–6.5 at physiological salt concentration, but it depends greatly on the quality of ions present and on ionic strength (McClean, 1943; Meyer, 1947; Rapport, Meyer, and Linker, 1950; Meyer and Rapport, 1952; Gibian, 1952,a; Weissmann, 1955). The speed of reaction decreases rapidly with the decrease of chain length of the substrate (Gibian, 1951; Rapport, Linker, and Meyer, 1951; Schoenberg *et al.*, 1951; Gibian, 1952,a; Weissmann, 1955).

The speed of reaction was related to the free energy of the complex formation between substrate and enzyme. The relationship between the free energy of the complex formation and the chain length has been used to show that the dissociation constant of the enzyme–substrate complex closely approximates an equilibrium constant (Houck and Pearce, 1957,a).

For hyaluronic acid and chondroitin 4-sulfate, the site of substrate–enzyme interaction and the energy of the activation of the enzyme–substrate complex are identical. The presence of the sulfate group tends to decrease the free energy of the complex formation by sterically hindering the union of enzyme and substrate (Houck and Pearce, 1957,a).

Application of kinetic methods to the enzymic degradation of hyaluronic acid and chondroitin sulfates is generally difficult, since this enzyme catalyzes both the hydrolysis of the β-hexosaminidic bond of the substrate and the transglycosylation of the reaction products. During the enzymic degradation, one is dealing with an ever-changing polydisperse mixture of substrate molecules.

Several authors studied the kinetics of the viscosity changes of hyaluronic acid caused by this enzyme (Madinaveitia and Quibell, 1941a; Werthessen *et al.*, 1945; Hultin, 1946, 1948; Dorfman, 1948; Swyer and Emmens, 1947; Lundquist, 1949; Rapport, Meyer, and Linker, 1950; Sundblad, 1953 (see also Volume I, Chapter 8).

b. Type IB. These hyaluronidases act on hyaluronic acid and chondroitin as Type IA does, but chondroitin sulfates are not degraded. These enzymes occur in the venom of snakes, spiders, scorpions, and bees (Reggianini, 1950; Kaiser, 1953,a; Habermann, 1957).

The enzymes prepared from the venoms of *Bothrops jararaca* (Linker, Meyer, and Hoffman, 1956) and *Crotalus terrificus* (Weissmann, 1955) were studied in detail and revealed that the degradation products are similar to those of testes enzymes.

c. Type IC. In 1954, Konetzka, Pelczar, and Burnett reported that suspensions of resting cells of *Proteus vulgaris* released ammonia and sulfate, and increased the reducing substance in the solution when incubated with chondroitin sulfate.

Dodgson and Lloyd (1957, 1958) showed that strain 4636NCTC of *Proteus vulgaris* contains sulfatases which act on the oligosaccharides of chondroitin sulfates (see Chapter 45) and glycosidases which degrade chondroitin sulfates, yielding saturated oligosaccharides (Fig. 2, structure 8). Meyer, Hoffman, and Linker (1960), using Dodgson and Lloyd's enzyme preparation, could confirm these results; on the other hand, using other enzyme preparations of *Proteus vulgaris* (strains 31M and 4636-NCTC), they could only detect unsaturated oligosaccharides as degradation products. Martinez, Wolfe, and Nakada (1959,a) made an enzyme preparation from strain 31M of *Proteus vulgaris,* cultured in media containing chondroitin sulfate, and found that hyaluronic acid is degraded at a rate six times slower than chondroitin sulfate is by this enzyme preparation. The same author also found evidence that unsaturated disaccharides are formed from chondroitin 4-sulfate (Nakada and Wolfe, 1961). Suzuki and Strominger (1960c) and Suzuki (1960), using Dodgson and Lloyd's preparation, could prepare only unsaturated disaccharides from chondroitin 4-sulfate and chondroitin 6-sulfate obtained from shark cartilage.

Meyer, Hoffman, and Linker (1960) reported that a hyaluronidase preparation from *Clostridium perfringens,* made by Baker *et al.* (1956), yielded saturated oligosaccharides "indistinguishable from those produced by testicular hyaluronidase." This preparation also degraded both hyaluronic acid and chondroitin 4-sulfate (Figs. 1 and 2, structures 2 and 8).

Based on all these data, it seems justifiable to include in Type IC hyaluronidase (and not chondroitinase) those bacterial enzymes which degrade both hyaluronic acid and chondroitin sulfates, yielding saturated oligosaccharides. The differences found in the degradation mechanism of various enzyme preparations of the same strains point to the necessity of more extensive studies on the effect of such factors as cations, nonenzymic degrading agents (oxidation), and the physical structure of the substrates (Nakada and Wolfe, 1961).

2. Hyaluronidases Type IIA and Type IIB

a. Type IIA. These enzymes split only the hexosaminyl linkages of the substrate through an intramolecular hydrolysis and elimination of water. As a result of this reaction, an unsaturated uranide disaccharide is formed (Fig. 1, structure 5). A separate dehydrase has not been found so far. Inasmuch as this enzyme does not degrade the substrate progressively from the end of the chain it is regarded as an endo-poly-β-hexosaminidase. The chain length of the substrate has no marked influence on the speed of reaction. Only nonsulfated polymer chains are substrates, and, probably, sulfated polysaccharides are split only at the nonsulfated parts of the chain. The tetrasaccharide degradation product of the Type IA enzyme is split into a saturated and an unsaturated disaccharide by Type IIA enzyme. No transglycosylation was observed with this enzyme (Linker and Meyer, 1954; Linker, Weissmann, and Meyer, 1954; Schütte and Greiling, 1955; Linker, Meyer, and Hoffman, 1956).

The kinetics of these enzymes using the decrease in viscosity as a test for degradation was studied by Andersen and Graae (1955) and Graae and Jensen (1956). The formation of the double bond on the uronic acid moiety leading to an absorption at 232 mμ permits one to follow the kinetics with means other than viscosity (Greiling, 1957; Greiling, Günther, and Eberhard, 1960; Nakada *et al.*, 1960). This method offers a more realistic approach, especially since the molecular weight of the substrate seems to be unimportant in the degradation process by Type IIA hyaluronidase. An enzyme preparation from staphylococci had a Michaelis constant $K_m = 1.1 \times 10^{-3}$ g per milliliter in 0.1 M NaCl and 0.04 M phosphate buffer at pH 6.4. This constant is in the same magnitude as that found for other carbohydrate-degrading enzymes (Greiling, 1957).

Hyaluronidase Type IIA was prepared from various bacteria (see Table I) (for review see Gibian, 1959, pages 135–136; Habermann, 1958–1959; Brunish and Mozersky, 1958). The enzyme from *Clostridium welchii* was prepared in a purity similar to that obtained for testis enzyme (Type IA) (Baker *et al.*, 1956; Habermann, 1958–1959).

b. Type IIB. This enzyme rapidly hydrolyzes not only hyaluronic acid but also chondroitin 4-sulfate and chondroitin 6-sulfate to unsaturated sulfated oligosaccharides and disaccharides (Fig. 2, structure 9). A sulfatase also present in the preparation will eventually produce sulfate-free oligosaccharides. Sulfated tetrasaccharides obtained from chondroitin sulfate are degraded by this enzyme to a saturated disaccharide and an unsaturated disaccharide, indicating that desulfation is not the prerequisite of degradation (Hoffman *et al.*, 1957; Linker *et al.*, 1960).

Type IIB enzyme was found only in *Flavobacterium heparinum* (Hoffman *et al.*, 1957) and *Proteus vulgaris* (Nakada *et al.*, 1960; Suzuki, 1960) when chondroitin sulfate was added to the culture medium.

3. Hyaluronidase Type III

This enzyme has the greatest substrate specificity inasmuch as it degrades only hyaluronic acid and higher oligosaccharides obtained from hyaluronic acid by other types of hyaluronidase. The degradation products are oligosaccharides with glucuronic acid as the reducing end group, and, on exhaustive digestion, tetrasaccharides are obtained (Fig. 1, structure 3). This enzyme splits the hexasaccharides obtained with Type IA enzyme into two different trisaccharides: one containing one glucuronic acid and two glucosamine moieties, and another containing one glucosamine and two glucuronic acid moieties (Linker, Hoffman, and Meyer, 1957). This enzyme is an endo-poly-β-glucuronidase which does not act on sulfated polysaccharides or on chondroitin (Hirst, 1941a; Reggianini, 1950, 1951; Linker, Meyer, and Hoffman, 1960).

The enzyme activity was demonstrated only in leech extract (*Hirudo medicinalis*), where it is present in the front segments of the animal (salivary glands) (Chain and Duthie, 1940; Claude, 1940; Favilli, 1940; Hirst, 1941a). The purification of the enzyme was first reported by Hahn (1945a), who also determined the isoelectric point by electrophoresis (pH 5.65). Further purification and characterization of the enzyme were made by Yuki and Fishman (1963).

D. Other Degrading Agents in Tissues

Agents which depolymerize hyaluronic acid were detected in many organs and tissue fluids—first of all, in the liver and spleen of cats and dogs and in the serum and saliva of several higher animal species. Their activity was totally confined to acidic pH ranges (for review see Gibian, 1959, page 137). These agents also have been demonstrated in human urine (Dicker and Eggleton, 1960; Knudsen and Koefoed, 1961; Cobbin and Dicker, 1962; see also Chapters 20 and 51) and in the saliva of carnivores (Schindler, 1960). It is not certain that an enzyme is involved in each case. The possibility of degradation by an oxidation–reduction system of low molecular weight, such as ascorbic acid–iron (see Chapter 47), was, in most cases, not excluded. Contamination with bacterial enzymes was, in many cases, another source of error; however, in several authors' experiments, this was eliminated by working under sterile conditions (Kiriluk, Kremen, and Glick, 1950; Balazs and von Euler, 1952; Fiore, 1952; Reggianini, 1953) or by finding that the pH optima of bacterial enzyme and of the tissue factor are different. The ability to degrade hyaluronic acid was also found in lower animals and protozoa (Romanini, 1954; Tempelis and Lysenko, 1957).

The mechanisms of these degrading agents are not established. It was found that compounds containing *N*-acetylhexosamine residues as end groups are formed. Paper chromatography indicated the formation of degradation products apparently different from those obtained by Type IA enzyme digestion (Gibian, unpublished). A Type IA enzyme was demonstrated in various tissue extracts by determining the release of *N*-acetylhexosamine from hyaluronic acid and chondroitin sulfate substrates (Bollet, Bonner, and Nance, 1963).

E. Enzyme Inhibitors

Testicular hyaluronidase is inhibited by sulfated polysaccharides and other polyanions. This nonspecific interaction between polyanions and hyaluronidase and other enzymes is discussed in Chapter 46. Heparin and dermatan sulfate are probably competitive inhibitors, but the tetrasaccharide of hyaluronic acid is not an inhibitor. These two polyanionic inhibitors compete for the same sites on the enzyme, as indicated by the fact that in both cases the inhibition is abolished in 0.5 *N* NaCl (Alburn and Whitley, 1951; Houck, 1957).

The mechanism of inhibition *in vitro* of another group of low molecular weight compounds and di- and trivalent metal ions is mostly unknown (Table II).

Mammalian serum contains proteins which inhibit Type I and Type II hyaluronidases. On the other hand, immunospecific antihyaluronidase can be produced in animals or can be detected in human serum. The various hyaluronidases, like any other proteins, when injected produce antibodies, specifically inhibiting the injected enzyme, probably through antigen–antibody interaction (Emmart *et al.*, 1958; Emmart and Turner, 1960) (for review see Mathews and Dorfman, 1955; and Gibian, 1959, page 198).

IV. Enzymic Degradation of Dermatan Sulfate

Despite its close chemical relationship to hyaluronic acid and the chondroitin sulfates (see Volume I, Chapter 7), dermatan sulfate, as a

TABLE II
SUBSTANCES WHICH INHIBIT HYALURONIDASES

	Substances	References
1. Metal ions	Fe^{3+}, Cu^{2+}, Fe^{2+}, Zn^{2+}	Meyer and Rapport, 1951; Weissmann, 1955
2. Phenols and their oxidation products	Phenol derivatives	Coste and Delbarre, 1956; Dorfman, Reimers and Ott, 1947; Swyer, 1948; Forrest *et al.*, 1952; Roseman, Pearson, and Dorfman, 1949
	Flavonoids	Beiler and Martin, 1947; Rodney *et al.*, 1950; Beiler, Brendel, and Martin, 1954; Martin, 1953; Preston *et al.*, 1953
	Coumarin derivatives	Caneghem, Marx, and Spier, 1956; Beiler and Martin, 1947; Vincent and Segonzac, 1953; Vincent, Segonzac, and Issandou-Carles, 1954
	Condensation products of phenol derivatives with formaldehyde	Beiler, Brendel, and Martin, 1954; Hahn and Fekete, 1953; Hahn and Frank, 1953; Rogers and Spensley, 1954
	Quinones	Forrest *et al.*, 1952; Löwenthal and Gagnon, 1948; Roseman and Dorfman, 1952
	Phenol phosphates Hesperidin phosphate Tocoferol phosphate	Martin, 1953; Preston *et al.*, 1953; Beiler and Martin, 1948; Miller and Dessert, 1949; Diczfalusy *et al.*, 1953; Ferno *et al.*, 1953
3. Acid dyes and detergents	Germanin Congo red Trypan blue Sulfonated detergents	Bergamini, 1948; Beiler and Martin, 1948; Vincent and Segonzac, 1956; Caneghem and Spier, 1954; Pacca, 1951; Miller and Dessert, 1949; Mathews, 1954
4. Miscellaneous	Porphyrins Bile salts Sulfated steroids Estrogen polyphosphates Urinary kallikrein	Caneghem and Spier, 1954; Wattenberg and Glick, 1949; Boissier, Gross, and Bonfils, 1954; Lienert and Thorsell, 1954; Barnard *et al.*, 1954; Dirscherl and Krüskemper, 1952; Opsahl, 1951; Diczfalusy *et al.*, 1959; Warren, Seifter, and Glassman, 1962

rule, is not degraded by hyaluronidases. Furthermore, β-glucuronidase does not react on oligosaccharides obtained from dermatan sulfate by acid hydrolysis. Only *Flavobacterium heparinum* produces an enzyme—particularly after it is cultured in a medium containing dermatan sulfate—which degrades dermatan sulfate. This enzyme also degrades chondroitin sulfate to give unsaturated, sulfate-containing oligosaccharides. Therefore, this enzyme seems to be a hyaluronidase with the lowest substrate specificity, since hyaluronic acid is, of course, also degraded. The disaccharide sulfates obtained from chondroitin 4-sulfate and dermatan sulfate are identical (Hoffman *et al.*, 1960).

V. Enzymic Degradation of Heparan Sulfate and Heparin

Hyaluronidases do not degrade heparan sulfate and heparin. It is possible, however, to adapt *Flavobacterium heparinum* by growth in a medium containing heparin or heparan sulfate, and thus to obtain an enzyme which degrades heparan sulfate and heparin in a way similar to the one described for dermatan sulfate (Payza and Korn, 1956; Hoffman *et. al.*, 1957; Linker *et al.*, 1958). Whether it is the same enzyme is still unknown. Apparently in this case also, unsaturated sulfate-containing oligosaccharides are formed which are similar to the products obtained by bacterial hyaluronidase. It is of interest that chemical hydrolysis of the sulfamate group prevents degradation of the chain. In heparan sulfate, this effect concerns only the parts of the molecule that contain sulfamate groups. The parts containing *N*-acetylglucosamine residues, however, are degraded, forming unsaturated *O*-sulfated disaccharides and oligosaccharides, and leaving a core which is only *O*-sulfated. The unsaturated oligosaccharides are finally degraded by an "anhydro-glucuronidase," as in chondroitin sulfates, to give α-keto acids and hexosamines with varying degrees of *O*- and *N*-sulfation and *N*-acetylation (Hoffman *et al.*, 1957; Linker and Sampson, 1960). Other bacteria can also utilize heparin for growth (Christman and Doherty, 1956), but the mechanism (for example, hydrolysis at first, or only oxidation) is unknown. There is still a possibility that specific heparinases may be found in other species, too.

Enzymic activities, which have been described as heparinases, have been detected in various organs of several animal species (Jaques, 1940; Jaques and Keeri-Szanto, 1952; Cho and Jaques, 1956). They have been established, however, only through the disappearance of the biological activity and through the decrease of the metachromasia with toluene blue. A chemical detection of this reaction is completely lacking.

VI. Enzymic Degradation of Keratan Sulfate

A *Micrococcus* which can degrade blood group substances (Gilmore and Howe, 1959) has also been found to split keratan sulfate into oligosaccharides, but so far no details are known (Meyer and Hoffman, 1960).

VII. The Action of β-Glucuronidase on Glycosaminoglycans

β-Glucuronidase splits the terminal glucuronic acid residue from the oligosaccharides but not from the disaccharide of glycosaminoglycans

(Linker, Meyer, and Weissmann, 1955; Hoffman, Meyer, and Linker, 1956; see for review Levvy and Marsh, 1959, 1960). The formed oligosaccharides have an odd number of residues with one reducing and one nonreducing hexosamine end group. Provided this oligosaccharide is not a large molecule, it is further susceptible to the effect of Type I hyaluronidase, but only after the terminal nonreducing *N*-acetylhexosamine residue is split off by β-*N*-acetylhexosaminidase (Meyer, 1958).

To what extent a hyaluronic acid molecule of high molecular weight can be depolymerized solely by the two "exoenzymes," β-glucuronidase and β-hexosaminidase, both acting on the nonreducing end of the molecular chain, is still unknown.

It is possible that the length of the chain will determine the speed of the reaction.

When *Flavobacterium heparinum* is adapted to chondroitin 4-sulfate, a β-glucuronidase is induced which is different from other β-glucuronidases. It degrades the unsaturated disaccharides of hyaluronic acid and chondroitin 4-sulfate, yielding hexosamines and α-ketouronic acid (Linker *et al.*, 1960).

Addendum

The following papers of interest have been published since the receipt of this chapter and are also incorporated in the reference list:

Lysozymes:

Epstein, C. J., and Goldberger, R. F. (1963). Study of factors influencing the reactivation of reduced egg-white lysozyme.

Hamaguchi, K., Hayashi, K., Imoto, T., and Funatsu, M. (1964). Structure of muramidase (lysozyme). IV. Effects of ethylene glycol, polyethylene glycol and sucrose on the physico-chemical and enzymatic properties of muramidase.

Hamaguchi, K., and Kurono, A. (1963). Structure of muramidase (lysozyme). III. Effects of 2-chloroethanol, ethanol and dioxane on the stability of muramidase.

Imai, K., Takagi, T., and Isemura, T. (1963). Recovery of the intact structure of muramidase (lysozyme) after reduction of all disulfide linkages in 8M urea.

Jollès, J., Jauregui-Adell, J., and Jollès, P. (1963). Disulfide bonds in hen's egg-white lysozyme.

Jollès, P. (1964). La structure chimique du lysozyme de blanc d'oeuf de poule.

Jollès, P., Sternberg, M., and Mathé, G. (1964). Étude de la teneur en lysozyme du sérum chez des patients atteints de leucémies et hématosarcomes.

Jollès, P., Petit, J. F., Charlemagne, D., Salmon, S., and Jollès, J. (1964). Étude comparée de quelques lysozymes humains.

Merigan, T. C., and Dreyer, W. J. (1963). Studies on the antigenic combining sites in bacteriophage lysozymes.

Parrot, J. L., Nicot, G., Laborde, C., and Canu, P. (1962). Inhibition of various biological actions of histamine by means of lysozyme.

Perri, G. C., Cappuccino, J. G., Faulk, M., Mellors, J., and Stock, C. C. (1963). Variations of the content of lysozyme in normal rats and in rats bearing Jensen sarcoma following surgery.

Petit, J. E. Panigel, M., and Jollès, P. (1963). Purification and analysis of lysozyme extract of human placenta.

Pletsityi, D. F., and Krasnyanskaya, V. G. (1963). Variation in the activity of lysozyme of egg protein in the process of embryogeny.

Sela, M., and Steiner, K. A. (1963). Inhibition of lysozyme by some co-polymers of amino acids.

Hyaluronidases:

Arata, L., and Pecora, P. (1962). Hyaluronidase content in testicle of rat on vitamin-E-deficient diet.

Barker, S. A., Bayyuk, S. I., Brimacombe, J. S., and Palmer, D. J. (1963). Characterization of the products of the action of bee venom hyaluronidase.

Belenkaya, G. M., Gladstein, A. I., Loran, I. D., and Tchertkova, F. A. (1962). Standardization of lydase, natural product of testicular hyaluronidase.

Clay, M. M., and Sinai, C. R. (1965). Stress effects on hyaluronidase activity.

Ispolatovskya, M. V., Levdikova, G. A., and Larina, I. A. (1962). Partition of lecithinase, collagenase and hyaluronidase activity of *B. perfringens* by means of ion-exchange cellulose.

Lycke, E., Lund, E., and Strannegard, O. (1965). Enhancement by lysozyme and hyaluronidase of the penetration by *Toxoplasma gondii* into cultured host cells.

Masaki, J., and Hartree, E. F. (1962). Distribution of metabolic activity. Phospholipid and hyaluronidase between the heads and tails of bull spermatozoa.

Mogilevsky, M. S. (1963). Isolation and purification of streptococcus hyaluronidase.

Schmidt, J. (1964,a,b, 1965,a). Untersuchungen über Staphylokokken-Hyaluronidase I—V.

Silbert, J. E., Nagai, Y., and Gross, J. (1965). Hyaluronidase from tadpole tissue.

Soru, E., and Ionescu-Stoian, F. (1965). The purification of testicular hyaluronidase by chromatography on a mixed column.

Sternieri, E. (1962). Evaluation of in vivo hyaluronidase activity of a substance by cutaneous clearance of a radioactivity tracer.

Turpeinen, P., Turpeinen, O., and Talanti, S. (1962). Effect of local heat in vivo on hyaluronidase succinic dehydrogenase and phosphatases of the rat testis.

Hyaluronidase Inhibitors:

Belenkaya, G. M., and Gladshtein, A. I. (1962). Nature of hyaluronidase inhibitors in some biological fluids of the body.

Faarvang, H. J. (1962). Influence of glucocortical steroids and corticotropic hormone on output of human urinary trypsin inhibitor (and hyaluronidase inhibitor).

Loran, I. D., and Galatch'iants, O. P. (1962). Standard for streptococcal anti-hyaluronidase.

Lotmar, R. (1960). Hyaluronidase-Hemmung durch Phenylbutazon, Prednisolon, Adrenalin und natürliche Moorsubstanz.

Lyampert, I. M., and Yarenshko, N. T. (1961). Anti-hyaluronidase and anti-O-streptolysin in the sera of patients suffering from acute nephritis.

Zakarian, L. M. (1962). Possibility of utilization of dried blood in detection of streptococcal anti-hyaluronidase in rheumatism.

Chapter 45

SULFATASES OF GLYCOSAMINOGLYCANS

K. S. Dodgson

The first observation of the enzymic release of inorganic sulfate from compounds containing sulfated amino sugar residues was made by Neuberg and Rubin (1914), who showed that a mixed culture of "putrefying bacteria" could liberate sulfate from chondroitin sulfate. Since this initial observation, surprisingly little progress has been made in our knowledge of the enzyme system or systems involved in the desulfation process. This can be attributed, first, to the fact that until recently the substrates of such enzymes were chemically ill-defined and, second, to the difficulty of the determination of inorganic sulfate on a scale suitable to enzyme experiments.

In this chapter, an attempt is made to show the confused state of the field at the present time and to point to the gaps in our knowledge. In much of the published work involving the chondroitin sulfates, the degree of purity of the substrates used is uncertain and it is not always clear which isomer has predominated. This should be borne in mind in accepting the frequent use of the term "chondroitin sulfate" in this review.

I. Desulfation of Sulfated Glycosaminoglycans

A. Enzymes Attacking Chondroitin 4-Sulfate and Chondroitin 6-Sulfate

After their early observations, Neuberg and co-workers established that pure cultures of an organism related to *Bacillus fluorescens non liquefaciens* (syn. *Pseudomonas non-liquefaciens*), as well as strains of *Bacterium pyocyaneum* (syn. *Pseudomonas pyocyanea*) and *Bacillus proteus* (syn. *Proteus vulgaris*) were capable of desulfating chondroitin sulfate (Neuberg and Hofmann, 1931,a; Neuberg and Cahill, 1934, 1936). Enzyme activity was still present in acetone-dried cells and acetone-dried extracts of whole cells, and desulfation was accompanied by depolymerization of the substrate with release of reducing materials.

The so-called mucoitin sulfate of Levene and López-Suárez (1918) was also desulfated and depolymerized. Enzyme preparations from fungi, snails, and higher plants (Cruciferae), containing "phenolsulfatase" (arylsulfatase) or "myrosulfatase" (myrosulfaminase), were without effect on chondroitin sulfate. Neuberg therefore concluded that a new sulfatase had been discovered and suggested that it should be called chondrosulfatase. It is now clear that this name is not entirely suitable.

Other workers have since shown that a similar enzyme is present in other bacteria (see, for example, Buehler, Katzman, and Doisy, 1951; Reggianini, 1950a; Candeli and Tronieri, 1951; Hartles and McLean, 1952), in fungi (Pincus, 1950), and in certain marine molluscs (see, for example, Soda and Egami, 1938a; Hayashi *et al.*, 1955; Horiguchi and Mikaya, 1954). In those cases in which a specific search was made, a depolymerizing enzyme (generally referred to as "chondroitinase") was associated with the chondrosulfatase. Most of these studies were of a fragmentary nature and threw little light on the properties or mode of action of the desulfating enzyme. Exceptions to this generalization were the studies on molluscan chondrosulfatase made by Soda and co-workers in Japan and those on bacterial chondrosulfatase made by Dodgson and co-workers.

The digestive gland of *Charonia lampas* was used as the source of the enzyme by the Japanese workers, who were able to purify the enzyme to some extent and to separate it from other sulfatases (glucosulfatase and arylsulfatase) which were present (Soda and Egami, 1938a; Soda, Katsura, and Yoda, 1940). The enzyme, which was strongly inhibited by phosphate, was shown to have a higher molecular weight and activation energy (ΔH) than either glucosulfatase or arylsulfatase from the same source (Soda and Yoshida, 1948,a).

Proteus vulgaris N.C.T.C. 4636 was the source of chondrosulfatase used by Dodgson, Lloyd, and Spencer (1957) and Dodgson and Lloyd (1957). A purified (30-fold) preparation of the enzyme (still containing chondroitinase) showed maximum activity toward ox-cartilage chondroitin sulfate (mainly chondroitin 4-sulfate) at pH 7.0 and at a substrate concentration of 0.15% (w/v). The enzyme was inhibited by 0.01 M phosphate, fluoride, or hydroxylamine (100, 87, and 83% inhibition, respectively) but was not affected by a similar concentration of cyanide or chloride.

1. Interdependence of Chondrosulfatase and Chondroitinase

The first clue to the relationship between the two enzymes came from Soda and Egami (1938a), who inactivated *Charonia* chondrosulfatase without affecting the ability of the chondroitinase to degrade chondroitin sulfate. Desulfation was therefore not an essential prerequisite for the enzymic depolymerization of the polysaccharide chain.

Subsequently, Konetzka, Pelczar, and Burnett (1954) found that resting cells of *Proteus vulgaris* could not desulfate cartilage chondroitin sulfate in the presence of sulfite or hydroxylamine, but were still able to depolymerize the substrate. In contrast, depolymerizing activity could not be inhibited without a parallel loss in sulfatase activity.

The nature of the interdependence of the two enzymes was finally firmly established by Dodgson and Lloyd (1957) who were able to separate the chondrosulfatase of *Proteus* from the associated chondroitinase. The chondroitinase-free sulfatase had little or no activity toward the polymerized form of chondroitin 4-sulfate, but was able to liberate sulfate from the sulfated oligosaccharides prepared by the exhaustive digestion of the substrate with testicular hyaluronidase. Chondroitinase activity must therefore precede sulfatase action and this conclusion has since received support from the work of Martinez, Wolfe, and Nakada (1959), who used *Proteus vulgaris* 31M, and from that of Linker *et al.* (1960), who used an unadapted strain of *Flavobacterium heparinum.*

It is somewhat surprising to find this reaction sequence for the enzymic degradation of chondroitin 4-sulfate in the light of the work of Houck and Pearce (1957). These workers, during the course of studies on the degradation of the polymer by testicular hyaluronidase, obtained results which suggested that the presence of the sulfate group hindered the formation of the enzyme–substrate complex. The Fischer–Hirschfelder–Taylor model of the repeating unit of the substrate indicated that the free rotation of the sulfate group allowed it to extend over the pyran ring of the hexosamine and effectively cover the labile glycosaminidic bond. Under these circumstances, it might be expected that complete degradation of chondroitin 4-sulfate would be more effectively achieved if desulfation were the primary reaction. However, Dodgson and Lloyd (1957) have suggested that the partial removal of sulfate in a primary reaction might lead to an increase in the degree of coiling of the substrate molecules. This may, in turn, decrease the availability of the remaining ester sulfate groups to the sulfatase enzyme. If this were so, then sulfatase action would be facilitated by the preliminary depolymerization of the highly coiled substrate molecule.

2. Specificity of Chondrosulfatase

a. Molluscan Chondrosulfatase. Little work on the specificity of this enzyme has been done, and the type of chondroitin sulfate used as substrate has not always been made clear. Some confusion did exist at one period (F. Egami, personal communication) following the observation that the endogenous sulfated polysaccharide (a β-linked polyglucan) of *Charonia lampas* was desulfated by a digestive-gland preparation containing chondrosulfatase. It is now known (Takahashi and Egami, 1960) that a new sulfatase (cellulose polysulfatase) is responsible for this activity. Takahashi and Egami (1961) have suggested that *Charonia* chondrosulfatase is an adaptive enzyme, the tissue concentration of which depends on the nutritional state of the organism.

b. Proteus Chondrosulfatase. The sulfated oligosaccharides (principally tetrasaccharide) resulting from the exhaustive degradation of chondroitin 4-sulfate with testicular hyaluronidase are readily desulfated by chondrosulfatase preparations containing no chondroitinase (Dodgson and Lloyd, 1957). The sulfated disaccharide obtained by the exhaustive degradation of chondroitin 4-sulfate with *Proteus* chondroitinase (purified 30-fold and preincubated for 30 min with 0.1 M Na_3PO_4 at pH 7.5, in order to inactivate the sulfatase) is also attacked. It has been suggested (Dodgson and Lloyd, 1958; Martinez, Wolfe, and Nakada, 1959) that this disaccharide is N-acetylchondrosin 4-sulfate. However, later work by Linker *et al.* (1960), using *Proteus vulgaris* 4636 grown in the United States, and by Suzuki and Strominger (1960,c) and Suzuki (1960), using a crude extract of the same organism grown in Britain, has thrown doubt on this conclusion. These workers observed that the degradation of chondroitin 4-sulfate yielded sulfated oligosaccharides containing $\Delta_{4,5}$-unsaturated uronic acid residues. *Proteus* preparations could desulfate these oligosaccharides. Similar findings have been obtained with *Proteus vulgaris* 31M (Nakada and Wolfe, 1961). Whatever the explanation of the conflicting results obtained by the different groups of workers (and it should be borne in mind that no two groups have used the same enzyme preparations or experimental conditions), it seems quite clear that both saturated and unsaturated oligosaccharides containing N-acetylgalactosamine 4-sulfate residues are substrates for *Proteus* chondrosulfatase. The degree of polymerization at which sulfatase action ceases is not yet known.

Unsaturated oligosaccharides derived from the enzymic degradation of shark chondroitin sulfate, and containing N-acetylgalactosamine 6-sulfate residues, are also substrates for the enzyme (Suzuki, 1960), but an unsaturated disaccharide containing two sulfate groups, which was also isolated as a minor product of the degradation, was only partially desulfated. The resistant sulfate grouping was considered to be located on the uronic acid residue. It is not yet certain whether saturated oligosaccharides containing N-acetylgalactosamine 6-sulfate residues can be desulfated by the enzyme.

A number of other compounds have been tested as substrates for

Proteus chondrosulfatase. A purified (30-fold) preparation, which still contained chondroitinase, showed no activity toward heparin, keratan sulfate, uridine diphospho-*N*-acetylgalactosamine sulfate and *N*-acetylgalactosamine sulfate (the last two prepared from hen oviduct and identified as 4-sulfates by Suzuki and Strominger, 1960), *N*-acetylgalactosamine 6-sulfate and *N*-acetylglucosamine 6-sulfate (prepared by the method of Lloyd, 1960), and toward a number of sulfated, nitrogen-free carbohydrates, including fucoidin, agar, carrageenan, *Chondrus ocellatus* mucilage, charonin sulfate, and glucose and galactose 6-sulfates (Dodgson, Lloyd, and Spencer, 1957, and unpublished). These particular results, as far as they apply to the polymeric substrates, must, of course, be viewed in the light of the chondrosulfatase–chondroitinase relationship, and the failure to detect sulfatase activity may simply reflect the inability of the chondroitinase to effect a preliminary depolymerization.

Further tentative conclusions may now be drawn from the various studies, which are, first, that chondrosulfatase will act on sulfate-ester linkages at either position 4 (secondary alcohol group) or 6 (primary alcohol group) of the *N*-acetylgalactosamine residue and, second, that the enzyme will not act in the absence of an adjacent uronic acid residue.

It is not yet known whether the sulfated polymer-building unit or units of heparin (where the hexosamine is 2-amino-2-deoxy-D-glucose) could act as a substrate for the enzyme, but this possibility should be borne in mind in the light of the observations of Linker *et al.* (1960) which will be described later (Section I,B,2).

c. Flavobacterium Chondrosulfatase. Flavobacterium heparinum can be adapted in such a way that it can depolymerize and desulfate heparin (Korn and Payza, 1956). However, Linker *et al.* (1960) have shown that unadapted strains of this organism can also degrade and desulfate chondroitin 4-sulfate and chondroitin 6-sulfate. Both saturated and unsaturated sulfated oligosaccharides are attacked by the sulfatase (see Volume I, Chapter 3). These findings suggest that a chondrosulfatase-type enzyme, of similar specificity to that of *Proteus,* is involved. Further comment on this will be made later (Section I,B,2).

B. Enzymes Attacking Heparin and Heparan Sulfate

The heparin-adapted strain of *Flavobacterium heparinum* is the only known source of enzymes capable of desulfating heparin. Enzymically liberated sulfate has never been measured during studies with this microorganism, but other evidence has suggested that at least two different types of sulfate-splitting enzyme (as well as a depolymerizing enzyme) are involved (Payza and Korn, 1956; Korn and Payza, 1956). One of these, tentatively referred to as a sulfamidase (Korn, 1957a), liberates sulfate which is bound to the amino group of the hexosamine residues, and the other, a sulfatase, attacks the ester sulfate groups. Heparan sulfates from various sources are also desulfated by *Flavobacterium* extracts (Linker *et al.*, 1958; Linker and Sampson, 1960; Suzuki and Strominger, 1960,c).

1. Interdependence of the Enzymes

Comparative studies on the degradation of heparin, hyaluronic acid, and chondroitin sulfate by preparations of unadapted and adapted *Flavobacterium* cells led Korn (1957a) to conclude that the only enzyme concerned in the adaptation was the sulfamidase. This enzyme must therefore be the one which acts directly on heparin, removing *N*-sulfate groups which, when present in the intact molecule, act as inhibitors of the depolymerizing enzyme. Although direct evidence has not been presented, it may be assumed that the subsequent stages in the degradation of heparin are depolymerization followed by desulfation by a chondrosulfatase-type enzyme, since chemically desulfated heparin is only slowly depolymerized by *Flavobacterium* preparations (Hoffman *et al.*, 1957).

2. Specificity

Little can be said regarding the specificity of the sulfamidase. No similar enzyme has previously been described, and further studies are most desirable. The specificity of the sulfatase enzyme is also uncertain. Preparations from unadapted or adapted strains of *Flavobacterium* can desulfate unsaturated or saturated oligosaccharides arising from the depolymerization of chondroitin 4-sulfate or chondroitin 6-sulfate, and it is therefore tempting to assume that a single enzyme, namely a chondrosulfatase identical with that present in *Proteus,* is responsible for the sulfatase activity exhibited toward the various substrates. If this were so, then the range of specificity of chondrosulfatase must be extended to include sulfate groups attached to glucosamine residues. However, the *Proteus* and *Flavobacterium* enzymes are different in one outstanding respect, which is that the former, in contrast to the latter, can be completely inhibited by phosphate.

It is not yet known whether *Flavobacterium* preparations can desulfate heparin completely, and this is a point which needs to be established in the light of the possibility that the compound contains ester sulfate groups of differing steric disposition and stability (see, for example, Danishefsky, Eiber, and Carr, 1960; Durant, Hendrickson, and Montgomery, 1962).

C. Enzymes Attacking Dermatan Sulfate

Linker *et al.* (1960) have reported that crude *Flavobacterium* and *Proteus* preparations are able to degrade dermatan sulfate slowly. Adaptation of *Flavobacterium* to dermatan sulfate was followed by greatly enhanced activity toward this substrate, sulfated and desulfated unsaturated oligosaccharides being produced by an enzyme preparation which had been pretreated at 56° for 5 min (Hoffman *et al.,* 1960). However, this does not necessarily mean that a second sulfatase, specific for oligosaccharides containing L-iduronic acid residues, is present in *Flavobacterium,* since the formation of a double bond between C-4 and C-5 of such residues, or of the glucuronic acid residues present in chondroitin 4-sulfate, would yield one and the same sulfated product.

Suzuki (1960) confirmed that crude extracts of *Proteus* can degrade dermatan sulfate with liberation of inorganic sulfate. Among the minor products of degradation was a $\Delta_{4,5}$-unsaturated disaccharide which appeared to be sulfated on both the uronic acid and hexosamine residues, and which was not desulfated when incubated further with crude *Proteus* extracts. The significance of this observation, in relation to the specificity of chondrosulfatase-type enzymes, is not at all clear.

D. Enzymes Attacking Keratan Sulfate

Preliminary work has suggested that extracts of a coccobacillus (Chase) can degrade keratan sulfate to give a mixture of oligosaccharides, D-galactose, *N*-acetylglucosamine, and inorganic sulfate (Rosen, Hoffman, and Meyer, 1960). It seems probable that a sulfatase is involved in this degradation, but this remains to be confirmed.

E. General Comments

It should be clear from the foregoing that much work still remains to be done on the sulfate-liberating enzymes. Indeed, most of the results described are unconfirmed and have been deduced from chromatographic and similar observations. At the moment, the apparently wide specificity of the chondrosulfatase type of enzyme should be regarded with some degree of caution, and it is possible that more than one enzyme is present in the crude preparations which have generally been used. There is ample precedence for this in the sulfatase field, and crude preparations originally thought to contain a single sulfatase have later been shown to contain two or three enzymes of related specificity (Dodgson, Spencer, and Thomas, 1955; Dodgson, 1961; Takahashi and Egami, 1960). There is now a great need for systematic studies on the chondrosulfatase-type enzyme, using conventional enzyme techniques and methods. Such studies will almost certainly underline the necessity for modifying the present nomenclature applied to this type of enzyme.

II. Desulfation of Sulfated N-Acetylhexosamines

Although the chondrosulfatase type of enzyme is apparently unable to act on sulfated amino sugars which are not attached to uronic acid residues, sulfated amino sugars can be desulfated by glucosulfatase (glycosulfatase). This enzyme was first discovered by Soda and Hattori (1931), who noted the ability of extracts of the Japanese land snail, *Eulota luhuana,* to desulfate glucose monosulfate. Subsequently, glucosulfatase was detected in other relatively simple organisms, particularly in marine molluscs (Soda, 1936).

Apart from the studies of Dodgson and Spencer (1954), Dodgson and Lloyd (1961), and Dodgson (1961) with *Littorina littorea,* most of the work on glucosulfatase is of Japanese origin and has been concerned with the digestive gland of *Charonia lampas,* where the enzyme coexists with chondrosulfatase and cellulose polysulfatase.

Charonia glucosulfatase has been purified by a variety of procedures (Soda and Egami, 1933, 1941; Soda, Katsura, and Yoda, 1940) and has been distinguished from arylsulfatase (Soda and Egami, 1934), chondrosulfatase (Soda and Egami, 1938a), and cellulose polysulfatase (Takahashi and Egami, 1961). The enzyme is strongly inhibited by borate, phosphate, and fluoride.

The *Littorina* enzyme has also been partially purified and separated from a number of enzymes which can participate in the degradation of heteroglycosaminoglycans (Dodgson, 1961). The purified enzyme exhibited properties similar to those of the *Charonia* enzyme.

A. The Specificity of the Enzyme

Glucosulfatase exhibits a relatively wide range of specificity and hydrolyzes a number of monosulfated, disulfated, and trisulfated, reducing and nonreducing monosaccharides and disaccharides (Soda, 1934, 1936), as well as adenosine 5′-sulfate (Egami and Takahashi, 1955) and kojic acid disulfate (the primary alcohol-bound sulfate only; Soda, Katsura, and Yoda, 1940). The suggestion that the enzyme was also responsible for the hydrolysis of cortisone 21-sulfate (Roy, 1956) has recently been disproved (Dodgson, 1961). The name glucosulfatase was originally suggested for the enzyme by Soda and his group, on the grounds that the enzyme exhibited greatest activity toward glucose 6-sulfate, a finding which has recently been substantiated by the work of Dodgson (1961).

Soda and Egami (1938a) showed that glucosulfatase was also active toward *N*-acetylglucosamine monosulfate (prepared by direct sulfation of *N*-acetylglucosamine with chlorosulfonic acid). Unpublished work done by Dodgson and Lloyd has recently confirmed that *N*-acetylglucosamine 6-sulfate is readily desulfated by *Littorina* and *Charonia* glucosulfatases. The enzymes also exhibit relatively feeble activity toward *N*-acetylgalactosamine 6-sulfate. Dodgson and Lloyd (unpublished) have further shown that glucosulfatase has no activity toward the sulfated oligosaccharides resulting from the degradation of chondroitin 4-sulfate by testicular hyaluronidase or toward the sulfated disaccharide resulting from the degradation of chondroitin 4-sulfate by *Proteus* chondroitinase. This may merely imply that the enzyme will not attack hexosamine residues which are sulfated at position 4, but in view of the relatively wide specificity of the enzyme toward nitrogen-free sulfated monosaccharides and disaccharides, it is more probable that the enzyme is inactive when the substrate contains a uronic acid residue.

The present indication, therefore, is that chondrosulfatase and glucosulfatase exhibit a reverse specificity, in that the former will act only when the sulfated hexosamine is associated with a saturated or unsaturated uronic acid residue, whereas the latter will act only in the absence of such residues. These tentative conclusions now need to be confirmed.

Lloyd (1961, 1962) has shown that bacteria which are present in the feces of rats can desulfate *N*-acetylglucosamine 6-sulfate and *N*-acetylgalactosamine 6-sulfate. It is not yet known whether a bacterial glycosulfatase (see Tankó, 1932) is involved or whether the findings merely reflect the ability of these microorganisms to degrade these sulfated hexosamines by other routes.

III. Enzymic Desulfation in Mammals

Comparatively little is known about the metabolic fate of sulfated heteroglycosaminoglycans and related compounds. It is known, for example, that the turnover rate of the sulfate groups of the chondroitin sulfates is reasonably rapid (see, for example, Boström, 1954), but it is still not clear whether sulfatases are involved.

Early attempts by Neuberg and Cahill (1936) to detect chondrosulfatase-type enzymes in mammalian tissues were unsuccessful. Similar negative findings came from a histological investigation of the activity of fresh frozen sections of rat and rabbit organs toward heparin and cartilage chondroitin sulfate (Dohlman and Friedenwald, 1955) and from investigations in which a sensitive isotopic-dilution technique, involving S^{35}-labeled cartilage chondroitin sulfate, was applied to homogenates of costal cartilage, cornea, liver, kidney, and spleen of ox, rabbit, and rat (Dohlman, 1956). Woodin (1952) also failed to detect sulfatase activity toward endogenous substrate (keratan sulfate) in corneal sections, and later, Davidson and Riley (1960) were unable to detect activity toward S^{35}-labeled dermatan sulfate by skin preparations from young rabbits or from chick embryos.

Despite these negative findings, other investigations have suggested that mammalian enzymes capable of desulfating sulfated heteroglycosaminoglycans and hexosamines may exist. Thus, Dziewiatkowski (1956) and Dohlman (1956) have shown that subcutaneous injection of S^{35}-labeled cartilage chondroitin sulfate is followed by the appearance of small but significant amounts of S^{35} inorganic sulfate in the urine. Dohlman's work, in particular, was most carefully controlled to eliminate the possibility of biliary circulation of substrate followed by desulfation by bacteria in the gut. Oral administration of the labeled substrate gave rise to large amounts of S^{35} inorganic sulfate in the urine, but this could be traced to the activity of gut bacteria.

In a similar type of study, Danishefsky and Eiber (1959) observed the appearance of labeled inorganic sulfate in the urine of dogs that received intravenous injections of S^{35}-labeled heparin. In this case, no strict precautions were taken to ensure that microorganisms were not responsible. Recently, Lloyd (1961, 1962) has shown that *N*-acetylglucosamine 6-sulfate and *N*-acetylgalactosamine 6-sulfate injected intraperitoneally appear to undergo some desulfation under experimental conditions designed to eliminate interference from microorganisms.

Dodgson and Lloyd (1961) have again searched for mammalian sulfatases which might account for these various findings. The substrates used were *N*-acetylglucosamine 6-sulfate and *N*-acetylgalactosamine 6-sulfate, chondroitin 4-sulfate, an unfractionated mixture of sulfated oligosaccharides obtained by degradation of chondroitin 4-sulfate with testicular hyaluronidase, and the sulfated disaccharide obtained by the degrading of chondroitin 4-sulfate with *Proteus* chondroitinase. These substrates were incubated at varying pH, in different buffers, for periods of up to 48 hr with homogenates of fresh and acetone-dried pancreas, lung, kidney, liver, spleen, testis, ovary, brain, and costal cartilage from rats aged 3 and 12 months and from 4-day-old pigs; and of acetone-dried post-mortem samples of pancreas, lung, kidney, liver, spleen, and brain from a human male (aged 58). In some of the rat experiments, the animals had previously received subcutaneous injections, on each of three successive days, of a saline solution containing 20 mg of chondroitin 4-sulfate.

In no case was it possible to detect liberation of inorganic sulfate (method of Dodgson and Spencer, 1953) by the tissue preparations.

The discrepancy between the results of *in vivo* and *in vitro* studies is still therefore unexplained. Simple ion exchange between the sulfate esters and the inorganic sulfate of the tissues can probably be ruled out in explaining the *in vivo* results (see Boström and Månsson, 1952), and it may be that the failure to detect sulfatase activity *in vitro* simply reflects the instability of the enzyme system. Further work now seems essential.

Addendum

More studies have been added to those on the metabolic fate of sulfated heteroglycosaminoglycans. Kaplan and Meyer (1962) have followed the blood levels and urinary excretion of chondroitin 4-sulfate, chondroitin 6-sulfate, shark chondroitin sulfate, dermatan sulfate, and heparan sulfate after injection into humans and dogs. Collectively, the results showed that the polymers disappeared rapidly from the circulation, but could not be recovered (or could not be recovered quantitatively) from urine. The suggestion was made that two distinct mechanisms exist for handling these polymers, namely, an intracellular uptake (possibly by mononuclear and reticuloendothelial cells) leading eventually to extensive degradation, and a minor pathway of excretion of unchanged polymers by the kidney. No sulfatases capable of attacking these polymers could be found in the tissues.

Similar studies of the metabolic fate of heparin labeled with S^{35} in dogs and rats have been reported by Loomis (1961) and by Day, Green, and Robinson (1962). The latter workers seem to show conclusively that extensive degradation of heparin labeled with S^{35} occurs *in vivo,* particularly in skin, aorta, lung, adrenals, glands, stomach, heart, and brain. The metabolites resulting from this degradation are dialyzable and include inorganic S^{35}-sulfate. Whether all the various types of sulfate groups present in heparin are liberated during this degradation is, of course, not known. Unfortunately, other studies (Levy and Petracek, 1962) on the metabolism of sulfamate S^{35}-resulfated heparin which might have yielded valuable information regarding *N*-desulfation *in vivo* were not designed to check on the form in which S^{35} was being eliminated in the urine.

These various results have thrown little further light on the desulfation of sulfated heteroglycosaminoglycans *in vivo* or on the possible role of sulfatase enzymes in the process. When considered together with the metabolic studies on *N*-acetylglucosamine 6-sulfate and *N*-acetylgalactosamine 6-sulfate (Lloyd, 1961, 1962) and with similar earlier studies on homopolysaccharide sulfates (Morrow *et al.*, 1952; Huseman *et al.*, 1952; Ricketts, Walton, and Saddington, 1954), the results, however, do indicate that molecular size is an important factor in determining whether injected sulfated carbohydrate material is retained sufficiently long in the body to undergo degradation. On the one hand, compounds of low molecular weight such as *N*-acetylglucosamine 6-sulfate and *N*-acetylgalactosamine 6-sulfate are excreted extremely rapidly via the kidney. In contrast, sulfated polymers are less readily excreted via the kidney and may therefore be more readily taken up and degraded, for example, by mononuclear and reticuloendothelial cells. The question of whether or not such degradation involves the action of sulfatase enzymes still remains to be settled.

The first positive claim for the existence of a mammalian chondrosulfatase was recently made (Mehl and Jatzkewitz, 1963). An enzyme fraction, separated from the lysosomes of hog kidney, showed sulfatase activity toward cerebroside sulfate esters. This fraction also appears to liberate S^{35}-inorganic sulfate from S^{35}-labeled chondroitin 4-sulfate.

Chapter 46

ACTIVATION AND INHIBITION OF ENZYMES BY POLYANIONS CONTAINING AMINO SUGARS

Peter Bernfeld

Certain substances which contain amino sugars have been recognized during recent years as being capable of influencing enzyme activity; some are enzyme activators, and others are enzyme inhibitors. The realm of these enzyme "effectors"—a term introduced by Bersin (1951) for substances of like action—may be limited to some individual enzymes or it may extend to rather large groups of enzymes. Although the presence of amino sugar in the enzyme effector is the common feature to be discussed in this chapter, the role of the amino sugar is variable in different enzyme effectors; it may be essential for the biochemical activity of one and merely coincidental in others.

Two of the most important prerequisites for the biochemical action of enzyme effectors that contain amino sugar appear to be their macromolecular character and their polyelectrolyte nature. Several polysaccharides thus qualify as enzyme effectors. Their negative charges come mainly from sulfate ester groups, whereas carboxyl groups from uronic acid residues appear to have only secondary importance. Among the naturally occurring macromolecular polysulfate esters, the most prominent ones, and the only ones to occur in the animal kingdom, happen to be glycosaminoglycans. Certain phenomena of enzyme inhibition appear to involve, however, glycan sulfates and glycuronan sulfates, as well. Positive charges on glycosaminoglycans can be introduced by deacetylation of *N*-acetylhexosamine units, and the resulting polycations may act as enzyme effectors although they are unphysiological. Various other substances of high molecular weight which are chemically totally unrelated to the polysaccharides may, in some cases, exhibit similar abilities to affect enzyme activity.

Although the electrostatic charge of a polymer is essential for the phenomena under discussion, the sign of its charge does not determine whether it is an activator or an inhibitor. In fact, both macromolecular polyanions and polycations may be either activators or inhibitors.

I. Activation

A. Glycosaminoglycans with Sulfate Groups

1. Lipoprotein Lipase Activation

a. Characterization of the Enzyme. Until 1943, the only known physiological function of heparin was its anticoagulant activity. In that year, another important biological role of heparin was discovered by Hahn (1943), when he found that transfusion of lipemic dogs with heparinized blood caused a rapid clearing of the lipemia. Anderson and Fawcett (1950) later reported that the administration of heparin to normal animals produced a factor in their blood which was capable of the *in vitro* clearing of lipemic sera from other lipemic animals and from human subjects. This factor was subsequently called "clearing factor" (Anfinsen, Boyle, and Brown, 1952), until it was recognized that clearing factor actually is an enzyme which is practically absent in normal blood. This enzyme appears in blood only upon the administration of heparin to animals or men and was called lipoprotein lipase because of its ability to hydrolyze the triglyceride moiety of low-density lipoproteins and of chylomicrons (Korn, 1955b). In addition to the *in vivo* action of heparin to stimulate the production of serum lipoprotein lipase, heparin has also been found to be capable of the *in vitro* activation of this enzyme isolated from acetone-dried heart powder (Korn, 1955). Excellent reviews by Korn (1959) and Robinson and French (1957) on the subjects of lipoprotein lipase and clearing factor have appeared in the literature.

The dual *in vivo* and *in vitro* effects of heparin are clearly differentiated as (1) the physiological process of stimulating the appearance of clearing factor in plasma and (2) the biochemical activation of a plasma and tissue enzyme. Although the former process can be satisfactorily explained by the appearance of lipoprotein lipase in plasma after heparin administration, definite differences have been noted between the *in vivo* and *in vitro* effects of macromolecular polyanions other than, but chemically more or less related to, heparin. After a brief discussion of the specificity of the enzyme, its mode of action, and its activation and inhibition, it will be attempted, in the framework of this presentation, to stress the relationship between the chemical nature of the macromolecular polyanions and their physiological or biochemical effects.

b. Specificity of Lipoprotein Lipase. Whereas simple triglyceride emulsions are hydrolyzed only very slowly by tissue lipoprotein lipase, a preliminary incubation of triglyceride emulsions with whole serum or, better, with α-lipoprotein (Korn, 1955a) appears to result in the formation of a triglyceride–lipoprotein complex which possesses a much higher affinity for the enzyme than do the fat emulsions themselves (Korn and Quigley, 1957). Chylomicrons appear to constitute the physiological substrate of lipoprotein lipase (Robinson and French, 1953), but soluble, low-density lipoproteins of flotation rates above S_f 10 are also hydrolyzed by the enzyme (Korn, 1955a), whereas human serum lipoprotein with the flotation rate S_f 6 is not a good substrate (Shore, 1955).

c. Mode of Action. The clearing action of lipoprotein lipase is the result of lipolytic breakdown of chylomicrons, or low-density lipoproteins, and the actual products of the enzymic reaction are unesterified fatty acids (Shore, Nichols, and Freeman, 1953), diglycerides, and monoglycerides (Carlson and Wadström, 1957), as well as glycerol. The fate of the lipoprotein part of the lipoprotein–triglyceride complex or of the chylomicrons is somewhat uncertain, and it is generally accepted that the flotation rates decrease during the action of lipoprotein lipase. In fact, the incubation of a group of S_f 20–100 lipoproteins with lipoprotein lipase yielded a quantitative conversion to S_f 0–20 lipoproteins i.e.,—to lipoproteins of higher hydrated density (Lindgren, Elliott, and Gofman, 1951), which probably represent a type of lipoprotein distinct from the parent compounds mainly because of the lower content of triglycerides; simultaneously, unesterified fatty acids were also detected.

d. Activation and Inhibition. Since unesterified acids are powerful inhibitors of the enzyme, fatty acid acceptors have been found to be necessary for a progressive action of lipoprotein lipase; serum albumin (Robinson and French, 1953; Gordon, 1955) or calcium ions (Korn 1955) have been successfully used for this purpose. In addition, divalent ions, such as calcium, have also been found necessary for the activity of tissue enzyme preparations (Korn and Quigley, 1955).

The *in vitro* activation by heparin of heart lipoprotein lipase was previously mentioned. Concentrations of about 5 μg of heparin per milliliter of digest have been found to give maximal activation effects, whereas higher heparin concentrations are progressively less effective in increasing the enzyme activity, and, upon further increase of the heparin concentration, inhibition finally occurs (Korn and Quigley, 1957).

The requirement of heparin for the *in vitro* activity of lipoprotein lipase becomes even more evident from observations by Korn (1957) that this enzyme can be inactivated by a specific bacterial heparinase from *Flavobacterium heparinum* (Payza and Korn, 1956), although it was not possible to restore enzyme activity upon addition of heparin. Another rather specific inhibitor of lipoprotein lipase is protamine sulfate (Brown,

Boyle, and Anfinsen, 1953). There is an analogy between the mechanism of inhibition by heparinase and protamine sulfate: heparinase acts by hydrolyzing the glycosidic bonds of heparin and protamine sulfate by forming a heparin–protamine complex. In addition, solutions of NaCl at 0.35 *M* and higher concentrations inhibit lipoprotein lipase, as also do a number of more-or-less general enzyme inhibitors.

e. Action of Other Macromolecular Polyanions on Lipoprotein Lipase. A considerable number of polyanions have been examined by different laboratories for *in vivo* antilipemic activity. It appears as an over-all result that there are only two prerequisites of the chemical structure of a substance for its ability to generate *in vivo* lipoprotein lipase in blood —namely, the presence of a certain number of negative charges per molecule and a high molecular weight. In fact, practically every macromolecular polyanion investigated has been found capable of generating plasma lipoprotein lipase *in vivo,* independently of the chemical nature of the polyanion. Many sulfated polysaccharides were found by Constantinides, Cairns, and Werner (1954) to possess more-or-less powerful antilipemic activity; these include sulfated starch, amylopectin sulfate, amylose sulfate, sulfated glycogen (weak antilipemic), cellulose sulfate, pectin sulfate, alginic acid sulfate, sulfated agar, sulfated mesquite gum, and sulfated gum arabic. The *in vivo* effect of sulfated pectin on blood lipids was also demonstrated earlier by Zinn, Field, and Griffith (1952), by Ackerman and Zilversmit (1953), and by Chandler *et al.* (1953), whereas dextran sulfate was found by Brown (1952) and by Robinson, Harris, and Ricketts (1958) to produce a phenomenon similar to the one obtained with heparin. In order to differentiate the *in vivo* antilipemic action of these substances from their anticoagulant activity, it should be mentioned here that, with the exception of dextran sulfate, none of these substances exhibit more than a weak potency to prolong the clotting time of blood (Constantinides, Cairns, and Werner, 1954). Hyaluronic acid and depolymerized hyaluronic acid also exhibited antilipemic activity (Seifter and Baeder, 1954), and phosphorylated hesperidin was reported by Messinger and Porosowska (1953) to induce clearing activity. Polyethylene sulfonate, administered to patients, was found to produce plasma lipoprotein lipase in levels exceeding those obtained with heparin (Duncan, Best, and McGaff, 1959). In addition, polymetaphosphate and inorganic heteropolyacids of high molecular weight have been found to produce lipoprotein lipase *in vivo*—e.g., phosphotungstate, phosphomolybdate, and silicotungstate (Bragdon and Havel, 1954; Havel and Bragdon, 1954).

In sharp contrast with the lack of specificity for the chemical nature of the substances inducing clearing factor *in vivo,* the *in vitro* activation of lipoprotein lipase is caused by a small and chemically well-delimited group of substances. Upon screening of more than twenty-five different polysaccharide sulfates in which molecular weight, sulfate content, absence or presence of branching, type and configuration of branching bonds, configuration of glycosidic bonds of the main chain, and nature of the repeating unit were the variables, only a few glycosaminoglycan sulfates were found to exhibit the capacity of activating lipoprotein lipase (Bernfeld and Kelley, 1960, 1962, 1963). These activators *in vitro* exhibited the common feature of containing *N*-sulfate groups, whereas all other polyanions were free of this type of group. *N*-Sulfate groups were determined by the method of Van Slyke (1929) as free amino groups liberated after mild acid hydrolysis, a procedure first employed by Wolfrom and McNeely (1945) to demonstrate *N*-sulfate groups in heparin. Bernfeld and Kelley showed that deacetylation of chitin and subsequent sulfation yielded a product which, at certain concentrations, efficiently increased the reaction rate of lipoprotein lipase. Sulfur content and the presence of hexuronic acid units in the polymer appeared to be without influence on its lipoprotein lipase–activating potency. Substances of low molecular weight containing *N*-sulfate groups, in particular 2-deoxy-2-sulfoamino-D-glucose (Wolfrom, Gibbons, and Huggard, 1957) had no effect on the activity *in vitro* of the enzyme. It therefore appears that *N*-sulfate groups occurring in macromolecular substances play an important role in the *in vitro* activation of mouse heart lipoprotein lipase.

It was also observed that all those polysaccharides that contained *O*-sulfate groups and no *N*-sulfate groups were more-or-less potent inhibitors of the *in vitro* activity of lipoprotein lipase (see also Section II,A). The inhibition by dextran sulfate is a typical example of this type of inhibition and is illustrated by curves A1 and A2 in Fig. 1. The simultaneous occurrence of both *O*-sulfate and *N*-sulfate functions in one and the same polymer should then be expected to produce an antagonism between the inhibiting and activating tendencies. The fact that this is actually the case has been known for heparin for some time, since this polyanion behaves as an *in vitro* activator only at relatively low concentrations (0.5 to 5 μg per milliliter). At higher heparin concentrations, the activating potency gradually diminishes, and, at concentrations above 25 μg per milliliter, heparin becomes an *in vitro* inhibitor of lipoprotein lipase (see curve E2, Fig. 1).

The same phenomenon has also been observed with other lipoprotein lipase activators. Deacetylated and subsequently sulfated chitin, which contained 0.21 *N*-sulfate groups and 0.23 *O*-sulfate groups per monosaccharide repeating unit, proved to turn from an activator to a powerful inhibitor at even lower concentrations than does heparin (curves D1 and

D2, Fig. 1). On the other hand, an acid-deacetylated and subsequently sulfated, partially nitrated chitin (0.41 *N*-sulfate, 0.47 *O*-sulfate, and 0.57 nitro groups per repeating unit—curves C1 and C2, Fig. 1) behaved as an activator *in vitro* up to concentrations of 20 μg per milliliter (Bernfeld and Kelley, 1963). It appears that the over-all activating or inhibiting effect depends on the ratio of *N*-sulfate to *O*-sulfate groups of the polyanion, and possibly also on the positions of the *O*-sulfate groups in the anhydrohexose unit. In the nitrochitin, some hydroxyl positions were protected against sulfation by nitro groups, and this resulted in the formation of a less inhibitory polyanion.

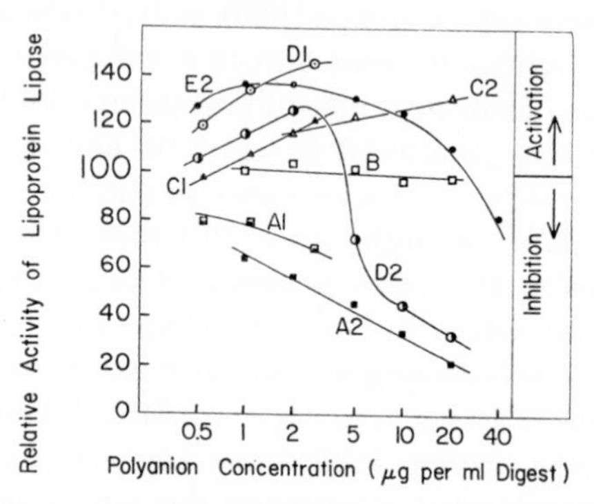

FIG. 1. Typical effects of several polyanions on the activity of mouse heart lipoprotein lipase. Enzyme activity without added polyanion was set equal to 100. Curves A1, C1, and D1 were obtained by titration of fatty acid liberated; curves A2, C2, D2, and E2 by glycerol assay; and curve B by both techniques.

Activity of lipoprotein lipase in the presence of:

A1 and A2—dextran sulfate (1.58 *O*-sulfate groups per glucose repeating unit); 5% α-(1 $\rightarrow$ 3) branching linkages; degree of polymerization, 440;

B—chondroitin 4-sulfate;

C1 and C2—acid-deacetylated sulfated nitrochitin (0.47 *O*-sulfate group and 0.41 *N*-sulfate group per repeating unit);

D1 and D2—alkali-deacetylated sulfated chitin (0.23 *O*-sulfate group and 0.21 *N*-sulfate group per repeating unit);

E2—heparin.

(According to Bernfeld and Kelley, 1963.)

It was also demonstrated that mild acid hydrolysis of heparin resulted simultaneously in the loss of *N*-sulfate groups and the abolishment of the potency to activate lipoprotein lipase (Bernfeld and Kelley, 1962). Subsequent sulfation yielded a polyanion which contained *N*-sulfate groups and a greater number of *O*-sulfate groups than did heparin, which activated the enzyme only at very low polyanion concentrations, however, and which was a powerful inhibitor at all other concentrations. Here again it was observed that the protection of some of the hydroxyl groups against sulfation—in this case by starting with a partially acetylated heparin—resulted in a polyanion after *N*-desulfation and subsequent sulfation that exhibited activating potency at much higher concentrations than did the nonacetylated heparin treated in the same way.

From these observations, it appears logical to predict that polysaccharides which contain only *N*-sulfate and no *O*-sulfate groups will behave as activators *in vitro* of lipoprotein lipase at any polyanion concentration. It is unknown whether tissue or plasma lipoprotein lipase contains small amounts of such or similar substances as naturally occurring activators.

f. Mechanism of Heparin Action. Obviously, the *in vivo* generation of clearing factor in plasma is caused by a much broader group of polyanions than is the *in vitro* activation of lipoprotein lipase. This observation suggests that the physiological and biochemical effects of heparin on lipoprotein lipase—i.e., its *in vivo* stimulation and its *in vitro* activation—are entirely different phenomena. Probably the best interpretation of our present knowledge of the relationship between heparin and lipoprotein lipase has been offered by Korn (1959d). This author came to the conclusion that "a mucopolysaccharide similar to heparin may be an integral part of the enzyme molecule," and he further stated that "it would seem not unreasonable that a heparinlike prosthetic group may be involved in the association of lipoprotein lipase and its substrate." Similarly, Engelberg (1958a) believed that heparin is a component of lipoprotein lipase and that it dissociates easily from the apoenzyme. This hypothesis would satisfactorily explain the *in vitro* activation of the enzyme by heparin and the rather narrow spectrum of substances capable of activating the enzyme, as well as its inactivation by heparinase and by protamine sulfate.

The physiological generation of the enzyme in blood might then be the result of a chain of reactions in which the active enzyme would be either synthesized or liberated from some insoluble form or from some localized site or transformed into the active form from a precursor state.

g. Increased Plasma Heparin and Plasma Lipoprotein Lipase Levels. So far, the discussion of the *in vivo* effects has been centered around the release of lipoprotein lipase into the blood stream under the influence of heparin or of other macromolecular polyanions. Conversely, human plasma heparin was increased during and after intravenous infusion of cottonseed oil emulsion (Engelberg, 1958), whereas clearing factor did not exactly parallel the fluctuations in circulating heparin. On the other hand, Havel and Boyle (1954) have shown that anaphylactic shock, produced in dogs by intravenous injection of peptone, was accompanied by both the release of a heparinlike substance into the blood and the appearance in plasma of lipemia clearing factor. In either of the two cases of heparinemia, the appearance of clearing factor in the blood may be the direct result of increased plasma heparin levels or, conversely, the higher plasma heparin concentration may be due to the release into the blood stream of lipoprotein lipase which, as pointed out before, is believed to contain heparin as an integral part.

2. Effect of Heparin on the Pepsin–Polylysine Complex

It was demonstrated by Herriott (1941) that pepsin, an enzyme with low isoelectric point, can be inhibited by a polypeptide containing a high percentage of arginine. With the assumption that the electrostatic interaction between the negative groups of the enzyme and the positively charged inhibitor is responsible for the formation of a pepsin-inhibitor complex in which the active sites of the enzyme are masked, Katchalski, Berger, and Neumann (1954) were able also to inhibit pepsin by other macromolecular polycations—namely, by the synthetic basic polyamino acids, poly-L-lysine, polyornithine, and poly-*p*-aminophenylalanine.

Katchalski, Berger, and Neumann (1954) were also able to demonstrate that the addition of heparin to the pepsin–polylysine complex caused restoration of the full activity of the enzyme, probably by the formation of a polycation–polyanion complex between polylysine and heparin and, hence, by releasing the pepsin. It is not known whether this reactivation of pepsin is limited to heparin alone or whether the "heparinoids" and other macromolecular polyanions behave in a similar fashion.

B. Glycosaminoglycans with Free Amino Groups

Two enzyme systems, i.e., hyaluronidase and β-glucuronidase, have been shown to be activated by chitosan, prepared from chitin by treatment with strong alkali at room temperature for several days. This phenomenon is not specific for deacetylated chitin and can also be observed with a number of other substances which have the common feature of being polycations; most of them are also of macromolecular nature. Consequently, the action of this type of enzyme effectors will be called "polycationic enzyme activation," which bears an analogy to the term of "macroanionic inhibition" introduced by Spensley and Rogers (1954). Unlike macroanionic inhibition, polycationic enzyme activation has been found to be closely related to, and to be absolutely dependent on, another phenomenon—i.e., the reversible decrease of enzyme activity upon dilution. Polycationic enzyme activation has only been observed under conditions in which the reversible decrease of enzyme activity becomes operative—i.e., upon sufficiently high dilution. Two other phenomena are also connected with both polycationic enzyme activation and reversible decrease of enzyme activity upon dilution; these are (1) macroanionic enzyme inhibition and (2) an irreversible loss of enzyme activity upon contact with rough surfaces.

1. Reversible Decrease of Enzyme Activity at High Dilutions

Studies on the kinetics of various enzymes at very high dilutions have shown that the specific enzyme activity (ratio of enzyme activity per enzyme concentration) progressively decreases upon dilution. There is a threshold of the enzyme concentration above which this phenomenon cannot be observed, and this threshold depends on the nature of the enzyme system under investigation. For example, highly purified preparations of calf liver and calf spleen β-glucuronidases exhibit extensive losses of specific activity below concentrations of 100 μg of enzyme protein per milliliter, as seen in Fig. 2 (Bernfeld *et al.*, 1954). Crude and purified

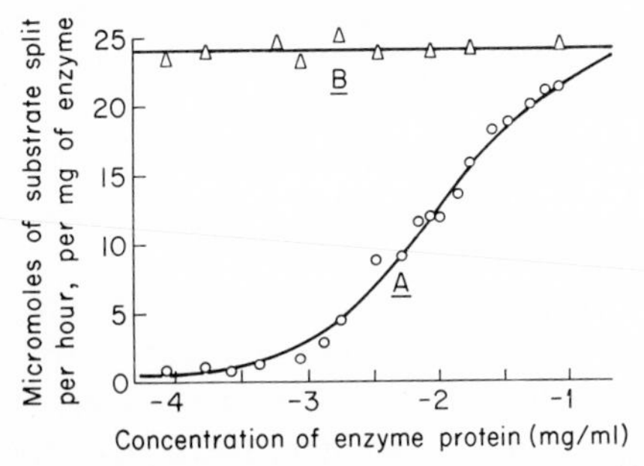

Fig. 2. Behavior of highly purified calf liver β-glucuronidase upon dilution in the presence and absence of chitosan (abscissa on logarithmic scale). Curve A: decrease of specific enzyme activity at high dilutions; Curve B: specific enzyme activity in the presence of chitosan (100 μg/ml).

testicular hyaluronidase showed the same behavior below concentrations of 1 USP unit per milliliter (Bernfeld and Tuttle, 1959; Bernfeld, Tuttle, and Hubbard, 1961). Crystalline preparations of porcine pancreatic α-amylase, sweet-potato β-amylase, rabbit muscle lactic dehydrogenase, and rabbit muscle aldolase also lose specific activity upon dilution (Bernfeld *et al.*, 1965). In all cases, the drop of specific activity progressed with the dilution of enzyme and appeared to be governed by the law of mass action.

The participation of surface forces during the decrease of specific enzyme activity at high dilutions has been ruled out (see Section I,B,3), and the best explanation for this phenomenon appeared to be the assumption of a dissociation of active enzyme protein into inactive products. Whether such a dissociation would cause the cleavage of intermolecular or intramolecular bonds of the enzyme, and whether the bonds in question would be of electrostatic nature or would involve the secondary or tertiary protein structure cannot be decided at the present state of our knowledge.

Whatever may be the nature of the bonds severed, it appears evident, however, that these bonds are essential for the enzymic activity.

Dissociation of active enzymes into inactive subunits under various conditions, other than dilution, has been described recently. Rabbit muscle aldolase reversibly dissociates into three subunits in the presence of urea, acid, or sodium dodecyl sulfate (Deal and Van Holde, 1962; Stellwagen and Schachman, 1962). Intramolecular reversible dissociation of ribonuclease, involving splitting of disulfide bonds, was described by Anfinsen *et al.* (1961), Haber and Anfinsen (1961), White (1961), and Anfinsen and Haber (1961). Lysozyme, fungal α-amylase (Isemura *et al.*, 1961), and alkaline phosphatase (Levinthal, Signer, and Fetherolf, 1962) also exhibited phenomena of reversible dissociation with concomitant loss and recovery of enzyme activity.

Loss of enzyme activity at high dilutions has been observed for prostatic acid phosphatase by Jeffree (1955, 1956) and for carbonic anhydrase by Stolkowski and Rosenberg (1953), but it is unknown whether these enzymes can be reactivated under proper conditions.

2. Enzyme Activation by Polycations

The reversibility of the decrease of enzyme activity at high dilutions can be demonstrated by complete reactivation of diluted hyaluronidase or β-glucuronidase upon addition of a number of substances with the common property of being polycations; these polycationic enzyme activators are mostly of macromolecular nature (Bernfeld *et al.*, 1954; Bernfeld, Tuttle and Hubbard, 1961; Bernfeld, Berkeley, and Bieber, 1965). The highest activation potency has been observed with chitosan (see Fig. 2) and other deacetylated glycosaminoglycans—in particular, deacetylated hyaluronic acid and deacetylated chondroitin 4-sulfate. Among the less potent activators are many purified or crystalline proteins—in particular, anionic proteins like protamine, certain preparations of deoxyribonucleic acid from salmon milt, and, to a lesser degree, α,ω-diaminoparaffins, especially 1,10-diamino-*n*-decan.

All these polycations are, therefore activators of the enzymes at appropriate dilutions; the activation becomes less and less important as the enzyme concentration is increased, and no activation at all is observed at high enzyme concentrations at which there was no dissociation. No matter how high the activator concentration, the specific enzyme activity will never exceed the activity obtained at high enzyme concentrations in the absence of activators. The enzyme activation by polycations is, therefore, the reversal of the dissociation occurring during dilution.

Attempts at demonstrating this reversibility by concentration of the enzyme solutions have failed, owing to the marked instability of the products of dissociation at high dilutions.

3. Stabilization of Diluted Enzyme Solutions

One of the phenomena closely connected with the reversible decrease of enzyme activity at high dilutions is an irreversible inactivation of the diluted enzymes through contact with rough surfaces, such as glass, quartz sand, filter cel, and others, as has been described for hyaluronidase by Rasmussen (1954) and for β-glucuronidase by Bernfeld, Jacobson, and Bernfeld (1957). The fact that this irreversible inactivation is actually a surface phenomenon and that it is related to the container material has been shown by Bernfeld, Jacobson, and Bernfeld (1957), who demonstrated the stability of equally diluted enzyme solutions in containers with smooth surfaces, such as polyethylene or silicone-coated glass. Elution of active enzyme from the inactivating surfaces, as well as any other attempt of reactivation, has been unsuccessful.

The loss of enzyme activity at contact with rough surfaces occurs only with highly diluted enzyme solutions, and it was shown that only the products of dissociation of the enzyme appear to be affected by the surface forces, whereas the enzymically active protein appears to be stable. The presence of activating polycations, which were found to counteract the dissociation of enzyme, also protects the diluted enzyme against surface inactivation. Consequently, chitosan, deacetylated hyaluronic acid, and deacetylated chondroitin 4-sulfate, as well as other macroanions, are powerful stabilizers of diluted hyaluronidase and β-glucuronidase. The stabilization of phosphatase by polyamines, reported by Jeffree (1956), is probably an analogous phenomenon.

II. Inhibition

Two types of enzyme inhibition by polyanions have been described. The first is a highly general and widespread phenomenon which was termed "macroanionic inhibition" by Spensley and Rogers (1954). The second type represents a special case of macroanionic inhibition and was called "activator competitive enzyme inhibition" (Bernfeld, Jacobson, and Bernfeld, 1957), in accordance with its characteristics and in analogy to the well-known term of "competitive enzyme inhibition," which implies that the inhibition is of the substrate competitive type.

A. The General Type: Macroanionic Enzyme Inhibition

A broad variety of macromolecular polyanions may inhibit many different enzymes, as can be seen from Table I. With the exception of reports on the inhibition of arginase and fumarase by ribonucleic acid, of lysozyme by ribonucleic and deoxyribonucleic acids, and of pepsin by carrageenan, the only naturally occurring substances among all poly-

TABLE I
POLYANIONS AS INHIBITORS OF ENZYME ACTIVITY

Inhibitor	Enzyme	References
Heparin	Alkaline phosphatase	Buruiana, 1957
Heparin	Alkaline phosphatase	Buruiana and Hadarag, 1958
Heparin	Acid phosphatase	Hummel, Anderson, and Patel, 1958
Heparin	α-Amylase	Myrbäck and Persson, 1953
Heparin	Hyaluronidase	Rogers, 1946
Heparin	Hyaluronidase	Seifter, Baeder, and Begany, 1949
Heparin	Hyaluronidase	Bernfeld and Tuttle, 1959; Bernfeld, Tuttle, and Hubbard, 1961
Heparin	Hyaluronidase	Balazs, Högberg, and Laurent, 1951
Heparin	Lysozyme	Kerby and Eadie, 1953
Heparin	Trypsin	Horwitt, 1940
Heparin	Pepsin	Levey and Sheinfeld, 1954
Heparin	Pepsin	Ravin, Baldinus, and Mazur, 1962
Heparin	Ribonuclease	Zöllner and Fellig, 1952
Heparin	Ribonuclease	Roth, 1953
Heparin	Ribonuclease	DeLamirande, Weber, and Cantero, 1956
Heparin	Ribonuclease	Vandendriessche, 1956
Heparin	Ribonuclease	Fellig and Wiley, 1959
Heparin[a]	Lipoprotein lipase	Bernfeld and Kelley, 1963
Heparin	Fumarase	Fischer and Herrmann, 1937
Chondroitin 4-sulfate	Fumarase	Fischer and Herrmann, 1937
Chondroitin 4-sulfate	Pepsin	Levey and Sheinfeld, 1954; Marini and Levey, 1955
Chondroitin 4-sulfate	Hyaluronidase	McClean, 1942
Chondroitin 4-sulfate	Acid phosphatase	Hummel, Anderson, and Patel, 1958
Chitin sulfate	Hyaluronidase	Astrup and Alkjaersig, 1950
Chitin sulfate	Ribonuclease	Fellig and Wiley, 1959
Hyaluronic acid	Lysozyme	Skarnes and Watson, 1955
Sulfated hyaluronic acid	Hyaluronidase	Balazs, Högberg, and Laurent, 1951
Amylopectin sulfate	Hyaluronidase	Bernfeld and Tuttle, 1959; Bernfeld, Tuttle, and Hubbard, 1961
Amylopectin sulfate	Ribonuclease	Fellig and Wiley, 1959
Amylopectin sulfate	Lipoprotein lipase	Bernfeld and Kelley, 1960, 1963
Amylopectin sulfate	β-Amylase	Bernfeld, Berkeley, and Bieber, 1965
Amylose sulfate	Pepsin	Ravin, Baldinus and Mazur, 1962
Amylose sulfate	Ribonuclease	Fellig and Wiley, 1959
Amylose sulfate	Lipoprotein lipase	Bernfeld and Kelley, 1960, 1963
Amylose sulfate	β-Amylase	Bernfeld, Berkeley, and Bieber, 1965
Rice starch sulfate	Pepsin	Ravin, Baldinus, and Mazur, 1962
Dextran sulfate	Ribonuclease	Walton, 1952
Dextran sulfate	Ribonuclease	Dickman, 1958
Dextran sulfate	Ribonuclease	Fellig and Wiley, 1959
Dextran sulfate	Lipoprotein lipase	Bernfeld and Kelley, 1960, 1963
Dextran sulfate	β-Amylase	Bernfeld, Berkeley, and Bieber, 1965
Cellulose sulfate	Hyaluronidase	Astrup and Alkjaersig, 1950

TABLE I (*Continued*)

Inhibitor	Enzyme	References
Cellulose sulfate	Ribonuclease	Fellig and Wiley, 1959
Carboxymethylcellulose sulfate	Ribonuclease	Fellig and Wiley, 1959
Carboxymethylcellulose sulfate	Lipoprotein lipase	Bernfeld and Kelley, 1960, 1963
Carrageenan	Pepsin	Ravin, Baldinus, and Mazur, 1962
Synthetic polyglucose sulfates	Lysozyme	Mora and Young, 1958, 1959
Synthetic polyglucose sulfates	Ribonuclease	Mora and Young, 1958, 1959
Synthetic polyglucose sulfates	Hyaluronidase	Mora and Young, 1959
Pectic acid sulfate	Hyaluronidase	Bernfeld and Tuttle, 1959; Bernfeld, Tuttle, and Hubbard, 1961
Pectic acid sulfate	Ribonuclease	Fellig and Wiley, 1959
Pectic acid sulfate	Lipoprotein lipase	Bernfeld and Kelley, 1963
Pectin sulfate	Ribonuclease	Vandendriessche, 1956
Pectin sulfate	Ribonuclease	Dickman, 1958
Sulfated pectic acid amide	Ribonuclease	Dickman, 1958
Galacturonan sulfate, methyl ester[b]	Ribonuclease	Roth, 1953
Galacturonan sulfate, methyl ester[b]	Deoxyribonuclease	Roth, 1953
Anhydromannuronan	Pepsin	Levey and Sheinfeld, 1954
Polyglutamic acid	Lysozyme	Skarnes and Watson, 1955
Polyglutamic acid	Trypsin	Dellert and Stahmann, 1955
Poly-L-aspartic acid	Ribonuclease	Vandendriessche, 1956
Ribonucleic acid	Fumarase	Fischer and Herrmann, 1937
Ribonucleic acid	Arginase	Moss, 1952
Ribonucleic acid	Lysozyme	Skarnes and Watson, 1955
Deoxyribonucleic acid	Lysozyme	Skarnes and Watson, 1955
Deoxyribonucleic acid	Hyaluronidase	Bernfeld, Tuttle, and Hubbard, 1961
Tetrametaphosphate	Ribonuclease	Vandendriessche, 1956
Polymetaphosphate	Acid phosphatase	Hummel, Anderson, and Patel, 1958
Phosphomolybdate	Ribonuclease	Dickman, 1958
Silicotungstate	Ribonuclease	Dickman, 1958
Polystyrene sulfonate	β-Amylase	Bernfeld, Berkeley, and Bieber, 1965
Polystyrene sulfonate	β-Glucuronidase	Bernfeld, Jacobson, and Bernfeld, 1957
Polystyrene sulfonate	Acid phosphatase	Hummel, Anderson, and Patel, 1958
Polystyrene sulfonate	Hyaluronidase	Spensley and Rogers, 1954
Polystyrene sulfonate	Hyaluronidase	Bernfeld and Tuttle, 1959; Bernfeld, Tuttle, and Hubbard, 1961
Polystyrene sulfonate	Lactic dehydrogenase	Bernfeld, Berkeley, and Bieber, 1965
Polystyrene sulfonate	Aldolase	Bernfeld, Berkeley, and Bieber, 1965
Polyvinyl sulfate	β-Amylase	Bernfeld, Berkeley, and Bieber, 1965

TABLE I (*Continued*)

Inhibitor	Enzyme	References
Polyvinyl sulfate	Pepsin	Ravin, Baldinus, and Mazur, 1962
Polyvinyl sulfate	Ribonuclease	Fellig and Wiley, 1959
Polyvinyl sulfate	Lipoprotein lipase	Bernfeld and Kelley, 1960, 1963
Polyvinyl sulfate	Lactic dehydrogenase	Bernfeld, Berkeley, and Bieber, 1965
Polysulfonic acid–formaldehyde polymers	Hyaluronidase	Rogers and Spensley, 1954
Polysulfonic acid–formaldehyde polymers	α-Amylase	Spensley and Rogers, 1954
Polysulfonic acid–formaldehyde polymers	Nuclease	Spensley and Rogers, 1954
Polysulfonic acid–formaldehyde polymers	Lysozyme	Heymann *et al.*, 1959
Polysulfonic acid–formaldehyde polymers	Pepsin	Heymann *et al.*, 1959
Hydroquinone sulfonic acid–formaldehyde polymer; dihydroxybenzene sulfonic acid–formaldehyde polymer; hydroquinone sulfonic acid–furfural polymer; hydroquinone sulfonic acid–acetaldehyde polymer	Pepsin, lysozyme	Heymann *et al.*, 1959
Polyacrylic acid	Catalase	Berdick and Morawetz, 1954
Polymethacrylic acid	β-Glucuronidase	Bernfeld, Jacobson, and Bernfeld, 1957
Polymethacrylic acid	Hyaluronidase	Bernfeld and Tuttle, 1959; Bernfeld, Tuttle, and Hubbard, 1961
Polycondensation products of dihydroxybenzoic or trihydroxybenzoic acids with formaldehyde, or their oxidation products	Hyaluronidase	Hahn, 1952; Hahn and Fekete, 1953; Hahn and Frank, 1953
Maleic anhydride copolymers	Catalase	Berdick and Morawetz, 1954
Phosphate polymers of various aromatic hydroxy and amino compounds	Acid phosphatase, alkaline phosphatase, urease, β-amylase, hyaluronidase, hexokinase	Diczfalusy *et al.*, 1953; Fernö *et al.*, 1953
Phosphate polymers of various aromatic hydroxy and amino compounds	Ribonuclease	Vandendriessche, 1956

TABLE I (*Continued*)

Inhibitor	Enzyme	References
Polyxenylphosphate	Acid phosphatase, chymotrypsin, ribonuclease, deoxyribonuclease, glyceraldehyde phosphate dehydrogenase, catalase	Hummel, Anderson, and Patel, 1958
Polyxenylphosphate	Ribonuclease	Hummel, Flores, and Nelson, 1958

[a] At concentrations above 25 μg per milliliter only.
[b] Described by Mangieri, Engelberg, and Randall, 1951.

anionic inhibitors appear to be glycosaminoglycans—in particular, heparin. Chondroitin 4-sulfate, hyaluronic acid, and alginic acid were found not to act as inhibitors of ribonuclease (Zöllner and Fellig, 1952), whereas chondroitin 4-sulfate was reported to inhibit fumarase and hyaluronidase, and hyaluronic acid was reported to inhibit lysozyme.

B. A Special Type: Activator Competitive Enzyme Inhibition

A special type of macroanionic inhibition has been detected for hyaluronidase (Bernfeld and Tuttle, 1959; Bernfeld, Tuttle, and Hubbard, 1961) and for β-glucuronidase (Bernfeld, Jacobson, and Bernfeld, 1957). In the case of both enzymes, the inhibition was clearly connected with the phenomena described earlier in this chapter (Section I,B,1 and 2)—i.e., the reversible decrease of enzyme activity at high dilutions and the reversal of this process by polycationic activators. Studies on the inhibition of these two enzymes by heparin, amylopectin sulfate, pectic acid sulfate, polystyrene sulfonate, and polymethacrylic acid have revealed that this inhibition was most marked at high enzyme dilutions in which the dissociation of the enzymes into inactive components is effective. Under these conditions, polycationic activator was added to the system, and kinetic studies revealed that the effect of the polyanions consisted in the sequestration of the activating polycations, rather than in their direct interaction with the enzyme. For this reason, the term of "activator competitive enzyme inhibition" had been introduced for this new type of enzyme inhibition.

The mechanism can best be explained by the assumption that the enzyme and the polyanionic inhibitor compete with each other for the polycationic activator, both aiming for the positive sites of the polycation. Whereas the activator was found to affect the enzyme activity by the reversal and prevention of the enzyme dissociation, the polyanionic inhibitor, at least in the case of β-glucuronidase and hyaluronidase, operates by sequestration of the activator through the formation of a polyanion–polycation complex, thereby promoting the dissociation of the enzyme and, hence, causing a decrease of specific enzyme activity.

In accordance with the theory is the observation that the inhibition of β-glucuronidase and of hyaluronidase by heparin and other macroanions is reversible, as long as the contact with the materials possessing rough surfaces is prevented; otherwise, it becomes irreversible.

A summary of the interrelationship between enzyme dissociation, polycationic activation, polyanionic inhibition, and surface inactivation is schematically represented in Fig. 3.

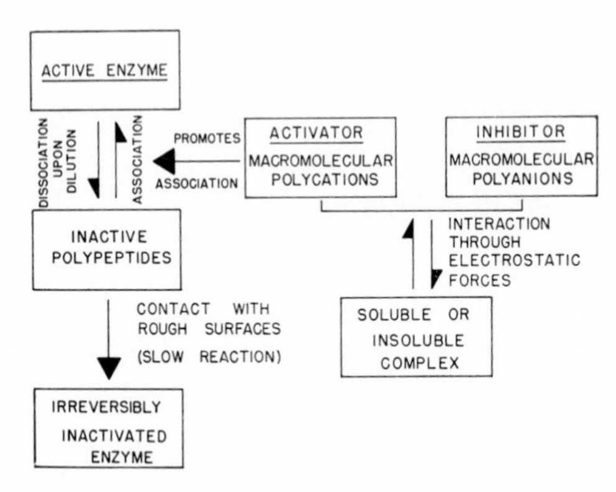

Fig. 3. Schematic representation of the interrelationship among dissociation, activation, inhibition, and stabilization against inactivation through contact with rough surfaces for the enzymes hyaluronidase and β-glucuronidase.

Chapter 47

CHEMICAL AND PHYSICAL CHANGES OF GLYCOSAMINOGLYCANS AND GLYCOPROTEINS CAUSED BY OXIDATION–REDUCTION SYSTEMS AND RADIATION

Lars Sundblad and Endre A. Balazs

I. Oxidation–Reduction Systems[1]

A. Glycosaminoglycans

1. Degradation by Oxidation–Reduction Systems

Shortly after the enzymic hydrolysis of hyaluronic acid had been described (Meyer, Dubos, and Smyth, 1937; Chain and Duthie, 1939, 1940), a number of reports on nonenzymic degradation of hyaluronic acid-containing substrates appeared. Robertson, Ropes, and Bauer (1939) found that fresh cattle vitreous contained a "mucolytic" agent, which was assumed to be ascorbic acid. The viscosity-reducing effect of ascorbic acid on synovial fluid or vitreous was later confirmed by several authors (McClean and Hale, 1940, 1941; Madinaveitia and Quibell, 1941a; Robertson, Ropes, and Bauer, 1941). It was evident that the effect of ascorbic acid was not accompanied by liberation of reducing sugars, in contrast to the action of hyaluronidase (McClean and Hale, 1941). Furthermore, the action of ascorbic acid was not limited to polysaccharides of mesothelial origin, since "mucins" of epithelial origin could be degraded with ascorbic acid, as could various other polysaccharides, such as starch, pectin, and flaxseed mucilage (Robertson, Ropes, and Bauer, 1941). The action of ascorbic acid is, to a great extent, independent of its concentration (McClean and Hale, 1941; Madinaveitia and Quibell, 1941), and it is accelerated by the presence of hydrogen peroxide (Robertson, Ropes, and Bauer, 1939, 1941; McClean and Hale,

[1] This section was prepared by Lars Sundblad.

1940, 1941), or traces of copper (Robertson, Ropes, and Bauer, 1939, 1941; Pirie, 1942). It was also found that the action of many other agents, such as organic reductants that contain an enediol group (Robertson, Ropes, and Bauer, 1941), diazotized compounds (Favilli, 1940; Madinaveitia and Quibell, 1941), thiolacetic acid, H_2S, quinol, pyrogallol, and many other reducing substances (McClean and Hale, 1941), was similar to that of ascorbic acid—viz., a decrease of the viscosity of solutions that contain hyaluronic acid without an increase of the amount of the reducing sugar of the solution.

Studies by Skanse and Sundblad (1943) showed that the presence of oxygen was necessary for the action of reducing agents on hyaluronic acid. When oxygen was carefully excluded from the reaction mixture, ascorbic acid was found to have no viscosity-decreasing effect on hyaluronic acid. Skanse and Sundblad found that hydrogen peroxide alone could cause a decrease in the viscosity of hyaluronic acid solutions and, also, that molecular oxygen was active at an elevated temperature (37° to 100°C), provided that traces of heavy metals were present. The presence of copper was found to be essential to the action of ascorbic acid in the presence of oxygen, and the reaction was almost completely inhibited in the presence of diethyldithiocarbamate. The same systems also caused degradation of other polysaccharides, such as chondroitin sulfate, heparin, and starch. Hale (1944) confirmed the finding that molecular oxygen is essential to the action of reducing agents on glycosaminoglycans. In experiments with various oxidation–reduction dyes (methylene blue, potassium indigo sulfonates, phenosafranine, rosinduline, and neutral red), the dyes were found to be active in the reduced form, but only if oxygen was present. The role of copper in the action of ascorbic acid was also pointed out, and it was shown that cuprous chloride alone could reduce the viscosity of hyaluronic acid solutions in the presence of air. It therefore appeared that cuprous ions undergoing oxidation might be the active agent in this system. Hale also found that hydrogen in the presence of catalytically active palladium could lower the viscosity of hyaluronic acid and starch solutions, but only in the presence of oxygen.

Jensen's (1949) experiments indicate that ferrous ions alone, or ferric ions in the presence of a reducing agent, such as hydrazine sulfate, degrade hyaluronic acid. Daubenmerkl (1951) confirmed previous observations that the effect of ascorbic acid is greatly accelerated by hydrogen peroxide. In later studies (Daubenmerkl, 1953,a), dihydroxymaleate was found to have a viscosity-reducing effect on hyaluronic acid solutions that was even more pronounced than that of ascorbic acid. The effect of this reductant was not influenced by the addition of hydrogen peroxide, whereas it was greatly accelerated by cupric, ferric, or ferrous ions. Suzuki and Sakakura (1953) also confirmed the viscosity-decreasing effect of various reducing agents on hyaluronic acid.

Jensen and his co-workers brought attention to the fact that reducing pigments produced by various *Pseudomonas* strains can decrease the viscosity of hyaluronic acid. They did not consider the possible catalytic effect of light in this reaction, but they did emphasize the importance of oxygen. A water-soluble greenish pigment, having a blue fluorescence, was isolated from cultures of *Pseudomonas calciprecipitans* and was found to cause a drop in the viscosity of hyaluronic acid (Bonde, Jensen, and Thamsen, 1957). Pyrocyanine prepared from *Pseudomonas aeruginosa* also caused a rapid decrease in the viscosity of hyaluronic acid solutions (Bonde, Jensen, and Schmidt, 1957). The presence of oxygen is essential for the reaction, and hydrogenated pigments do not show a viscosity-decreasing effect (Bonde and Jensen, 1956).

In recent years, the effect of oxidation–reduction systems on glycosaminoglycans has again received considerable attention, mainly owing to the awareness of the role that such reactions have in the degradation that often occurs during the preparation procedures. In 1945, it was suggested by Blix and Snellman that an oxidative type of degradation might, in part, be responsible for the loss of viscosity of hyaluronic acid solutions during certain preparation procedures. These authors found that hyaluronic acid prepared in a nitrogen atmosphere retained a higher viscosity than when it was prepared in air, and suggested that oxidative depolymerization, catalyzed by heavy metals, might occur during preparation. Lundquist (1949) found that 8-hydroxyquinoline inhibited the spontaneous decrease in viscosity occurring during the preparation of hyaluronic acid when iron-contaminated trypsin had been used to remove the proteins. Pigman and Rizvi (1959) found that the degradation often occurring during lyophilization of hyaluronic acid solutions was accelerated in the presence of phosphate ions. Phosphate ions were found to increase the effect of various reducing agents and oxygen on hyaluronic acid solutions or synovial fluid, indicating that the degradation noted on lyophilization of hyaluronic acid solutions might be due to reactions of this type. Merthiolate, often used as a bacteriostatic agent in preparation procedures, was also found to cause degradation of hyaluronic acid in the presence of oxygen (Pigman and Rizvi, 1959). It was shown, however, that this happens only when freshly prepared merthiolate solutions are used (Balazs and Sundblad, unpublished data). The loss in non-Newtonian viscosity noted on treatment of protein-containing hyaluronic acid with papain (Blumberg and Ogston, 1957, 1958) is not due to the splitting of a presumed hyaluronic acid–protein complex

(Ogston and Stanier, 1950, 1952), but to the agents, such as cysteine or EDTA, used to activate papain (Balazs and Sundblad, 1959; Ogston and Sherman, 1959). Balazs and Sundblad (1959) found that nonactivated papain also could decrease the viscosity of hyaluronic acid, most likely because of the reducing thiol groups of the inactive papain (E. L. Smith, 1958). On the other hand, a decrease in the viscosity of hyaluronic acid solutions of low ionic strength ($\Gamma/2 < 0.1$) may occur when nonactivated papain is added, owing to the interaction between papain and hyaluronic acid (Balazs and Sundblad, 1959). Experiments by Pigman *et al.* (1960) indicate that the irreversible loss of viscosity after acetic acid precipitation of hyaluronic acid from biological fluids (Ropes *et al.*, 1947; Ogston and Stanier, 1950) may also be due to reactions of this type. The viscosity decrease of synovial fluid at acid pH was found to be accelerated by phosphate ions and inhibited by ethanol in a manner the same as that observed for the degradation of hyaluronic acid by reducing agents in the presence of oxygen (Pigman and Rizvi, 1959).

Brinkman, Lamberts, and Zuideveld (1961a) found that sodium dithionite, which is a so-called radiomimetic substance, decreases the viscosity of synovial fluid in the absence of oxygen and that this effect can be partially inhibited by cystamine, serotonin, and sodium thiosulfate.

The collected data indicate that reactions of the oxidation–reduction type account for most of the degradation occurring during the previously used methods for the preparation of hyaluronic acid. This is supported by the finding (Balazs and Sundblad, 1959; Pigman, Rizvi, and Holley, 1961) that protein-free hyaluronic acid may be prepared from synovial fluid without loss of viscosity if degradation caused by oxidation–reduction systems can be prevented.

2. Degradation by Photosensitive Systems

Castellani (1954) was the first to report degradation of hyaluronic acid by a photosensitive system. A progressive decrease in the viscosity of hyaluronic acid from umbilical cord or synovial fluid could be produced by hematoporphyrin when irradiated with visible light in the presence of oxygen. These observations were confirmed by Castellani and Torlone (1956), who also demonstrated a similar action with two other "photosensitizers"—phylloerythrin and hypericin. None of these compounds had an effect on hyaluronic acid in the dark or in a vacuum.

Pigman and Rizvi (1959) found that visible light did not affect the rate of degradation of hyaluronic acid by the oxidation–reduction systems of oxygen with ascorbic acid, ferrous sulfate, or cysteine. Balazs, Sund-

TABLE I

EFFECT OF VISIBLE LIGHT AND OXYGEN ON THE DEPOLYMERIZATION OF HYALURONIC ACID BY THE EOSIN–ASCORBIC ACID SYSTEM

Conditions[a]	Degradation rate ($\times 10^3$)
Air and light	7.82
Air and reduced light	3.13
Evacuated tubes and light	1.04
Evacuated tubes and reduced light	0.35

[a] Experimental conditions: hyaluronic acid (2 mg/ml), ascorbic acid (4×10^{-3} M), and eosin (2×10^{-6} M) in phosphate buffer (pH 7.0) incubated at 4°C for 30 hours in tubes evacuated or open to air, either in darkness or illuminated with a 75-watt tungsten lamp. Viscosity determinations were carried out in reduced light, using eosin solution as the light filter. Degradation rates were calculated according to Sundblad (1953).

blad, and Dewey (1959) reported, on the other hand, that visible light catalyzed the degradation of hyaluronic acid by some oxidation–reduction systems, such as oxygen with reducing agents and eosin, methylene blue, or copper.

The role of light in the action of oxidation–reduction systems on hyaluronic acid was recently studied in detail by Balazs and Sundblad (unpublished data). Certain synthetic dyes, such as acriflavine, acridine

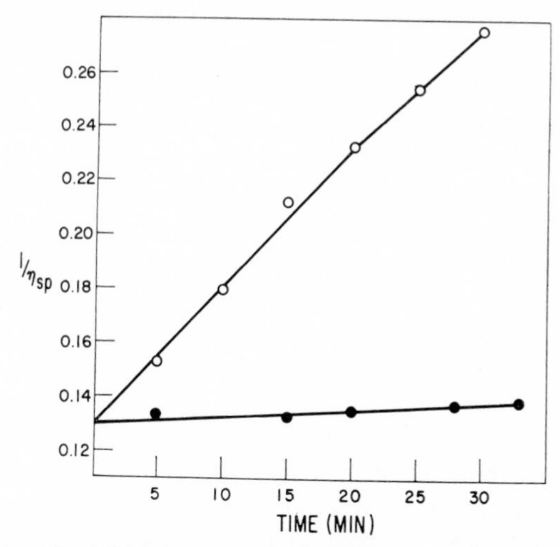

FIG. 1. Effect of visible light on the depolymerization of hyaluronic acid by riboflavin and ascorbic acid. Experimental conditions: Hyaluronic acid (0.6 mg/ml), ascorbic acid (2×10^{-3} M), and riboflavin (2×10^{-5} M) in Veronal buffer (pH 6.2) at 37°C in reduced light (●) and illuminated with a 300-watt tungsten lamp (○). Initial degradation rates (for definition, see Sundblad, 1953): in reduced light, 0.2×10^{-3}; illuminated, 5.3×10^{-3}.

orange, crystal violet, eosin, methylene blue, and neutral red, known to be reducible by visible light and suitable electron donors (Oster, 1954; Oster and Wotherspoon, 1954), were found to cause a rapid decrease in the viscosity of hyaluronic acid in the presence of ascorbic acid or phenylhydrazine, visible light, and oxygen (Table I).

Some compounds of biological interest were also tested. Riboflavin and ascorbic acid degraded hyaluronic acid in the presence of visible light, the viscosity-decreasing effect being insignificant in reduced light (Fig. 1). Other oxidation–reduction systems, such as ascorbic acid or phenylhydrazine and Cu^{++}, were found to degrade hyaluronic acid in the dark, although visible light accelerated the reaction to a variable extent. Some other oxidation–reduction systems that caused a decrease of viscosity were not affected by light.

3. Mechanism of Degradation

The finding that various reducing agents degrade glycosaminoglycans in the presence of oxygen, whereas the oxidized forms of the reducing agents are inactive (Hale, 1944; Pigman and Rizvi, 1959), suggests that a free-radical mechanism may be involved in this type of depolymerization. Observations that glycosaminoglycans also are depolymerized by ionizing radiation (see Section II of this chapter) support this idea.

It was suggested (Balazs and Sundblad, unpublished data) that the mechanism for the degradation of glycosaminoglycans by oxidation–reduction systems is similar to those observed in the experiments on the polymerization of vinyl compounds. The oxidation–reduction systems that contain dye and are dependent on light and oxygen produce free radicals and initiate the polymerization of vinyl compounds (Oster, 1954; Oster, Oster, and Prati, 1957). The reducing agents probably act only as electron donors in the reduction of the dye by visible light, and the free radicals are formed in the course of the reaction of the reduced dye with oxygen (Oster, 1954). The chelating agent EDTA, which was found to decrease the non-Newtonian viscosity of hyaluronic acid (Balazs and Sundblad, 1959; Ogston and Sherman, 1959), is known to form photoreducible metal complexes with, e.g., ferric ions (Jones and Long, 1952; Hill-Cottingham, 1955). Ethylenediaminetetraacetate (EDTA) is also known to act as an electron donor in dye-sensitized photoreductions (Oster, 1957; Oster and Oster, 1959). Oxalate complexes of ferric ions produce free radicals on illumination (Ingram *et al.*, 1955) and may also degrade hyaluronic acid in the presence of oxygen and visible light (Blix, 1944, personal communication).

Electron-spin-resonance studies have shown that free radicals are formed from ascorbic acid in the reaction between this substance and hydrogen peroxide in the presence of peroxidase and in the reaction with molecular oxygen in the presence of ascorbic acid oxidase (Piette, Yamazaki, and Mason, 1961). Lagercrantz (1964) recently demonstrated that free radicals are formed on oxidation of ascorbic acid with molecular oxygen.

Studies on inhibitors of various oxidation–reduction systems also support the theory that free radicals are involved in the degradation of glycosaminoglycans. Free-radical scavengers, such as ethanol and toluene, were shown to inhibit the action of ascorbic acid, cysteine, ferrous sulfate, and hydroquinone on hyaluronic acid (Pigman and Rizvi, 1959). Aminothiol compounds of the type known to prevent radiation damage (Alexander *et al.*, 1955; Doherty, Burnett, and Shapira, 1957) also inhibit the action of certain oxidation–reduction systems on hyaluronic acid (Pigman, Rizvi, and Holley, 1961; Balazs and Sundblad, unpublished data). Figure 2 shows the marked effect of cystamine on the degradation of hyaluronic acid by the eosin–ascorbic acid system.

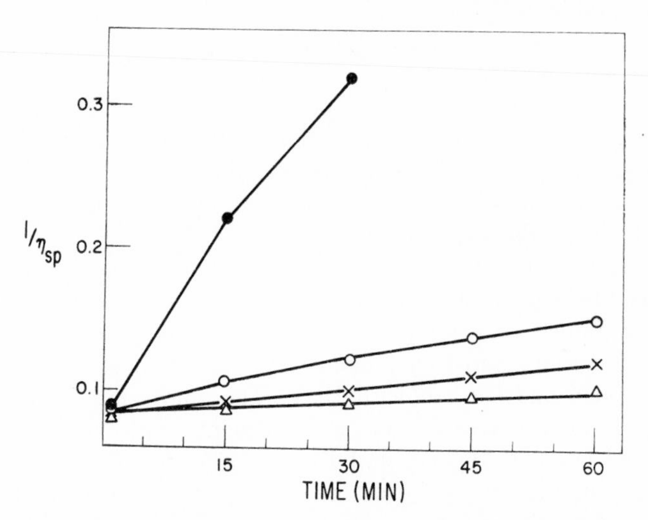

FIG. 2. Cystamine inhibition of the viscosity decrease of hyaluronic acid solutions caused by eosin and ascorbic acid. Experimental conditions: hyaluronic acid (2 mg/ml), ascorbic acid ($1 \times 10^{-3} M$), and eosin ($1 \times 10^{-5} M$) in tris buffer (pH 7.4) at 37°C, illuminated with visible light. Cystamine concentrations: none (●), $1 \times 10^{-5} M$ (○), $1 \times 10^{-4} M$ (X), $1 \times 10^{-3} M$ (△).

The action of reducing agents such as ascorbic acid or cysteine probably requires the presence of trace amounts of heavy metals. Skanse and Sundblad (1943) found that diethyldithiocarbamate or cyanide abolishes the effect of ascorbic acid almost completely. Pigman, Rizvi, and Holley (1961) reported, on the other hand, only slight inhibition by metal-complexing agents other than diethyldithiocarbamate. Balazs and Sundblad (unpublished data) found that, when scrupulous heavy-metal "sterility" was maintained, ascorbic acid had only an insignificant effect on most of the hyaluronic acid preparations tested. With some preparations, however, a markedly different reaction was obtained—viz., on the addition of ascorbic acid, the viscosity dropped simultaneously with the oxidation of the ascorbic acid and, after all of the ascorbic acid had been oxidized, the viscosity decrease stopped. It seems likely, therefore, that some of the hyaluronic acid preparations are contaminated by small amounts of metallic ions, not removable by dialysis, which catalyze the autoxidation of the ascorbic acid.

The decrease in the viscosity of glycosaminoglycans brought about by oxidation–reduction systems appears to be due to a true depolymerization. Skanse and Sundblad (1943) observed a rapid disappearance of the birefringence of flow when hyaluronic acid solutions were treated with ascorbic acid or hydrogen peroxide. On prolonged treatment (several days), a dialyzable nitrogen-containing material was formed. Pigman and Rizvi (1959) found no dialyzable material after treatment of hyaluronic acid with various oxidation–reduction systems for three hours. A broadening of the hyaluronic acid peak on the ultracentrifugal and electrophoretic patterns, similar to that found after mild treatment with hyaluronidase, was noted, however. An irreversible decrease in the intrinsic viscosity of hyaluronic acid was observed by Pigman, Rizvi, and Holley (1961) in similar experiments.

The chemical nature of the cleavage of the glycosaminoglycan molecule remains unclarified. An oxidative type of depolymerization was postulated by Skanse and Sundblad (1943), based on the observed increase in acidic groups noted on prolonged treatment of hyaluronic acid with ascorbic acid and Cu^{++} or with H_2O_2. The glucosamine content of the hyaluronic acid decreased during treatment, with no change in glucuronic acid content. Pigman and Rizvi (1959) found no detectable decrease in glucuronic acid or hexosamine after treatment of hyaluronic acid with ascorbic acid or ferrous sulfate.

4. Biological Significance

It was early noted (McClean and Hale, 1940, 1941; Parrot and Fasquelle, 1949) that reducing agents which had an *in vitro* "mucolytic" effect also acted as "spreading factors"—i.e., they increased the spreading of colored indicators injected intracutaneously into rabbits. The increase in diffusion in the dermis caused by such agents as ascorbic acid or ascorbic acid and H_2O_2 was found to be marked, although it developed slowly over a period of several hours (McClean and Hale, 1941), in contrast to the rapid spreading effect of hyaluronidase. In experiments on rabbits and human subjects, Daubenmerkl (1951) found that ascorbic acid and H_2O_2 markedly increased the absorption of physiological saline from the subcutaneous tissue; he suggested the use of such agents instead of hyaluronidase for therapeutic purposes. Daubenmerkl later (1953) found dihydroxymaleic acid and ferrous sulfate to be even more active, increasing the normal subcutaneous infusion rate up to five times. Fabianek *et al.* recently (1962) reported a general parallelism between the *in vitro* effect on hyaluronic acid and the *in vivo* effect on tissue permeability for several oxidation–reduction systems (ascorbic acid, ferrous sulfate, hydroquinone, and cysteine).

The findings just described indicate that the hyaluronic acid in the intercellular matrix may be modified by oxidation–reduction systems. Consequently, such systems may well be of importance in the control of connective tissue permeability. It should be noted, however, that serum proteins, especially α_2-globulins, have been shown to protect hyaluronic acid from degradation by oxidation–reduction systems (Salegui *et al.*, 1962; Abrams and Sandson, 1964).

The very rapid drop in the viscosity of hyaluronic acid in the adult bovine vitreous has been known for some time, and it has been suggested that it is caused by the presence of a high concentration of ascorbic acid (Robertson, Ropes, and Bauer, 1939). It was found recently (Balazs and Sundblad, unpublished data) that the viscosity decrease and the probable underlying degradation of the hyaluronic acid in the bovine vitreous is a reaction sensitive to light and that factors other than ascorbic acid, probably glutathione and pigments, are also involved.

Castellani and Torlone (1956) found that a "photodynamic disease" of both acute and chronic form could be produced in laboratory animals by subjecting the animals to visible light after injection of certain photosensitizers, such as hematoporphyrin. Histological examination of the skin (toluidine-blue staining) showed that the normal metachromatic substance of rat skin became orthochromatic under these conditions, indicating an effect on the skin glycosaminoglycans. Possibly, such effects may be of pathogenetic significance in the light-sensitive types of porphyria.

B. Glycoproteins

As early as 1941, Robertson, Ropes, and Bauer were able to show that oxidation–reduction systems, such as ascorbic acid and H_2O_2, cause an alteration of viscosity and precipitability of "mucins" of epithelial origin (gastric and salivary). Ericsson and Stjernström (1951) found that the viscosity of saliva was rapidly reduced by ascorbic acid in the presence of H_2O_2 or traces of Cu^{++}. The viscosity-decreasing effect, as well as the strong bacterial, fungicidal, and virucidal effects of an ascorbic acid–Cu^{++}–H_2O_2 system (Ericsson, 1954; Ericsson and Lundbeck, 1955,a), has been utilized in the treatment of oral infestions (Berghagen, Ericsson, and Stjernström, 1954; Muth, 1960) and in the treatment of chronic bronchitis with highly viscous bronchial secretion (Palmer, 1961).

A marked effect of various sulfhydryl compounds on the viscosity of glycoproteins from gastric mucin was reported by Sheffner (1963). The decrease in viscosity was attributed to a breaking of the disulfide bonds. Ascorbic acid was reported to have no effect.

It is not known whether or not the effect of ascorbic acid with Cu^{++} or H_2O_2 on the viscosity of epithelial mucins is due to a true depolymerization. A cleavage of the sialic acid of submaxillary mucin can be expected to cause a decrease in viscosity by folding of the molecule (Gottschalk and Thomas, 1961).

II. Radiation[2]

A. Glycosaminoglycans

1. Hyaluronic Acid

a. Physicochemical Changes. Ragan *et al.* (1947) showed, for the first time, that the relative viscosity of hyaluronic acid solutions decreases 20–30% during X-irradiation at a dose of approximately 3000 r. These authors also demonstrated that the viscosity of pathological human synovial fluids can also be decreased by X-irradiation. No postirradiation effects were observed. Balazs and Laurent (1951) studied, by viscometry, the polyanionic behavior of hyaluronic acid as a function of counter-ion concentration. They found that irradiation with ultraviolet light causes a decrease in the intrinsic viscosity of both hyaluronic acid and its sodium salt. The polyanionic character of hyaluronic acid did not change, however, even after a dose of ultraviolet radiation which decreased the intrinsic viscosity to 10% of its original value. This indicates that, although a decrease in the size of the molecule or a change in its shape, or both, occurs, the carboxylic groups are not affected. Mogilevskiĭ and Laufer (1951) also found that irradiation with ultraviolet light causes a decrease in the relative viscosity of hyaluronic acid solutions and that hyaluronic acid irradiated in the presence of proteins does not precipitate in solutions at pH 4.5. Schoenberg *et al.* (1950, 1951) reported further physicochemical studies on hyaluronic acid after X-irradiation. The relative viscosity of hyaluronic acid solu-

[2] This section was prepared by Endre A. Balazs.

tions (0.4–0.6%) decreases considerably after a dose of 9000 r; moreover, a decrease (23%) in viscosity was observed within the first 4 hours after irradiation. A decrease in light scattering at a 90° angle was also found during the 12-hour postirradiation period. These authors, as well as other investigators (Ragan *et al.*, 1947; Mogilevskiĭ and Laufer, 1951), found that irradiated hyaluronic acid solutions show a further decrease in viscosity upon incubation with testicular hyaluronidase.

Caputo (1957) found that X-irradiated (2×10^5 r) hyaluronic acid in phosphate buffer solution ($\Gamma/2$ 0.1, pH 7) shows three components, in free electrophoresis, with mobilities of 7.6, 4.2, and 1.3×10^5 cm^2 sec^{-1} V^{-1}, all lower than the mobility of the single boundary of the unirradiated hyaluronic acid (10.5×10^5 cm^2 sec^{-1} V^{-1}). The sedimentation coefficient, measured at various concentrations, was found to be lower for the irradiated samples than for the unirradiated, but only one boundary could be observed in all samples.

Setlow and Doyle (1955) irradiated hyaluronic acid in solid state with electrons, deuterons, and α-particles of varying energy at room and liquid air temperatures. The irradiated samples were dissolved in phosphate buffer, and, after albumin was added and the pH was adjusted to 4.2, the turbidity of the solution was measured. After irradiation, the turbidity decreases as the energy absorbed by the molecules increases. The data obtained were consistent with the picture of the direct action of ionizing radiation on hyaluronic acid, provided that the molecular model assumed was a long (770–1750 Å) and thin (10–15 Å) cylinder randomly oriented in the dry sample. When hyaluronic acid and testicular hyaluronidase were dried together and then irradiated in solid state, the enzyme was more susceptible to radiation damage than it was when irradiated without the substrate. The authors suggested that this was the result of radiation damage to the hyaluronic acid which, owing to a specific substrate–enzyme combination, causes an enhanced inactivation of the enzyme.

Balazs *et al.* (1959) observed that the molecular weight of a hyaluronic acid preparation, calculated from sedimentation and diffusion constants, decreased from 80,000 to 19,700 after irradiation with ultraviolet light. They found that the average molecular weight of hyaluronic acid irradiated with ultraviolet light or fast electrons decreases considerably with increasing doses and that a large part of the molecules split into small molecular fractions which pass through dialysis membranes, thus clearly demonstrating that intensive radiation causes degradation of the molecular chain.

A temperature-sensitive postirradiation viscosity drop was observed in hyaluronic acid solutions (0.2 mg/ml) after irradiation with doses of

2000–4000 r of 220-kv X-rays (Lamberts and Alexander, 1964). The molecular weight of hyaluronic acid, measured by light scattering, decreased from 2.75×10^6 to 1.75×10^6 when irradiated in 0.2 M NaCl or KCl. No postirradiation effect was observed in the absence of added electrolytes or in the presence of 0.2 M NaF or $NaClO_4$. Sodium thiosulfate protected the hyaluronic acid from degradation and stopped the postirradiation effect when added to the macromolecular solution immediately after irradiation, probably by scavenging the OH radicals of the solvent (Brinkman, Lamberts, and Zuideveld, 1961a; Lamberts and Alexander, 1964). When the irradiation was carried out in the absence of oxygen, the decrease in the viscosity was greater than it was in the presence of oxygen. It was suggested that "oxygen stabilizes an intermediary product of hyaluronic acid and reduces the likelihood of a break in the main chain being produced" (Lamberts and Alexander, 1964).

Relatively low doses of radiation cause rapid decrease of the limiting viscosity number measured with a rotating-cylinder viscometer at low shear rates (0.2–2 sec^{-1}). When hyaluronic acid solutions (1 mg/ml) of high molecular weight (MW $= 2 \times 10^6$; limiting viscosity number, 5760 cc/g) are exposed to 50 and 500 rads of γ-irradiation (CO^{60}), the limiting viscosity number drops to 5350 and 3810 cc/g, respectively. The chemical determinations carried out on these samples were not sensitive enough to detect any significant changes. Molecular weight calculations obtained from sedimentation and diffusion experiments indicate very little change after irradiation with these low doses, suggesting that the considerable change in the viscosity is caused by a change in the shape, deformability, or internal structure of the molecule, rather than by a change in its size (Balazs, unpublished data[3]).

b. Chemical Changes. Chemical changes observed in irradiated hyaluronic acid solutions are of two types: (1) those which indicate degradation of the macromolecule, and (2) those which suggest the formation of new chemical compounds.

Caputo (1957) observed that the dimethylaminobenzaldehyde reaction used for the determination of hexosamines (Elson and Morgan, 1933) yields a more intense color in hyaluronic acid solutions X-irradiated with $2\text{–}6 \times 10^5$ r. Whether this increased color density indicates an increase in the number of glucosamine end groups or whether it indicates the formation of a compound which gives a chromogen with a higher color yield was not established. Balazs *et al.* (1959) determined the hexosamine content of hyaluronic acid solutions irradiated with 2.6 Mev of $0.5\text{–}4 \times 10^6$ rads. The samples, after hydrolysis with 6 N HCl

[3] Reported at the International Symposium on Energy Transfer in Radiation Processes, Association for Radiation Research, Cardiff, Wales, January 7–9, 1965.

for 16 hr at 95°C, showed that the total hexosamine content decreases with increasing doses. A similar decrease in hexuronic acid content was also observed. These chemical determinations indicate that both the glucosamine and the glucuronic acid moiety of hyaluronic acid undergo destruction as a result of irradiation with electrons. Measurement of the reducing substance by the ferricyanide method suggests an increase in the number of end groups as the result of ultraviolet irradiation. The drop in relative viscosity is accompanied by only a very small increase in the reducing-substance values, however. The cationic dyebinding of hyaluronic acid also decreases rapidly upon irradiation with large doses of ultraviolet light or electrons, indicating partial decarboxylation of the glucuronic acid moiety (Balazs *et al.*, 1959).

A rapid decrease in the pH of water solutions of hyaluronic acid, when irradiated with ultraviolet light or with electrons, indicates the formation of acid. Parallel with the formation of acid, an absorption band at 267 mμ develops (Fig. 3). When the acidity of the solution drops below pH 5, the absorption maximum shifts toward the shorter wavelengths; at $<$pH 3, the maximum is at 245 mμ. With increasing doses of radiation, more and more of the ultraviolet-absorbing material becomes dialyzable, indicating that the unsaturated compound responsible for the ultraviolet absorption is present in both large and small molecular weight fractions (Balazs *et al.*, 1959). The chemical nature of this ultraviolet-absorbing substance is not known, but it should be pointed out that the irradiation of glucose and other hexoses, and of their C-1 acids, with ultraviolet light or with various ionizing radiations, gives, among other products, a product which exhibits similar ultraviolet absorption characteristics (Laurent and Wertheim, 1952; Laurent, 1956; Bothner-By and Balazs, 1957; Coleby, 1957). This product forms in greater quantity when the sugar solution is irradiated in alkaline (pH 8–11) solution. Since all enediol structures, such as L-ascorbic acid, have similar absorption characteristics, the authors suggested that this product belongs to that group of substances.

The electron-spin-resonance spectrum of the free radical formed upon γ-irradiation of hyaluronic acid in solid state was studied recently by Balazs, Baugh, and Phillips (unpublished data, 1964). The g value (spectroscopic-splitting factor) of the single-line spectrum was found to be 2.0012, which is close to the free-electron value (2.0023). The singlet nature of the spectrum (Fig. 4a) indicates that the unpaired electron produced during irradiation in solid state does not interact with neighboring protons and, hence, is localized in the molecule by hydrogen ejection from a carbon chain which has no other protons attached to it. The evidence seems to point to the elimination of a hydrogen atom from C-5

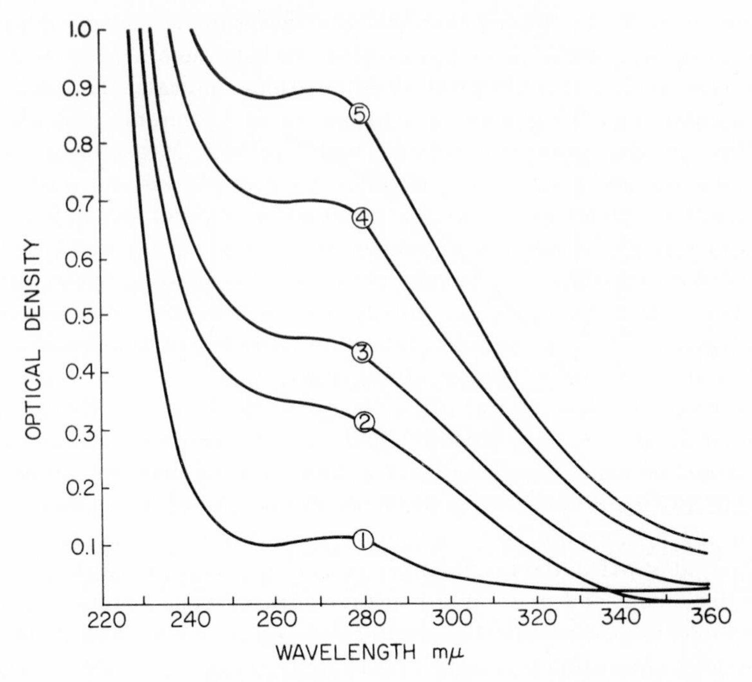

FIG. 3. Absorption spectra of hyaluronic acid irradiated with 2.6-Mev electrons. Experimental conditions: 5.2 mg of hyaluronic acid in 1 ml of water (pH 7.0) (1), irradiated with 1×10^6 rads (2), 2×10^6 rads (3), 3×10^6 rads (4), and with 4×10^6 rads (5) (taken from Balazs *et al.*, 1959).

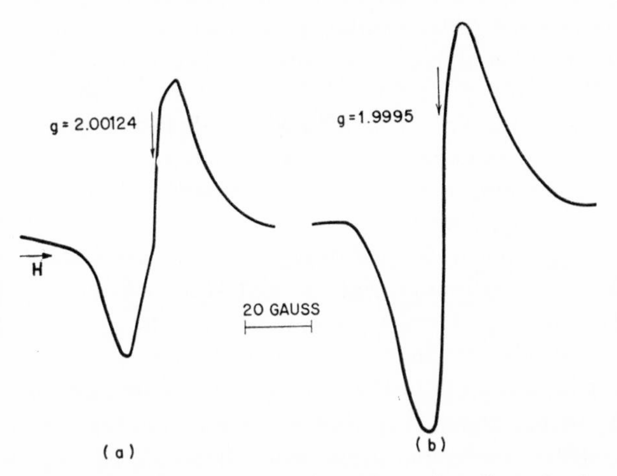

FIG. 4. The electron-spin-resonance absorption of sodium hyaluronate after irradiation with γ-rays (a) and the electron-spin-resonance absorption of the hyaluronic acid–azure A complex before irradiation (b) (Balazs, Baugh, and Phillips, unpublished data, 1964).

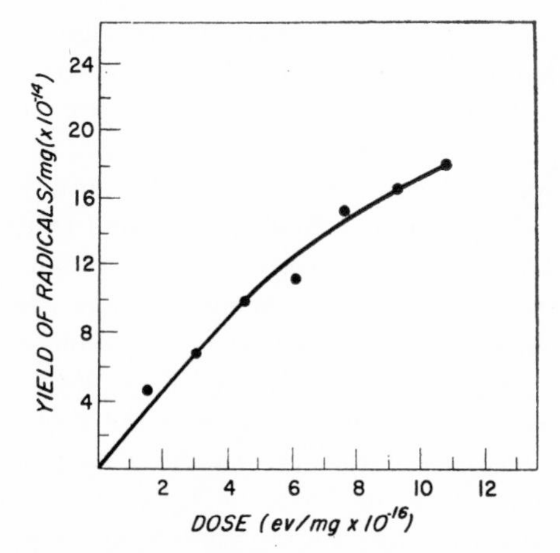

FIG. 5. Increase in concentration of radicals during γ-irradiation of sodium hyaluronate (Balazs, Baugh, and Phillips, unpublished data, 1964).

of the glucuronic acid moiety because, otherwise, a radical such as this would be stabilized by resonance interaction with the carboxyl group.

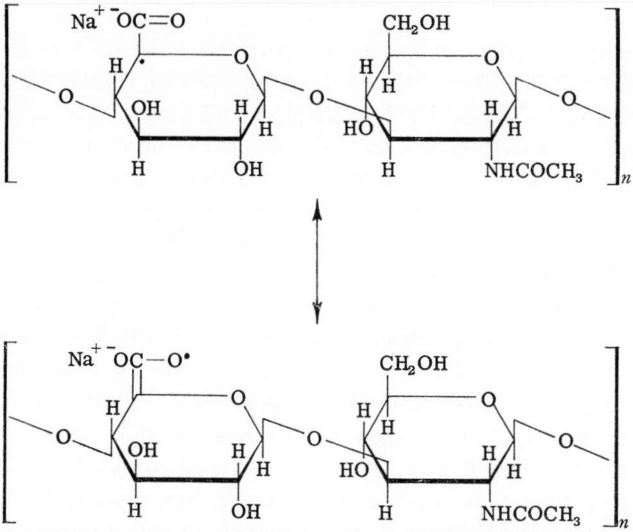

The yield–dose curve (Fig. 5) for the formation of radicals gives initial G (radical) values (number of radicals formed per 100-ev energy input) of 2.0–2.5, which are in the same order of magnitude as has been observed for other carbohydrate systems (Phillips and Baugh, 1963; Ehrenberg, Ehrenberg, and Löfroth, 1963).

The metachromatic complex formed by hyaluronic acid and the

cationic thiazin dye azure A (7-dimethylamino-3-imino-3 *H*-phenothiazine hydrochloride) exhibits strong paramagnetic properties in solid state even before irradiation (Fig. 4b). Irradiation of the complex resulted in subsequently greater degradation of the hyaluronic acid, as evidenced by limiting viscosity number measurements, than did irradiation of sodium hyaluronate alone. It was suggested that the metachromatic dye–polyanion complex represents a greater electron delocalization process than the sodium hyaluronate does, thereby producing a more efficient energy-transport system which results in increased degradation of the macromolecule (Balazs, Baugh, Phillips, unpublished data, 1964). This observation and its interpretation are compatible with the recently suggested energy-transfer characteristics of carbohydrates. During the irradiation of carbohydrates in solid state, in which only the direct-action effects are encountered, the physical state of the carbohydrate profoundly influences the course of the radiation decomposition (Phillips, 1963). These findings suggest the existence of a mechanism of energy transport which is facilitated by a highly ordered crystal system. Lattice imperfections, for example, appear to act as energy traps and hinder the transport of energy, apparently resulting in less radiation decomposition. Furthermore, energy transfer appears to be extremely facile during the irradiation of oligosaccharides and of polysaccharides. Such effects have been demonstrated in complexes of Schardinger dextrins (cyclic dextrins composed of 6, 7, or 8 α-D-glucose units joined by $1 \rightarrow 4$ links) and aromatic molecules. The characteristic electron-spin-resonance spectrum associated with γ-irradiated dextrin is not evident when the complex with aromatic molecules is irradiated; the spectrum is characteristic of the aromatic molecule. Moreover, the presence of the aromatic molecule appears to confer considerable radiation stability upon the dextrin as a direct consequence of the facility of energy transfer from the carbohydrate to the aromatic molecule, which acts as an efficient energy "sink" (Phillips, 1963).

Carbohydrates in solid state or in aqueous solution have been shown to be very susceptible to radiation damage (for a review, see Phillips, 1961). The results of irradiation in aqueous solution cannot be satisfactorily interpreted solely in terms of H atoms, solvated electrons, and OH radicals produced on irradiation of water, but seem to be indicative of a significant contribution from processes of the direct-action type, even in solute concentrations of the order of 10^{-2} *M* (Phillips and Davies, 1964). Glycosaminoglycans of very high molecular weight exhibit great sensitivity to radiation.

2. Other Glycosaminoglycans

The degradation of heparin and sulfated hyaluronic acid by ultraviolet light and by fast electrons (2.6 Mev) was studied by Balazs *et al.*

(1959). When aqueous solutions of heparin (13.0–13.3% S content) are irradiated with ultraviolet light, the anticoagulant activity and the cationic dyebinding power of the polyanion decrease. Destruction of the molecules is also manifested by an increase in reducing substance and an increase in the amount of the fractions which will pass through dialysis membranes. The results obtained after irradiation of the same heparin preparations with fast electrons were similar. More than half of the hexosamine and hexuronic acid moieties of the heparin samples was destroyed after irradiation with 4×10^6 rads. More than 50% of the undestroyed hexosamine and hexuronic acid was present in fractions of low molecular weight that passed through the dialysis membranes.

B. Biological Systems

1. Mast Cells

For a long time, the mast cells of normal connective tissues were assumed to contain heparin. Direct chemical evidence for this assumption was presented only for the mast cells of the rat peritoneum (Schiller and Dorfman, 1959; Bloom and Ringertz, 1960), however. The possibility that mast cells, or similar connective tissue cells, contain other glycosaminoglycans was suggested by the finding that polysaccharides of varying sulfate content, containing glucosamine and galactosamine, are present in mast cell tumors of mice and dogs (Ringertz, 1960a; Ringertz and Bloom, 1960) (see also Chapter 27).

Since hemorrhages and general changes in the permeability of the blood capillary walls are among the most characteristic symptoms of radiation damage in man and in animals, the attention of investigators turned early to heparin, a biological anticoagulant, and to the mast cells, the site of its synthesis and storage. Allen and Jacobson (1947) found an increase in the blood clotting time of humans and animals exposed to large doses of radiation in Hiroshima and Nagasaki. Cationic molecules, such as toluidine blue, thiamine, or protamine, which interact with, and thereby "neutralize," heparin, restored the clotting time to normal; consequently, a "hyperheparinemia" was assumed to result from total-body irradiation. Dogs receiving X-ray doses of 450 r or more showed similar symptoms, and an anticoagulant with the properties of heparin could be isolated from the blood of these animals (Allen *et al.*, 1948). Studies by later investigators, however, did not confirm that an increase in blood clotting time always occurs in animals after irradiation, nor did they confirm that it is caused by an increase in the concentration of heparin in the blood when it does occur (Rekers and Field, 1943; Holden *et al.*, 1949; Rosenthal and Benedek, 1950; Cronkite, 1950).

The first histochemical study on the glycosaminoglycan content of the intercellular space of connective tissue and of mast cells after irradiation was made by Sylvén (1940). In the skin of the rat, after irradiation with X-rays and radium, increased metachromasia was observed in the intercellular matrix, and the mast cells seemed to have fewer granules than they have in normal skin. These findings, interpreted as a release of metachromatic substance, presumably heparin, from the granules of the mast cells as a result of radiation damage, were confirmed by Campani (1948). Disintegration of mast cells after total-body irradiation of rats was also observed by other authors (Kelényi, 1953; Riley, 1953; Smith and Lewis, 1953; van den Brenk, 1959).

Quantitative determinations of the number of mast cells per unit area of tissue section were made by Smith and Lewis (1954) in the cheek pouch of hamsters 3–33 days after total-body X-irradiation (600 r). Three days after exposure there was no difference in the mast cell count, but between 10 and 33 days, the count had dropped significantly. Pettersson (1954) made a thorough study of the mast cell count per unit volume of tissue in guinea pig skin after weekly total-body X-irradiation with 220 r. The mast cell count decreased approximately 50% after the animals had received an accumulated dose of 660 r. An increase of the dose to 1320 r did not further alter the mast cell count.

It was reported that the antihistamine pyrilamine maleate protects the mast cells against radiation damage (Maynard *et al.*, 1955), although this protective effect is species specific and is localized to the region where the drug is applied (D. E. Smith, 1958). Adrenalectomy, hypophysectomy, and treatment with corticosteroids do not alter the response of mast cells to X-irradiation (Smith and Lewis, 1954a, 1958). In certain connective tissues of some species, large numbers of mast cells disappear on irradiation or become so damaged that they can no longer be detected by the usual histological methods. A direct relationship between the radiation damage to heparin, or to any other glycosaminoglycan, and changes in the morphology or in the physiology of any of the cellular elements of connective tissue has not been established, however.

2. Vitreous

The vitreous, in most animals and in humans, is a collagen gel which contains hyaluronic acid and proteins, the concentrations of which vary with the species and age of the animal and with the topography of the gel. It was suggested that the frictional interaction of the large hyaluronic acid molecules serves to "reinforce" the gel (Balazs, 1961; for a review see also Chapter 37). It was shown that the viscosity of the hyaluronic acid in the bovine, ovine, and avian vitreous decreases after the enucleated eyeball or the isolated vitreous gel is irradiated with ultraviolet light or with γ-rays (Howe, 1955; Toth, Balazs, and Howe, 1962; Howe and Balazs, unpublished data). As a result of radiation-caused changes in the hyaluronic acid, the "stability," or stress resistance, of the vitreous gel decreases, as was demonstrated by subjecting ovine and bovine gels to centrifugation after irradiation. Under the centrifugal force, a liquid phase separates from the gel, the amount of liquid formed being proportional to the radiation dose (Fig. 6). A concomitant drop in

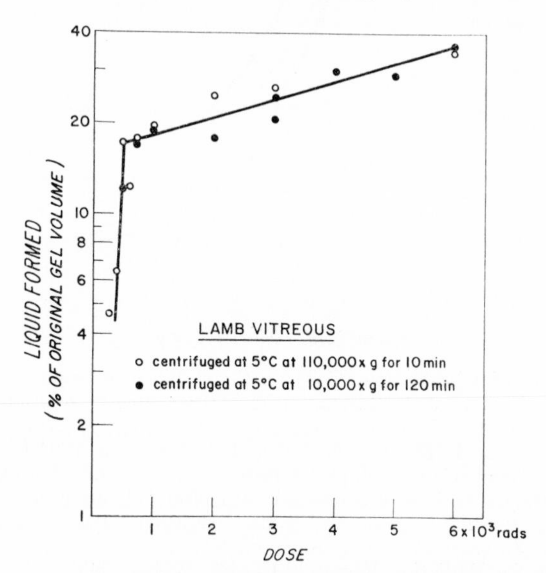

FIG. 6. Radiation sensitivity of the ovine vitreous. Enucleated eyeball irradiated with γ-rays (Co^{60}) (Toth, Balazs, and Howe, 1962).

the intrinsic viscosity of the hyaluronic acid was observed in both the liquid and the gel. The change in the rate of liquid formation at doses higher than 1000 rads was interpreted as a sign of radiation damage to the collagen network (Toth, Balazs, and Howe, 1962).

The radiation sensitivity of the intercellular matrix was also demonstrated in collagen gels which contained various concentrations of hyaluronic acid of large molecular weight ($1–2 \times 10^6$). The stability of these gels, under mechanical stress, was tested by centrifuging them at various forces, which led to partial collapse of the gel and a separation of the liquid. The concentrations of collagen and hyaluronic acid, as well as the centrifugal force applied, determine the volume of the liquid formed. Irradiation does not alter the liquid formation in gels which contain no hyaluronic acid. In the presence of hyaluronic acid, depending on the concentration of the polysaccharide, the gel is "stabilized," but, after irradiation, this stabilizing effect of the hyaluronic acid decreases or

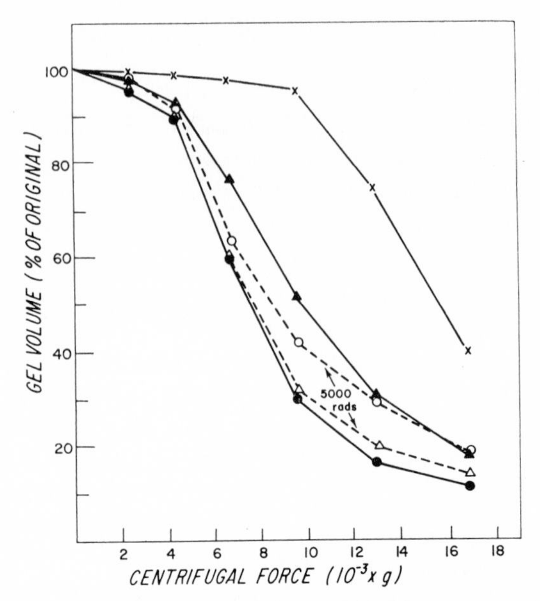

FIG. 7. Effect of γ-irradiation (Co^{60}) on the stability of tropocollagen gels in the presence and absence of hyaluronic acid. Tropocollagen solutions (1.5 mg/ml) containing hyaluronic acid concentrations of 1.0 mg/ml (X) and 0.5 mg/ml (▲), and no hyaluronic acid (●) were heated and then kept at 37°C for 2 hours before centrifugation. Other gels containing hyaluronic acid in concentrations of 1.0 mg/ml (○) and 0.5 mg/ml (△) were irradiated with 5000 rads after incubation and then centrifuged (dotted line) under the same conditions (Balazs, unpublished data, reported at the International Symposium on Energy Transfer in Radiation Processes, Association for Radiation Research, Cardiff, Wales, 1965).

disappears completely, depending on the radiation dose (Fig. 7). Thus, the radiation sensitivity of the intercellular matrix caused by the breakdown of the hyaluronic acid molecule was demonstrated not only in the simplest connective tissue of the vertebrate body—the vitreous—but also in a reconstituted extracellular matrix (Balazs, unpublished data, 1964).

3. Other Connective Tissues

Brinkman and Lamberts (1958,a), Brinkman, Lamberts, and Zuideveld (1961,a), and Brinkman *et al.* (1961) showed that the flow of 0.9% NaCl solution through freshly excised fasciae of the abdominal muscles of guinea pigs and rats is increased after X-irradiation with 2000 r. In another series of experiments, the pressure necessary to maintain, at constant velocity, a slow flow of physiological salt solution into the mucoid layer of the rooster comb and human and rat dermis was recorded. After X-irradiation (100–500 r), the resistance set up by the matrix of the tissue to the fluid motion dropped considerably. When cystamine (0.01%) was added to the salt solution, the drop in resistance after irradiation was prevented. Inasmuch as the addition of hyaluronidase to the infusion fluid causes a similar drop in the tissue resistance and in the permeability of the fasciae (Day, 1952), and the viscosity of synovial fluid decreases after irradiation (see Section II,A,1 of this chapter), the authors concluded that the effect observed is the result of a breakdown of the intercellular matrix of the tissue.

Cystamine, serotonin, and molecular oxygen showed a protective effect on the radiation-caused viscosity drop of synovial fluid (Brinkman, Lamberts, and Zuideveld, 1961,a).

It may be of some interest to mention that Brinkman and Veninga (1962) and Veninga and Brinkman (1962) reported the liberation of serotonin and other biogenic amines as a result of X-irradiation of frog skin and rat uterine horns. In view of the possible interaction between biological amines and polyacids, such as the glycosaminoglycans, the possibility exists that the radiation damage to the polyacids results in a change in the binding capacity of the amines.

Only a few studies were made on the effect of radiation on the metabolism of glycosaminoglycans *in vivo*. Degenerative changes in the epiphyseal cartilage of knee joints of mice were observed after X-irradiation of 900 and 2000 r, respectively (Dziewiatkowski and Woodard, 1959). Parallel with the histological changes, a decrease in the uptake of S^{35} was demonstrated on autoradiograms after the administration of $S^{35}O_4$. Münich (1962) showed that the S^{35} uptake of the glycosaminoglycans of another connective tissue, the cornea, decreases after β-irradiation of 600–1000 rep.

Anderson and Odell (1960) measured the hexosamine and hexuronic acid concentrations of various glycosaminoglycan fractions obtained from the costal cartilage of rats between 56 and 730 days of age. Although the total glycosaminoglycan content decreased with age, X-irradiation of the whole body with one single dose (range, 100–900 r) did not change the amount of glycosaminoglycans which could be prepared from the cartilage 6, 9, and 12 months after irradiation. Gerber *et al.* (1962) studied the incorporation of S^{35} and uniformly labeled glucose-C^{14} into the sulfate and hexosamine of glycosaminoglycan fractions of rat skin after X-irradiation. A slight increase in the specific activity of sulfate and of hexosamine was observed after X-irradiation with 500 and 1000 r and was interpreted as a decreased rate of replacement of glycosaminoglycans.

Further indication that radiation influences the metabolic apparatus of the cells responsible for the turnover of the sulfate groups of glycosaminoglycans comes from Schuster's (1964) systematic studies on the effect of radiation on the proliferation of fibrocytes and S^{35} incorporation into the vascularized corneal stroma of rats after the infliction of penetrating wounds (see also Chapter 37, Section II,C,3). Vascularization was induced by the injection of alloxan into the anterior chamber or of turpentine into the stroma. Eight days later, penetrating wounds, 2-mm long, were made in the tissue, and then there was immediate local application of β-radiation (600–6000 rep, Sr^{90}). Two days before the animals were killed (2, 5, 10, and 20 days after irradiation), $Na_2S^{35}O_4$ was injected intraperitoneally. The number of fibrocytes and the number of silver grains per unit area of tissue at various distances from the edge of the wound were then counted in the histological sections and in the autoradiograms. Most of the S^{35} was localized in the intercellular matrix, and both grain and cell counts were highest in the immediate vicinity of the wound edge, gradually decreasing until a constant value was reached at a distance of approximately 300 μ from the wound edge after 2–10 days of healing. On day 20 of healing, a higher grain number was observed only in the immediate vicinity ($<$100-μ distance) of the wound.

When the cornea was irradiated with 2400 and 6000 rep, fewer fibrocytes were observed in the vicinity of the wound edge ($<$300 μ) throughout the healing process that was studied (2–20 days), but a significant decrease in S^{35} incorporation was observed only from the 10th day of healing. Irradiation with 2400 rep caused an inhibition in the vascularization process of the stroma, induced by the injection of turpentine, and a parallel decrease in S^{35} incorporation (Schuster, 1963).

Scaife (1964) presented evidence that the release and the activity of extracted hyaluronidase from freshly isolated spermatozoa of rats and guinea pigs are not affected by 2000 rads of X-irradiation.

NOTE: The following papers of interest are hereby added to make the survey of the literature more comprehensive. These articles are also included in the reference list:

Anderson, A. J. (1965). The effect of chondromucoprotein on the solubility and peroxidatic properties of haemoglobin and methaemalbumin in aqueous solution and blood.

Galzinga, L., and Reggiani, A. (1965). Mucolytic activity mechanism of *N*-acetyl-L-cysteine.

Matsumura, G., and Pigman, W. (1965). Catalytic role of copper and iron ions in the depolymerization of hyaluronic acid by ascorbic acid.

Valtonen, E. J., Jänne, J., and Siimes, M. (1964). The effect of the erythemal reaction caused by ultra-violet irradiation on mast cell degranulation in the skin.

Wilson, C. W. (1965). The effect of a single 2,000 R exposure of X rays upon the uptake of ^{35}S by soft tissue of the mouse hind limb.

Chapter 48

INTERACTION OF POLYANIONS WITH BLOOD COMPONENTS

Peter Bernfeld

Substances containing amino sugar have been known for a long time to fulfill important biological functions. The first report on the physiological role of a substance which later was recognized to be made up, in part, of amino sugar was the discovery by McLean (1916) of a potent anticoagulant of normal blood, termed heparin by Howell and Holt (1918) because of its presumed relationship to the liver from which it was first obtained. Hahn (1943) later observed lipemia-clearing activity of intravenous heparin, a phenomenon which had subsequently been shown to consist in the mobilization of clearing factor (lipoprotein lipase) in the blood (Anfinsen, Boyle, and Brown, 1952) (see Chapter 46). Sulfated glycosaminoglycans were further found to inhibit the growth of marine eggs (Heilbrunn and Wilson, 1949) and of mammalian cells in tissue culture (Balazs and Holmgren, 1949) (see Chapter 51). *In vitro* activation and, especially, inhibition of enzymes by heparin and related substances are discussed in Chapter 46. The present chapter deals with the interactions between blood components and polyanionic macromolecular substances that contain amino sugar and either hexuronic acid or sulfate ester groups, or both. In many instances, it has been observed that macromolecular polyanions that do not contain amino sugar are also capable of interacting with plasma proteins in a similar fashion. The present discussion will, therefore, be centered around the general problem of complex formations of proteins with macromolecular polyanions, and emphasis will be placed on the influence of amino sugars on such complex formation.

Inasmuch as the anticoagulant activity of heparin and related substances may be considered to be the result of an interaction of these polyanions with certain blood components, this problem, as well as the mobilization of clearing factor in plasma, will also be briefly discussed in this chapter.

I. Nonspecific Protein–Polyanion Complexes

The *in vitro* interaction between polyanions and proteins is generally considered as being due, at least in a major part, to electrostatic attractive forces or salt formation, as pointed out by Bettelheim-Jevons (1958). It depends greatly on the charge density of both the polyanion and the protein and, hence, on the number of dissociable acidic groups of the polyanion (Mathews, 1960), as well as on the number of dissociable basic groups of the protein. The pH of the medium, the content of basic amino acids of the protein, the isoelectric point of the protein, and the nature of the acidic groups of the polyanion (sulfate, carboxyl, or other) are of the highest importance, therefore, for such complex formation. On the other hand, the chemical composition of the polyanion and of the protein, besides the content of acidic and basic groups, respectively, as well as the physicochemical and biological characteristics of these polyelectrolytes, appears to have little if any influence on the interaction. Consequently, this interaction is particularly nonspecific with regard to the nature of the participating proteins and polyanions, and a great many protein–polyanion complexes have been described, involving a great variety of each of the participating polyelectrolytes.

Naturally occurring protein complexes of chondroitin 4-sulfate and of hyaluronic acid have been discussed by Meyer (1953) (see Volume I, Chapter 8). Chargaff, Ziff, and Moore (1941) obtained definite proof of complex formation by studying the effect of rather high concentrations of heparin, chondroitin 4-sulfate, and cellulose sulfate on whole plasma. Interactions between heparin and casein, gelatin, and protamine, respectively, were investigated by Jaques (1943). Gorter and Nanninga (1952, 1953) described complexes of heparin or chondroitin 4-sulfate with bovine serum albumin, ovalbumin, and thrombin. The precipitation of euglobulins from normal human serum with small amounts of chondroitin 4-sulfate has been reported by Badin and Schubert (1955) (see Volume I, Chapter 8).

Among macromolecular polyanions not containing amino sugars, complex formation with various proteins is manifold. Singer, Timasheff, and Kirkwood (1952) observed the interaction between bovine serum albumin and fish sperm deoxyribonucleic acid. Changes in the viscosity of proteins upon addition of nucleic acids have been interpreted by Greenstein and Jenrette (1941) to be the result of interactions. Many synthetic high polymers, such as polymethacrylic acid, methacrylic–vinylpyridine polymers, polyvinylamine, maleic anhydride–styrene copolymers, and methacrylic acid–diethylaminoethyl methacrylate copolymers, were found by Morawetz and Hughes (1952) to undergo complex formation with bovine serum albumin, and Berdick and Morawetz (1954) observed interaction of polyacrylic acid, maleic anhydride–styrene copolymers, and maleic anhydride–vinyl methyl ether copolymers with beef and pork liver catalases and with bovine hemoglobin. Even certain anionic detergents of low molecular weight form a complex with proteins (Neurath and Putnam, 1945). Thus, β-lactoglobulin forms a crystalline derivative with two equivalents of firmly bound dodecyl sulfate (McMeekin *et al.*, 1949), and dodecylbenzene sulfonate has been shown to combine with bovine serum albumin, zein, and ovalbumin (Foster and Yang, 1953). The formation of complexes between proteins and detergents, macroanions, and other substances was reviewed by Putnam (1948), Klotz (1953), and Bettelheim-Jevons (1958).

In almost all cases of these nonspecific interactions, the complex formation was observed in acid medium or on the acid side of the isoelectric point of the protein. Chargaff, Ziff, and Moore (1941) worked at pH 7.58, however, and used much higher polyanion concentrations (0.4% heparin) than did most other investigators. It appears, therefore, that the protein behaves in most or all of the instances just mentioned as nothing more than a nonspecific polycation which tends to form a salt with any kind of polyanion, particularly so with polyanions of a macromolecular nature.

II. Specific Complexes between Polyanions and Certain Proteins

In contrast with the large number of the just-mentioned nonspecific protein–polyanion interactions, a few instances are known in which the polyanions appear to be highly selective for certain proteins. Serum β-lipoproteins are capable of interacting with polyanions not only in an acid medium but also in a weakly alkaline medium, the pH of which is well above the isoelectric point of the lipoprotein. The interaction of β-lipoproteins with polyanions proceeds, therefore, under conditions in which the negative charges of the protein are in considerable excess over its positive charges. Among all serum proteins, β-lipoproteins are the only ones to react with polyanions at pH 8.6, and only a very few other proteins, such as fibrinogen, are known to undergo complex formation with polyanions on the alkaline side of their isoelectric points. It is for this reason that the formation of such complexes is designated as a specific type.

In addition, the chemical nature of the polyanion also influences this type of interaction. As an example, serum β-lipoproteins exhibit different affinities for various polyanions, depending on the chemical and physicochemical nature of the latter.

Consequently, in contrast with the lack of specificity of the protein–polyanion complexes discussed in the preceding section of this chapter, the complex formation between serum β-lipoproteins and certain polyanions is a specific reaction.

A. Interaction of Macromolecular Polyanions with Serum Lipoproteins

1. *In Vitro* Effects

a. Specificity of Interaction. A great many polysaccharide sulfates, such as heparin and the polysulfate esters of hyaluronic acid, chitin, polymannuronic acid, polygalacturonic acid, cellulose, dextran, amylopectin, amylose, and many others, are known to interact with certain specific serum proteins. This interaction takes place not only in slightly acid and neutral medium but also in a weakly alkaline medium, up to the pH of 9. When amylopectin sulfate is added to normal or pathological human sera, a marked precipitate is obtained, and a sharp decrease in β-globulin can be observed in the electrophoretic pattern (Bernfeld, Berkowitz, and Donahue, 1957). The β-globulin–amylopectin sulfate precipitate can be disintegrated into its components by dissolving it in 12 to 18% sodium chloride solution and precipitating the polysulfate as the barium salt. The remaining protein was identified by chemical, electrophoretic, and ultracentrifugal analyses and was found to be a β-lipoprotein containing 70 to 80% lipids (Bernfeld, 1957, 1958), and having a flotation rate between S_f 4 and 8 (Bernfeld, 1959); this β-lipoprotein is similar in composition and properties to the one obtained by Oncley, Walton, and Cornwell (1957) using dextran sulfate as the precipitant. Evidence of complex formation between other macromolecular polyanions and human serum proteins in weakly alkaline media (pH 8.6) is shown by either a yield of precipitates or the production of significant changes in the electrophoretic patterns. When whole serum is first treated with amylopectin sulfate and the resulting precipitate removed, no further interaction between any polyanion and the remaining serum proteins is observed. It appears evident, therefore, that the interaction between polysaccharide sulfates and serum proteins at pH 7.5 to 8.6 is limited to those β-globulins which may be precipitated by amylopectin sulfate and which, according to their chemical and physicochemical analyses, are low-density β-lipoproteins (Bernfeld, Donahue, and Berkowitz, 1957).

b. Various Types of Complexes. The specific interaction between macromolecular polyanions and serum β-lipoproteins was observed to yield several different types of complexes according to the chemical nature of the polyanion involved. When the interaction was studied by means of two independent techniques—namely, by nephelometric measurement of the formation of insoluble complexes and by the moving boundary electrophoresis to detect and analyze soluble complexes—it was possible to classify the types of complex formed between serum β-lipoprotein and macromolecular polyanions into three distinct groups (Bernfeld, 1954, 1955). It was assumed that no interaction at all had occurred when both of these techniques gave negative results.

These three types of interaction between β-lipoprotein and polyanions were characterized by Bernfeld, Donahue, and Berkowitz (1957) (see Table I). Type I represents the formation of an insoluble complex, as

TABLE I
TYPES OF INTERACTION BETWEEN HUMAN SERUM β-LIPOPROTEIN AND MACROMOLECULAR POLYANIONS[a]

Interaction			Means of characterization of interaction[b]		
			Nephelometry (increase in light scattering)	Electrophoresis (increase in mobility)	
Type of complex	Solubility	Ability to dissociate		Ascending limb	Descending limb
I	Insoluble	—	+		
II	Soluble	no	−	+	+
III	Soluble	yes	−	+	−
None	—	—	−	−	−

[a] Data from Bernfeld *et al.*, 1960.
[b] −: no change observed; +: change observed.

indicated by an increase in turbidity; type II, the formation of a soluble, irreversible complex, as represented by an acceleration of the electrophoretic mobility of β-lipoprotein in both ascending and descending limbs of the electrophoresis cell; and type III, the formation of a soluble, reversible complex, as depicted by an acceleration of the electrophoretic mobility of β-lipoprotein in the ascending limb of the cell only.

The absence of an acceleration of the mobility in the descending limb of the electrophoresis cell is due to the dissociation of the complex into its components, whereby the fast-migrating polyanion rapidly moves away from the descending limb; its concentration remains constant, however, in the ascending limb of the cell during the experiment.

Under normal experimental conditions, the rapid depletion of polyanions, capable of forming type III complexes with β-lipoprotein, occurs

TABLE II

RELATIONSHIP BETWEEN THE CHEMICAL NATURE OF THE POLYANION AND THE TYPE OF COMPLEX FORMATION WITH β-LIPOPROTEINS[a]

	Functional groups				Interaction			
	No. of sulfate ester groups							
Polyanion	Per monosaccharide unit	Per repeating unit	Carboxyl group	*N*-Acetyl or *N*-sulfate or both	Type I	Type II	Type III	None
Amylopectin sulfate	1.25–2.45	—	—	—	+	—	—	—
Amylose sulfate	1.45–2.1	—	—	—	+	+	—	—
Glycogen sulfate	1.7–1.9	—	—	—	+	+	—	—
Dextran sulfate	1.1–1.7	—	—	—	+	+	—	—
Cellulose sulfate	1.7–2.9	—	—	—	+	+	—	—
Carrageenan (λ or κ)	0.6–1.0	—	—	—	+	+	—	—
Polyvinyl sulfate	—	0.64	—	—	+	+	—	—
Polystyrene sulfonate	—	0.61	—	—	+	+	—	—
Agar	0.10	—	—	—	—	—	—	+
Galacturonan sulfate	1.4	—	+	—	—	+	—	—
Mannuronan sulfate	1.15	—	+	—	—	+	—	—
Carboxymethyl-cellulose sulfate	0.66	—	+[b]	—	—	+	—	—
Chitin sulfate	0.68	—	—	+	—	—	+	—
Deacetylated chitin sulfate	0.23	—	—	+	—	—	+	—
Heparin	—	1.45–2.68	+	+	—	—	+	—
Hyaluronic[c] acid sulfate	—	0.58–1.33	+	+	—	—	+	—
Sulfated chondroitin 4-sulfate	—	1.6–2.35	+	+	—	—	+	—
Chondroitin 4-sulfate	—	0.94	+	+	—	—	—	+

TABLE II (*Continued*)

Polyanion	Functional groups: No. of sulfate ester groups: Per monosaccharide unit	Per repeating unit	Carboxyl group	N-Acetyl or N-sulfate or both	Interaction: Type I	Type II	Type III	None
Chondroitin 6-sulfate	—	1.0	+	+	—	—	—	+
Dermatan sulfate	—	0.77	+	+	—	—	+	—
Carboxymethylcellulose	—	—	+	—	—	(+)	—	—
Polymethacrylic acid	—	—	+	—	—	(+)	—	—
Galacturonan (pectic acid)	—	—	+	—	—	—	—	+
Mannuronan (alginic acid)	—	—	+	—	—	—	—	+
Hyaluronic acid	—	—	+	+	—	—	—	+

[a] According to Bernfeld *et al.*, 1960.
[b] 0.75 carboxymethyl group.
[c] Derived from either bovine vitreous body or human umbilical cord.

not only in the descending limb of the cell of free electrophoresis but also during zone electrophoresis (e.g., paper electrophoresis). This is owing to the fact that, in contrast with moving boundary electrophoresis, the average distance of migration of the proteins in zone electrophoresis is a multiple of the distance from one end of the protein sample to the other, measured in the direction of electrophoretic migration. Type III complex formation cannot be observed, therefore, by paper electrophoresis or by other techniques of zone electrophoresis.

c. Relationship between Chemical Nature of the Polyanion and Type of Complex. The results summarized in Table II clearly show that the type of complex formed by β-lipoprotein and polyanion is governed mainly by the chemical nature of the polyanion—i.e., by the presence or absence therein of sulfate, carbonyl, and *N*-acetyl groups (Bernfeld *et al.*, 1960; Bernfeld and Nisselbaum, 1956).

Most macromolecular polysulfate esters and polysulfonic acids, possessing no other functional groups besides hydroxyl and the sulfate ester or sulfonic acid groups, have been found to form insoluble complexes of type I with β-lipoprotein. There are differences in the solubility of the complex within this group and, as the complexes of type I become more soluble, they are gradually replaced by type II complexes. The molecular weight, the presence or absence of a branched structure (e.g., amylopectin vs. amylose), the type of glycosidic bonds (amylopectin vs. dextran), the configuration of the bonds (amylose vs. cellulose), and the nature of the repeating unit (glucose vs. galactose, in amylopectin and carrageenan, respectively) do not appear to affect the type of complex. The sulfur content exerts relatively little influence on the interaction. When the amount of sulfate groups is decreased below a certain threshold, however (0.6 sulfate per anhydrohexose unit), interaction ceases altogether.

Polyanions with carboxyl groups such as polymannuronic acid, polygalacturonic acid, and hyaluronic acid do not interact at all with β-lipoproteins, whereas carboxymethylcellulose and polymethacrylic acid exhibit only a very weak tendency for complex formation. When carboxyl groups and sulfate ester groups occur together in the same polymer, however, such as in sulfated carboxymethylcellulose, sulfated galacturonan, and mannuronan sulfate (acid sulfate), the complex formation is of type II, which is the soluble and irreversible type. The presence of carboxyl groups therefore appears to increase markedly the solubility of the lipoprotein–polyanion complexes.

N-Acetyl and *N*-sulfate groups have been found to decrease even more considerably the affinity between polyanion and lipoprotein than do carboxyl groups. Consequently, sulfated glycosaminoglycans, such as chitin sulfate, chitosan sulfate, sulfated hyaluronic acid, sulfated chondroitin 4-sulfate with at least 1.6 sulfate groups per repeating unit, dermatan sulfate, and heparin, interact with β-lipoprotein to form soluble and reversible complexes that are of type III. Chondroitin 4-sulfate and chondroitin 6-sulfate did not show any signs of complex formation.

An increase in the electrophoretic mobility of globulins upon the *in vitro* addition of heparin to serum at pH 7.5 to 8.6 has been repeatedly reported in the literature. Chargaff, Ziff, and Moore (1941), using as much as 400 mg of heparin per 100 ml of serum, obtained not only an acceleration of β-globulin but also some interaction with albumin. Nikkilä (1952) found an increase of α-globulin with a simultaneous decrease of β-globulin. The use of even higher heparin concentrations, ranging from 0.5 mg to 10 g per 100 cc of serum, led Blasius and Seitz (1952) to similar observations. At these extremely elevated polyanion concentrations, these authors noted increased electrophoretic mobilities also for α- and γ-globulins.

2. *In Vivo* Effects

The intravenous injection of heparin into humans and experimental animals obviously produces a multiple effect on the blood components. The prolongation of the clotting time of blood by heparin has been known for a long time. The antilipemic action of *in vivo* administered heparin is another important phenomenon that has been studied thoroughly during the past years and is known to result in the liberation of unesterified fatty acids (Shore, Nichols, and Freeman, 1953) (see Chapter 46). If heparin would stay in the blood long enough, it would certainly interact with the plasma proteins in the same way as it does *in vitro.* It is difficult to distinguish, however, between heparin–protein interactions and fatty acid–protein complexes resulting from the antilipemic action of heparin (Gordon, 1955). Some of the phenomena observed upon *in vivo* administration of heparin will be presented, and, in a few cases, an attempt will be made to analyze whether these phenomena are due to interaction of plasma proteins with unesterified fatty acids, with heparin, or with some heparinoid which might originate from heparin *in vivo.*

a. Ultracentrifugal Observations. Graham *et al.* (1951) have studied the low-density lipoproteins in humans and rabbits after intravenous heparin injection, using the method of ultracentrifugal flotation. They found a profound reorientation in the distribution of these lipoproteins and a successive shift from molecules of higher flotation rates to those of lower flotation rates. In the light of our knowledge on the induction by heparin of plasma lipoprotein lipase which, in turn, breaks down the triglycerides in lipoproteins, the findings of Graham *et al.* indicate that lipoproteins with a high content of triglycerides and, hence, with high flotation rates are transformed into lipoproteins with less neutral fat and, therefore, with lower flotation rates.

b. Electrophoretic Findings. Numerous reports have appeared in the literature on the effects of intravenous heparin on plasma proteins and, in particular, on lipoproteins, as measured by moving boundary or paper electrophoresis. Lever, Smith, and Hurley (1953) found a decrease of β-globulin in two of seven normal subjects after heparin injection, as well as increases in the β-globulins or in albumin. In addition, abnormally high β_1-globulins were drastically reduced after heparin injection in six of eight patients with hypercholesteremic xanthomatosis, while the α_2- or α_1-globulins, or both, or the albumin of these patients was increased. No simultaneous changes occurred, however, in the amounts of neutral fat or phospholipids—a fact which would seem to indicate that triglycerides have not been more than insignificantly broken down to fatty acids, and that the plasma protein changes were due to the combination of heparin or of a similar polyanion, derived from heparin, with β-lipoprotein, rather than to an interaction of lipoprotein with unesterified fatty acids.

In contrast with these considerations, Eiber and Danishefsky (1959) isolated various plasma protein fractions, after intravenous injection of heparin S^{35}, by means of ultracentrifugal flotation and chemical fractionation by Cohn's Method IV. They did not find more than minute amounts of radioactivity in the low-density lipoproteins, denoting that no complexes between β-lipoprotein and heparin (or any heparinoid derived from heparin) could have been formed. Herbst *et al.* (1955) isolated α- and β-lipoproteins from subjects with idiopathic and alimentary hyperlipemia after heparin injection; these authors observed greatly increased electrophoretic mobilities of the isolated proteins which were interpreted as being due to complex formations of the lipoproteins with unesterified fatty acids liberated as a result of the lipolytic effect of heparin. Herbst, Lever, and Hurley (1955), using paper electrophoresis, also noted an increase in the mobility of β-lipoprotein after heparin injection. This finding is of interest with regard to the explanation of the phenomena described by Herbst *et al.* (1955). Reversible complexes between β-lipoprotein and heparin are known to belong to type III and to dissociate readily. Such complexes cannot be detected by zone electrophoresis, in particular by paper electrophoresis (see Section II,A,1,*b*). It appears unlikely, therefore, that the acceleration of β-lipoprotein by heparin *in vivo* is owing to an interaction between these two components; this phenomenon is probably caused by the formation of type II complexes between lipoprotein and fatty acids released by the action of lipoprotein lipase.

The study of the interaction between serum proteins and polyanions has shown that, among all polyelectrolytes studied so far, only polyanions containing amino sugar are capable of forming reversible complexes of type III. It appears to be of some interest, therefore, to recall some instances in which electrophoretic plasma protein patterns have been obtained which show differences between ascending and descending boundaries in analogy to those produced by lipoprotein–glycosaminoglycan sulfate complexes. For example, characteristic electrophoretic patterns in patients with idiopathic thrombocytopenia and other hemorrhagic conditions (Bernfeld and Stefanini, 1951) and in families with hemophilia (Bernfeld *et al.*, 1953) have been observed. There appeared in the ascending boundaries an α-globulin with a mobility as high as 4.4 to 4.5×10^{-5} cm^2 volt^{-1} sec^{-1}, while the mobilities of the α_2-globulins in the corresponding descending boundaries were completely normal—i.e., between 3.9 and 4.1×10^{-5} cm^2 volt^{-1} sec^{-1}. It was also possible to distinguish, on the ground of moving boundary electrophoretic analyses, between acute and chronic idiopathic thrombocytopenic purpura (Stefanini, Dameshek, and Bernfeld, 1953). Although no attempt to isolate anomalous substances from the serum of subjects with any of these hemorrhagic disorders has been made, the behavior of the plasma proteins on moving boundary electrophoresis strongly suggests the occurrence of type III complexes in the plasma of these patients. The existence in pathological plasma of glycosaminoglycan sulfates may have to be considered as the cause of this phenomenon, although these substances are chemically and physiologically different from heparin and contain higher amounts of sulfate than do the chondroitin sulfates.

B. Interaction of Polyanions with Fibrinogen

In studying streaming potentials of fibrinogen–heparin mixtures, Sheppard and Wright (1954) found that heparin increased the ζ potentials of fibrinogenated Pyrex and Teflon surfaces. These authors therefore assumed the existence of a fibrinogen–heparin complex which has a decreased affinity for coating-out on the negative capillary wall.

Definite proof of a complex formed by fibrinogen and heparin has been obtained by Bernfeld, Donahue, and Berkowitz (1957), using moving boundary electrophoresis. Fibrinogen was found to behave like β-lipoprotein with respect to heparin and most other macromolecular polyanions. All three types of complexes were observed to occur with fibrinogen, and the same individual polyanions were found to produce the same type of interaction for both plasma proteins, with the only exception being that the fibrinogen–polyanion complexes were usually more soluble than the corresponding β-lipoprotein–polyanion complexes. As in the case of β-lipoprotein, polyanions containing amino sugars were the only substances to produce type III interaction.

The precipitation at low temperatures (cold precipitation) by heparin of gelatinous protein material from normal human plasma and, in particular, from the plasma of patients with acute rheumatic disease and from the plasma of rabbits after injection of meningococcal endotoxin has been reported by Thomas, Smith, and Von Korff (1954). The plasma protein involved in this precipitation at low temperatures (cold precipitation) has been identified as being closely related to fibrinogen.

III. Interaction of Polyanions with Blood Components as Observed by Physiological Changes

The interactions discussed in this chapter so far were adequately characterized by physicochemical methods. In contrast, heparin and similar glycan sulfates are also well known for their effect upon certain blood components, resulting in such physiological changes as the prolongation of the clotting time of blood or the generation in blood of a lipid clearing activity. The existence of complex formation has not, however, been established by chemical or physicochemical methods. The occurrence of interactions is indirectly evident from the physiological changes in the coagulation and lipolytic systems, respectively.

A. Anticoagulant Activity of Heparin

1. Mechanism

The mechanism of blood coagulation is an extremely intricate system which involves a great number of more-or-less undefined blood components. This subject has been repeatedly reviewed in the literature (Chargaff, 1945; Seegers, 1953, 1955; Stefanini, 1953; Quick, 1954; Stefanini and Dameshek, 1955; and Macfarlane, 1960). For the better understanding of the anticoagulant action of heparin, a "drastically simplified scheme of coagulation," according to Macfarlane (1960), is shown in Fig. 1.

It has long been known that heparin, despite its remarkable effect on

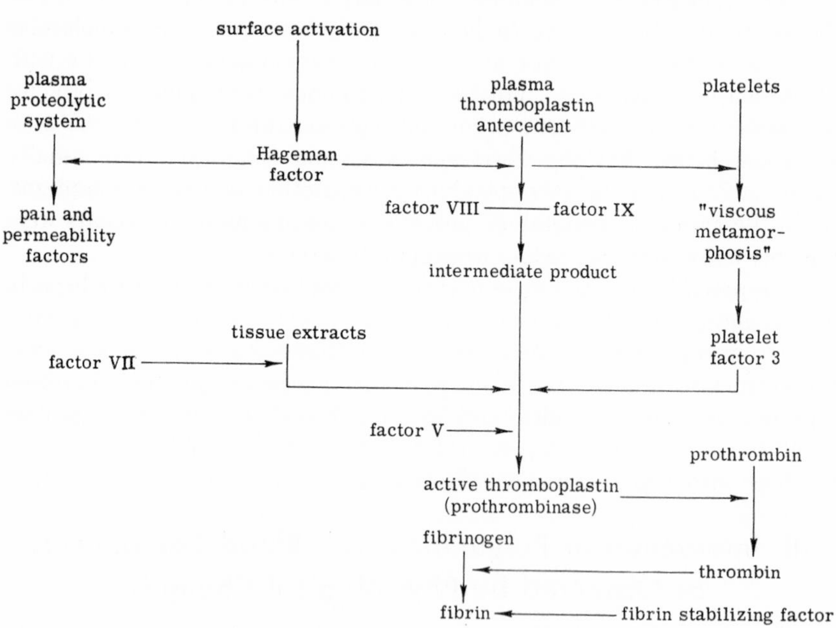

FIG. 1. Diagram illustrating some of the factors believed to be concerned in clotting and their possible relationships, according to Macfarlane (1960).

whole blood or plasma, does not inhibit the conversion of pure fibrinogen to fibrin by purified thrombin (Howell and Holt, 1918) nor is it capable of preventing the transformation of isolated prothrombin to thrombin in the presence of purified thromboplastin (Mellanby, 1934; Quick, 1936). The anticoagulant action of heparin is generally thought to be involved in at least four different steps of the clotting mechanism.

(1) In the presence of a certain plasma protein, called "heparin complement" by Ziff and Chargaff (1940), which frequently accompanies impure albumin preparations, heparin is believed to possess "antithrombin activity" by inhibiting the enzymic activity of thrombin (Ziff and Chargaff, 1940). In fact, thrombin disappears from the blood after coagulation, and this disappearance has been ascribed mainly to the action of antithrombin II, a serum protein with the electrophoretic mobility of albumin; antithrombin II may be activated by heparin (Seegers, 1955). Whether "heparin complement" or any other heparin cofactor is identical with the natural antithrombin is a controversial issue (Walton, 1955). In this connection it appears interesting, however, that a heparin–lipoprotein complex with antithrombin activity has been isolated from mast cells (Snellman, Sylvén, and Julén, 1951). The lipoprotein moiety, after dissociation from this complex, was capable of recombining with heparin and, thus, regaining antithrombin activity. In view of the acceleration of the electrophoretic mobility of serum β-lipoproteins by heparin through complex formation, discussed earlier in this chapter (see Section II,A,1), and in accordance with electrophoresis findings by Chargaff, Ziff, and Moore (1941) and with views expressed by Chargaff (1945), natural antithrombin, or one of the natural antithrombins, could be considered as a complex formed by antithrombin II or "heparin complement"—possibly a serum β-lipoprotein—and heparin in which the latter functions as a prosthetic group. It has been suggested that the action of heparin consists in an acceleration of the normal binding between thrombin and the protein cofactor (Loeb, 1956).

"Heparin complement" was found to act only above a certain critical concentration (Ziff and Chargaff, 1940). Above this threshold concentration, the occurrence of clotting depended entirely on the concentration of "heparin complement."

It has also been suggested that heparin exerts its antithrombin action by means of a coupled phosphorylation reaction (Green, 1952).

(2) In combination with a similar, or possibly the same, plasma protein, heparin has been found to inhibit prothrombin conversion to thrombin (Brinkhous *et al.*, 1939). It is not known, however, whether this effect is due to an action on prothrombin or on thromboplastin. An activation of prothrombin by heparin-sequestrating agents, such as protamine sul-

fate, was observed (Seegers, 1955), and it thus appears that heparin normally inhibits prothrombin, and that normal clotting involves the removal of heparin from its combination with a clotting factor (Macfarlane, 1960). This suggests an "antiprothrombin action" of heparin, in addition to its "antithrombin" effect.

(3) An interaction between heparin and thromboplastin, a lipoprotein prepared from beef lung (Cohen and Chargaff, 1940, 1941a; Chargaff, Bendich, and Cohen, 1944), was observed by Chargaff, Ziff, and Cohen (1940). It results in a complex formed by heparin and the protein moiety of the lipoprotein, while the lipid constituents of the thromboplastic protein are released. These lipids were found to consist of phosphatides with marked clotting activity, and of sphingomyelin (Cohen and Chargaff, 1941). A similar mechanism was suggested by Overman (1949) for the action of heparin on plasma thromboplastic protein.

(4) Finally, Best, Cowan, and MacLean (1938) found that heparin prevents the disintegration of blood platelets; it therefore also interferes with one of the initial steps of the coagulation of blood. In addition, the release of serotonin, the vasoconstrictor substance associated with blood clotting, is known to be inhibited by heparin (Janeway, Richardson, and Park, 1918).

2. Relation between Chemical Structure and Anticoagulant Activity

The role of the amino sugar in heparin and heparinlike anticoagulants and the requirement of *N*-sulfate groups and sulfate ester groups for their anticoagulant activity have been widely discussed by a number of workers, and this subject has been summarized by Walton (1955).

Wolfrom and McNeely (1945) found that heparin gradually loses its biological activity as its *N*-sulfate groups are hydrolyzed by weak acid. This observation was later confirmed by Wolfrom *et al.* (1950), by Meyer and Schwartz (1950), and by Jorpes, Boström, and Mutt (1950). The high importance of the contribution of *N*-sulfate groups to the anticoagulant activity has been further pointed out by Wolfrom, Shen, and Summers (1953) and by Doczi, Fischman, and King (1953) by the demonstration of high anticoagulant potency of *N*-sulfated, deacetylated chitin.

On the other hand, alkaline degradation of heparin with ammonium hydroxide yielded a biologically inactive substance in which the *N*-sulfate groups were essentially left intact, while a certain amount of the *O*-sulfate groups had been split off (Jorpes, Boström, and Mutt, 1950). Later, Foster, Martlew, and Stacey (1953) showed that the anticoagulant activity of heparin does not necessarily follow its content in sulfoamino groups when they observed that some heparin preparations with high *N*-sulfate content actually exhibited low anticoagulant potency. In addition, the long list of synthetic and naturally occurring anticoagulants which do not contain hexosamine demonstrates that the presence of sulfoamino groups, although undoubtedly contributing to the anticoagulant activity, is not a prerequisite for this biological effect (Bergström, 1936; Chargaff, Bancroft, and Stanley-Brown, 1936; Constantinides, Cairns, and Werner, 1954). In most instances, however, the anticoagulant potency of the sulfated polysaccharides which do not contain sulfoamino groups amounts to only a fraction of that of heparin itself; the potency of these polysaccharides does not exceed 25% of that of heparin except in a very small number of cases, such as in dextran sulfates of very high molecular weights (Walton, 1955).

Some influence must be attributed to the content of total sulfate in heparin as a determinant of the anticoagulant potency therein. Jorpes and Bergström (1939) found, indeed, that the biological activity of heparin preparations from various sources increased with the content of total sulfate of the polysaccharide, although there was no strict proportionality between these two parameters. Dextran sulfates did not exhibit anticoagulant activity unless they contained at least 1 sulfate group per glucose residue (Ricketts and Walton, 1952); their biological activity then rose with the increasing sulfate content until they reached about 1.7 sulfate groups per glucose unit. An additional increase in sulfate content did not produce any further rise in their anticoagulant activity.

The influence of the molecular weight of polysaccharide sulfates on their anticoagulant properties was studied by Ricketts (1952, 1954), who found little activity in low molecular species (degree of polymerization below 9), even when the sulfate content was high (from 2 to 2.8 sulfate groups per glucose residue). Sulfated dextrans with the same content of sulfate but different molecular weight showed a higher anticoagulant activity for the compound possessing a higher molecular weight (degree of polymerization about 17).

It thus appears that anticoagulant activity is determined by more than a single factor and that it depends on the presence of both sulfoamino groups and sulfate ester groups, while the molecular shape contributes to the reaching of optimum conditions for such biological activity.

B. Anticoagulant Activity of Other Polyanions

Among the many substances known to interfere in one way or another with the clotting mechanism of blood, there are numerous anticoagulants which act in a manner completely different from that of heparin; these are 3,3′-methylene-bis-(4-hydroxycoumarin) (dicumarol), hirudin, oxalate, citrate, fluoride, rare earth salts, protamines, and reducing agents like cysteine, glutathione, and bisulfite. Polysulfate esters of numerous macromolecular substances, in particular of polysaccharides, and other polyanions of high molecular weight have been found, however, to parallel the action of heparin, in that they may either inactivate thrombin or inhibit prothrombin conversion to thrombin. Both naturally occurring and synthetic anticoagulants of this type are known. Thus, a polysaccharide (galactan sulfate) from *Irideae laminarioides* (Chargaff, Bancroft, and Stanley-Brown, 1936), agar and carrageenan from *Chondrus crispus* (Elsner, Broser, and Bürgel, 1937), a hexosamine-free polysaccharide sulfate from *Charonia campas* (Soda and Egami, 1938), an unidentified polysaccharide from mollusks (Frommhagen *et al.*, 1953), dermatan sulfate (Marbet and Winterstein, 1951), and sulfated hyaluronic acid (Balazs, Högberg, and Laurent, 1951) all have heparinlike action. Among the synthetic anticoagulants are sulfated products of starch, amylose, amylopectin, glycogen, and cellulose (Bergström, 1936), those of hyaluronic acid (Balazs, Högberg, and Laurent, 1951), dextran (Walton, 1952), xylan, mannuronan (alginic acid) (Sorenson and Wright, 1950), galacturonan methyl ester (Mangieri, Engelberg, and Randall, 1951; Field *et al.*, 1953), chitin (Roth, Shepperd, and Richards, 1954), polyvinyl alcohol (Chargaff, Bancroft, and Stanley-Brown, 1936), and, in addition, various inorganic substances of high molecular weight such as phosphotungstate and silicotungstate (Bragdon and Havel, 1954).

With the exception of dermatan sulfate, chitin sulfate, and sulfated hyaluronic acid, none of these substances contains amino sugars, and the amino groups of the two glycosaminoglycans, just mentioned, are known to occur as *N*-acetyl derivatives. *N*-Sulfate groups are not involved, therefore, in the biological activity of any of these products. All of the heparinlike anticoagulants have high molecular weights and are polyanions, mostly sulfate esters of polysaccharides. Almost all of them have been found to be also capable of generating lipoprotein lipase *in vivo* (see Chapter 46).

Chapter 49

IMMUNOCHEMISTRY

Georg F. Springer†

In 1917, Dochez and Avery found a soluble substance in cell-free filtrates of pneumococci, which precipitated specifically with antiserum of the corresponding type.* By 1923, Zinsser and Parker described protein-free "residue antigens" from pneumococci which gave specific precipitates. Heidelberger and Avery, however, in 1923, were the first to demonstrate unequivocally the carbohydrate nature of type II pneumococcal capsular substance. Based on this fundamental observation, Heidelberger and his colleagues showed the general immunochemical importance of polysaccharides, many of which contained hexosamine (Heidelberger, 1956). The original antigen in the intact pneumococcus was the principal part which could give rise to type-specific antibodies. The isolated purified polysaccharides, on the other hand, reacted with the antibodies in horse or rabbit sera, but did not appear to induce their formation. Not until Schiemann and Casper (1927), Finland and Sutliff (1931,a), Felton (1932), Finland and Sutliff (1932), and Felton, Sutliff, and Steele (1935) studied the effect of these polysaccharides on mice was it known that extremely small quantities of polysaccharide material could be antigenic in some animal species (compare Heidelberger, 1956) and, as shown by Tillett and Francis

† I have attempted to treat the immunochemistry of amino sugars comprehensively up to and including 1963. The delay in publication of this tome and the rapid progress in many of the areas of research covered have made it impossible to refer to original work (including that from my laboratory) which became known after the summer of 1964.

* In view of the nature of this book, the editors requested omission of explanation of the essential terminology used in this chapter. A definition of terms and how they were arrived at may be found in: Ehrlich, 1904, 1957; Arrhenius, 1907; Landsteiner and Lampl, 1918; Landsteiner, 1921; Avery and Heidelberger, 1923; Zinsser and Parker, 1923; Avery and Goebel, 1929; Goebel and Avery, 1929; Marrack and Smith, 1932; Haurowitz and Breinl, 1933; Marrack, 1938; Heidelberger, Treffers, and Mayer, 1940; Race, 1944; Wiener, 1944; Landsteiner, 1945; Oudin, 1946; Doerr, 1948; Ouchterlony, 1948; Singer and Campbell, 1952; Grabar and Williams, 1953; Kabat and Berg, 1953; Heidelberger, 1956; Westphal, 1957a; Mayer, 1958; Schmidt, 1959; Boyd, 1961; Kabat and Mayer, 1961; Raffel, 1961; Crowle, 1961.

(1929, 1930) and Francis and Tillett (1930) and others after them, also in man (compare Boivin and Delaunay, 1944).

In general, circulating-antibody response varies in its nature, depending on whether the antigen injected is of predominantly protein or polysaccharide character. In the antitoxin type (representative of antiprotein type), antibodies rise rapidly to a maximum and recede quickly to low levels. Further injection of the homologous protein antigen then leads to a prompt "recall," often to antibody levels considerably higher than those induced by the original injection. In contrast, anticarbohydrate

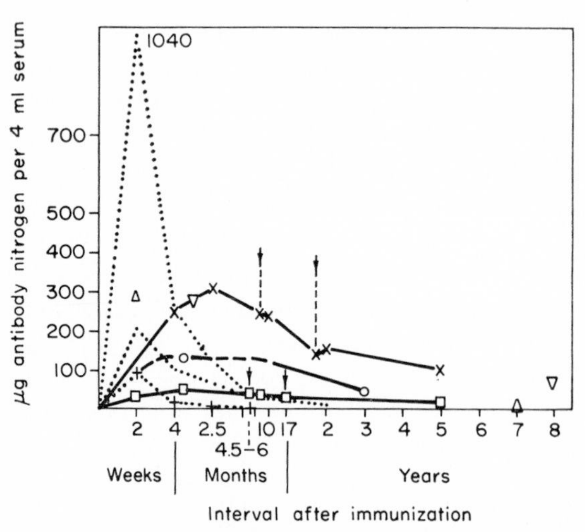

FIG. 1. Persistence of antibodies after immunization. Curves indicate the amount of antibody nitrogen found in human subjects at various intervals after immunization. Arrows indicate reinjections after bleeding analyzed (from Heidelberger, 1953).
· · · ·, diphtheria antitoxin;
○,□,×, antibody to type-specific polysaccharide of pneumococcus;
△,▽, type-specific antibody after pneumococcal infections.
The sections marked *weeks, months, years* are not directly comparable, since successively smaller units of length are used.

antibodies, which include those against the blood group substances (compare Kabat, 1956), rise more slowly, reach a somewhat lower peak, and form a long plateau near the maximum; the decline in antibody level begins slowly after about 6 months and lasts for years. During this period, reinjections with polysaccharide have little effect on existing antibody levels (see arrows in Fig. 1) (Heidelberger *et al.*, 1950; Murray, Ludwig, and Foter, 1950). An illustration of this situation is given in Fig. 1 (Heidelberger *et al.*, 1946, 1950; Heidelberger, 1953). An explanation for the strikingly different effect caused by these two classes of antigens was given by Heidelberger (1953), who reasoned that polysaccharides persist in the body for a long time and thus exert continuous antigenic stimuli, whereas proteins are speedily broken down by the body's own proteolytic enzymes.

The presence of hexosamine in highly purified, potentially antigenic compounds of both mammalian and bacterial origin was demonstrated over 30 years ago. Heidelberger (1927) suspected an amino sugar as a component of the type I pneumococcal soluble specific substance, and the presence of nitrogenous sugars in a number of polysaccharides isolated from pneumococci was again reported by Heidelberger and Kendall (1931, 1932), even though one of these polysaccharides may have been identical with the blood group A substance present in the growth medium employed (Goebel, 1938). At about the same time, the occurrence of hexosamine in blood group substances was established (Schiff and Weiler, 1931; Freudenberg and Eichel, 1934). This last group of compounds will be considered in detail first. The chemical structure of glycoproteins with blood group A, B, H(O), and Le^a activity is reviewed in Volume I, Chapter 13.

I. Blood Group Substances

A. A,B,H(O), and Lewis (Le^a) Blood Group Substances

The immunological importance of blood group substances has been established since their discovery by Landsteiner in 1900 (Landsteiner, 1900, 1901). Landsteiner was the first to show that when serum and erythrocytes from different individuals were mixed, red cell agglutination frequently, but not always, resulted. He found that, according to these clumping reactions, human blood could be classified into four groups. The serologically specific agent in the plasma occurred, so it seemed, naturally, and an individual's plasma or serum could not contain, under physiological circumstances, antibodies reactive against antigens on his own erythrocytes. On these early observations the modern concepts of the A, B, and O groups are built. There are known today at least fourteen human blood group systems, with over sixty different recognized agglutinogens (compare Boorman and Dodd, 1957) ; Race and Sanger, 1962; Stratton and Renton, 1959; Wiener, 1961). The chemical nature of only very few of these antigens has been determined, and for these materials alone can immunochemical studies be mentioned. The agglutinogens in question are those of the A, B, O(H), and closely related Lewis systems, all of which contain hexosamines. Their abundance in epithelial secretions and normal organs, as well as in malignant tissues (compare Springer, Rose, and György, 1954), has led to the isolation of these substances in large amounts and highly active form from sources such as saliva or pseudomucinous ovarian cyst fluids. In consequence, almost all detailed chemical and immunological knowledge of the A,B,H(O), and Lewis systems is based on such water-soluble substances, although the first observations pertaining to the physical and chemical nature of the A and B agglutinogens of erythrocytes were those of Schiff and Adelsberger (1924) and Landsteiner, van der Scheer, and Witt (1925), showing that these substances could be extracted from the red cells with ethanol. By their solubilities, these substances were characterized as being lipid (Schröder, 1931). There is little, however, to indicate that the serological specificity of the blood group A, B, and O agglutinogens is due to the lipid part of the extracted molecule. Schiff (1931) demonstrated the role of carbohydrate in the blood group specific groupings when he saponified the lipid part of the extracted A substance without destroying the activity of blood group A. Hallauer (1934) extracted A-, B-, and H(O)-active substances from human erythrocytes and stroma. These materials, which behaved as haptens, were water-soluble; no protein was demonstrable. Hallauer believed them to be of cerebroside-like nature, with additional carbohydrates.

More recently, Yamakawa and Iida (1953) isolated glycolipid structures of low activity from human erythrocytes which specifically inhibited blood group agglutinins; similar observations were made by Radin (1957), Kościelak and Zakrzewski (1960), Klenk (1960), Stalder and Springer (1960), and Hakomori and Jeanloz (1961). The activity of these glycolipids was uniformly low, usually well below 1% of that observed for water-soluble blood group glycoproteins.

If it is assumed that no water-soluble contaminant accompanied these glycolipids, then the low activity may be explainable in part by the poor solubility of these substances and their correspondingly reduced surface area. Recent experiments by Kościelak (1962, 1963), who obtained glycolipids of high blood group A and B activity from human erythrocytes, indicate that, in addition, favorable molecular shape and proper distance between chemical groups of the native blood group substance have to be secured by an "inert carrier" of the active groups for optimal combination with antibody molecules. The terminal, oligosaccharide structures essential for specificity may be the same as in the ovarian cyst glycoproteins of A and B specificity (Watkins, Kościelak, and Morgan, 1964). The blood group molecule, however, differs.

The substances isolated from A and B erythrocyte stroma, respectively, by Hakomori and Jeanloz showed great similarity in chemical composition and physical properties. Both contained the sugars thought to be predominantly responsible for A and B specificity. The chemical results of Kościelak and Zakrzewski are compatible with those obtained by Hakomori and Jeanloz, whereas those of Yamakawa and Irie (1960) and Yamakawa, Irie, and Iwanaga (1960) are not. Yamakawa and Irie stated that their purified blood group A glycolipid isolated from human erythrocytes was precipitable by rabbit anti-A serum from which it was subsequently isolated essentially unchanged.

Some chemical knowledge on the M and N substances has also accumulated which will be mentioned here, as will some data on the "I antigen," the "Lutheran antigens," a P-like antigen, the Forssman antigen, and the "heterogenetic mononucleosis receptor" of sheep and beef erythrocytes; all of these structures contain hexosamine. No agreement exists as to the chemical nature of the clinically important antigens of the Rh system. Recent claims by one group of workers (employing weak antibodies) which indicate direct participation of certain sialic acids in the specificity of the Rh_0 (D) antigen (Bigley, Chandler, and Dodd, 1958; Dodd, Bigley, and Geyer, 1960; Boyd and Reeves, 1961) have not been confirmed by others (Mäkelä, Cantell, and Penttinen, 1959; Johnson and McCluer, 1961; Springer, Williamson, and Brandes, 1961). None of the most recent claims (Dodd, Bigley, and Geyer, 1963; Bigley *et al.*, 1963), which differed from earlier ones by the same authors, has been confirmed in this laboratory (Wolff and Springer, 1964). Pirofsky and Cordova (1964) confirmed earlier studies by Kout and Kubickova (1959) and by Boyd, McMaster, and Waszczenko-Zacharczenko (1959) which indicated that streptomycin at very high concentrations (>30 mg/ml) inhibits specific agglutination of anti-Rh antibodies. Pirofsky and Cordova (1964) thought it unlikely that the hexosamine part of the streptomycin molecule was involved in the apparent Rh specificity of this antibiotic, since the basic streptidine part of the molecule was as active by itself as streptomycin was. Springer and Tegtmeyer (1964) found that twigs of most angiospermous plants and some lignin precursors contain nondialyzable material which inhibits the specific action of anti-Rh antibodies but is without effect on most other blood group reactions with specific human and animal agglutinins. The activity of these extracts, which contained no demonstrable hexosamine, sialic acid, or methylpentose, was about fifty times that of streptomycin.

1. Reactions *in Vivo*

The immunogenicity of highly purified blood group substances depends somewhat on which experimental animal is used. Although in man and chickens it is established that blood group substances may stimulate antibodies corresponding to their specificity (compare Kabat, 1956), their antigenicity in rabbits, unless coupled to protein, was open to doubt until Baer and Rasmussen (1960) reported production of anti-A and anti-B specific antibodies in a significant proportion of rabbits after intravenous injection of alum-precipitated blood group substances. A simple anamnestic response (i.e., enhanced response due to prior, possibly accidental, immunization with these substances) appears unlikely in some of these animals, since they formed potent antibodies and possessed no demonstrable preimmunization titer.

The antibodies against human blood groups A, B, and O(H) are unusual in that they are present, without deliberate stimulation, in all humans (after early infancy) lacking the particular antigen against which these antibodies are directed. This "natural" occurrence seemingly is at variance with the definition of an antibody and has even led to the opinion that anti-human blood group A and B agglutinins are not antibodies (Ehrlich, 1900; Thomsen, 1929–1930; Lederberg, 1959). More generally upheld however, was the view that blood group agglutinins are antibodies but that they are inherited and are products of genes linked to the A, B, and O genes (Bernstein, 1925; Hirszfeld, 1926; Furuhata, 1927; cf. Wilson and Miles, 1955).

Substantial evidence for the immunogenic origin of these anti-blood group antibodies (Dupont, 1934; Wiener, 1951; Kabat, 1956; Springer, 1960; and others), however, has been furnished by the demonstration that "germ-free" chicks do not form anti-human group B antibodies up to the age of 60 days, whereas ordinary chicks from the same hatch possess anti-B antibodies by the 30th day of life (Springer, Horton, and Forbes, 1959). Anti-human group B antibodies can be readily elicited in germ-free chicks 20–25 days old either if they are fed live blood group B active *E. coli* O_{86} (Springer, 1956,a, 1958,a) or if human group B meconium is fed to them and dusted into their cages. Furthermore, extensive serological studies of gram-negative bacteria, especially Enterobacteriaceae, have shown that a large number of them cross-react with human A, B, and H(O) substances (compare Springer, Williamson, and Brandes, 1961). The case for the immunogenic origin of anti-A and anti-B isoantibodies was strengthened by the findings of McDuffie and Kabat (1956) and Muschel, Osawa, and McDermott (1958) (see also Kabat, 1956,a), who were unable to demonstrate in actively immunized human beings the reported differences between so-called natural and immune anti-A and anti-B isoagglutinins. Springer, Tritel, and Leuterer (1963) recently showed that anti-B and anti-A isoagglutinin production is stimulated in humans with severe intestinal disorders when they are fed large quantities of killed blood group active *E. coli* O_{86}.

Purified blood group substances may raise pre-existing isoagglutinins to higher levels in man. Kabat and Bezer (1945) injected subcutaneously a total of only 2 mg of blood group substances—and 1 mg suffices (Kabat, 1956); a quarter to a third of the individuals so treated showed a very good rise in hemagglutinin titers. These high titers persisted for 1 to 2 years without any further injection. Highly purified human, water-soluble, blood group glycoproteins produced circulating antibodies in the guinea pig when injected intradermally with adjuvant. Holborow and Loewi (1962) and Janković and Waksman (1962) reported that delayed hypersensitivity to subsequent injection of these substances was found against water-soluble A, B, H(O), and Le^a substances, regardless of which of these had been used for immunization. The authors attributed the delayed reaction to a "backbone" structure, probably the polypeptide moiety plus some part of the carbohydrate shared by the water-soluble blood group substances. In contrast, erythrocyte-derived blood group A and B specific glycolipids were stated not to give a delayed reaction. A delayed hypersensitivity response, however, was observed by Springer and Readler (1961) in humans who received injections of highly purified amino acid-rich "mononucleosis receptor" isolated from beef erythrocytes. The possibility that some contaminant is the agent causing these delayed sensitivities, although unlikely, has not been excluded.

2. Reactions *in Vitro*

a. Hemagglutination. Agglutinating antibodies and some plant proteins are specific reagents used to detect antigenic structures on insoluble carriers of large size, such as erythrocytes. Also, antigens can be fixed onto erythrocytes or other large particles and then measured by agglutination. The latter procedure is called "passive agglutination" (compare Neter, 1956). Hemagglutination tests are among the most sensitive serological procedures known. The agglutination by anti-blood group antibodies and, in the presence of complement, lysis of erythrocytes, form the basis of blood group serology on which blood-banking procedures depend in order to ensure safe blood transfusions without which no modern hospital can exist. These tests are also indispensable in genetical, anthropological, and forensical studies of blood groups, for all of which the interested reader is referred to a number of excellent texts, among them those by Race and Sanger (1962), Wiener (1943, 1961), Mollison (1951), Mourant (1954), Stratton and Renton (1959), Boorman and Dodd (1957), Dacie (1960), and Prokop and Uhlenbruck (1963).

Hemagglutination tests may also be employed for semiquantitative measurement of concentration of antigens and for detailed genetical analysis, in addition to simple detection. As was first shown by Landsteiner and Levine (1927), some sera in a number of blood group systems, but not in the ABO system, will give a dosage effect—i.e., the strength of the reaction indicates whether a given agglutinogen is present as the heterozygous or homozygous gene product, the latter giving stronger reactions. This demonstrated the possibility of using antibodies to determine at least the relative number of antigenic sites on erythrocyte surfaces, as was first done by Wiener and Gordon (1953) for agglutinogens $Rh_o(D)$, K, Fy^a, and A (see also Race, Sanger, and Lehane, 1953; Boyd *et al.,* 1962). Boursnell, Coombs, and Rizk (1953) first employed I^{131}-labeled antibodies to count the receptor sites on erythrocyte surfaces. Masouredis (1960,a) much refined the I^{131} technique and was able, by means of labeled anti-$Rh_o(D)$ isoantibody, to determine (granting certain reasonable assumptions) the $Rh_o(D)$ genotype and the $Rh_o(D)$ antigen content on human erythrocytes. He arrived at a figure of about 10,300 $Rh_o(D)$ antigenic sites per homozygous cell and 6400 per heterozygous erythrocyte, whereas Hughes-Jones, Gardner, and Telford recently (1963) found a considerably higher number of $Rh_o(D)$ antigenic sites. It is obviously of great importance to know the amount of antigen which one may expect in a given volume of erythrocytes.

Hemagglutinating antibodies have also been used with advantage in the determination of changes induced in hexosamine-containing antigens by physical, chemical, or enzymic means. The determination of inactivation of blood group A, B, and H(O) substances on erythrocyte surfaces by enzymes serves as an example (Schiff and Burón, 1935; Iseki and Okada, 1951; Watkins and Morgan, 1954; Howe *et al.,* 1957; Fujisawa, Furukawa, and Iseki, 1963). The action of other agents (compare Springer, 1963) such as the periodate ion (Moskowitz and Treffers, 1950; Morgan and Watkins, 1951) may also be cited. The extent of agglutination is measured before and after treatment with these agents. This kind of measurement, however, is still only an approximation of the extent of change induced, and cannot be rigidly quantitated (compare Hummel, 1961). It also does not give information on the finer structural changes afflicted by the action of enzymes and other agents.

More detailed, although still only semiquantitative, information has been obtained on the blood group specific structures of the erythrocyte surfaces by hapten inhibition of hemagglutination (compare Landsteiner, 1920) which was first employed in the blood group field by Morgan and King (1943) and Morgan and Van Heyningen (1944). Instead of measurement of hemagglutination inhibition, it may be advantageous to absorb a given serum, preferably with insoluble substances, and measure the serum's titer before and after absorption. The difference in titer allows conclusions as to the blood group activity of the absorbant.

One important limitation of this procedure is that measurement of antigenicity may, in some instances at least, be of greater sensitivity than hemagglutination inhibition in the detecting of low blood group activity (Allen and Kabat, 1959,a). It had been observed earlier (Beiser and Kabat, 1952) that a bovine substance virtually inactive in the hemagglutination-inhibition tests stimulated anti-B hemagglutinins on injection into humans. This also has been noted for an *Escherichia freundii,* which, although only faintly A-active in the hemagglutination-inhibition test, nevertheless evoked potent anti-A agglutinins in the rabbit (Springer, 1956,a).

b. Precipitation. Essential for the strict quantitation of antigen–antibody interactions is the precipitin assay, which, however, is less sensitive than are procedures using the principle of hemagglutination. Also, precipitin tests are obviously restricted in their use to antigenic substances in solution. The quantitative microprecipitin technique was first applied to blood group studies by Kabat and Bezer (1945) and is based on the test of Heidelberger and MacPherson (1943,a) (see also Beiser and Kabat, 1951; Beiser, Kabat, and Schor, 1952). The most rigorous data as to purity of the blood group substances have been provided by use of this technique. Kabat and his colleagues have shown that substances for which no definite difference in activity could be established in the hemagglutination-inhibition assay could be clearly differentiated by precipitation methods (Kabat, 1956; Howe and Kabat, 1956). Furthermore, it was recently found that the degree of activity of various substances as measured with the hemagglutination-inhibition assay may not show the same relationship in the precipitin-inhibition test (Springer and Williamson, 1962, 1963; Springer, Desai, and Kolecki, 1964).

Precipitin data permit accurate measurement of the quantities of a given antibody present in human sera; *vice versa,* determination of quantitative precipitin curves of several different blood group substance preparations with the same antiserum is a rather precise measure (within 10%) of their relative activities (Kabat, Bendich, and Bezer, 1946; Howe and Kabat, 1956; Kabat, 1956,a).

Bendich, Kabat, and Bezer (1947) reported that they were able to differentiate, by means of the quantitative precipitin technique, between homozygous blood group AA hogs and heterozygous group AO(H) hogs, indicating that A specificity, on the one hand, and H(O), on the other, were carried by different antigen molecules. The best commercial mucin fraction obtained from a large number of hogs chosen at random, however, approached 75 to 80% of the potency of the best hog AA substances, even in antibody excess (Howe and Kabat, 1956).

The question of whether, in secretions having more than one specific serological activity, each specificity is associated with a different molecular entity, or whether more than one specificity may be present on an individual glycoprotein molecule, has been investigated by Morgan and Watkins (1958) because of its genetical importance (Morgan, 1960) and because of the inseparability of A, B, H(O), and Le^a substances by physical and chemical fractionation procedures. In carefully controlled tests with selected monospecific but heterologous precipitins, these authors found that, in the epithelial fluids of secretors, a large proportion, but not all, of the macromolecules possessed all specificities which are demonstrable in a given secretion (A, B, H(O), and Le^a) on the same molecule (Watkins and Morgan, 1956–1957; Morgan and Watkins, 1958, 1959). The observation that serological characteristics which result from the activity of nonallelomorphic genes, such as Le^a and A, can occur on the same macromolecule is not only of immunological but also of biosynthetic and genetical interest (Morgan, 1960). Similarly, Beiser and Kabat (1952) noted that bovine materials, isolated from stomach linings, were blood group specific, as well as species specific, and these two specificities were linked to the same molecule. These authors made the additional interesting observation that the ability to absorb anti-B may be a property of most bovine blood group substances, even if they do not exhibit blood group B activity in the hemagglutination-inhibition test.

Springer, Readler, and Williamson (1961) showed that cross-reactive substances, such as highly purified blood group B active lipopolysaccharide preparations from *E. coli* O_{86}, precipitate about 50% of anti-human blood group B antibody (human serum) at the point of maximal precipitation of a highly purified human blood group B glycoprotein. Similarly, highly H(O)-active material isolated from smooth *E. coli* O_{128} precipitated, in the equivalence zone of human H(O) cyst material–eel serum system, approximately one half as much nitrogen as did the most active human H(O) cyst glycoprotein or *Sassafras* polysaccharide (Springer, Williamson, and Readler, 1961, 1962; Springer and Williamson, 1963).

Bendich, Kabat, and Bezer (1946) determined the hexosamine and methylpentose content of the A and B substances precipitable by homologous antibody and showed that essentially all of the hexosamine and methylpentose of the A and B substances was found in the antigen–antibody precipitate. This excluded for the first time the possibility that the blood group activity of these preparations was associated with contaminants of undetermined nature. Johns and Marrack (1953) applied these principles to the analysis of H(O)-specific precipitates obtained with O(H) cyst substances from Morgan's laboratories. It was found that virtually all of the blood group substance hexosamine was precipitated by antibody. The interpretation of their results, however, is complicated because only heterologous sera, produced by injection of the H(O) substance combined with the conjugated protein from *Shigella dysenteriae*, were available.

c. Hapten Inhibition. Most structural information on blood group substances has been obtained with hapten inhibition of either hemagglutination or precipitation. The first studies which showed that carbohydrates were involved in blood group specificity were the previously cited observation of Schiff in 1931 and the finding by Cohn and his group in 1951 (Cohn, 1953) that the interaction between red cells and isoagglutinins is inhibited by the addition of simple sugars which naturally occur in specific blood group substances. The usefulness in the possible elucidation of blood group specific terminal groups was shown by Watkins and Morgan (1952), who found that heterologous eel anti-H(O) serum could be specifically inhibited in its action on erythrocytes by minute quantities of L-fucose. Because of an activity of methyl α-L-fucopyranoside higher than that of the β anomer or the parent sugar, Watkins and Morgan concluded that L-fucose must be linked to the H(O) blood group glycoprotein in α-glycosidic linkage.

Plant agglutinin inhibition by haptens also has yielded information on the nature of structures responsible for blood group specificity (Morgan and Watkins, 1953). Studies with the agglutinins from the seed of *Lotus tetragonolobus* confirmed the observations in the H(O) system with eel serum. Two other plant anti-H(O) agglutinins, those from *Laburnum alpinum* and *Cytisus sessilifolius*, could not be inhibited by L-fucose but were inhibited by much smaller amounts of intact human H(O) substance than was the agglutinin from *Lotus*. This may indicate that these antibody-like substances possess affinity for a larger structure more closely related to the complete H(O) substance receptor than is a fucoside. Watkins and Morgan (1962), however, showed that *O*-2-acetamido-2-deoxy-β-D-glucopyranosyl-(1 → 4)-2-acetamido-2-deoxy-D-glucopyranose was a moderate inhibitor of these reagents. The likelihood of the presence of a 2-acetamido-2-deoxy-β-D-glucopyranosyl structure in addition to an α-L-fucopyranosyl grouping as part of the terminal unit involved in the H(O) specific structure was further substantiated by Rege *et al.* (1963), who isolated from H(O), A, B, and also from Le^a substance (thought to be the precursor of H(O) substance) the trisaccharide *O*-2-acetamido-2-deoxy-β-D-glucopyranosyl-(1 → 3)-*O*-β-D-galactopyranosyl-(1 → 3)-2-acetamido-2-deoxy-D-galactose. This trisaccharide inhibited the *Cytisus* extract.

N-Acetyl-D-galactosamine was implicated in A specificity when it was found that agglutination of group A erythrocytes by anti-A agglutinins from *Vicia cracca* and Lima beans was inhibited by this monosaccharide (Morgan and Watkins, 1953; see also Yosizawa and Miki, 1963). Subsequently, it was shown that 3-*O*-(2-acetamido-2-deoxy-α-D-galactopyranosyl)-D-galactose, a disaccharide isolated from human A substance, inhibited human anti-A serum (Côté and Morgan, 1956), although the monosaccharide *N*-acetyl-D-galactosamine did not. Results obtained by inhibition of heterologous reagents may give chemically inaccurate information and, must, therefore, be interpreted with great caution, as pointed out by Springer and Williamson (1963).

The generally observed failure of human or rabbit anti-H(O) or anti-A reagents to be inhibited by simple sugars in the agglutination of O or A cells, respectively, suggests that the combining sites of these antibodies are directed against a more extensive chemical structure.

Similar results by Kabat and Leskowitz (1955) and by Kabat (1958) showed, with the more precise quantitative precipitation technique, the importance of *N*-acetyl-D-galactosamine for A specificity (see also Yosizawa, 1962). More recently, blood group A specific trisaccharides were isolated. Schiffman and Kabat (1961) and Schiffman, Kabat, and Leskowitz (1962) obtained, after mild hydrolysis of ovarian cyst fluid A substance, the trisaccharide *O*-2-acetamido-2-deoxy-α-D-galactosyl-(1 → 3)-*O*-β-D-galactosyl-(1 → 3)-2-acetamido-2-deoxy-D-glucose. This trisaccharide, according to the authors, is the most potent haptenic inhibitor of A–anti-A precipitation yet isolated. Cheese and Morgan (1961) described two A-specific trisaccharides isolated from the cyst fluid from an individual donor. They concluded that trisaccharide I is most likely *O*-2-acetamido-2-deoxy-α-D-galactosyl-(1 → 3)-*O*-β-D-galactosyl-(1 → 4)-2-acetamido-2-deoxy-D-glucose. Trisaccharide II is believed to be *O*-2-acetamido-2-deoxy-α-D-galactosyl-(1 → 3)-*O*-β-D-galactosyl-(1 → 3)-2-acetamido-2-deoxy-D-glucose. This finding indicated that the A specific substance could contain at least two different carbohydrate chains. In hemagglutination-inhibition tests, both trisaccharides were of an activity equal, within the limits of error, to that of the previously described disaccharide 3-*O*-(2-acetamido-2-deoxy-α-D-galactopyranosyl)-D-galactose. It is noteworthy that both trisaccharides also inhibited the lysis of sheep erythrocytes by rabbit immune anti-A serum in the presence of complement. Trisaccharide I was the most active and more than ten times as potent in this respect as the disaccharide (Table I). Cheese and Morgan (1961) concluded from their findings that the unique association of blood group A antigens with both isoagglutinins and Forssman antibodies (Schiff and Adelsberger, 1924) depends on similar but overlapping specificities of these antigens. The common part is probably represented by *O*-2-acetamido-2-deoxy-α-D-galactosyl-(1 → 3)-D-galactose. Fucose, a sugar present in considerable amounts in all human substances whose specificity falls within the ABO and Le^a systems, is almost certainly attached glycosidically in the form of many branching units on the main carbohydrate chains of each of the specific substances and is readily removed by mild acid hydrolysis. Fragments containing this sugar do not normally survive in the acid hydrolysis products in appreciable amounts, but oligosaccharides containing fucose residues are readily obtained if hydrolysis is brought about by a mild alkaline reagent. Such fragments have now been tentatively identified as oligosaccharides containing *N*-acetylgalactosamine, galactose, *N*-acetylglucosamine, and fucose residues in which fucose is linked glycosidically as a branching

TABLE I

AMOUNTS OF HUMAN BLOOD GROUP A SUBSTANCE AND AMINO SUGARS WHICH GIVE INHIBITION OF HUMAN ISOAGGLUTININS AND RABBIT ANTI-A SHEEP CELL HEMOLYSINS[a]

Substance	Minimum amount of substance giving inhibition (μg/0.1 ml)	
	Human isoagglutinins	Rabbit anti-A sheep cell hemolysins
Human blood group A substance	0.04	0.01
2-Acetamido-2-deoxy-D-galactose	>1000	>1000
Methyl 2-acetamido-2-deoxy-α-D-galactopyranoside	500	500
3-*O*-(2-Acetamido-2-deoxy-α-D-galactopyranosyl)-D-galactose	60	250
3-*O*-α-D-Galactopyranosyl-D-galactose	>1000	>1000
2-Acetamido-2-deoxy-3-*O*-(β-D-galactopyranosyl)-D-glucose	>1000	>1000
2-Acetamido-2-deoxy-4-*O*-(β-D-galactopyranosyl)-D-glucose	1000	>1000
Trisaccharide I	60	15
Trisaccharide II	60	30

[a] Data from Cheese and Morgan, 1961.

unit, either to a galactose or to an *N*-acetylglucosamine residue (Morgan, Painter, and Watkins, 1964; Schiffman, Kabat, and Thompson, 1964a). One fragment from A substance was more A active when measured by hemagglutination and hemolysis-inhibition tests than are the A-active trisaccharides isolated from A substance by acid hydrolysis. Removal of the fucosyl unit from the fragment by mild acid hydrolysis gave an oligosaccharide which had less A activity.

A structure probably containing *N*-acetyl-D-galactosamine and D-galactose and apparently common to A and B blood group antigens was detected with a *Sophora japonica* extract. Agglutination by this extract of both A and B erythrocytes could be inhibited rather specifically by *N*-acetyl-D-galactosamine and D-galactose (Morgan and Watkins, 1953).

The first evidence as to the nature of structures involved in blood group B specificity was furnished by Kabat and Leskowitz (1955) with the demonstration that an α-D-galactoside inhibited in the B–anti-B system. It was found subsequently that the disaccharide 3-*O*-(α-D-galactopyranosyl)-D-galactose was the most potent of the inhibitors tested, and Painter, Watkins, and Morgan (1962) isolated this disaccharide from human blood group B substance. The role of hexosamine as a third unit involved in B specificity has now been defined by the same authors (1963) who isolated and characterized two blood group B active trisaccharides from the same B substance. These were 3-*O*-(α-D-galactopyranosyl)-*O*-β-D-galactopyranosyl-(1 → 4)-2-acetamido-2-deoxy-D-glucose and 3-*O*-(α-D-galactopyranosyl)-*O*-β-D-galactopyranosyl-(1 → 3)-2-acetamido-2-deoxy-D-glucose. On a molar basis, the first of these trisaccharides was a more active inhibitor than was 3-*O*-(α-D-galactopyranosyl)-D-galactose. The second trisaccharide was equally as active as the disaccharide.

Inhibition studies with model compounds showed it to be likely that the oligosaccharide side chains determining blood group A and B specificity are not larger than hexasaccharides (see also Kabat and Leskowitz, 1955; Schiffman, Kabat, and Thompson, 1964). Such a conclusion may substantially simplify the problem of A, B, O(H), and Lewis (Le^{a}) specificity, since it implies that the bulk of the blood group substance molecule functions as a "carrier" for multiple specific oligosaccharide side chains which are responsible for blood group specificity (Painter, Rege, and Morgan, 1963). Support for this conclusion comes from the studies which indicate that the specific immunological ability of the A and B substances to react with homologous antibodies is associated with the carbohydrate portion of these materials. Further supporting evidence for the part played by the just-mentioned carbohydrates in H(O), B, and A specificity has been obtained in enzyme experiments (see e.g., Iseki and Masaki, 1953; Watkins and Morgan, 1955; Morgan and Watkins, 1959; Watkins, Zarnitz, and Kabat, 1962; Springer, 1963; Springer, Nichols, and Callahan, 1964). The only chemical difference between the determinants of the A and B glycoproteins appears to be the nature of the substituent at C-2 of the terminal monosaccharide.

Human blood group H(O) specificity has been associated with nonreducing fucopyranosyl structures, and it was only recently that hexosamine-containing structures have also been implicated (Watkins and Morgan, 1962; Painter, Rege, and Morgan, 1963). It was found by these authors that *N,N*-diacetylchitibiose—i.e., 4-*O*-(2-acetamido-2-deoxy-β-D-glucopyranosyl)-2-acetamido-2-deoxy-D-glucopyranose—inhibited the two anti-H(O) reagents from the seeds of the plants *Cytisus sessilifolius* and *Laburnum alpinum.* This indicated that *O*-2-acetamido-2-deoxy-β-D-glucopyranosyl structure may be a serological determinant unit in human H(O) substance, in addition to an α-L-fucopyranosyl residue. Such a disaccharide, however, has not been found in blood group H(O) glycoprotein (Rege *et al.*, 1964), and the observed activity of *N,N'*-diacetylchitobiose may be another example of the limitations of structural serological analysis, especially with heterologous reagents in the blood group H(O) system (compare Springer and Williamson, 1962; Springer and Williamson, 1963; Springer, Desai, and Kolecki, 1964). Rege *et al.* (1964) have now reported the isolation of a number of oligosaccharides which are moderately active inhibitors of human and rabbit anti-H(O) sera, as well as of the plant seed and eel serum agglutinins. Two blood group H(O) active trisaccharides were isolated. The terminal group of both is 2-*O*-(α-L-fucosyl)-*O*-β-D-galactosyl, whereas the third sugar in both instances is 2-acetamido-2-deoxy-D-glucose linked either 1:4 or 1:3 (Rege *et al.*, 1964; see also Lloyd and Kabat, 1964). The activities observed with the various reagents for the oligosaccharides were generally $<1\%$ of that activity found for the intact H(O) substance. An oligosaccharide, also isolated from human H(O) substance, believed to be a tetra- or pentasaccharide (Rege *et al.*, 1964), was slightly more active than the trisaccharides. This and the rather low activity of the fragments indicate that a trisaccharide unit does not represent the complete H(O) determinant structure. The eel serum showed an anomalous behavior, as compared with the other anti-H(O) agglutinins, in that the trisaccharide tested was a considerably poorer inhibitor than the disaccharide was. This observation may be explained by recent findings that the eel serum and Lotus agglutinin react with structures smaller than an entire sugar unit and by the "steric" interference by large, serologically inactive groups (compare Springer, Desai, and Kolecki, 1964). No studies with the Lotus reagent were reported by Rege *et al.* (1964). It is noteworthy, in view of the earlier findings by Watkins and Morgan (1962) just described, that the *Cytisus sessilifolius* reagent was inhibited by these oligosaccharides which had no terminal nonreducing 2-acetamido-2-deoxy-β-D-glucopyranosyl grouping.

Enzyme-inhibition and antibody-inhibition techniques were combined to obtain evidence for the structure which is most likely responsible for the specificity of Lewis (Le^a) substance (Morgan and Watkins, 1959). None of the monosaccharides tested was active in the hemagglutination-inhibition assay, although L-fucose did inhibit inactivation of Le^a substances by an enzyme preparation from *Trichomonas foetus* (Watkins, 1953). When a novel class of oligosaccharides (see Volume I, Chapter 3) isolated from human milk (Kuhn *et al.*, 1957) was investigated serologically, it was found that an α-L-fucopyranosyl structure was involved in Le^a specificity (see original serological observations on blood group substances in milk by Springer, Rose, and Gyorgy, 1954). Three oligo-

TABLE II

LEWIS-ACTIVE (Le[a] AND Le[b]) OLIGOSACCHARIDES OF HUMAN MILK[a]

(1) Lacto-*N*-fucopentaose II

O-β-D-Galactosyl-(1 → 3)-*O*-2-acetamido-2-deoxy-β-D-glucosyl-(1 → 3)-*O*-β-D-galactosyl-(1 → 4)-D-glucose
| (1 → 4) [on the 2-acetamido-2-deoxy-β-D-glucosyl residue]
O-α-L-Fucosyl

(2) Lacto-*N*-difucohexaose I

β-D-Galactosyl-(1 → 3)-*O*-2-acetamido-2-deoxy-β-D-glucosyl-(1 → 3)-*O*-β-D-galactosyl-(1 → 4)-D-glucose
| (1 → 2) [on the β-D-galactosyl residue] *O*-α-L-Fucosyl
| (1 → 4) [on the 2-acetamido-2-deoxy-β-D-glucosyl residue] *O*-α-L-Fucosyl

(3) Lacto-*N*-difucohexaose II

O-β-D-Galactosyl-(1 → 3)-*O*-2-acetamido-2-deoxy-β-D-glucosyl-(1 → 3)-*O*-β-D-galactosyl-(1 → 4)-D-glucose
| (1 → 4) [on the 2-acetamido-2-deoxy-β-D-glucosyl residue] *O*-α-L-Fucosyl
| (1 → 3) [on the D-glucose residue] *O*-α-L-Fucosyl

(4) Lactodifucotetraose

O-β-D-Galactosyl-(1 → 4)-D-glucose
| (1 → 2) [on the β-D-galactosyl residue] *O*-α-L-Fucosyl
| (1 → 3) [on the D-glucose residue] *O*-α-L-Fucosyl

[a] After Morgan, 1960, and Kuhn and Gauhe, 1960.

saccharides inhibited anti-Le^a antibody (Watkins and Morgan, 1957; Kuhn and Gauhe, 1960; Morgan, 1961). The most active one, possessing approximately 5% of the activity of human Le^a substance, is lacto-*N*-fucopentaose II, and the next most active structure was found to be lacto-*N*-difucohexaose II. These, together with structures active in the Le^b system only, are listed in Table II.

Morgan and Watkins (Morgan, 1960) suggested that the Le^a activity resides in a branched trisaccharide unit which contains two nonreducing end units, α-L-fucosyl and β-D-galactosyl, which are linked 1 → 4 and 1 → 3, respectively, to 2-acetamido-2-deoxy-D-glucose (Fig. 2). The re-

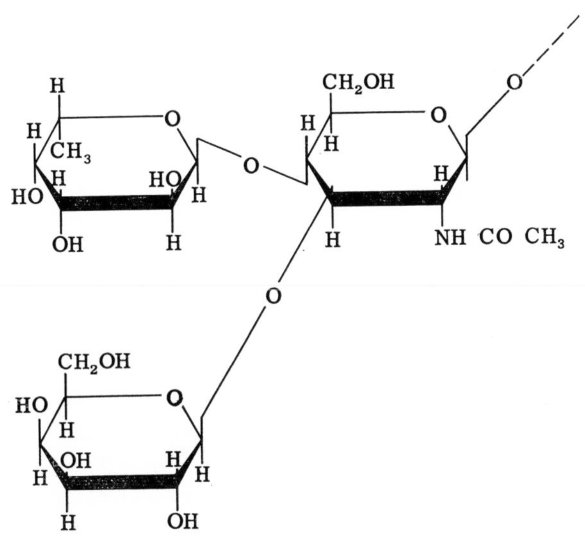

FIG. 2. Trisaccharide structure proposed for Le^a specificity (from Morgan and Watkins, 1959).

maining part of this oligosaccharide does not appear to be involved significantly in serological specificity, and, indeed, the inhibiting power of lacto-*N*-fucopentaose II is not decreased when the end unit D-glucose is reduced to sorbitol (see Table II). An additional α-L-fucosyl residue joined (1 → 2) to the galactose residue, as in lacto-*N*-difucohexaose I, impairs the activity, apparently due to "steric hindrance."

Le^a active substances were also reported to occur, in dialyzable form only, in the urine of human secretors of Le^a substances of large molecular size. In contrast, none of the A, B, and H(O) active substances in human urine was found to be dialyzable ([Price-]Evans, McConnell, and Donohoe, 1963). These as yet undefined substances may be similar to the Le^a haptens of human milk. The urinary substances were thought to be breakdown products of blood group macromolecules.

As far as the Le^b substance is concerned, preliminary observations by Watkins and Morgan (1956–1957, 1957) on Kuhn's substances (Kuhn and Gauhe, 1960; Watkins and Morgan, 1962) showed that none of the simple saccharides tested was active, whereas, of the fucose-containing oligosaccharides, lacto-*N*-difucohexaose I and lacto-*N*-difucotetraose were the only ones which gave weak, but definite, inhibition. It is therefore not unlikely that two fucose structures as arranged in these compounds are concerned in Le^b specificity (see Table II).

It is to be noted that the branched structure lacto-*N*-fucopentaose II is a considerably more potent inhibitor than the simple straight-chain sugars described in the A and B systems. The degree of agglutination inhibition, however, as also shown in Table I for A-active di- and trisaccharides, even by the most active of the low molecular weight carbohydrate inhibitors and, as observed by Painter, Watkins, and Morgan (1963), by Springer, Nichols, and Kolecki (1964), and by Springer (1965) for B-active oligosaccharides, is only a fraction of that given by undegraded blood group substances. This indicates that orientation and proper structural integration of the specific carbohydrate—even if branched—into the macromolecule are essential for the full immunological activity of these glycoproteins and that larger units, possibly branched as the pentasaccharide in the Le^a system, most likely comprise the specific structures (Rege *et al.*, 1963; Schiffman and Kabat, personal communication, 1963).

The Lewis (Le^a) system may shed light on the puzzling and important observation that only certain blood group antibodies are complement fixing (compare Rosenfield, Haber, and Gilbert, 1960), since only an aggregate containing erythrocyte, antibody, and complement gives a positive antiglobulin test. Lysis does not result, however, which is in contrast to the usual reactions in which complement is involved. As was demonstrated by Dacie, Crookston, and Christenson (1957), the antiglobulin reagent in these instances united not with antibody but with the adsorbed complement component C'_4. There is evidence that C'_2 enhances the absorption of C'_4. The fact that C'_4, and not the hemolytically active C'_3, acts as an agglutinogen serves to explain the lack of hemolysis of erythrocytes in such unusual antigen–antibody reactions. According to Pillemer (1943), C'_2 and C'_4 both have the character of muco-euglobulins and therefore may be expected to possess hexosamine.

d. Cross-Reactions with Antisera against Type XIV Pneumococcus. Blood group A, B, H(O), and Le^a substances react with anti-type XIV pneumococcus horse serum—a reactivity much enhanced by mild acid hydrolysis (Kabat *et al.*, 1948,a). The amount of nitrogen precipitated by undegraded material in some cases was quite small (Kabat, 1956, p. 202).

This cross-reacting property provides an immunochemical indication of the similarity of the blood group glycoproteins, despite their multiplicity, both within and without a species. Horse anti-type XIV pneumococcus serum also agglutinates A_1, A_2, B, O, and A_1B erythrocytes to a high titer, whereas rabbit antiserum prepared against this bacterial type agglutinated only A and AB erythrocytes (Finland and Curnen, 1938)—and these to a lower titer. The antibodies from rabbits appeared to be in the nature of Forssman antibodies only (see also Bailey and Shorb, 1931, 1933,a). The observations on agglutination by antipneumococcus antibodies were made some time ago, and it was not then taken into consideration that all or nearly all antipneumococcus sera were obtained with antigen preparations which contained blood group substances of animal origin as contaminants from the growth medium (Goebel, 1938).

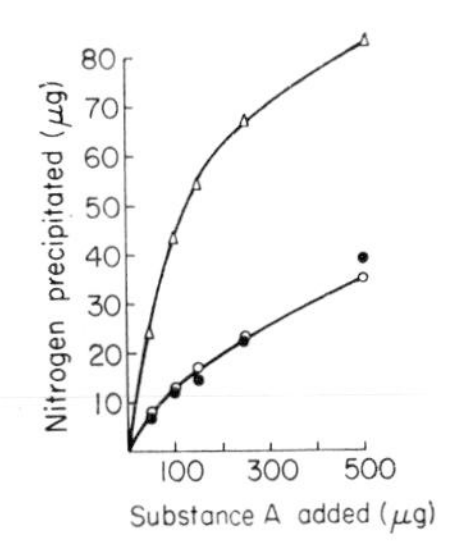

FIG. 3. Effect of mild acid hydrolysis on the reaction of porcine blood group A substance with anti-type XIV pneumococcus horse serum (from Kabat, 1956, p. 204).
○, unheated;
●, heated for 2 hr at pH 4.75;
△, heated for 2 hr at pH 1.5.

The type XIV pneumococcus cross-reactivity, however, appears to be caused, in fact, by pneumococcal structures and not by components of the medium. It is believed that anti-type XIV pneumococcus agglutinins have been responsible for at least some of the fatal hemolytic reactions which occasionally followed therapeutic administration of anti-pneumococcus type XIV sera (Finland and Curnen, 1938; Beeson and Goebel, 1939). It is remarkable that polysaccharide of type XIV pneumococcus does not inhibit human and animal anti-A, anti-B, and anti-H(O) sera (Springer, 1956), thus indicating absence of reciprocity between this polysaccharide and the blood group substances with respect to their corresponding antibodies.

The effect of mild acid hydrolysis on a hog A-substance preparation of fairly low cross-reacting activity is shown in Fig. 3. Hydrolysis at pH 1.5 and 100°C for 2 hr increased the capacity to precipitate type XIV pneumococcus antibody almost threefold, whereas the anti-A hemagglutination-inhibiting potency of the blood group A preparation declined to less than 0.3% of its original level (Kabat *et al.*, 1948). Heating at pH 4.75, as well as autoclaving at around pH 7, did not increase cross-reacting capacity (Gibbons and Morgan, 1954). Blood group substances from individual hog stomachs each showed their own characteristic precipitin curve with type XIV pneumococcus antibody. These variations were not due to different blood group activity, as five different substances precipitated blood group antibodies and inhibited hemagglutination to the same extent, yet they showed as much as a fourfold difference in their anti-type XIV pneumococcus precipitating capacity. None of the preparations, however, precipitated more than 40% of the total anti-type XIV pneumococcus nitrogen (Beiser and Kabat, 1952). These hydrolytically induced changes are accompanied by liberation of reducing sugars, of which fucose is the major part. Kabat and co-workers (1948,a) believed that the fucose residues in the blood group glycoproteins are projecting outward, thus restricting the reactivity of the specific substances with type XIV pneumococcus antibody. It is in agreement with this hypothesis that Annison and Morgan (1952) noted that unhydrolyzed Le^a glycoproteins, which contain less fucose than do H(O), A, and B substances, reacted more strongly with type XIV pneumococcus antibodies than did the A, B, and H(O) substances.

It was first pointed out by Springer, Rose, and György (1954) that highly purified human blood group glycoproteins, A, B, and H(O), as well as Le^a, generally contain small amounts of sialic acid and is now generally recognized (Rege *et al.*, 1963). A physicochemically homogeneous sialic acid-containing glycoprotein, with blood group Le^a specificity, was described (Pusztai and Morgan, 1961,a) which contained 19% sialic acid (as *N*-acetylneuraminic acid). Quantitative release of this sialic acid by purified "receptor-destroying enzyme" (R.D.E.) from *Vibrio cholerae* led to a sharp increase in cross-reactivity with anti-type XIV pneumococcus serum, indicating that the sialic acid covered the structures essential for this cross-reactivity in a way similar to that postulated for fucose in the ordinary blood group glycoproteins.

D-Galactose and *N*-acetyl-D-glucosamine units are components of all the mammalian blood group glycoproteins investigated and also of the polysaccharide of type XIV pneumococcus (Goebel, Beeson, and Hoagland, 1939). It was, therefore, suspected that cross-reactivity arises from the presence of common galactose-*N*-acetylglucosamine structures (especially those with $1 \rightarrow 3$ and $1 \rightarrow 6$ linkages) (Heidelberger, 1955). Indeed, Morgan and his collaborators (Morgan, 1960) and Allen and Kabat (1959,a) found that the precipitation of slightly degraded blood group substances by type XIV pneumococcus antiserum is inhibited strongly by disaccharides which have been isolated from blood group A substances after mild acid hydrolysis. A more detailed discussion of the structures thought to be responsible for the cross-reactivity with type XIV pneumococcus antisera will be given in the section on pneumococcal polysaccharides (Section VII,A,1).

Based on immunochemical and enzymic studies (Howe and Kabat, 1953; Watkins, 1956; Howe *et al.*, 1959), evidence has been obtained for three different types of D-galactosyl-containing structures in blood group B substance, and each is believed to be implicated with a specific immunochemical property (Allen and Kabat, 1959a)—namely, blood group B specificity, type XIV pneumococcus cross-reactivity, and B P1 specificity. The latter will be discussed after consideration of cross-reactivity with the Forssman antigen. It is possible that all these galactose structures are linked to hexosamine as the subterminal unit.

e. Forssman Reactivity. Schiff and Adelsberger (1924) were the first to observe that undegraded blood group A substance inhibits hemolysis of sheep erythrocytes by rabbit anti-human blood group A serum. This "heterophil" activity increases considerably after brief acid hydrolysis of blood group A substance (Aminoff, Morgan, and Watkins, 1948, 1950; Kekwick, 1950) and increases similarly after treatment with formamide at 150°C (Landsteiner and Harte, 1940). This heterophil activity is present in blood group A substance, but not in B and H(O) substances; it is not completely identical with blood group A specificity and hence should not be used as an exclusive measure of A specificity, as was done by Freudenberg and Molter (1939) during their attempts to isolate blood group A substance. Recent work points to a close association between Forssman and blood group A characteristics (Cheese and Morgan, 1961).

The Forssman antigen was one of the first heterogenetic antigens to be discovered (Forssman, 1911; Frouin and Lisbonne, 1911), and many of the early studies on heterogenetic antigens were carried out with it (see also Tomcsik, 1945; Jenkin, 1963). Brunius (1936) first reported the presence of hexosamine in the Forssman antigen, and this finding was later confirmed by Chase and Landsteiner (1939). This antigen has recently gained some interest as a component of egg-grown virus vaccines and purified myxoviruses and their ability to engender hemolytic anti-A antibodies (Springer and Tritel, 1962; Springer, 1963; Tritel and Springer, 1963; Springer and Schuster, 1964,a). Highly purified Forssman substance appears to be a typical hapten, which, in order to be antigenic, must be combined with a carrier such as serum proteins; if the Forssman substance has not been overly purified, kaolin or charcoal will render the hapten antigenic (compare Boyd, 1956).

Papirmeister and Mallette (1955,a) reported on isolation and some properties of the Forssman hapten from sheep erythrocytes. These investigators considered the Forssman substance to be a glycolipid with 18% hexosamine and believed it to contain galactosamine. The material was stated to have a molecular weight of about 1000, and, despite its small size, it precipitated antibody, apparently as a result of extensive aggregation of the Forssman-hapten molecules. In addition, it was said that in order to become active in inhibiting assays the specific hapten needed a nonspecific activator (see also Kościelak, 1963). Yamakawa, Irie, and Iwanaga (1960) found galactosamine and glucosamine in a proportion of 4:1 in a Forssman-active glycolipid which contained 17.4% hexosamine.

f. The P1 Specificities. Nondialyzable serologically specific structures were obtained by mild acid hydrolysis (pH 1.5 to 1.8, 100°C, 2 hr) of human and animal blood group glycoproteins and designated as P1 fractions. They were obtained from A and B blood group substances, and are antigenic in some humans (Allen and Kabat, 1959) wherein they give rise to precipitins specific for the P1 fractions from A and the P1 fractions from B substances, respectively. A P1 fractions differ from untreated A substance, among other properties, in their ability to stimulate the formation of A P1 specific precipitins in group A individuals. Similarly, B P1 fractions sometimes give rise to B P1 specific precipitins in group B and AB persons. These antibodies are not directed against the original specific structure. Schiffman, Kabat, and Thompson (1964a) showed that the P1 structures are associated with the A and B determinants but are blocked by fucose residues before hydrolysis.

Some individuals possess a low concentration of precipitins against the P1 fractions prior to deliberate stimulation. In general, the amount of precipitin which could be evoked was much less than that produced by the undegraded blood group substances.

It may also be mentioned here that Westphal and Schmidt (1952) noted that partially degraded blood group A substances from hog stomach mucus, but not the intact material, inhibited the precipitation of protein-coupled *p*-aminophenyl 2-acetamido-2-deoxy-β-D-glucopyranoside by its corresponding antibody.

The amino acid-containing moiety of human blood group substances has been less intensively studied than has the carbohydrate portion, since the peptide part of these macromolecules is not directly involved in their serological specificity. Although there are some early reports on the effect of proteolytic enzymes on blood group substances, it was only a few years ago that an extensive, but incomplete, destruction of the hemagglutination-inhibiting activity of the A, B, H(O), and Le^a substances by crystallized ficin and papain was reported (Pusztai and Morgan, 1958).

It was suggested by the results that the kind of linkages broken by these enzymes are common to all the group-specific substances tested by the authors (Pusztai and Morgan, 1961a).

3. Miscellaneous Immunological Techniques Found Useful in the Study of A,B,H(O) Blood Group Active Substances

a. Immunofluorescence. This technique (Coons and Kaplan, 1950) has permitted a topographical study of the distribution of the various blood group antigens throughout an organism on the assumption that the fluorescent antibody used has a high specificity. The sensitivity of this method is limited (Glynn and Holborow, 1959). Glynn, Holborow, and Johnson (1957) used the fluorescent-antibody method first in a study of the distribution of blood group A, H(O), and Lewis substances in human stomach and duodenum, employing heterologous antisera from the rabbit. An extensive investigation on the distribution, within the human body, of blood group A and B substances was published by Szulman (1960). Fluorescein-labeled human anti-A and anti-B sera, obtained by immunization with animal substances, were used. This technique distinguished, with some exceptions, between those antigens which were dependent on the secretor (S,s) genes of Schiff and Sasaki (1932a) and those which were thought to be clearly independent.

b. "Passive" Hemagglutination. Human blood group substances A, B, and Le^a were fixed onto tanned erythrocytes (and also other particulate material, such as cocci) (Brading, 1956; Hornung and Baer, 1958; Levine and Celano, 1960). Similarly, Levine, Celano, and Staveley (1958) coated tanned human or sheep red cells with blood factor P, which is present in *Echinococcus* cyst fluid. The adsorbed factors were antigenic for rabbits. Springer and Ansell (1960), Springer and [Ansell] Hahn (1962), and Springer and Horton (1964) were successful in coating human and chicken erythrocytes with blood groups B- and H(O)-active polysaccharide material from gram-negative bacteria. In distinction to the experiments with human and sheep echinococcal cyst blood group substances, no pretreatment of the erythrocytes with tannic acid is required, as native erythrocytes are coated irreversibly by the bacterial substances (compare Keogh, North, and Warburton, 1947, 1948; Neter, 1956) of the kind employed in these studies. These *in vitro* studies were confirmed by Andersen (1961). Some purified fractions from human meconium also irreversibly coat human erythrocytes (Springer and Horton, 1964), although there is some possibility that this coating effect is due to contaminating bacterial products.

c. Mixed Agglutination. This qualitative micromethod (Boyden, 1951; Coombs, Bedford, and Rouillard, 1956) is based on early work by Heidelberger and Kabat (1937) and Wiener and Herman (1939). A suspension of isolated epidermal cells of blood group A, for example, is incubated with anti-A serum and washed. Mixed agglutinates are formed when these cells are then incubated in a suspension of group A red cells, but not when incubated with B or O cells. With this technique, the presence of the H(O) antigen, as well as the absence of A and B (Kelus, Gurner, and Coombs, 1959), on HeLa (human cervical carcinoma) cells has been shown. These findings are in agreement with earlier observations in the hemagglutination-inhibition technique (Springer and McLimans, unpublished data). Kelus and his colleagues (1959), employing this technique, also found the MN and P antigens on HeLa cells. Högman (1959) studied the distribution of blood group antigens in various fetal tissues with this method.

B. M, N, and Lutheran Blood Group Substances

Some chemical knowledge has been gained for the M and N system and, to a lesser degree, for the Lutheran system. It was found by Springer and Ansell (1958,a, 1959), and, later, independently, by Mäkelä and Cantell (1958) (MN antigens only) that these factors are inactivated by purified influenza viruses. Based on present knowledge of the enzymic activity of influenza viruses (compare Gottschalk, 1960), only one enzyme is assumed to be present: a ketosidase. M- and N-active substances, isolated from human erythrocyte stroma by a procedure which was first described by Hohorst (1954), contain large amounts of sialic acid and hexosamine and are inactivated by influenza viruses (Baranowski *et al.*, 1959; Klenk and Uhlenbruck, 1960; Stalder and Springer, 1962; Nagai and Springer, 1962; Springer and Hotta, 1963). Similar material has been isolated by Kathan, Winzler, and Johnson (1961). In the opinion of this writer, the significance of sialic acid or its derivatives for M and N specificity cannot be fully deduced as yet, although they are undoubtedly involved directly in M specificity and in N specificity, as judged by measurements with some sera. Free sialic acid and numerous sialic acid derivatives did not significantly inhibit any of a number of anti-M and anti-N agglutinins (Springer, Williamson, and Brandes, 1961). In addition, the M^g antigen, which is thought to be the product of a gene allelomorphic to the M and N genes, was not inactivated by influenza viruses and receptor-destroying enzyme under conditions which destroy M and N agglutinogens (Springer and Stalder, 1961). It is noteworthy that appropriate hydrolysis of isolated MM receptors by influenza viruses or mild acid increased pre-existing N activity of the MM receptors when measured with *Vicia graminea* agglutinins. Mild acid hydrolysis released large amounts of dialyzable materials, some of which specifically inhibited

Vicia anti-N, whereas others inhibited a human anti-N serum; in addition, the nondialyzable residue, which had lost its M activity, had acquired N activity *de novo* when measured with human anti-N antibodies (Nagai and Springer, 1962). These authors found that L-aspartic acid (not neutralized) was a weak but specific inhibitor of *Vicia graminea* anti-N. D-Aspartic acid and the glutamic acids were inactive. Glucosamine and galactosamine were found in addition to sialic acid in hydrolyzates of these receptor preparations (see also Romanowska, 1961; Springer and Hotta, 1964; Cook and Eylar, 1964). A highly purified and highly N and anti-influenza virus active receptor from human NN red cells contained 24% sialic acid, 9% hexosamine, and 7.1% N, and glutamic and aspartic acid, threonine and serine were among the major amino acid components. It had a molecular weight of 150,000 although the most highly purified NN antigen from a different lot had a molecular weight of 595,000 (Springer and Hotta, 1964). Material inhibiting anti-M and anti-N agglutinins was also found in human kidney medulla by Stalder and Springer (1960), and substances inhibiting anti-N agglutinins of *Vicia graminea* only were prepared by Springer and Hotta (1963) from meconium of babies possessing all possible combinations of MN antigens on their red cells (Springer, 1965,a). These authors have also noted that the sialic acid (>9%) and hexosamine (20%) rich N receptor materials isolated from human erythrocytes or meconium of blood groups MM, MN, or NN were not inactivated (measured with anti-N from *Vicia graminea*) by mild hydrolysis with acid and R.D.E. from *Vibrio cholerae,* even though up to 100% of the bound sialic acid was released by this treatment. It was concluded, therefore, that sialic acids were not involved in N specificity as measured by *Vicia* anti-N. Ethanol ether-soluble substances having low sialic acid content and inhibiting agglutination of M and N erythrocytes by their corresponding antibodies have also been isolated from human erythrocytes (Stalder and Springer, 1960, 1962). Levine *et al.* (1955) have reported that N-like antigens are present on horse erythrocytes. Extracts from horse erythrocyte stroma inhibited action of plant anti-N on human NN and horse erythrocytes. None of the other anti-N reagents was inhibited (Stalder and Springer, 1962; Lisowska, 1963). Lisowska (1963) confirmed that sialic acid is not involved in N specificity as measured with *Vicia graminea* extracts (see also Uhlenbruck and Krüpe, 1963).

C. I Blood Group Antigens

Blood group I specificity was first described by Wiener *et al.* (1956). Anti-I antibodies are found among the cold agglutinins, which frequently are autoantibodies and may cause hemolytic anemias. The I antigen shows great variations in strength in different individuals, and its ontogenetic development is slower than that of other blood group antigens; it is extremely common. It was further shown by Wiener and his colleagues (1956) that the I antigen is resistant to treatment with ficin. Interestingly enough, Race and Sanger (1962) found that some anti-I sera were inhibited by the same hydatid cyst fluid from sheep livers which inhibits anti-P.

Marcus, Kabat, and Rosenfield (1963) have inactivated I antigenic determinants on human erythrocytes by the combined action of partially purified β-galactosidase and β-glucosaminidase isolated from *Clostridium tertium*. Both enzymes were required for optimal inactivation. Galactose and *N*-acetylglucosamine were released concomitantly with the loss of activity and may thus be involved in I specificity. Neither of these sugars in high concentration nor a number of low molecular weight compounds containing these sugars inhibited anti-I agglutinins.

It is remarkable that the I determinants of blood group A_1 erythrocytes and stroma were found to be altered more rapidly and more extensively than were those of blood group O.

D. P Blood Group Substances

This system was discovered by Landsteiner and Levine (1927), and more recent studies indicate its serological complexity (Sanger, 1955). The P-system antigens and antibodies are analogous, in many serological and genetical aspects, to A_1A_2 H(O) groups in the ABO system. Cameron and Staveley (1957) made the surprising observation that live scolices containing cysts from *Echinococcus* of sheep livers have a fluid which specifically inhibits anti-P_1 agglutinins. The antigenicity of this P factor has been investigated by Levine, Celano, and Staveley (1958). They succeeded in obtaining anti-P_1 sera by injection of rabbits with rabbit erythrocytes which had been exposed to hydatid cyst fluid of sheep or human origin. Prokop and Oesterle (1958) failed in similar experiments using hydatid cyst fluid from pigs, but Kerde *et al.* (1960) obtained high-titer anti-P_1 sera from goats upon immunization with pig hydatid cyst fluid. Staveley sent his heat-resistant fluid to Morgan and Watkins, who isolated a highly active P_1-like material from it (Morgan and Watkins, 1964; Watkins and Morgan, 1964). This hapten material was physicochemically and immunochemically inhomogeneous. It was nondialyzable and contained galactose and hexosamine (ca. 20%) as carbohydrates. Threonine predominated among the amino acids. When the P_1-active material was conjugated to *Shigella shigae* protein, it was found to be a potent antigen in rabbits. Antisera were produced which specifically precipitated the P_1 substance. The only cross-reaction noted was with horse anti-type XIV pneumococcus serum. *O*-α-D-galactopyranosyl-$(1 \rightarrow 3)$-D-galactose and O-α-D-galactopyranosyl-(1 → 4)-D-galactose weakly but specifically inhibited the agglutination of P_1 cells by human anti-P_1 sera. Other tests also implicated D-galactose in P_1 specificity, although it could not be firmly established whether this sugar's linkage had to be α or β. Levine, Celano, and Falkowski (1963) noted that all sera of patients with paroxysmal cold hemoglobinuria tested possessed antibodies of anti-P + P_1 specificity. The specificity was revealed by agglutination in the cold, cold-warm lysis, and absorption experiments. The antibodies were neutralized by sheep cyst fluid but not by the P_1-like material prepared by Morgan and Watkins from it.

E. T Antigen

Neuraminidase not only destroys erythrocyte agglutinogens but, also, concomitantly with the removal of sialic acid, uncovers a structure of new immunologic specificity, the so-called T antigen. This antigen is responsible for the Thomsen–Friedenreich phenomenon of panagglutination (Thomsen, 1927; Friedenreich, 1928; compare Uhlenbruck, 1961)—i.e., the enzyme renders all human and most animal erythrocytes agglutinable by sera from all individuals except infants (compare Springer, 1963). It is in agreement with earlier observations that Klenk and Uhlenbruck (1960) were able, under special conditions, to inhibit T agglutination by isolated sialidase-treated M and N receptors. The chemical nature of the specific structures of the T receptor is unknown, but it is likely that the sugars to which sialic acids are ketosidically linked play a decisive role in the specificity of the T antigen. These sugars are probably N-acetyl-D-galactosamine or D-galactose, or both (compare Gottschalk, 1960, p. 65). The T agglutinins belong in the group of so-called natural agglutinins, which, if true antibodies, are most likely formed in response to ubiquitous antigens.

F. Blood Group Substances of Animal Origin

Substances related serologically to the human A, B, and H(O) substances are widely distributed in nature and quite common in higher and lower animals (see, e.g., Springer, Rose, and György, 1954). In general, antibodies produced with these materials react with A, B, and H(O) substances (compare Kabat, 1956). These substances are of a chemical composition similar to those of human origin (compare Kabat, 1956). It is noteworthy, in this connection, that all preparations of Castle's "intrinsic factor"—i.e., the substance which makes possible the absorption of vitamin B_{12} across the intestinal mucosa and which is lacking in patients with pernicious anemia (see, e.g., Castle, 1953)—have been shown to possess the same blood group specificity as does the gastric mucosa or gastric juice from which they were isolated (Cresseri, 1954; Springer, Rose, and György, 1954). The observed activities were high. Most "intrinsic factor" preparations were obtained from hogs—A-active and H(O)-active—but some were from humans. Highly purified "intrinsic factor" preparations possess galactose, fucose, galactosamine, and glucosamine (Prusoff *et al.*, 1953; Latner, Merrills, and Raine, 1954; Holdsworth and Otteson, 1955)—the same sugars which are also present in human blood group substances. Interestingly enough, gastric juice, as well as saliva, from pernicious anemia patients possesses blood group activity (Springer and György, 1955). It has not been established whether blood group specificity is located on the same molecule as is the "intrinsic factor" activity in individuals possessing "intrinsic factor" and secreting blood group substances (see Chapters 22, 23). The physiological importance of sialic acid in intrinsic-factor preparations has been pointed out by Faillard and Pribilla (1964).

Among the lower animals, it was found that frog spawn mucin, which contains hexosamine, was blood group active (Hiyama, 1949,a,b; Folkes, Grant, and Jones, 1950; Springer, Rose, and György, 1954). Similarly, oyster polysaccharide was blood group A specific (Springer, Rose, and György, 1954), thus suggesting the presence of *N*-acetylgalactosamine in this polysaccharide. The ubiquitous occurrence of blood group active substances as surface structures is further made likely by our recent observation (Springer, 1965) of blood group A, B, and H(O) activity, as well as of some N-like activity (with *Vicia graminea* extracts only), in sponge cell surface glycopeptides isolated by MacLennan (1963). Determination was with the hemagglutination-inhibition test only. In some instances, the inhibition was strictly specific for one blood group only, H(O) being the most common. None of the ten different samples tested had B specificity only. Some of them may not be specific in their action. These glycopeptides were found by MacLennan to be species-specific surface antigens. The moderate blood group activities found by us are, therefore, only due to partial antigens of the glycopeptides. MacLennan found that all the glycopeptides possessed, among other components, the four sugars characteristic of the human blood group A, B, H(O) glycoproteins.

Little knowledge has accumulated on the composition of blood group substances characteristic for a given animal species. One exception is the J substance of cattle, which coats their erythrocytes. This is a water-soluble blood group substance found in various body fluids and tissues other than those which produce erythrocytes (Stormont, 1949). This material has been reported to be immunologically and chemically related to human A substance (Stormont, 1949). It was said to contain glucosamine but, strangely enough for an A-active material, no galactosamine

(Sørensen, Rendel, and Stone, 1954; Hayashi *et al.*, 1958). In addition to glucosamine, fucose and galactose in proportions similar to those of human blood group substances have been found in the J substance of cattle. J substance evoked a moderate immune response in a number of chickens, rabbits, and cows. The antibodies were directed against human, hog, and horse A substance, but not against J—a surprising and unexplained observation. Some of the J preparations inhibited also reactions of human O substances with cattle anti-H(O) sera. Anti-J occurs "naturally" in cattle.

The serological relationship of J substance to human A and also sheep R substance is demonstrated by the capacity of body fluids containing J, R, or A to inhibit hemolysis in the J–anti-J system and also by the removal of anti-J by absorbing with cattle J, sheep R, or human A erythrocytes (Sørensen, Rendel, and Stone, 1954). Lately, Horowitz, Hashimoto, and Pigman (1963, 1964) isolated J substance from bovine submaxillary mucin. Preliminary tests indicated that this material was physicochemically homogeneous. This J substance did cross-react with human blood group A substance (Springer, 1964, unpublished data) and showed some blood group H(O) specificity. From this J substance, most of the sialic acid could be removed without loss of J specificity. Acid-hydrolyzed or neuraminidase-treated J substance from bovine submaxillary mucin cross-reacted with type XIV pneumococcus antiserum.

Glycopeptide preparations obtained by pronase digestion and Sephadex separation had hapten activity and contained 28% hexosamine (both *N*-acetylgalactosamine and *N*-acetylglucosamine), 1.2% sialic acid, 3.5% fucose, and more than 4% hexose.

The isolation of cattle blood group active receptors from beef erythrocyte stroma was reported by Royal, Ferguson, and Sutton (1953) and later by Uhlenbruck and Schmid (1962). The extracted material was stated to contain about 20% hexosamine and approximately 15% sialic acid. It inhibited sera against numerous different blood group factors of cattle. No quantitative comparisons as to the activities against the various antisera were given. Royal, Ferguson, and Sutton reported a rather remarkable chromatographic separation of their material into fractions containing only one to three haptens; they also found their fractions to be nonantigenic in the rabbit. The F factor specificity of cattle erythrocytes appears to be associated with sialic acid (Hatheway, Ludwick, and Weseli, 1964).

G. Heterogenetic Infectious Mononucleosis Receptor

Paul and Bunnell (1932) first described powerful anti-sheep erythrocyte agglutinins, in the sera of patients suffering from infectious mononucleosis, that led to a diagnostic test for this disease (cf. Springer, 1963).

It is assumed that the agent causing infectious mononucleosis (probably a virus) and the sheep erythrocyte surface have structures in common with which the agglutinins react. These agglutinins are distinct from Forssman and other antibodies, which also react with sheep erythrocytes but which are usually of low titer and present in the sera of most individuals.

A receptor reacting with "infectious mononucleosis antibodies" is also found on beef erythrocytes, although its serological and chemical properties differ from those of sheep erythrocyte agglutinogen (compare Springer, 1963) even though preparations of both contain sialic acid and hexosamine. Beef and sheep erythrocytes also contain an agglutinogen which reacts with antibodies developed by patients suffering from serum sickness, a hypersensitivity reaction resulting mainly from therapeutical horse serum administration.

It was shown by Springer and Rapaport (1957) that the infectious mononucleosis receptor of sheep erythrocytes is inactivated by influenza viruses, with the concomitant release of sialic acid. These authors also noted that papain treatment of intact sheep and beef erythrocytes released predominantly nondialyzable substances which were not coagulable by heat and which contained sialic acid and other carbohydrates besides amino acids. The released substances from sheep erythrocytes retained some of their original serological specificity. It is possible, therefore, that a situation similar to that discussed above for the M, N, and Lutheran antigens pertains. The receptor on beef erythrocytes, however, differs and is apparently not influenced significantly by plant proteases and influenza viruses. The isolated serologically highly active receptor from beef red cell stroma was not inactivated by either papain or pronase (Springer and Callahan, unpublished data). Schwarzweiss and Tomcsik (1948, 1949) were the first to isolate crude "infectious mononucleosis" and "serum sickness" receptors from beef erythrocytes and reported that they contained glucosamine. The mononucleosis receptor material had about twice the amount of hexosamine (8.56%) that they observed for the serum sickness antigens. Preparations of this receptor corresponding in N content to that reported by Schwarzweiss and Tomcsik (1949) were found to contain as much as 4% sialic acid (Springer and Frank, 1962). About 30% of the dry weight can be removed as lipids from these fractions without loss of activity. More highly purified mononucleosis receptor preparation from beef erythrocytes, however, had 1.5 to 2% N and 0.5 to 1.5% sialic acid (Springer and Readler, 1961; Springer and Frank, 1962). Highly purified active fractions were shown by chromatography to contain galactose and two hexosamines, besides minor carbohydrate components and lipids (Springer and Frank, 1962). The most active preparation contained only 1 to 3% hexosamine (Springer and Callahan, unpublished data). The receptor preparations gave quantitative precipitin curves of the cross-reacting type with the majority of sera from patients suffering from infectious mononucleosis and reacted in agar gel diffusion tests in which the purer preparations gave one band only. They also cross-reacted with human anti-blood group B sera. Their skin-sensitizing properties have been described by Springer and Readler (1961).

H. Blood Group Active Substances of Bacteria and Higher Plants*

The occurrence in bacteria of genetically determined substances with close serological relationship to A and H(O) erythrocyte agglutinogens was first demonstrated unequivocally by Schiff (1934) for one strain of the genus *Shigella*. Other gram-negative bacteria (for gram-positive see Section VII,A,1; for type XIV pneumococcus see Section I,A,2,*d*) have been reported by Japanese (compare Iseki, 1952) and German (compare Hohorst, 1954a) workers to be related serologically to human blood

TABLE III
BACTERIA WITH HIGH BLOOD GROUP ACTIVITY AND WITH KNOWN O ANTIGEN CARBOHYDRATES[a]

			Sugars common to O antigen and to human blood group glycoproteins			
Bacteria	O antigen	Specificity	Fucose	Galactose	Galactosamine	Glucosamine
E. coli	86	B	+	⊕	+	+
	127	H(O)	⊕[b]	+	+	+
	128	H(O)	⊕	+	+	+
S. poona	13, 22	H(O)	⊕	+	+	+
S. grumpensis	13, 23	H(O)	⊕	+	+	+
S. atlanta	13, 23	H(O)	⊕	+	+	+
S. berkeley	43	B	+	⊕	+	+
S. arizona	9	H(O)	⊕	+	—	+
	21	B	+	⊕	+	+

[a] From Springer, Williamson, and Brandes, 1961; see there for additional references.
[b] ⊕ = sugar responsible for most of a given activity in human blood group glycoproteins.

groups A, B, and H(O), but the pre-existence of blood group active substances in the growth media used in these latter studies is almost certain. Studies by Springer (1956,a) and by Springer, Williamson, and Brandes (1961), in which extraneous blood group substances were absent, emphasized the presence of similar serological and chemical structures in

* For blood group active substances in viruses and fungi, see Sections IX and X of this chapter.

groups as widely separated phylogenetically as bacteria and man. Table III demonstrates that all bacteria which were found to be highly blood group active contain at least three of the four monosaccharides making up the human blood group glycoproteins. Enzymic and antibody inhibition studies, in Iseki's laboratory, also implicated the appropriate monosaccharides in blood group specificity of bacteria (Yamamoto *et al.*, 1963).

Four blood group B specific oligosaccharides, possessing galactose, fucose, glucose and, in all but one of the four, hexosamine, have been isolated from the blood group B active *E. coli* O_{86} lipopolysaccharide which was as active as human blood group B mucoid (Springer, Nichols, and Callahan, 1964; Springer, 1965,a). One of these oligosaccharides was approximately thirty times as active as 3-*O*-(α-D-galactopyranosyl)-D-galactose. A further indication of the close relationship between human blood group B glycoproteins and the B specific lipopolysaccharide from *E. coli* O_{86} is the recent finding that coffee-bean α-galactosidase destroys the blood group B specificity of blood group B active bacterial lipopolysaccharide of *E. coli* O_{86} and an oligosaccharide fraction isolated from it (Springer, Nichols, and Callahan, 1964) as it does human blood group B glycoprotein (Zarnitz and Kabat, 1960). Concomitantly, blood group H(O) specificity occurs *de novo* in both materials, although to a lesser degree in the bacterial products (Watkins, Zarnitz, and Kabat, 1962; Springer, Nichols, and Callahan, 1964).

On the other hand, bacteria possessing all sugars of the human blood group substances do not necessarily have blood group activity. Presumably, the sugars of these inactive bacteria are linked in such a way as to be unavailable for reaction with the blood group antibodies or they are present as the inactive enantiomorphs.

Two polysaccharides of higher plants, one from yew (*Taxus cuspidata*) and one from sassafras (*Sassafras albidum*), were found to possess high and specific blood group H(O) activity in the heterologous eel anti-H(O) serum–human O erythrocyte system and thus were serologically similar to human blood group H(O) glycoproteins. In contrast with the human and bacterial substances, however, these plant materials contain no fucose or hexosamine, but the blood group specific haptenic sugar of *Taxus* is 2-*O*-methyl-L-fucose (Springer, 1958), and that of sassafras 3-*O*-methyl-D-galactose (Springer *et al.*, 1964; Takahashi and Springer, 1964; Springer, 1965,a).

Quantitative precipitin tests with eel serum on highly active human H(O) cyst glycoprotein, sassafras polysaccharide, *Taxus* polysaccharide, and an *E. coli* O_{128} H(O) specific polysaccharide preparation (Springer, Williamson, and Readler, 1961, 1962) gave similar curves for sassafras and ovarian cyst polysaccharides, although they are chemically quite different. Hexosamine- and fucose-containing *E. coli* O_{128} polysaccharide precipitated in the equivalence zone of the human cyst–eel serum system approximately one half as much nitrogen as did the human cyst glycoprotein, sassafras, or taxus polysaccharide (Fig. 4). Agar gel diffusion studies of the same four H(O)-active materials showed that, in general, a fusion of the bands resulted when eel serum was used as antibody (Springer, Readler, and Williamson, 1961). In agar gel studies, human B cyst glycoprotein, B meconium, and *E. coli* O_{86} polysaccharide also fused after reacting with human anti-B serum (Springer, Williamson, and Readler, 1961, 1962).

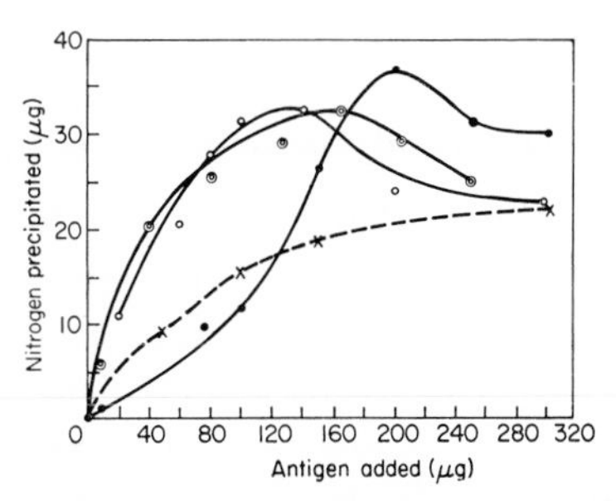

Fig. 4. Quantitative precipitin curves of blood group H(O) active substances: 0.5 ml of eel serum was added; total volume, 1.5 ml (from Springer, Williamson, and Readler, 1961).
●, *Taxus* PRXXI;
⊙, *Sassafras* C-70 PRXXIV;
○, Morgan, Human Ovarian Cyst 277/P1/WS PRXXXIII;
×, *Escherichia coli* O_{128} ΦOH, 16,000.

The very close immunochemical similarity between human blood group H(O) active substances and those from higher plants in the blood group H(O)–eel anti-H(O) system is surprising because of their great chemical differences and points to the limitation of immunochemical analysis with heterologous reagents, even if the assumption is made that the eel antibody reacts with little more than a methyl group in a special conformational arrangement of a pyranosidic sugar (Springer, Desai, and Kolecki, 1964). Blood group active substances of bacterial origin, on the other hand, probably have chemical groups identical to those found in the blood group glycoproteins (Springer, Williamson, and Brandes, 1961).

Blood group active substances can serve as models for most immunological situations. There may be mentioned two more phenomena of immunological and, probably, general significance.

I. Blood Group Chimerism and Acquired Tolerance

Owen's (1945) paper on the "immunogenetic consequences of vascular anastomoses between bovine twins" was the first-described example of immune tolerance. Here, primordial erythrocytes of one bovine twin changed over into the other, where they produced, during the entire life span of the host, erythrocytes with genetically foreign antigens against which the host did not produce demonstrable antibodies. Similar observations of a permanent mixture of two different bloods in one individual have been made in humans (Dunsford *et al.*, 1953). The importance of this observation for tissue grafting cannot be discussed here, and the reader is referred to the literature (compare Billingham, Brent, and Medawar, 1953, 1956; Raffel, 1961).

J. Transient Acquisition of Blood Group Antigens by Human Erythrocytes

In 1959, British authors (Cameron *et al.*, 1959; Giles *et al.*, 1959; Marsh, Jenkins, and Walther, 1959) surprisingly observed that human beings of blood group A with severe intestinal, genitourinary, or extensive gangrenous disorders may temporarily acquire blood group B-like antigens on their erythrocytes. Stratton and Renton thought (1959) that the acquired B antigen may be due to bacterial polysaccharides (compare Springer, Horton, and Forbes, 1959); microbial enzymes have also been implicated (Marsh, 1960). The suggestion that blood group A and B substances may interconvert without extraneous influence (Masamune, 1953) has not found followers (compare Kabat, 1956). Acquisition of extraneous substances by erythrocytes implicates, on the one hand, these cells in transport and detoxification, and, on the other hand, the coating substances as possible pathogenetic agents in some hemolytic anemias. Studies on humans from infancy to adulthood and on ordinary and germ-free chicks have shown that, although irreversible coating of erythrocytes with B- and H(O)-active *E. coli* is easily achieved *in vitro* (in the absence of albumin and plasma lipoproteins), *in vivo* coating of erythrocytes with blood group active bacterial polysaccharides, although it does occur, is accomplished only rarely, even under severe pathological conditions of the host (Springer and Ansell, 1960; Springer and [Ansell-]Hahn, 1962; Springer and Horton, 1964).

II. Hormones

Many hormones can function as antigens, and antibodies to them may have clinical importance, as is the case for insulin. Only two hexosamine-containing hormones, however, will be given here as examples.

A. Chorionic Gonadotropin

This hormone (isolated from human urine) has been shown to contain hexosamine (5 to 6%) and to have a molecular weight of about 100,000 (see Volume I, Chapter 12; Gurin, 1942; Lundgren *et al.*, 1947). This material also contains sialic acid (compare Whitten, 1948; Friedmann, 1949; Brossmer and Walter, 1958). Bussard and Eyquem (1947) reported that anti-human group A serum from the rabbit (prepared with A erythrocytes) precipitated gonadotropin from various sources and neutralized its hormone effect in immature rats. Rabbit antisera to gonadotropin, on the other hand, had no significant effect on A substance. Eyquem and Bussard (1949), however, observed that antigonadotropic sera from horses, rabbits, goats, and chickens reacted with type XIV pneumococci and their isolated specific polysaccharide. The authors believed, therefore, that this hormone is more closely related to the polysaccharide of type XIV pneumococcus than to blood group A substance. It should be noted that Gurin, Bachman, and Wilson (1939), in earlier experiments, failed to find A activity for chorionic gonadotropin when using human anti-A sera (see also Gurin, Bachman, and Wilson, 1940)—an observation which was confirmed with the use of highly purified chorionic gonadotropin (Springer, unpublished data). It may be mentioned that Zilliacus, Widholm, and Pesonen (1954) reported that the concentration of chorionic gonadotropin in the urine and in the placenta is significantly lower in blood type Rh-negative-immunized mothers than it is in mothers not so immunized.

The formation of an antigonadotropic factor was demonstrated by its capacity to impair the gonadotropic reaction in rodents (Zondek and Sulman, 1937). An antigonadotropic factor was demonstrated by *in vitro* serological methods (Brody and Carlström, 1960) after immunization of rabbits with purified gonadotropin preparations plus adjuvants. The presence of antibodies against human chorionic gonadotropin was demonstrated with the complement-fixation test (Brody and Carlström, 1960), with precipitin (McKean, 1960), and with hemagglutination-inhibition tests (Wide and Gemzell, 1960, 1962). The serological procedures were found to be sensitive and specific (Brody and Carlström, 1961, 1962). Semiquantitative estimations of chorionic gonadotropins by agar gel and red cell hemagglutination techniques with the use of antisera to chorionic gonadotropin correlated well with the results of bioassays (see, e.g., Butt, Crooke, and Cunningham, 1962).

Histochemical localization of human chorionic gonadotropin by fluorescent rabbit antibodies against biologically active human chorionic gonadotropin and indication of the syncytiotrophoblast as the site of production or storage of human chorionic gonadotropin were recently reported (Midgley and Pierce, 1962).

B. Thyroglobulin

Thyroglobulin, the specific protein to which the thyroid hormones are bound when stored in the thyroid follicles, contains, in addition to other sugars, between 2 and 4% hexosamine (Brand, Kassell, and Heidelberger, 1939; Boas and Foley, 1955; Ujejski and Glegg, 1955; Gottschalk and Ada, 1956). There also is evidence that not only thyroglobulin but also the pituitary hormone, thyrotrophin, and the thyroxine-binding protein of serum are all glycoproteins (see Volume I, Chapter 10; see also Bettelheim-Jevons, 1958).

The serological specificity of thyroglobulin was discovered by Hektoen and Schulhof (1925) and Hektoen, Fox, and Schulhof (1927) and was confirmed by Witebsky (1929). This protein is capable of eliciting organ-specific antibodies, which precipitate thyroglobulins of various mammalian species but no other organ globulins. Stokinger and Heidelberger (1937) demonstrated quantitatively that thyroglobulin, in addition to being organ specific, is also species specific. Lerman (1942) was of the opinion that organ-specific antithyroglobulin sera act as antihormones. The serological interrelationship among thyroid extracts of various animal species was investigated by Rose and Witebsky (1955, 1956). In normal rabbits, injection of the animals' own thyroid produced antibodies which reacted with the remaining lobe of the thyroid.

Antibodies in humans against an individual's own thyroglobulin were first demonstrated by Roitt and co-workers (1956), Doniach and Roitt (1957), Witebsky *et al.* (1957), and Roitt, Campbell, and Doniach (1958) and represent a striking example of autoimmunity and its apparent detrimental effects in man. Autoantibodies may be the cause of chronic noninfectious thyroiditis—i.e., Hashimoto's thyroiditis and Riedel's thyroiditis (struma) (compare Boyd, 1947). The patient's serum in such cases may contain up to 5.2 mg of antibody protein per milliliter of serum, which reflects the presence of precipitating autoantibodies against thyroglobulin. Thyroglobulin precipitins were also found by Doniach and Roitt (1957) in some patients with spontaneous nongoitrous myxedema and untreated thyrotoxicosis. Autoantibodies may cause damage in organs against which they are directed. Thyrotoxicosis is known to precede Hashimoto's disease in certain cases, and spontaneous nongoitrous myxedema may be the end result of thyroid autoimmunity (Doniach and Roitt, 1957). After thyroidectomy for Hashimoto's goiter, the antibody level gradually decreased, most likely reflecting the decrease in antigenic stimulus. The antibody obtained from patients suffering from

Hashimoto's disease reacts very strongly with thyroglobulin from normal thyroids. Although unlikely, it is still possible that the antibodies found in Hashimoto's disease may be merely indicators of an immune process and not actually the destructive agents (Witebsky, Rose, and Shulman, 1958).

The antithyroglobulin antibodies are evidently either 7S or 19S α-globulins exclusively (Korngold, Van Leeuwen, and Brener, 1959; Shulman, Rose, and Witebsky, 1960). It was recently noted (Roitt, Campbell, and Doniach, 1958; Balfour *et al.*, 1961) that autoantibodies against three different antigenic components—namely, thyroglobulin, microsomes, and colloid—were present in patients with Hashimoto's disease with antibodies against the colloid in all of them. Pulvertaft, Doniach, and Roitt (1961) also reported cytotoxic effects of sera from patients with Hashimoto's disease or thyrotoxic goiter. The cytotoxic factor showed organ and species specificity and required complement (see also Trotter, Belyavin, and Waddams, 1957). The authors believed it to be the complement-fixing antibody against the lipoprotein "microsomal antigen" (Roitt *et al.*, 1964).

With the classic quantitative precipitation procedure, two types of curves were obtained by Roitt, Campbell, and Doniach (1958) for thyroglobulin–antithyroglobulin in different patients. One curve was similar to a usual rabbit protein–antiprotein system, whereas the other resembled that seen with horse flocculating antibodies. A low molar ratio of antibody to antigen (4:1 to 2:1) was found in the precipitates. This indicates a small number of combining sites on the antigen and suggests that only restricted parts of the molecule provide antigenic stimuli during autoimmunization. This reasoning appears justified, since Heidelberger (1938) —see also Stokinger and Heidelberger (1937)—obtained ratios of up to 60:1 with thyroid heterologous immune systems. Roitt, Campbell, and Doniach (1958) postulated that the confinement of thyroglobulin in closed follicles prevents the establishment of immunological tolerance (compare Owen, 1945; Billingham, Brent, and Medawar, 1956) in early life so that any subsequent release of thyroglobulin antigens might set up an autoimmunization process which gradually destroys the follicles.

III. Glycoproteins in Body Fluids

Antibodies to glycoproteins were described long ago, although it was found to be exceedingly difficult to elicit production of precipitins against this class of hexosamine-containing compounds (Goodner, 1925). In addition, the potency and specificity of the antibodies formed were considered to be low. The low degree of specificity noted by the early investigators appears to be due to lack of purity of the antigens employed. No sufficiently accurate determination has yet been made as to which groups on these macromolecules (except for the blood group substances) determine antigenic specificity.

A. Urinary Glycoproteins and Related Virus Inhibitors

The first specific antibodies against an apparently homogeneous glycoprotein, human urinary virus inhibitor, seem to have been obtained by Fraser (1951) and by Tamm and Horsfall (1952). These authors gave rabbits injections of urinary glycoproteins which have an average molecular weight of 7 to 8×10^6 and contain 9.1% sialic acid, 7.8% glucosamine, and 1.6% galactosamine (see Chapters 12, 50). Antibodies of narrow specificity were obtained which did not cross-react with human proteins, with human salivary or ovarian cyst glycoprotein, or with glycoproteins of other species.

The serological activity of urinary glycoprotein, as measured with the precipitin technique, was found to be undiminished if the glycoprotein was treated before exposure to antibody with receptor-destroying enzyme (isolated from *Vibrio comma*). This strongly indicates that the specific antigenic determinant is not the sialic acid portion released by the receptor-destroying enzyme. On the other hand, the union of urinary inhibitor with specific antibody neutralized the viral hemagglutination-inhibiting properties of the antigen. This applied regardless of whether there was a visible antigen–antibody complex precipitate or not. This phenomenon indicates blocking of virus receptor on the antigen macromolecule by the large antibody molecules. The fact that virus receptor sites and antigenic sites can be separate parts of the same macromolecule was clearly shown by Pusztai and Morgan (1961), who described an Le^a-active glycoprotein which, in addition to the usual constituents of human blood group glycoproteins, contained 18% sialic acid and was a potent inhibitor of influenza virus hemagglutination. It was possible to selectively destroy with different enzymes one of these two distinct biological activities without destroying the other.

Tamm and Horsfall (1952) also reported that antibodies against urinary glycoproteins did not agglutinate chick or human erythrocytes, nor did they prevent infection of chorioallantoic membrane with swine influenza virus. All these structures carry virus receptors closely similar to those found on the glycoprotein.

The urinary glycoprotein gave a single precipitation line with its corresponding antiserum when examined immunoelectrophoretically (Grant and Everall, 1957). Vaerman and Heremans (1959) reported that this line, however, presented two distinct maxima, and they assumed that a series of closely similar urinary glycoproteins of different degrees of aggregation represent the so-called Tamm–Horsfall glycoprotein. None of the numerous other related glycoproteins with virus-inhibitory activity (e.g., those from bronchial mucus or meconium) have been sufficiently studied immunologically to warrant inclusion here (see Chapter 50). The erythrocyte MN antigens are very powerful influenza-virus inhibitors (see Section I,B).

B. Plasma Glycoproteins

All plasma proteins migrating electrophoretically as globulins, with the possible exception of some lipoproteins, appear to contain hexosamine (see Volume I, Chapter 10). Early in this century, Bywaters (1909) found glucosamine in seromucoid. It appears that most or all of the plasma globulins are moderately immunogenic under appropriate conditions (Goodner, 1925; Lewis and Wells, 1927). In the plasma lipoproteins (α_1, α_2, β) significant amounts of carbohydrate are found, but less than 0.5% hexosamine and neuraminic acid, respectively (Epstein and Block, 1959; Schultze and Heide, 1960). Plasma lipoproteins, therefore, will not be discussed here.

1. Antibodies

Most antibodies are γ- or β-globulins (see the early studies by Heidelberger and Kabat, 1936; Tiselius and Kabat, 1939), which are groups of proteins arbitrarily defined by their physicochemical properties under specific conditions. In human and, probably, other mammalian sera, there are three main globulin types which may possess antibody activity. These antigenically distinct types cross-react with each other. According to present terminology, the following alternative names for the three types are used: (*i*) γ_2, 7S, or γ-globulin; (*ii*) 19S, γ_M, or β_{2M}-globulin; (*iii*) γ_{1A}- or β_{2A}-globulin. It was shown, based on the relationship to Bence Jones proteins, that there are two antigenic types in each of the three classes of immunoglobulins (Franklin, 1962; Mannik and Kunkel, 1962, 1963; Migita and Putnam, 1963; Fahey, 1963). Serum globulins increase in general during immunization and tend to be less in germ-free animals (compare Boyd, 1956; Reyniers *et al.*, 1959).

There is no indication to date that the hexosamine of these globulins is involved in specific antibody functions (see, however, one recent report on the effect of *p*-aminophenyl *N*-acetylgalactosaminide coupling on plant agglutinin specificity—Matsubara and Boyd, 1963), whereas the individual antigenic specificity of globulins appears to be associated with the carbohydrate portion of the molecule. The great importance of the exclusion of carbohydrate-rich contaminants in these studies has been stressed by Clamp, Bernier, and Putnam (1964). No effort will be made, therefore, to give here a detailed account of the nature of antibodies or to correlate physical and chemical properties with biological function. For this and for a discussion of different γ- and β-globulin types, the reader is referred to Volume I, Chapter 10, and to a number of extensive reviews (Campbell and Bulman, 1952; Boyd, 1954; Biserte, 1957; Isliker, 1957; Montreuil, 1957; Schultze, 1958; Heremans, 1960; Porter, 1960, Kunkel, 1960; Winzler, 1960; Kabat and Mayer, 1961; Putnam, 1965; Singer, 1965). The genetically important problem of intraspecies gamma globulin group differences which are demonstrated by serological methods (compare Oudin, 1962) will also be disregarded here, and the interested reader is referred to, among others, the summary by Grubb (1959; see also the end of this section on Antibodies).

The valence of antibodies appears to be 2 for most precipitating antibodies (Eisen and Karush, 1949; Karush, 1958; Kabat, 1961, p. 352; Boyd, 1956, p. 65; Wiener, 1961). The areas responsible for antibody specificity are unevenly distributed over the globulin molecules, and it has therefore been possible to degrade antibodies with enzymes with preservation of specific structures (compare von Behring, 1912; Pope, 1939,a; Petermann and Pappenheimer, 1941; Schultze, 1941; van der Scheer, Wyckoff, and Clarke, 1941; Pope and Stevens, 1951; Petermann, 1946; Porter, 1950, 1958; Porter and Charlwood, 1959; Porter, 1960; Deutsch, Thorpe, and Fudenberg, 1963).

Certain antibodies in human and horse sera are of higher molecular weight than are other antibodies. As was first shown by Heidelberger and Pedersen (1937), the weight of the heavier molecules is close to 1×10^6, as compared with the ordinary 150,000. Immunization of horse, pig, or cow with type-specific pneumococcus leads to exclusive formation of this heavy component (Heidelberger, Pedersen, and Tiselius, 1936; Kabat and Pedersen, 1938; Kabat, 1939). In contrast, man, monkey, and rabbit form antibodies of the "usual" size. The heavier component has been considered to be an aggregate of the lighter one (Treffers, Moore, and Heidelberger, 1942). Studies by Müller-Eberhard, Kunkel, and Franklin (1956) have shown, however, that the 18–20S component (γ_1 and α_2) contained about four times more carbohydrate, on a per cent basis, than did the lighter one. The hexosamine content, excluding sialic acids, was twice as high, and the sialic acid content was eight to ten times more than that of ordinary γ-globulin. It is also noteworthy that Kunkel and his colleagues (Wallenius *et al.*, 1956) found no reduction in the α_2 heavy component in patients suffering from so-called agammaglobulinemia, whereas γ_1 was not detectable. The 18–20S group of proteins does not represent, therefore, a simple aggregate of molecules of the main 7S type, even though 19S proteins can be dissociated into 6–7S units by SH compounds (Deutsch and Morton, 1957; Fudenberg and Kunkel, 1957; Kunkel, 1960).

More recent studies by Reisner and Franklin (1961) stressed, apart from cross-reactions, the difference in chemical, physical, and, antigenic properties between native 7S γ-globulin and the 7–8S cleavage product of normal and pathological 19S γ-globulins (see Deutsch, Thorpe, and Fudenberg, 1963). Franklin and Stanworth (1961) also presented evidence that the cross-reactions between 7S, 19S, and β_{2A}-globulins and the closely related (see, e.g., Kanzow, Böhm, and Kuhn, 1961) pathological γ- and β-myeloma proteins and macroglobulinemia proteins of Waldenström's disease (Waldenström, 1944) are due to those fragments of 7S γ-globulins which carry the antibody-combining sites. (For discussion of Bence Jones proteins found in patients with multiple myeloma, see Hässig, 1961.) Most of the "common" antibodies are located in the 7S fraction (compare Franklin and Kunkel, 1957), although isoagglutinins, Wassermann, complete Rh antibodies, and cold agglutinins in man are frequently associated with the 19S component (Gordon, 1953).

Kunkel, Franklin, and Müller-Eberhard (1959) (see also Lospalluto and Ziff, 1959) indicated that the pathological rheumatoid factor macroglobulins (cf. Fudenberg and Kunkel, 1961) have a carbohydrate pattern almost identical with that of 19S globulins. Schultze and co-authors (1960) found a γ-x-globulin in sera of patients with inflammatory or malignant diseases that appears to be closely related to the C-reactive proteins found in humans and monkeys in a variety of pathological conditions (Francis and Tillett, 1930; Tillett and Francis, 1930; MacLeod and Avery, 1941). The isolated γ-x-globulin which was not homogeneous contained about 1.5 times as much *N*-acetylhexosamine and almost six times as much sialic acid as normal 6–7S globulin does. Turumi, Hamagami, and Kenkel (1959) did not find sialic acid in C-reactive protein, the isolation method of which was not described.

Antibodies of the 19S globulin class fail to sensitize guinea pigs for cutaneous anaphylaxis reactions, do not fix to the skin (Ovary, Fudenberg, and Kunkel, 1960), and do not cross the placenta as the 7S γ-globulins do in man, rabbit, and some other species (Brambell, Hemmings, and Rowlands, 1948; Moore, Du Pan, and Buxton, 1949).

The immunological specificity of the pathological macroglobulins was recognized before that of the ordinary macroglobulins (Wuhrmann *et al.*, 1949; Wuhrmann, Wunderly, and Hässig, 1950; Habich, 1953; Korngold and Lipari, 1956,a) from which they differ to some slight extent (Deutsch, Kratochvil, and Reif, 1955; Franklin and Kunkel, 1957; Korngold and Van Leeuwen, 1957,a; Morton and Deutsch, 1958; Heremans, Heremans, and Schultze, 1959; Hässig, 1961; Fahey and Askonas, 1962). Both pathological and ordinary macroglobulins cross-react with 7S γ-globulins (Kratochvil and Deutsch, 1956; Franklin and Kunkel, 1957; Korngold and Van Leeuwen, 1957,a).

Chemical analyses of antibodies and "normal" globulins have shown no difference between them. The immunological relationships between antibodies and "normal" serum globulin have been investigated by the use of antibodies as antigens (being proteins, antibodies have specificities as antigens in addition to specificities as antibodies). The resulting antibodies may react with the normal serum of the donor species (Hamburger and Dehne, 1904; Landsteiner and Prašek, 1911; Eisler, 1920; Smith and Marrack, 1930; Wright, 1942). This production of antibody against antibody was demonstrated especially clearly by immunizing with washed specific polysaccharide precipitates, whereby antigenic protein material other than antibody was virtually eliminated. Antibodies of different function originating from the same species were antigenically essentially alike, as long as comparisons were made within the two different fractions of globulin types (antitoxic and precipitin types of horse antibodies) (Ando, Takeda, and Hamano, 1938; Treffers and Heidelberger, 1941,a; Treffers, Moore, and Heidelberger, 1942). Only occasionally were minute differences noted (Treffers and Heidelberger, 1941; Treffers, 1944).

Antibodies employed as antigens apparently do not differ significantly from "normal" serum globulin used for the same purpose. In no instance studied did the antigenic specificity of the antibody involve that part of the antibody molecule which reacts with the antigen. The only antigenic specificity of antibodies appears to be due to their common origin, and the groups responsible for their antibody function are either only a small part of the total protein molecule or else nonantigenic.

The immunochemical similarity between "normal" globulins and specific antibodies forms the basis for the widespread use of antiglobulin tests which employ antibodies to normal globulins in order to detect coating of erythrocytes or bacteria by "blocking" antibodies (Moreschi, 1908,a; Coombs, Mourant and Race, 1945).

Despite their apparent antigenic homogeneity, given serum globulins show fine differences among individuals within one species (Oudin, 1956,a). The antigenically different types of γ-globulin, evidently genetically controlled, were named allotypes (Oudin, 1956,a; Grubb and Laurell, 1956; see also Scheiffarth, Götz, and Warnatz, 1958; Dray and Young, 1959; Grubb, 1959; Hirschfeld, 1959; Oudin, 1960; for β-globulins see, e.g., Smithies and Connell, 1959).

2. Fetuin

Among the plasma proteins, fetuin and α_1-acid glycoprotein have attracted attention because of their high sialic acid content (Deutsch, 1954; Klenk and Stoffel, 1955; Klenk and Faillard, 1957). Both will be mentioned here briefly, since the former may conceivably have some function in resistance and since both have been studied extensively immunologically.

Fetuin is present in high concentration in fetal calf serum, as well as in other mammalian fetuses (Pedersen, 1944). Its biological function is unknown. The chemical and physical structure of fetuin are described in Volume I, Chapter 10.

Meyers and Deutsch (1955) found that antibodies to fetuin were made by rabbits against only a small portion of the purified protein. Their data suggested that electrophoretically "homogeneous" fetuin contains six or more antigenic components. The heterogeneity was established by agar gel diffusion and by the shape of quantitative precipitin curves. After being heated for 15 min at 100°C and pH 7, fetuin failed to precipitate with its antibody, although it gave evidence of combination with antibody by its inhibition of specific precipitin formation between native antigen and its antibody.

3. α_1-Acid Glycoprotein and Haptoglobins

The α_1-acid glycoprotein (Weimer, Mehl, and Winzler, 1950) (see also Volume I, Chapter 10, and Volume II, Chapter 34) contains ca. 12% hexosamine and 12% sialic acid. It is of weak antigenicity in chickens. No more than one precipitation band was found in the α_1-acid glycoprotein—anti-α_1-acid glycoprotein system by the Oudin agar gel technique (Silberberg *et al.*, 1955). A procedure to quantitate the content of a serum by the precipitin reaction was also described by Silberberg *et al.* (1955). Native α_1-acid glycoprotein is of low immunogenicity in the rabbit, but removal of the sialic acid leads to a highly immunogenic substance (Winzler, personal communication).

Haptoglobin, the hemoglobin-binding component of plasma, is a glycoprotein which increases during infectious diseases, collagen disease, and "stress" conditions (Jayle and Boussier, 1954). The different genetical groups of haptoglobin (Smithies, 1955, 1959) can be separated by electrophoresis and by immunoelectrophoresis (compare Allison, 1958; Hirschfeld, 1960). Haptoglobin is said to contain 5.7% *N*-acetylglucosamine and 5.1% sialic acid (Cheftel *et al.*, 1960).

IV. Amyloid

Amyloid is a collective term for a group of substances found in various tissues of persons with primary and secondary amyloidosis. The chemical nature and origin of these substances are controversial (Calkins, Cohen, and Larsen, 1960) (see also Chapters 19, 20, 33). Amyloid is thought by many to be the result, at least in part, of an antigen–antibody reaction and to consist of both components of this reaction (Loeschcke, 1927; Letterer, Caesar, and Vogt, 1960; Tal, Laufer, and Zlotnick, 1964)—the consequence of a chronic antigenic stimulus (compare Vogt and Kochem,

1960) in which the stimulation of plasma cells was shown to be preeminent (Ehrich, 1952). Amyloid produced experimentally in the rabbit by casein application, however, is more than a casein–γ-globulin complex (Giles and Calkins, 1958). Amyloid (Friedreich and Kekulé, 1859) contains a mixture of glycoproteins possessing, in general, between 1.0 and 1.6% hexosamine (compare also Meyer, in Springer, 1959, p. 140). This content is higher than that found in the corresponding normal tissues from which it was isolated (Faber, 1948; Giles and Calkins, 1958). Calkins, Cohen, and Larsen (1960) believed that glucosamine was the predominant amino sugar in amyloid-laden tissues, in which they found also galactosamine (Giles and Calkins, 1955; Calkins, Cohen, and Larsen, 1960), but there is no report for analysis of sialic acid.

Klenk and Faillard (1955) reported on the occurrence of much sialic acid in amyloid of the liver of a patient without recognizable underlying disease. This observation was considered to be consonant with the derivation of part of the amyloid from α- or β-globulins (see also Schneider, 1964).

Conclusions from fairly recent experiments with rabbits and also from study of the human disorder (Calkins, Cohen, and Gitlin, 1958; Calkins, Cohen, and Larsen, 1960) disagree with the earlier statements (Mellors and Ortega, 1956; Vazquez and Dixon, 1956) that gamma globulin is preferentially bound in the sites of amyloid accumulation. Schmitz-Moormann (1964) reported on the analysis of uronic acid and sialic acid–containing polysaccharides from the liver of a patient with amyloidosis. He found the amyloid liver to contain the same sugars as did a healthy one, but in increased amount, especially sialic acid and uronic acid. There were about three times as many macromolecules containing sialic acid as polysaccharides containing uronic acid. Among the latter, chondroitin sulfate predominated. One glycoprotein containing sialic acid was considered to be characteristic of amyloidosis. It has also been stated that the proteins and polysaccharides which are deposited in primary and secondary amyloidosis differ in nature (see e.g., Clausen and Christensen, 1964). There is no agreement of opinion on this, however (cf. Schneider, 1964), nor are there enough well-defined cases of primary amyloidosis which have been studied properly by physical and chemical means.

V. Gangliosides and Related Lipids

These lipids, which are found in the brain and other organs and whose fundamental chemistry has been established by Klenk, generally, but not always, contain, as carbohydrates, sialic acid and 2-acetamido-2-deoxygalactose besides galactose and glucose (Klenk and Gielen, 1960,

1961; Weicker *et al.*, 1960; L. Svennerholm, 1962; Kuhn and Wiegandt, 1963,a).

Yokoyama, Trams, and Brady (1963) have investigated the immunological properties of gangliosides, after Rapport *et al.* (1959) had reported on the antigenicity of a ceramide lactoside, cytolipin H (Rapport, Graf, and Yariv (1961). Yokoyama and his colleagues noted that injection of purified gangliosides caused the production of anti-ganglioside antibodies in rabbits when administered with carrier substances such as red cells, Freund's adjuvant, or serum proteins. Furthermore, they noted that high concentrations of gangliosides weakly inhibited numerous anti-blood group antibodies of different specificities. This very low and unspecific inhibiting activity with exorbitant amounts of gangliosides was also noted by Springer, Williamson, and Brandes (1961) and by Wolff and Springer (1964). These authors could not confirm the reportedly specific inhibition of anti-Rh_0 (D) antibodies by gangliosides (Dodd, Bigley, and Geyer, 1963). It is well established, however, that numerous acidic polymers unspecifically inhibit the action of agglutinating antibodies (cf. Springer, 1963). Related and apparently immunologically specific substances are naturally occurring cytolipin K, which originates from human kidney (Rapport, Graf, and Schneider, 1964), and human red-cell "globoside" (Yamakawa, Yokoyama, and Handa, 1963). Quite possibly, both these ceramide tetrasaccharides, which have the same over-all composition, with 1 mole galactosamine as hexosamine, will turn out to possess the same structure.

VI. Glycoproteins of Hen Egg White

The antigenicity of the ovomucoids was established early (Lewis and Wells, 1927), and anaphylaxis due to ovomucoid was demonstrated more than 50 years ago (Wells, 1911). Egg albumin, because of its ready availability and the comparative ease with which it may be obtained in highly purified crystalline form, has been used widely in immunochemical studies (compare Kabat and Mayer, 1961). The chemical and physical structure of these glycoproteins is described in Volume I, Chapter 12 (compare Seemann, 1898; Langstein, 1900; Neuberger, 1938; Stacey and Woolley, 1940; Levene, 1941; Johansen, Marshall, and Neuberger, 1961). No relation has been established between the hexosamine content of the ovomucoids and their immunological properties, except that some blood group A specificity was reported for hen ovomucoid (Bray, Henry, and Stacey, 1946).

Pérez and Sergent (1958) found no difference in quantitative precipitin curves given by ordinary recrystallized egg albumin and that which had been treated with formaldehyde. The effect of irradiation on the serological properties of ovalbumin has also been studied (Leone, 1960).

Ovalbumin, even in its crystallized form, is inhomogeneous (see, e.g., Durieux and Kaminski, 1956). It was pointed out, however, that the three physically and chemically different constituents found in ovalbumin had the same immunological behavior in the agar gel diffusion test.

VII. Fertilizin and Antifertilizin

Lillie (1913) found that "egg water" of some sea urchins and of polychaete annelids may agglutinate homologous spermatozoa. He termed the active agent, which could be removed from the eggs, fertilizin. Tyler (1948) and Vasseur (1948) showed that fertilizin is derived from the gelatinous coat of the sea urchin egg and is an acid polysaccharide which contains fucose (and other sugars depending on the species) and sulfate esters (Vasseur, 1947). At various times, this material has been thought of as a "mucopolysaccharide." Physicochemically homogeneous fertilizin preparations, however, probably do not contain hexosamine (Tyler, 1949; Vasseur and Immers, 1949; Runnström, 1951; Vasseur, 1952), although this problem is not yet resolved unequivocally (Tyler, personal communication).

Fertilizin preparations have been tested by Morgan (1950) for their capability to inhibit blood group agglutinins but were found to be inactive. Surprisingly enough, it was reported that the neutral blood group H(O) substance acted like jelly-coat material of sea urchin eggs in inhibiting fertilization (Wicklund, 1954). More recently, fertilizin activity was related to the acidity of the jelly-coat polysaccharides and their action as enzyme inhibitors (Runnström and Immers, 1956).

The substance on the sperm with which fertilizin reacts is named antifertilizin (Tyler, 1949). Antifertilizin appears to be an acidic protein, and its hexosamine content is unknown. In many ways, the action between fertilizin and antifertilizin resembles that of an antibody–antigen reaction (Tyler, 1948, 1949; Perlmann, 1954, 1956, 1959).

VIII. Microbial Polysaccharides

Hexosamine-containing structures in bacteria are legion, and Heidelberger (1959) indicated in the title of his paper at the fourth International Congress of Biochemistry in Vienna in 1958 that "all polysaccharides are immunologically specific." There are some comprehensive reviews on this subject, such as those by Burger (1950), Tomcsik (1953), Davies (1960), and Stacey and Barker (1960). Therefore, it will be attempted here to list only those antigen–antibody reactions of hexosamine-containing bacterial substances for which it is reasonably likely that hexosamines are involved in the specific reaction or for which the immunochemical mechanism of a given microbial antigen–antibody reaction is of more general significance.

Early in this century, Pick (1902) showed that typhoid cultures could be digested with proteolytic enzymes and that polysaccharide material could be recovered. This material gave a specific precipitate with antiserum. Perlzweig and Steffen (1923) believed in the "nonprotein nature of the immunizing pneumococcus antigen." The participation of carbohydrates in immune reactions was firmly established by Heidelberger and Avery (1923, 1924) and by Heidelberger, Goebel, and Avery (1925). The consequence of this discovery was the recognition of polysaccharides as determinants of the immunological specificities of many microorganisms. For most hexosamine-containing microbial polysaccharides, however, sufficient evidence has not been gathered to indicate the rôle that amino sugars play in their serological specificity.

Recent studies on the chemical composition of bacterial cell walls point to a similar basic structural component in all bacteria investigated (Cummins and Harris, 1958; McQuillen, in Springer, 1960a, p. 93). This basic structure, designated as cell wall peptidoglycan, contains two hexosamines: *N*-acetylglucosamine and *N*-acetylmuramic acid. Peptidoglycans are compounds of large molecular weight (see Volume I, Chapter 9). They are combined with the cell wall in such a way that it is likely that their major function consists in the preservation of integrity of the bacterial cell (compare Park, 1961; Weidel, 1964). Peptidoglycan, however, does not appear to play an active role in immunization, and no antibodies against it are known. This may, perhaps, be explained by the observations of Weidel, Frank, and Martin (1960), who concluded that the peptidoglycan was present as the innermost layer of the three-layer cell wall of an *E. coli* B and thus did not come in contact with the host tissues. There also appears to be no information on the serological specificity or immunological significance of the monomer muramic acid.

A. Gram-Positive Bacteria

In addition to the peptidoglycan, the cell wall of gram-positive bacteria may possess up to 60% of a ribitol phosphate or glycerophosphate polymer containing glycosidically linked sugars and esterified D-alanine (teichoic or teichuronic acids) (Mitchell and Moyle, 1951a; Armstrong *et al.*, 1958a; Armstrong, Baddiley and Buchanan, 1959; McCarty, 1959; Janczura, Perkins, and Rogers, 1961). *N*-Acetylamino sugar may be the glycosidically attached carbohydrate, as is the case for *Staphylococcus aureus* H, *Staphylococcus albus*, and *Streptococcus faecalis* (Armstrong *et al.*, 1958; Baddiley, 1962) (see Volume I, Chapter 9). Not enough is known about the antigenic properties of these recently discovered polymers. The following observations, however, are relevant. Rebers and Heidelberger (1959) showed that the type VI pneumococcus specific substance is similar in general structure to teichoic acids. Furthermore, McCarty (1959) isolated polyglycerophosphate as an antigenic component of various gram-positive bacterial species. Sanderson, Juergens, and Strominger (1961) and Sanderson, Strominger, and Nathenson (1962) noted that the ribitol teichoic acid from *Staphylococcus aureus* (strain Copenhagen) bears 85% *N*-acetylglucosamine in β-linkage, whereas the remainder is α-linked. Immunization of rabbits with staphylococci led to anti-cell wall agglutinins which could not be neutralized by phenyl 2-acetamido-2-deoxy-β-D-glucoside but which were neutralized only by rather high concentrations of the α anomer. It was concluded from these inhibition experiments that the α anomer probably is the most terminal nonreducing structure of this ribitol phosphate. Antibodies with anti-*N*-acetyl-β-D-glucosaminide specificity obtained with streptococcal antigens were, nevertheless, able to react with the β structures in this teichoic acid. Strominger (personal communication) believes that the type-specific immediate skin reactions due to staphylococci first described by Julianelle and his colleagues (Julianelle and Wieghard, 1935,a; Wieghard and Julianelle, 1935; Julianelle and Hartmann, 1936; Julianelle, 1939) are due to teichoic acid (see also Strominger, 1962a). Similarly, Baddiley (1962) reported that the group-antigenic polysaccharides of *Staphylococcus aureus* and *Staphylococcus albus* are the teichoic acids.

The linkage of the *N*-acetylglucosaminyl residue remained a major problem. Teichoic acid isolated from *Staphylococcus aureus* was a polyribitol phosphate of α-, β-, or α- and β-*N*-acetylglucosaminyl and D-alanine ester residues (Baddiley *et al.*, 1962,a; Sanderson, Strominger, and Nathenson, 1962). Juergens, Sanderson, and Strominger (1960, 1963) and Nathenson and Strominger (1962) reported that sera obtained by immunization with *Staphylococcus aureus* strain Copenhagen possessed anti-teichoic acid antibodies specific for α-*N*-acetylglucosaminyl residues only. Haukenes *et al.* (1961) and Haukenes (1962) in their studies of cross-reactions of teichoic acids from *Staphylococcus aureus* strain H with *Staphylococcus* immune sera noted, however, that their antisera reacted with teichoic acids which contained little or no α-linked *N*-acetylglucosamine residues. Morse (1962a) found, by hemagglutination inhibition and precipitation inhibition, that β-linked *N*-acetylglucosaminyl residues were the determinant groups of the teichoic acid of *Staphylococcus aureus* strain NYH-6. Nathenson and Strominger (1962) also found β-*N*-acetylglucosaminyl specificity. They ascribed the apparent discrepancies in the antibody specificities to different teichoic acids in the *Staphylococcus* strain used for immunization. A careful investigation in Kabat's laboratory (Torii, Kabat, and Bezer, 1964), however, revealed that the teichoic acids from the Copenhagen and NYH-6 strains were each mixtures of two distinct polysaccharides: α- and a β-teichoic acid, depending on the linkage of the *N*-acetylglucosaminyl residue to ribitol, which was at least predominantly and probably entirely α for one polymer and β for the other. These investigators were able to separate the two teichoic acids by immunochemical methods. They proved the importance of the α- and β-linkage for the two different teichoic acids by precipitin-inhibition test with α- and β-linked *N*-acetylglucosaminides. During their studies, the authors found that humans possess some antibodies to teichoic acids of *S. aureus,* probably as a consequence of prior contact with this microorganism. Teichoic acid itself was found to be antigenic in man and to produce a rise in titer when injected. Human immune sera were obtained after injection of a total of 0.8 to 1.0 mg of teichoic acid from *S. aureus* Copenhagen and used for the *in vitro* studies. Haukenes *et al.* (1961) and Haukenes (1962) reported that antibodies to teichoic acid could not be produced in rabbits and mice. It was found by Torii, Kabat, and Bezer (1964) that, in general, teichoic acid from *S. aureus* NYH-6 precipitated considerably more nitrogen from the same antisera than did the Copenhagen material. On the other hand, teichoic acid from *S. albus* did not precipitate any significant amount of nitrogen from the antisera tested. The α- and β-teichoic acids could be separated from each other with one antiserum by specific precipitation under appropriate conditions, since the equivalence zone for α-teichoic acid and its homologous antibody differed significantly from that of the β-teichoic acid and its antibody. The separated α- and β-teichoic acids could be recovered from the specific precipitates. The α- and β-teichoic acids could also be clearly distinguished by two-dimensional agar gel diffusion. The distinction was easier for teichoic acid from *S. aureus* NYH-6 than for that from the Copenhagen strain.

1. Pneumococci

The various pneumococcal types are classified according to the make-up of their capsules (Heidelberger and Kendall, 1933). The capsular polysaccharides from the pneumococci have been studied especially thoroughly (compare Heidelberger, 1959). More than seventy-five different types of pneumococci are known, but the chemical nature of less than a third of them has been investigated, and not all of these contain hexosamine (compare Heidelberger, 1956).

The purified capsular polysaccharides precipitated in dilutions of up to greater than 1 to 10^6 with their specific antisera. Acid hydrolysis inactivated the macromolecule, but yielded degradation products which inhibited agglutination, as well as precipitation. These split products were of the order of trisaccharides (Heidelberger and Kendall, 1933).

The unusual immunologic relationship between the capsular polysaccharide of type XIV pneumococcus and human blood group substances has already been discussed. The earliest observations pointing to an immunological relation were those by Finland and Curnen (1938) and Weil and Sherman (1939). *N*-Acetyl-D-glucosamine and D-galactose were first described as components of the polysaccharide of type XIV pneumococcus by Goebel, Beeson, and Hoagland (1939), who also showed that blood group A substances isolated from pepsin precipitated with type XIV pneumococcus antiserum. The importance of *N*-acetyl-D-glucosamine for the determinant specificity of the type XIV pneumococcus antibody has been inferred from inhibition studies by Watkins and Morgan (1956). There is little doubt that the cross-reactivity arises from the presence of a common galactose-*N*-acetyl-D-glucosamine disaccharide in both the human blood group substances and polysaccharides of type XIV pneumococcus. This structure of the blood group substances is free to react strongly with the type XIV pneumococcus antibody after mild hydrolysis of the A, B, and H(O) substances, whereas the unhydrolyzed glycoproteins react only weakly (compare Kabat, 1956; Morgan, 1960). The most active disaccharide in inhibiting this cross-reaction was *O*-β-D-galactopyranosyl-(1 $\rightarrow$ 4)-2-acetamido-2-deoxy-D-glucose (Watkins and Morgan, 1956; Schiffman, Howe, and Kabat, 1958). It was therefore concluded that the cross-reactivity of the blood group substances with anti-type XIV pneumococcus serum was, at least in part, due to this disaccharide which is a component of human blood group substances. It has, however, not been isolated from the polysaccharide of type XIV pneumococcus (Barker *et al.*, 1958; Barker, Keith, and Stacey, 1961). It has been shown, though, that human blood group A substance (Côté and Morgan, 1956) and polysaccharide of type XIV pneumococcus (Barker *et al.*, 1958; Barker, Keith, and Stacey, 1961) both contain the disaccharide 3-*O*-(2-amino-2-deoxy-β-*O*-glucosyl)-D-galactose and both also possess nonreducing terminal D-galactopyranoside structures (see also Section I,A,2). Recently, in Morgan's laboratory (Rege *et al.*, 1963) two trisaccharides, isolated from human blood group A,B,H(O), and Le^a substances, inhibited the cross-reaction of blood group substances with anti-type XIV pneumococcus horse serum. They were *O*-β-D-galactosyl-(1 $\rightarrow$ 3)-*O*-2-acetamido-2-deoxy-β-D-glucosyl-(1 $\rightarrow$ 3)-galactose and *O*-β-D-galactosyl-(1 $\rightarrow$ 4)-*O*-

2-acetamido-2-deoxy-β-D-glucosyl-(1 → 3)-galactose; the latter was the more active. These findings are in agreement with studies on model compounds by Kabat (1962) and studies by Watkins and Morgan (1962).

Capsular-specific polysaccharide of types I, IV, and V pneumococcus has also been reported to contain *N*-acetylamino sugar residues (Heidelberger and Kendall, 1931; Heidelberger, Kendall, and Scherp, 1936; Barker *et al.*, 1961) (see Volume I, Chapters 14, 15). A role of these sugars in the immunological specificity is suspected but not established. The presence of amino sugar (or sugars) is also indicated in the capsular polysaccharide of types VII, IX, and XII pneumococcus (Heidelberger, Barker, and Stacey, 1954; Stacey and Barker, 1960). Capsular polysaccharides of types XV through XXXIV pneumococcus in all but seven strains have been reported to contain hexosamine (Brown, 1939; Brown and Robinson, 1943), but the immunological significance of this finding is unknown.

The isolated purified capsular polysaccharides are antigenic for some species, such as man and mouse, but are only haptens for the rabbit. These haptens, however, can elicit an anamnestic reaction in the rabbit (C. M. MacLeod, personal communication). The somatic portion of all pneumococci contains the so-called cellular, or C, carbohydrate (Tillett and Francis, 1930; Tillett, Goebel, and Avery, 1930), which is a characteristic of the species pneumococcus. It contains amino sugar (Heidelberger and Kendall, 1931, 1932) and forms a portion of the heterophil antigen of pneumococcus (Goebel and Adams, 1943).

Pneumococcal capsular polysaccharides have been useful in practical immunology. As first shown by Tillett and Francis (1929) and by Francis and Tillett (1930) the isolated polysaccharides of pneumococcus are antigenic in man and may be used in cutaneous tests to indicate the state of immunity. Immunization by subcutaneous injection of purified capsular polysaccharides can prevent pneumococcal pneumonia (MacLeod *et al.*, 1945; Heidelberger *et al.*, 1946). Injection of 50 μg each of up to six type-specific pneumococcal polysaccharides elicited in humans, in most instances, type-specific antibodies which reached peak levels in 2 to 6 weeks and slowly decreased after 6 to 8 months (Heidelberger *et al.*, 1947; Heidelberger, MacLeod, and DiLapi, 1948). Human subjects who received injections of type-specific pneumococcal polysaccharide usually showed measurable and, frequently, up to one half of the maximum antibody content against the polysaccharides 3 to 8 years later. In cases in which antibody had disappeared or remained only at a low level, reinjection generally caused antibody to reappear or increase, but at a submaximal level (Heidelberger *et al.*, 1950).

2. ANTHRAX

Ivánovics (1940,a,b) isolated the agar and protein-free specific polysaccharide from *Bacillus anthracis* (compare Tomcsik, 1927) and found it to be composed of equimolecular amounts of D-glucosamine and galactose. Acetic acid was likewise found, probably also in equimolecular amounts. These compounds, which are also components of the human blood group glycoproteins, prompted Ivánovics to investigate immunological relationships among these substances. He observed that human A substance reacts with horse antianthrax serum only after some acid treatment and then not particularly well.

As Heidelberger and Kendall (1937) had noted, gentle acid hydrolysis of pneumococcal polysaccharide will leave it reactive with horse antipneumococcus serum, but not with rabbit antipneumococcus serum. Heidelberger and Kendall (1933) showed that precipitating haptens may have a molecular size no larger than 550 to 1800 (see also Landsteiner and van der Scheer, 1932) provided that horse (but not rabbit) antisera are employed. The reason for the distinctive behavior of rabbit and horse antisera appears to be the different molecular weight of the antibodies produced by these animal species (Heidelberger and Pedersen, 1937). Similarly, Ivánovics (1940a) found that gentle hydrolysis rapidly decreased the capability of the anthrax polysaccharide to react with its homologous rabbit antibodies, whereas the capability to precipitate horse antibodies persisted much longer. Although there was no precipitation between partially degraded anthrax polysaccharide and its rabbit antibody, it nevertheless retained its serological specificity and functioned as a hapten. Rather extensively degraded anthrax polysaccharide inhibited precipitation, but it was not possible to inhibit precipitation of undegraded anthrax polysaccharide by horse antiserum with a mixture of the constituent sugars, galactose and glucosamine (each in 2% concentration). The failure of the rabbit serum to precipitate was shown not to be due to lack of antibody. Ivánovics also demonstrated (1940b) that polysaccharide type XIV pneumococcus precipitated antianthrax horse serum. The reciprocal of this reaction—namely, the precipitation of anti-pneumococcus type XIV antiserum by somatic anthrax polysaccharide—could not be shown. Surprisingly enough, however, this was demonstrated later by Heidelberger, Barker, and Björklund (1958) with one anthrax polysaccharide preparation only, obtained from a *Bacillus anthracis* isolated from guinea pigs. A significant part of the cross-reactivity of the anthrax polysaccharide with pneumococcus type XIV serum is due to nonreducing galactose end groups; periodate oxidation indicated that these units were not responsible for the entire cross-reactivity, since some glucosamine residues were also involved (see also Mester and Ivánovics, 1957).

The amino sugar-containing polysaccharide of a closely related organism, *Bacillus subtilis* (Sharon, 1957; Sharon and Jeanloz, 1959), was not investigated for the chemical basis of immunological specificity.

3. Streptococci

The division of hemolytic streptococci into serological groups by Lancefield (1941) is based in large part on the serological specificity of the bacterial cell wall carbohydrates, in which the teichoic acids play a role (compare McCarty, 1959). Streptococci groups A to G all contain hexosamine and rhamnose. Hyaluronic acid which is produced by streptococci (Kendall, Heidelberger, and Dawson, 1937) will be discussed in Section XI.

The group A streptococci have been investigated from the immunochemical and chemical point of view by McCarty (1959), mainly because of their relationship to human disease. The major component of the cell wall of group A streptococci is the specific polysaccharide which can be brought into solution without disturbing the integrity of the glycopeptide of the cell wall. Its specificity was believed to be associated with rhamnose and hexosamine (Schmidt, 1952). Most of the hexosamine occurs as *N*-acetyl-D-glucosamine, and it was shown by McCarty (1956) that *N*-acetyl-D-glucosamine side chains are responsible for the serological specificity of the group A polysaccharide. That at least a large part of the L-rhamnose in the cell wall polysaccharide of group A hemolytic streptococcus must be linked α-1 $\rightarrow$ 3 was recently shown by Estrada-Parra, Heidelberger, and Rebers (1963). In their study this polysaccharide was treated with periodate, destroying the terminal *N*-acetylglucosamine but leaving intact all L-rhamnose. The oxidized polysaccharide lost its precipitability by anti-streptococcus A rabbit serum but strongly precipitated with types II and VI antipneumococcus horse sera and an antiserum to a streptococcal group A variant, whose specificity appears to be directed against α-1 $\rightarrow$ 3-linked L-rhamnose structures.

Variants of group A strains may arise during their passage through animal hosts. These variants seem to have lost their group-specific carbohydrate, since extracts of them do not react with group A antisera (Wilson, 1945). The variants, however, still contain a cell wall carbohydrate with the same monosaccharides as the specific group A carbohydrate, although in different proportions (rhamnose-to-hexosamine ratio about 5 against 1.5 to 2.0 for the ordinary A carbohydrate) (McCarty and Lancefield, 1955). On the basis of enzymic studies, McCarty (1956) explained the chemical and serological difference of the variant carbohydrate by the absence of a hexosamine side chain which is responsible for group A specificity. In streptococcus of group A, this side chain masks those structures of the macromolecule which confer the specificity to variant (V) carbohydrate. The relationship between chemical alteration and serological specificity of the group A carbohydrate is shown in a simplified manner in Fig. 5 (McCarty, in Springer, 1960a, p. 163).

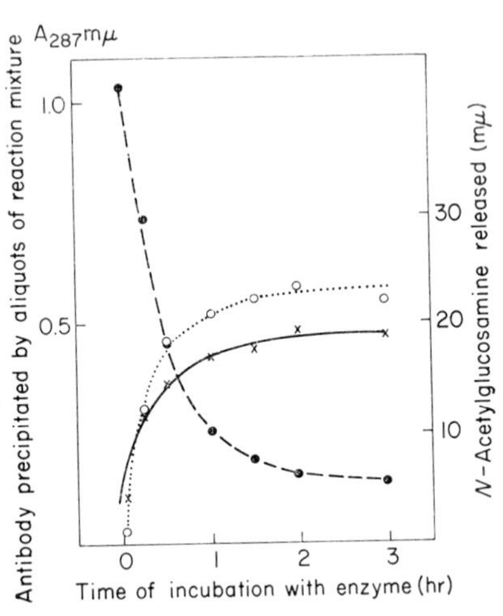

FIG. 5. Relationship between the decrease in the reactivity of specific group A streptococcus and the increase in the cross-reactivity of the V antiserum during enzymic removal of *N*-acetylglucosamine side chains from group A carbohydrate (from McCarty, in Springer, 1960a, p. 163).
●, antibody precipitated from group A antiserum;
×, antibody precipitated from variant (V) antiserum;
○, *N*-acetylglucosamine released.

Araujo and Krause (1963) presented evidence that certain variant strains of group C streptococci possess a carbohydrate antigen similar to group A variant streptococci. The major hexosamine of the group C carbohydrate is *N*-acetylgalactosamine, however. Studies on A and C variant strains suggested that the carbohydrates of groups A and C streptococci have a similar rhamnose structure, but that the antigenic specificity is dependent on the particular terminal *N*-acetylhexosamines.

McCarty (1958) also investigated the chemical basis for serological specificity of group A streptococcal carbohydrate with an "artificial" azoantigen prepared according to established procedures (Landsteiner, 1945; Westphal and Schmidt, 1952). Phenyl *N*-acetylglucosaminides inhibited the reaction of A carbohydrate with homologous antiserum, the β anomer being over twice as effective an inhibitor as either the α anomer or *N*-acetyl-D-glucosamine. It would be of interest to know whether the α anomer is contaminated with some of the β form or not. These "artificial" antigens reacted only with ordinary group A antisera and with none of the variant antisera, and this was taken as further evidence for the decisive role of *N*-acetyl-D-glucosamine in A group specificity. The cross-reaction, however, was not reciprocal—i.e., antibodies to the azo-antigen did not react with the group A carbohydrate. This lack of reciprocal cross-reactivity is quite common for serological reactions. Kabat (in Springer, 1960a, p. 164) suggested that the cause in this particular instance was the small size of the subterminal benzene ring in the artificial antigen in comparison with the subterminal sugar units of the natural antigens. This explanation appears to be valid if the antibody resulting from immunization with these artificial antigens is pictured as having combining sites fitting closely to the determinant group of the antigen (Kabat, 1958).

Structures containing *N*-acetylgalactosamine apparently are involved in the serological specificity of some of the type antigens of group F streptococci (Willers *et al.*, 1964). This was shown to be the case for type antigens I and II and, possibly, IV. Interestingly enough, *N*-methylglucamine (1-methylamino-1-deoxy-D-glucitol) was a good inhibitor, even of reactions with F antigenic determinants, against which hexosamines showed no activity.

4. Staphylococci

The study of the chemical composition of staphylococcus cell constituents used to take second place to the investigation of the toxins elaborated by these bacteria. Twenty years ago, however, Fellowes and Routh (1944) noted the presence of "glucosamine" in polysaccharide fractions of young cultures of *Staphylococcus aureus*. The significance of the teichoic acids for staphylococcus specificity was mentioned in Section VIII,A, of this chapter.

Staphylococcus carbohydrate has been used in skin testing (Julianelle and Hartmann, 1936; Julianelle, 1939). By means of specific immunoprecipitation of polysaccharides isolated from staphylococci, Julianelle and Wieghard (1935,a and Wieghard and Julianelle, 1935) separated the staphylococci into two large groups designated as "type A" (pathogenic) and "type B" (not pathogenic) (see also Losnegard and Oeding, 1963). Recent studies suggest that these type-specific carbohydrates are teichoic acids (cf. Torii, Kabat, and Bezer, 1964, and Section VIII,A, of this chapter).

Morse (1962) isolated a component from the growth medium of an originally virulent staphylococcal strain. This immunochemically inhomogeneous material was presumed to contain about 25% glucosamine. Although it precipitated antibodies *in vitro,* the material was not antigenic in rabbits. Rabbits previously immunized with heat-killed whole staphylococci, however, exhibited cutaneous hypersensitivity to small quantities of the injected isolated staphylococcus component. When this soluble material was injected subcutaneously 12 to 14 days in advance, it protected mice from subsequent death due to intraperitoneal challenge with the staphylococcus from which the soluble compound was isolated. Perkins (1963) adduced evidence that this antigen contained 2-amino-2-deoxyglucuronic acid, which has also been described in *O*- and *N*-acetylated form as the sole carbohydrate building stone of a homogeneous polysaccharide isolated from *Staphylococcus aureus* of the pathogenic Smith-type strains (Haskell and Hanessian, 1963). This antigen was shown to possess high immunizing activity for mice (Fisher, Devlin, and Erlandson, 1963).

This short immunochemical review of gram-positive bacteria containing hexosamine does not pretend to be complete and does not discuss organisms containing hexosamine or hexosamine derivatives, such as *Micrococcus lysodeikticus* where 2-amino-2-deoxymannuronic acid was found, as well as glucosamine and muramic acid (Hawthorne, 1950; Perkins, 1963), *Lactobacillus casei,* and *Streptococcus faecalis* (Ikawa and Snell, 1956), or *Clostridium* (Tardieux and Nisman, 1952). Hexosamine is also said to occur in the *Leptospira* (Schneider, 1954). The chemistry of amino sugar-containing compounds of the microorganisms just mentioned is discussed in Chapter 18.

B. Mycobacteria

The polysaccharides and glycolipids of the mycobacteria, including such pathogenic members of this group as the tubercle and leprosy bacilli, have been investigated by numerous authors, but the role of the polysaccharides of tubercle bacilli in the pathogenesis of and immunity to tuberculosis has only recently become clearer. It is now well established that tuberculous hosts may become hypersensitive to tubercle bacillus polysaccharides. This hypersensitivity, however, is of the anaphylactic, and not the tuberculin, type (Enders, 1929). Zinsser and Parker (1923) and Laidlaw and Dudley (1925) were the first to show a serologically specific carbohydrate substance in tubercle bacilli, and, subsequently, Heidelberger and Menzel (1937) described gentle procedures for its isolation. Hexosamine was not then reported as a constituent. A somatic polysaccharide of *Mycobacterium tuberculosis* was subsequently described by Anderson (1941), which was bound to lipid and retained D-glucosamine after saponification (see also Haworth, Kent, and Stacey, 1948,a).

Recently, Miyano (1958) published his finding of significant amounts of hexosamine in serologically active polysaccharides isolated from human tubercle bacilli. These crude polysaccharide preparations have been reported to possess preventive and curative properties against human tuberculosis when applied in vaccinations (Nagao *et al.*, 1958).

Also, Sorkin, Boyden, and Rhodes (1956) and Rhodes, Sorkin, and Boyden (1957) found that highly purified α-hemosensitin—isolated from culture filtrates of tubercle bacilli—which sensitizes erythrocytes to agglutination by anti-*Mycobacterium tuberculosis* sera (Middlebrook and Dubos, 1948) does contain hexosamine (1.3%). This sensitizing capacity is lost by mild acid, as well as alkaline, hydrolysis, whereas ability to neutralize antibodies in the hemagglutination-inhibition test was destroyed only by acid hydrolysis. Cummins (1962) found glucosamine and muramic acid in the cell walls of all actinomycetes studied. Occasionally, also galactosamine was detected (see also Takeya, Hisatsune, and Inoue, 1963).

C. Gram-Negative Bacteria

The serology and immunochemistry of gram-negative bacteria are complicated by the endless number of species (compare Kauffmann, 1954). There appear to be relatively few, however, in which the amino sugars have much to contribute to the major serological characteristics and immunological specificities, but those organisms (and those closely related to them) for which such information exists will be described in the following paragraphs.

1. Neisseria

The two clinically most important species of *Neisseria* are the gonococcus and the meningococcus.

Casper (1930) probably was the first to report the isolation of two type-specific serologically active carbohydrates from gonococcus (type I and type II), which he later obtained free of protein and in a state of sufficient purity to be used in skin tests (Casper, 1937). Positive reactions with this sensitive test were only found in patients with acute gonorrhea. It is unknown whether this polysaccharide or another one isolated by Miller and Boor (1934; Boor and Miller, 1934) which was type, but not species, specific, contained hexosamines, but, in view of the hexosamine content of related species, their presence would not be surprising. It must be mentioned, however, that Stokinger, Carpenter, and Plack (1944) found no evidence for type-specific serologically active polysaccharides in gonococcus.

It was established early that meningococcus contains type-specific, as well as species-specific, antigens (Zozaya and Wood, 1932; Rake, 1933; Rake and Scherp, 1933). The species-specific "C" fraction contained protein and carbohydrate. The type-specific substance (later shown to be a mixture of substances—Scherp, 1939) was an acidic polysaccharide, one of its components being a nitrogen-containing sugar (Scherp and Rake, 1935). Quantitative precipitin studies to determine the antibody nitrogen content of antisera against type-specific polysaccharide of group I meningococcus were carried out by Rake (1937). Scherp and Rake (1945) also showed that antibodies that protect mice against infection with meningococcus are type-specific and correspond to polysaccharide components of meningococci. An interesting study on horse, rabbit, chicken, and human convalescent antimeningococcus sera was published in 1945 by Kabat and co-workers.

Later, Watson and Scherp (1958) and Watson, Marinetti, and Scherp (1958) isolated the capsular polysaccharide of group C (II α) meningococcus which they reported to be predominantly a sialic acid polymer with some (reportedly, acid labile) hexosamine, in addition. This was the first such polysaccharide of serological activity to be isolated. Dilutions as high as $1{:}4 \times 10^6$ of the purified specific substances from all three representative strains of group C meningococcus investigated gave positive reactions with the group C antiserum but did not react in dilutions of between 1:100 and 1:100,000 with a potent group A antiserum. Data on passive protection and absorption studies indicated, however, that the specific substances had undergone some degradation during isolation (Scherp, in Springer, 1960a, p. 54).

Although it was not possible to actively immunize mice with these polysaccharides, intra-abdominal injection of 30 μg of polysaccharide preparation per mouse strongly inhibited subsequent active immunization with an effective whole-cell vaccine—i.e., the polysaccharide induced a state akin to "immunological paralysis," and behaved like a hapten. Kabat (in Springer, 1960a and personal communication) obtained evidence of the antigenicity in man of the material isolated by Scherp and his colleagues.

A recently isolated group C meningococcal endotoxin (Mergenhagen, Martin, and Schiffmann, 1963) was stated to contain sialic acid besides glucosamine. Serological, as well as physicochemical, differentiation of lipopolysaccharide from capsular polysaccharide was reported.

2. Enterobacteriaceae

There are numerous components of gram-negative bacteria which have been characterized sufficiently for immunological and chemical correlations and are dealt with elsewhere in this book (see Volume I,

Chapter 14). It may suffice here to say that all O somatic antigens or lipopolysaccharides from Enterobacteriaceae (Morgan, 1936; Westphal and Lüderitz, 1954; Davies, 1960; Shrivastava, 1961), *Vibrio comma, Pasteurella,* and at least of some *Hemophilus* strains appear to contain amino sugars (always, glucosamine and, frequently, galactosamine, as well as hexosaminuronic acids). Glucosamine has also been stated to be the major carbohydrate component of an antigen said to be common to Enterobacteriaceae (Kunin, 1963). Recently, Rüde and Goebel (1962) found mannosamine in addition to glucosamine in the somatic antigen of *E. coli* O_1. This was the first isolation of mannosamine from a bacterium. It was not stated whether mannosamine is involved in the serological specificity of this microorganism. As far as is known to this reviewer, glucosamine and galactosamine do not enter as major terminal determinants into homologous antigen–antibody reactions of these microorganisms, be they rough (r) forms or smooth (s) forms. Possible exceptions are recently described type-specific substances of *Hemophilus* strains (Williamson and Zamenhof, 1963). *N*-Acetyl-D-galactosamine and *N*-acetyl-D-glucosamine may both be involved, however, in major cross-reactions such as the blood group A and probably also B and H(O) (as subterminal units) specificities of a number of gram-negative bacteria (compare Springer, Williamson, and Brandes, 1961; Springer, Nichols, and Kolecki, 1964). It is necessary to bear in bind that the lipid A component of somatic antigens (Westphal, 1957; Davies, 1960) apparently always contains *N*-acetyl-D-glucosamine, and this sugar may or may not be present in the specific polysaccharide itself. Nothing is known that would indicate that the lipid-bound *N*-acetyl-D-glucosamine would partake in any immunological reaction. The lipoprotein part of gram-negative bacteria has been used associated with polysaccharides to produce aggregates which are antigenic in rabbits, although the polysaccharides were not by themselves antigenic in these animals (Partridge and Morgan, 1940; Morgan, 1959); the role of the hexosamine of the lipoprotein, however, has not been assessed.

There are, though, structures containing hexosamine or hexosamine derivatives in some Enterobacteriaceae whose remarkable immunological properties deserve to be mentioned here.

a. Vi Antigen. Typhoid bacilli possess an unusual hexosamine component, the Vi antigen, which is shared with some *E. coli* (Kauffmann and Møller, 1940; Kauffmann, 1941). Felix and Pitt (1934,a, 1935) first showed that the then-known O and H antigens of typhoid bacilli could not explain certain anomalous immunological reactions of these bacteria. One of the most striking observations was that those smooth strains, which were inagglutinable in anti-O sera, were more virulent than the agglutinable ones and that this phenomenon was not related to the H antigen. Felix and Pitt inferred the presence of a third, hitherto unknown, antigen which they termed virulence, or Vi, antigen. They related the presence of this antigen to virulence of the typhoid bacillus, its O inagglutinability, and the immunity it was able to evoke. It is known today, however, that there exists no direct relationship between virulence and Vi antigen.

Almon (1943) pointed out that mild methods are essential in order to isolate the Vi antigen, which is thought to envelop the cell and thus to prevent access of anti-O agglutinins to their homologous somatic antigens. Isolated Vi antigen may interfere with the agglutinability of other antigens by their homologous sera, as was first demonstrated by Spaun (1951) and later by Ceppellini and De Gregorio (1953). The degree of interference in various antigen–antibody reactions depends on the system investigated. In hemagglutination-inhibition assays, a disproportional activity in the inhibition of the heterologous blood group A–anti-A hemagglutination reaction was observed (Springer, 1956,a). Furthermore, Muschel, Osawa, and McDermott (1958) found that the Vi antigen stimulated anti-A agglutinins in rabbits. This latter effect, however, may have been due to trace contamination with A substance from the medium in which the bacterium from which the Vi antigen was isolated had been grown.

In addition to enhancing the antigenicity of typhoid vaccines for man (Landy, 1953) and mice (Landy, 1957), the Vi antigen by itself is also immunogenic in man (Landy, 1954; Clark, McLaughlin, and Webster, 1958; Huang, 1959), giving rise to precipitins. This is noteworthy, as the Vi antigen appears to be a homopolymer of *N*-acetyl-D-galactosaminuronic acid (Heyns *et al.*, 1959). This unusual composition, which imparts to the Vi antigen its strongly acidic properties, also appears to be responsible for its largely unspecific interference with the interaction between other antigens and their corresponding antibodies. Acetyl groups are of importance for the immunological properties of the Vi antigen. Preparations of the antigen, from which 70 to 80% of the acetyl was removed, precipitated only approximately 25% of the anti-Vi antibody in rabbit and horse antisera. Reacetylation restored precipitating activity so that it was equal to 60 to 75% of that of the intact antigen. Inhibition of Vi hemagglutination (in the hemosensitization test) by the deacetylated Vi antigen was also greatly reduced in comparison with the native antigen. The deacetylated and the original Vi antigens, however, both evoked quite similar antibody levels in human beings (Landy, Johnson, and Webster, 1961). This observation has its parallel in earlier studies by Heidelberger, MacLeod, and DiLapi (1951), who noted that the polysaccharides of types I and V pneumococcus retained their antigenicity for man (in the case of S-1 polysaccharide there was possibly even a slight enhancing effect) but only about 40 and 20%, respectively, of their original precipitating power on partial degradation with sodium hydroxide.

Baker and colleagues (1959) prepared highly purified Vi antigens by a method considerably more gentle than any used by earlier investigators and studied (Whiteside and Baker, 1959, 1960) their immunological and biological properties. The Vi antigens isolated from *Paracolobactrum ballerup, Escherichia coli,* and *Salmonella typhosa* were found to be identical by agar gel diffusion technique. The Vi antigens were nontoxic and of poor immunogenicity in rabbits, although quite potent immunologically in mice. These authors found Vi antigens from the three organisms to have approximately the same immunogenic potency, a finding which contrasts with earlier work, in which the three different Vi antigens were stated to be immunologically distinct (Landy, Webster, and Sagin, 1954). Absorption of *Paracolobactrum ballerup* antiserum with deacetylated Vi antigen did not remove all antibody capable of reacting with Vi antigen, whereas nondeacetylated Vi antigen did remove all antibody. The data further indicated that the two bands observed in agar gel diffusion studies in reaction of "undegraded" Vi antigen were due to presence of both fully acetylated and partially deacetylated antigens.

b. Colominic Acid. This macromolecule of the bacterial surface ($>$10,000 molecular weight) was discovered by Barry in Goebel's laboratory (1958) and described as a sialic acid homopolymer (see Volume I, Chapters 7, 9).

Escherichia coli K_{235} possesses a capsular anti-O agglutination factor in addition to its O antigen. Heating of bacteria containing colominic acid removed both the anti-O agglutination factor and colominic acid together. A strain of *E. coli* K_{235} which was naturally O agglutinable was found to be free of colominic acid. These two pieces of evidence suggest, therefore, that colominic acid is identical with the anti-O agglutination factor. All *E. coli* strains possessing the K_1 antigen, regardless of the kind of O antigen present, contained colominic acid. Similarly, K_5 strains gave positive, although weaker, reactions for this acid polymer (Barry, 1959). Colominic acid, just like Vi antigen, appears to be a component of, or perhaps even the complete, capsular antigen of these strains.

Colominic acid has been shown to possess no serological specificity in any of the homologous systems tested (Barry, 1958). In heterologous systems, no specific reaction was observed for this acidic compound, even when tested in substantial concentrations (10 mg per milliliter against four hemagglutinating doses) (Springer, Williamson, and Brandes, 1961). *In vitro* reactions observed when concentrations still much larger were used (Boyd and Reeves, 1961) may be due to some physical interference by this large acidic molecule.

c. Acidic Polysaccharides. Hexosamine-containing acidic polysaccharides from *E. coli* capsules have been described by Ørskov *et al.* (1963) and by Barry and Tsai (1963). They occurred in about 20% of all *E. coli* strains investigated and appeared to be identical with the K antigens of these strains. They reacted specifically in gel diffusion and absorption tests but were found to be nonantigenic in rabbits. The part played by the hexosamine in the serological specificity of these polysaccharides is unknown.

IX. Substances of Viruses and Rickettsiae with Potential Antigenicity

In the consideration of serological reactions given by hexosamine-containing structures of viruses, it must be borne in mind that serological procedures are extremely sensitive, and viruses cannot be grown like numerous bacteria on fully defined media composed solely of compounds of low molecular weight. It is, therefore, extremely difficult to exclude a host impurity in a virus preparation. Only biological observations with good chemical correlation will be judged sufficient to be incorporated in this discussion (see also Knight, 1946, 1947).

Hoyle (1957) found purified influenza virus to contain 3.5% carbohydrate. The carbohydrate was believed to be present in glycoprotein components of the virus envelope, including the hemagglutinin, which may have been derived from the membrane of the host cell. If this is so, then the "envelope carbohydrate" could possibly partake in immunological reactions. Knight, who had described hexosamine as a constituent of influenza virus (1946, 1947), later reported that he found the influenza virus to contain both glucosamine and galactosamine in addition to galactose and fucose (1957).

Ada and Gottschalk (1956) found the PR-8 virus to contain a glycoprotein with an average of 2.6% glucosamine; it was very similar to the glycoprotein fraction from allantoic fluid which also contained a little galactosamine. The virus-purification process and the amount of glycoprotein separated present some evidence that the latter is an integral part of the virus particle. It is conceivable that immunochemical studies would allow a decision as to whether this glycoprotein is acquired as an entity from the host cell—or perhaps in part even from the conventional virus-diluting fluid used for inoculation which is known to contain A-like substances (Springer and Tritel, 1962)—or whether it is a genetically controlled viral product synthesized *de novo* in response to viral invasion. It may be mentioned that Springer and Tritel (1962) found that purified egg-grown influenza viruses (diluted in buffered saline) possess A-like activity. Upon treatment with ether and subsequent separation of the resulting fractions, it was found that blood group A and Forssman-like activity are found predominantly in the ether layer and in the hemagglutinin fraction of influenza virus grown on chicken eggs (Springer, 1965; Springer and Schuster, 1964, and unpublished observations) (for blood group specificity of another myxovirus, see Isacson and Holden, 1962).

The presence of A-like substances, including Forssman antigen, in chicken eggs and embryos has been known for a long time (Amako, 1914; Schiff and Adelsberger, 1924; Bray, Henry, and Stacey, 1946; Harris, Harrison, and Rondle, 1963), and, since it is thought by many authors that influenza viruses consist in part of host cytoplasmic substances, the finding (Springer and Tritel, 1962; Springer, 1963; Tritel and Springer, 1963) that purified influenza virus preparations, when given in doses of 2 to 10 mg, stimulate anti-A and anti-Forssman antibodies in humans of blood groups O and B is not too surprising. It is noteworthy that the most highly purified (by chromatography) influenza virus preparations available, isolated from chicken eggs, also possessed the highest group A activity and induced powerful isohemolysins and isohemagglutinins in humans (Springer and Schuster, 1964,a). The potential harmful implications of these findings in mother–foetus relationships were also considered by these authors.

Perkins and Allison's researches (1963) strongly indicate that rickettsiae and organisms of the psittacosis–lymphogranuloma group all contain muramic acid—a hexosamine compound considered specific to the peptidoglycans found in bacterial cell walls. This was taken as an indication of the close relationship of these organisms to bacteria.

X. Fungi

Little is known about the participation of hexosamine-containing macromolecular substances from fungi in immunological reactions. Chitin is present in aspergilli, neurospora, and yeasts, as well as in the pathogenic fungi *Coccidioides immitis* and *Histoplasma capsulatum* (see Chapter 18), but no immunological phenomenon has been ascribed to it. Landau *et al.* (1964), however, have carried out carefully controlled experiments in which they found certain members of *Phycomycetes, Ascomycetes,* and *Fungi imperfecti* to possess human blood group A and B activity.

Zymosan, the immunologically well-studied component with anticomplement activity (compare von Dungern, 1900) of yeast (*Saccharomyces cerivisiae*), has been reported to be a polysaccharide and to contain hexosamine (glucosamine, 0.7 to 0.9%) (Di Carlo and Fiore, 1958; Voluyskaya *et al.*, 1959), although other authors did not find hexosamine in zymosan (Northcote and Horne, 1952; Rozenfel'd, Poznanskaya, and Rudakova, 1959).

XI. Protozoa

There is one well-investigated representative: *Trichomonas foetus*, a protozoan flagellate which causes abortion and infertility in cattle. Feinberg and Morgan (1953) isolated from this organism a polysaccharide–amino acid complex which possessed the dominant serological specificity of the intact protozoon (see Chapter 18). This specific substance, containing 9% glucosamine, was rapidly inactivated serologically by a purified enzyme mixture from *Clostridium perfringens* which also destroyed the serological properties of the human A, B, and H(O) substances.

The polysaccharide had the properties of a hapten, in that it did not induce antibody formation in rabbits, whereas rabbits given injections of living or dried *Trichomonas foetus* cultures generally formed antibodies. The soluble specific substance produced a local swelling (immediate type of reaction) when injected into the skin of cattle sensitized to *Trichomonas foetus*, but not in unsensitized cattle. In contrast, rabbits immunized with *Trichomonas foetus* preparation showed a delayed, but not an immediate, skin reaction; rabbits not immunized did not show a significant reaction to this specific substance.

Recently, an acid mucopolysaccharide was isolated from the protozoan slime mold, *Dictyostelium discoideum*, and related species (White and Sussman, 1963). The cellular slime molds are free-living amebae, which, after cessation of growth, aggregate in compactly organized multicellular assemblies with fruiting bodies. The antigenic acid polysaccharide is synthesized during the last stages of fruit construction. It is composed of galactose, galactosamine, and galacturonic acid. The hexosamine content is ca. 25%. The serologically determinant terminal sugar of this carbohydrate seems to be galactose, of which the polymer contained ca. 54%. The material was antigenic in rabbits and reacted in agar gel diffusion and complement fixation tests.

XII. Macromolecular Compounds without Known Antigenic Properties

In general, it can be said that antigenicity has not been demonstrated unequivocally for any of the glycosaminoglycuronans.

Lack of antigenicity of hyaluronic acid prepared from group C streptococci and bovine vitreous humor was observed by Seastone (1939). This recalls similar observations by Kendall, Heidelberger, and Dawson (1937), who described a nonantigenic polysaccharide (hyaluronic acid) isolated from three strains of group A hemolytic streptococci. Furthermore, Meyer, Smyth, and Dawson (1939,a) were unable to obtain antisera to hyaluronic acid from bovine synovial fluid and to a polysaccharide of group A hemolytic streptococci in rabbits.

Hyaluronic acid was not antigenic in the hands of Seifter, Baeder, and Beckfield (1954). In addition, hyaluronic acid does not determine antigenic specificity when it is coupled to protein (Humphrey, 1943). The problem of whether glycosaminoglycuronans may become antigenic, and especially autoantigenic, is important, nevertheless, from the clinical point of view in possible interpretations of the pathogenesis of diseases affecting the connective tissue (e.g., periarteritis nodosa, rheumatic fever, rheumatoid arthritis, lupus erythematosus). Zavázal (1957) presented data on patients with rheumatic fever purporting to indicate autoantibodies against hyaluronic acid, as demonstrated in the collodion agglutination test. No chemical data or statements relating to the purity of the hyaluronic acid used in this study were given. The purity of the materials studied by Di Ferrante (1964) was not reported. He found slight, specific immunogenicity, in the rabbit, for protein–polysaccharide from bovine nasal cartilage. The polysaccharide part alone showed no *in vivo* or *in vitro* immunological activity. Carefully controlled experiments were carried out by Quinn and Singh (1957) with crude and purified human umbilical cord hyaluronic acid and streptococcal hyaluronic acid. The experimental animals were rabbits. Intravenous, intramuscular, and subcutaneous inoculation of these substances in amounts which led to good antibody production against streptococcal group-specific C carbohydrate and M protein did not produce precipitating or nonprecipitating (Prausnitz–Küstner type) antibodies against hyaluronic acid, nor did the umbilical cord hyaluronic acid become a specificity-determining component when exposed to streptococci or staphylococci and subsequently injected simultaneously with them. There was no clear result in production of skin sensitivity. In a few of the rabbits, small areas of erythema and induration formed, suggesting that in these rabbits some tuberculin-like sensitivity might conceivably have developed.

Closely similar results were obtained by Quinn and Cerroni (1957) with chondroitin sulfates from human costal cartilage. Saunders, Mathews, and Dorfman (1962) noted a slight response in a cutaneous hypersensitivity test when a chondroitin sulfuric acid–protein complex from bovine nasal septa was tested in rats. It was necessary, however, to include in these experiments *B. pertussis* as adjuvant. The conclusion drawn by Quinn and colleagues was that hyaluronic acid and chondroitin sulfates are not antigenic and they do not act as specific haptenic groups. Hence, they failed, as did Glynn, Holborow, and Johnson (1956), to confirm earlier work in which antigenicity of these substances was claimed (Glynn and Holborow, 1952). Kabat (personal communication) injected hyaluronic acid into each of ten human beings under conditions identical to those used to produce antibodies against dextran and blood group substances (Kabat and Berg, 1953; Maurer, 1953) and observed no response.

It is believed that none of these substances are antigenic, since they appear to be identical for all species (Kendall, Heidelberger, and Dawson, 1937; Meyer, personal communication). It is relevant also in considering the immunological properties of these linear polymers that Heidelberger (1956, p. 109) stated that poor antigenic reactivity might be caused by the presence of relatively few immunologically reactive groupings per large molecule. Branching does not seem to be the sole requirement, and such factors as size, rigidity of the molecule, surface charge, and configuration have to be taken into account in addition to end groups.

Sulfated glycosaminoglycuronans may enter in some immunological reactions which are not due to well-recognized antigen–antibody interactions. For example, *in vitro* inhibition of phagocytosis by hyaluronic acid has been reported (Ludányi, Orbán, and Vajda, 1952; compare Gibian, 1959). Heparin inactivated complement and delayed or decreased precipitation, whereas it had no effect (at concentrations of 0.1 to 0.5%) on immune agglutination of either erythrocytes or bacteria (Klopstock, 1932; Schmidt, 1959). It also seems to play a role in hypersensitivity reactions (Waters, Markowitz, and Jaques, 1938; McCluskey, 1959).

XIII. Immunochemistry in Amino Sugar Research

In general terms, the usefulness of immunochemical procedures in determination of chemical structures lies in their sensitivity and in the capability of antibodies, under appropriate conditions, to discern between very similar structures. This is demonstrated by the fact that not only will enantiomorphs usually be strictly distinguished, but also, as was shown by Goebel and Avery (1929), antibodies can differentiate clearly between D-galactose and D-glucose molecules which differ in the spatial arrangement of the hydroxyl and hydrogen on one C atom only. Antibodies will also differentiate between the same sugar in α or β linkages (Avery, Goebel, and Babers, 1932) or between different linkages in oligosaccharides (1:2, 1:3, or 1:4—Kabat, 1956,a). The extreme sensitivity and high specificity of antibodies and their usefulness in the hands of a resourceful investigator were demonstrated by Heidelberger and coworkers when they determined, with strictly immunochemical methods, that the uronic acid which was present in beef lung galactan to the extent of only 1 in 35 to 40 sugar residues was glucuronic acid, and that it was an impurity (Heidelberger *et al.*, 1955; compare Heidelberger, 1956, pp. 105 and 113). Both these results were borne out by strictly physical and chemical studies.

Despite the considerable resolving power and reliability of antibodies when used appropriately, they are, nevertheless, only one of a number of tools for establishing purity and structure of a compound. In evaluating the great measure of success of the hapten-inhibition method (Pauling *et al.*, 1942; Watkins and Morgan, 1952; Kabat, 1954; Davies *et al.*, 1958; McCarty, 1958; Staub and Tinelli, 1960; Springer, Williamson, and Brandes, 1961), one must consider that its limitations, in rare instances, are shown, for example, by the very high inhibiting activity of galactinol (α-galactopyranosyl-myoinositol) in the B–anti-B blood group system (Kabat *et al.*, 1953), although this compound is not present in B blood group substances. Similarly, in the admittedly heterologous human H(O)–eel anti-H(O) system, which was thought to be specific for α-L-fucopyranoside structures (Kuhn and Osman, 1956), inhibition was observed not only with L-fucose (Watkins and Morgan, 1952) but also to the same degree with 3-*O*-methyl-L-fucose and its enantiomorphous isomer D-digitalose and with the enantiomorphous 2,3-di-*O*-methylfucoses (Springer, Williamson, and Ruelius, 1960; Springer and Williamson, 1962; Springer and Williamson, 1963) and with some anomeric methyl glycopyranosides of L- and D-fucose ethers (Springer, Desai, and Kolecki, 1964). Also, 3-*O*-methyl-D-galactose was as active as L-fucose (Springer *et al.*, 1964). In these examples, conclusions based solely on immunochemical procedures would have merely led to a rather crude approximation but not to the structurally correct information.

The state of purity of macromolecules may not infrequently be reliably determined with immunochemical methods; these methods may also reveal hitherto unrecognized complexities of various macromolecules (compare Kabat and Mayer, 1961, p. 384). The question frequently arises whether or not such complexities are due to minor variations in the composition of the individual antigen under study or due to impurities. The former instance—variation in the antigen molecules themselves—is called microheterogeneity (Colvin, Smith, and Cook, 1954; compare Kabat and Stern in Springer, 1956b, pp. 159, 166).

In establishing immunochemical homogeneity, antisera may be used which contain antibodies against suspected impurities, and the amount of impurity in a given preparation may be established by a number of precipitin methods (compare Weil, 1916; Kabat and Mayer, 1961; Kendall, 1937; Cohn, Wetter, and Deutsch, 1949; Wetter, Cohn, and Deutsch, 1952).

Serological reactions then are not only indispensable in immunology in order to extend our still rather fragmentary knowledge of the relationships between chemical composition and immunological specificity, but carefully chosen antisera, when used with proper caution, are valuable tools in structural chemical studies. Four principally different and supplementary major serological approaches are available for this purpose:

(1) Mixtures of physicochemically closely related macromolecules may be separated by selective precipitation of the desired antigen. Also, it is a rather good criterion of the purity of the antigen if an excess of the specific antibody precipitates all of the antigen (Bendich, Kabat, and Bezer, 1946; Kabat, Baer, and Knaub, 1949; Annison and Morgan, 1952; Kabat, 1956, 1958);
(2) When cross-reaction occurs between heterologous sera specific for a known determinant and structures present on various other macromolecules, it indicates a chemical similarity between the determinant of the cross-reacting structure and that of the homologous antigen (Landsteiner, 1945);
(3) The inhibition of antigen–antibody interactions by specific haptens or closely related compounds aids in pinpointing the groups responsible for the over-all reactions of the macromolecules;
(4) Partial degradation of serologically specific groupings by chemical or enzymic means followed by examination of the split products and the residual structure can lead to subsequent correlation between serological activity and chemical change.

Important limitations of structural analysis by immunological techniques are that antibodies are generally specific only for end groups (Kabat, 1961) or structures close to them (see however, Uchida, Robbins, and Luria, 1963) and that the actual size of the antibody combining site is rarely known. The interior of a molecule containing groups separated by more than two to seven monosaccharides from the surface of the molecule (Kabat, in Springer, 1960a, p. 201) will probably not be accessible to studies by antibodies unless it is exposed after degradation of the outer part of the molecule.

Another limitation of the analytical value of antigen–antibody reactions rests in the difficulty of obtaining antigen–antibody systems consisting of but a single specificity and an entirely homogeneous antibody population (see Schlossman and Kabat, 1962). Hence, several kinds of heterogeneity are to be distinguished (Karush, 1959)—even if only one antigen population is present, several different antigenic groups on a single molecule are the rule (compare Landsteiner, 1945; Wiener and Wexler, 1952; Morgan, 1960; Kabat and Mayer, 1961). There is also a variation in the degree of complementarity of antibody sites directed against a single antigenic group. A closely allied difficulty consists in obtaining antigens completely free from contaminants and, correspondingly, antisera which are free of antibody against contaminating components (compare Vaughan and Kabat, 1954). An additional problem, which as yet has not been sufficiently investigated, is the possibility that host enzymes may partially hydrolyze immunogenic substances, with resultant formation of antigenic components of slightly different specificities (see, e.g., Ishizaka, Campbell, and Ishizaka, 1960). Weak cross-reactions may then conceivably be due not only to similarly linked related structures but also to the presence of a small amount of another antigen produced by host enzymes. This consideration is especially important when structural inferences are to be drawn on the basis of cross-reactions (see Dorfman, in Springer, 1960a, p. 203; Roseman, in Springer, 1960a, p. 203, 204). On the other hand, the observation that specificity of anti-carbohydrate antibodies may be directed toward relatively small groupings (75% of the antibody being directed against a disaccharide or even smaller grouping) might advantageously be employed in the preparation of "artificial" or conjugated antigens (Landsteiner and Lampl, 1918; Landsteiner, 1945). Indeed, vaccines may thus be synthesized, as was clearly demonstrated by Goebel (1939, 1940) who prepared a cellobiuronic acid conjugate which stimulated anti-cellobiuronic acid antibodies, which in turn conferred on mice passive protection against infection with virulent pneumococci of types II, III, and VIII, in which cellobiuronic acid has a determining structural role. Rabbits immunized with this antigen acquired active resistance to infection with virulent type III pneumococcus. This is the first recorded instance of production of effective immunity against a disease by injection of an "artificial" antigen. "Artificial" antigens containing hexosamine as determinant structure have already been described (see Section VIII).

Hexosamine structures may contribute to the comprehension of immunological phenomena in the broadest sense and not necessarily in strict antigen–antibody reactions only. Interferon, which has been reported to contain 2.4% hexosamine, may be an example (Burke, 1961). Interferon (Isaacs and Lindenmann, 1957) is a virus-related substance which acts on host cells in such a way that they will subsequently be unable to fully support the growth of a second virus.

Hexosamine-containing macromolecules may further the understanding of basic immunological mechanisms, even if they neither induce antibodies nor show any *in vitro* immunological specificity, as is the case for many mesodermal glycosaminoglycans which possess the appropriate particle size and structural rigidity (compare Haurowitz, 1952; Boyd, 1956; Sela and Arnon, 1960) but are not antigenic. They may thus shed light on phenomena related to immunological tolerance.

Hexosamine-containing substances, notably bacterial lipopolysaccharides (see, e.g., Johnson, Gaines, and Landy, 1956), can act as powerful adjuvants in immunizations—i.e., if they are mixed with an antigen, they cause an increase in specific antibody response against that particular antigen (compare Pasteur and Joubert, 1877; Freund, 1947). The mechanisms underlying the adjuvant effect are not as yet fully understood.

Immunological methods are also helpful in genetical investigations, as was alluded to in the paragraphs on blood group substances (Section I). With the increasing number of hexosamine-containing macromolecular substances which are found to show fine intraspecies differences (such as the γ-globulins), one may expect a more general application of immunological methods to genetical problems (compare Oudin, 1956,a, 1960; and Grubb, 1959) including embryonic development, mother–foetus relationships (see, e.g., Springer, 1963), and biosynthesis of microorganisms (see, e.g., Springer and Tritel, 1962), including sequential enzyme induction (Barker *et al.*, 1963). In order to detect small intraspecies differences, it would seem to be promising to employ isoantibodies rather than antibodies produced in a different species.

Immunochemical methods are being employed in the hope of throwing light on the significance and interrelationship between normal globulin and hexosamine-containing macromolecular constituents or products of malignant tumors, such as the myeloma globulins and the Bence Jones protein (compare Korngold and Lipari, 1956,a; Putnam, 1960; Askonas and Fahey, 1961; Migita and Putnam, 1963).

Finally, investigation of the dynamic nature of body constituent production may avail itself of immunochemical methods. This has already been done in the study of synthesis and metabolism of antibodies (Heidelberger *et al.*, 1942; Schoenheimer *et al.*, 1942). The effectiveness of the human physiological apparatus when charged with the immune response was clearly demonstrated by the production (over a period of 4 years) of about 50 g of antibody globulin in response to injection of three times 50 μg of pneumococcal polysaccharides (Heidelberger, 1956).

ACKNOWLEDGMENT

The author acknowledges the evaluation of an early version of the manuscript by Peter Williamson.

The writer's work described in this chapter is being supported by the U. S. National Science Foundation, the U. S. National Institutes of Health, and the U. S. Atomic Energy Commission.

Chapter 50

INTERACTION BETWEEN GLYCOPROTEINS AND VIRUSES

Alfred Gottschalk

Microbes provide many instances of evolution of specific enzymes or enzyme systems in response to environmental factors. The more marked and the better defined the chemistry of the environment is, the easier will be the recognition of the enzymes which have evolved as a mechanism of survival in a given surrounding. A recent addition to our knowledge in this field comes from virology. The essence of virus multiplication is the replication within the host cell of the genetic material which determines virus-specific components. The natural host cells for the viruses of the influenza group (myxoviruses) are the lining cells of the respiratory tract; natural infection spreads by droplets passing from individual to individual. Since the lining cells of the respiratory tract are covered with a protective layer of mucus, the invading virus particles will soon find themselves enwrapped in a coat of mucus which threatens to interrupt their life cycle. The realization that the myxoviruses contain, embedded in their surface, an enzyme which acts on a large family of glycoproteins containing sialic acid, including those present in the epithelial secretions of the respiratory tract, has added much to an understanding of the initial phases of influenza-virus infection (Gottschalk, 1959). Beyond that, this realization has provided a powerful tool for probing into the fundamental structure of glycoproteins which contain sialic acid and has greatly stimulated research in this previously rather neglected field. In this chapter, the influenza-virus and glycoprotein interaction in its chemical, physicochemical, and biological aspects will be described, as well as the association between some other viruses and hexosamine-containing compounds.

I. Interaction between Influenza Virus and Cellular Receptor

Research in this field was initiated when Hirst (1941) and McClelland and Hare (1941) observed independently that fluids containing infective influenza-virus particles agglutinated chicken red blood cells. In subsequent work, Hirst (1942,a) showed that at 4°C the influenza virus was quickly adsorbed to the red cells and remained attached to the cells for as long as 18 hr. When the reaction was carried out at 37°C, adsorption of the virus to the red-cell surface was equally rapid, but, after 6 hr, nearly complete elution of the virus had taken place. Red cells from which the virus had eluted spontaneously were stabilized—i.e., they neither adsorbed nor were agglutinated by fresh virus. The eluted virus, however, was found to be functionally intact. Hirst (1942a) also presented evidence that the virus hemagglutinin is an intrinsic component of the virus particle itself. In essence, viral hemagglutination is an adsorption phenomenon—by simultaneous adsorption of a virus particle to two red blood cells, aggregates of cells are built up. Hirst interpreted these phenomena in terms of an enzyme–substrate interaction, with the enzyme being possessed by the virus, and the substrate, or receptor, being located at the surface of the red blood cell. The same series of events (*viz.*, adsorption of the virus to, and spontaneous elution from, cell surfaces) was demonstrated with the system influenza virus and respiratory cells of the excised ferret lung (Hirst, 1943).

It was further established that the capacity of the virus to agglutinate red cells was more stable than its capacity to infect and to elute. Hence, influenza virus after heat treatment at 55°C for 30 min lost both its infective and its eluting powers, but retained virtually undiminished its agglutinating property (Hirst, 1942a; Briody, 1948). Such crippled virus has been termed "indicator virus" (Stone, 1949).

Hirst visualized the adsorption of virus to, and the spontaneous elution from, appropriate cells as an enzyme–substrate combination followed by an enzyme–substrate interaction and resulting in free enzyme (unchanged virus particle) and in reaction products, one of them being the altered cellular receptors. This concept was strongly supported when Burnet and associates discovered in the culture filtrate of *Vibrio cholerae* an enzyme closely imitating the biological effect of active influenza virus on cellular receptors (Burnet, McCrea, and Stone, 1946). This enzyme was adsorbed to red cells at 0°C and, when the temperature was raised, eluted spontaneously from the cells, rendering them inagglutinable by all strains of influenza virus. The fact that the *Vibrio* enzyme and the virus did indeed act on the same site at the red-cell surface was demonstrated in the following three sets of experiments: (1) red cells, the receptors of which had been "destroyed" at 37°C by one agent, failed to adsorb the other agent; (2) adsorption to cells of one agent at 0°C blocked the adsorption of the other agent, just as coating of red cells with one type of influenza virus blocked the adsorption of another type; and (3) both the virus particle and the *Vibrio* enzyme rendered cells agglutinable by normal human sera (T agglutination) to equivalent titers (Stone, 1947). The *Vibrio cholerae* enzyme was termed "receptor destroying enzyme" or, briefly, RDE (Burnet and Stone, 1947).

Another observation pointing in the same direction was the change in the net electric charge of the red blood cells after treatment with living influenza virus or with RDE. Action of RDE on human red cells reduced their electrophoretic mobility from the normal value of 1.30×10^{-4} cm^2 $volt^{-1}$ sec^{-1} to a value of 0.17×10^{-4} cm^2 $volt^{-1}$ sec^{-1}. Different strains of influenza virus were found to decrease the electrophoretic mobility of red cells to different levels, although no strain decreased the mobility to the level attained with RDE. When partial or complete treatment of red cells with any virus strain was followed by RDE action, the electrophoretic mobility was reduced to the same value as that obtained with RDE alone. This lack of cumulative effect suggested that the chemical groupings susceptible to the various influenza viruses were also sensitive to RDE (Ada and Stone, 1950; Stone and Ada, 1950).

With the excised mouse lung and the chorioallantois of the chick embryo (killed by formalin), adsorption of influenza virus to, and spontaneous elution from, the respective lining cells proceeded as in Hirst's experiments with the excised ferret lung. Moreover, pretreatment of the systems with RDE prevented adsorption of active influenza virus and indicator virus to the respiratory cells and to the allantoic endothelium of the chorioallantois, respectively. Finally, it was shown that RDE instillation could also prevent viable host cells from adsorbing influenza virus, thus protecting them, at least to a certain degree, against viral infection (Fazekas de St. Groth, 1948,a; Stone, 1948).

Taken together, these intriguing results at the biological and biophysical level left little doubt of the presence of an enzyme at the influenza-virus surface and of a substrate (virus receptor) embedded in the outer membrane of the red blood cells, the lining cells of the respiratory tract, and the endothelium of the chorioallantoic membrane. The inferred viral enzyme was imitated in nearly every detail by an exoenzyme of *Vibrio cholerae* (RDE), first purified by Burnet and Stone (1947) and, after many improvements of the technique, recently crystallized independently by Schramm and Mohr (1959) and by Ada and French (1959).

The first suggestion as to the carbohydrate nature of the cellular substrates (receptors) came from Hirst's observation (1945) that treatment of erythrocytes with potassium periodate "destroyed" the cellular receptors, rendering the cells inagglutinable by influenza virus. Fazekas de St. Groth (1949) showed that by more gentle periodate treatment—

e.g., 0.2 to 2.0 mg KIO_4 per milliliter of packed red cells—the cell receptors were modified in such a way that they were no longer substrates for the viral enzyme or for RDE, but retained their ability to adsorb the influenza-virus particle. Cellular receptors in the excised mouse lung and in the formalinized allantoic cavity were modified by 0.01 *M* KIO_4 in the same way: they still adsorbed influenza-virus particles but did not allow spontaneous elution or displacement of the virus by RDE.

II. Soluble Glycoproteins as Receptor Analogues: Their Composition, Structure, Inhibitory Capacity, and Enzymatic Inactivation

Obviously, only a direct chemical approach could provide an insight into the chemical structures and chemical reactions underlying the phenomena of virus and red-cell or virus and host-cell interactions. Since the isolation and purification of cellular receptors in quantities sufficient for chemical analysis and structural investigations would have been an arduous task, it was fortunate that body fluids, secretions, and excretions were found to contain appreciable amounts of cell-receptor analogues. The observation initiating this rewarding approach was Francis's (1947) finding that normal human and animal sera strongly inhibited hemagglutination by the Lee strain of influenza B virus, provided that the virus was in the indicator state. Subsequently, Anderson (1948) showed that the Francis serum inhibitor was inactivated by RDE and by active influenza virus. From human and rabbit sera, McCrea (1948) isolated a heat-stable glycoprotein fraction, identical with Rimington's (1940) "serum mucoid" fraction, which inhibited hemagglutination by indicator viruses. At the same time, de Burgh *et al.* (1948) prepared from human red cells small amounts of carbohydrate-containing material which inhibited hemagglutination by virus. Gottschalk and Lind (1949) found in ovomucin, a glycoprotein fraction of hen egg white, a potent and easily available inhibitor of the influenza-virus hemagglutinin. The inhibitory capacity of these materials was lost upon treatment with active influenza virus, with RDE, or with periodate (0.01 *M*). The inference drawn from these results was that certain soluble glycoproteins inhibited hemagglutination by competing with the red-cell receptors for the influenza-virus particle, that the cellular receptors and their soluble analogues had some structural feature in common, probably of carbohydrate nature, and that this common grouping served both the viral enzyme and RDE as substrate.

None of the various hemagglutinin inhibitors just mentioned, however, was homogeneous. To date, only two glycoproteins, inhibiting influenza-virus hemagglutination in high dilution, have been prepared from secretions in a homogeneous state as judged from their electrophoretic and sedimentation patterns. In addition, a highly purified blood-group substance with Le^a specificity, prepared from human ovarian-cyst fluid, was shown to be a potent inhibitor of hemagglutination. The physical characteristics and carbohydrate constituents of these compounds are summarized in Tables I and II. The protein moieties of both the ovine submaxillary-gland glycoprotein (Gottschalk and Simmonds, 1960) and the glycopeptide from human ovarian-cyst fluid (Pusztai and Morgan, 1961) were rich in serine, threonine, and proline residues, but contained only small amounts of aromatic and sulfur-containing amino acids (see Volume I, Chapter 12).

The urinary glycoprotein which inhibits hemagglutination is a conjugated protein which contains as prosthetic groups a large number of relatively small polysaccharides linked covalently to the polypeptide. This conclusion was based on the total carbohydrate content of the glycoprotein and the dialyzability of the individual carbohydrate prosthetic groups (Gottschalk, 1952, 1958). This concept of the basic structure of a glycoprotein which inhibits hemagglutination by virus was confirmed and extended by a comprehensive study of the glycoprotein isolated from ovine submaxillary glands. It proved to be the most potent inhibitor of influenza-virus hemagglutinin obtained so far; when tested before lyophilization against PR8 indicator virus, its inhibitory titer was 14.6×10^6 per milligram of glycoprotein (see Table III). The close similarity between the purified material and the native glycoprotein, as secreted by the glands, was seen from an examination of the sedimentation pattern of the first crude aqueous extract of the minced glands (Gottschalk and McKenzie, 1961).

The prosthetic group isolated from the glycoprotein of ovine submaxillary gland is a disaccharide, D-*N*-acetylneuraminyl-(2 → 6)-*N*-acetylgalactosamine (Graham and Gottschalk, 1960); about 800 of these groups are distributed along the polypeptide chain (Gottschalk, 1963). The linkages between the prosthetic groups and the protein core were shown to be glycosidic linkages involving the reducing group of *N*-acetylgalactosamine and the carboxyl groups of aspartyl and glutamyl residues (Gottschalk and Murphy, 1961) and the OH-groups of serine and threonine, respectively (Carubelli, Bhavanandan, and Gottschalk, 1965).

In bovine submaxillary-gland glycoprotein, a compound with a carbohydrate content, composition, and structure closely similar to that of the glycoprotein prepared from ovine submaxillary glands, the prosthetic groups are linked in a fashion similar to that of the polypeptide

TABLE I
PHYSICAL CHARACTERISTICS OF GLYCOPROTEINS INHIBITING HEMAGGLUTINATION

Source	Particle weight	$s^{\circ}_{20,w}$ (S)	$[\eta]$ 20° (ml/g)	$\bar{V}$ (ml/g)	Electrophoretic mobility (10^{-5} cm^2 volt^{-1} sec^{-1})	References
Human urine (male)	7×10^6	29.5	370	—	−9.1 (prep. A) −8.3 (prep. B) (phosphate buffer, pH 6.8, Γ/2 0.05)	Perlmann, Tamm, and Horsfall, 1952; Tamm, Bugher, and Horsfall, 1955
Ovine submaxillary glands	1×10^6	8.5	340	0.68	−7.4 (phosphate buffer, pH 7.3, Γ/2 0.2)	Gottschalk and Simmonds, 1960; Gottschalk and McKenzie, 1961
Human ovarian-cyst fluid—blood phenotype ALe (a+)	3.5×10^5 [a]	7.7 [a]	60	0.63	−7.6 (phosphate buffer, pH 8, Γ/2 0.2)	Pusztai and Morgan, 1961
Human erythrocytes (type O Rh-positive blood)	3.1×10^4	2.16	[b]	0.71 (assumed)	—	Kathan, Winzler, and Johnson, 1961

[a] These figures are calculated from the experimental data given by Pusztai and Morgan, 1961.
[b] $D_{20,w}$ 0.575×10^{-6} cm^2 sec^{-1}.

TABLE II

CARBOHYDRATE CONTENT OF GLYCOPROTEINS INHIBITING HEMAGGLUTINATION

Source	Galactose	Mannose	Fucose	Glucosamine[a]	Galactosamine[a]	Sialic acid[a]	Total carbohydrate residue[b]	References
	(g/100 g dry glycoprotein)							
Human urine	5.4	2.7	1.1	5.7	1.9	9.1	25	Gottschalk, 1952; Odin, 1952
Ovine submaxillary glands	0.3	0.1	0.4	Trace	15.0	25.4	42	Graham and Gottschalk, 1960
Human ovarian-cyst fluid	28.8	0	8.4	20	6	18	73	Pusztai and Morgan, 1961
Human erythrocytes	12.4	0	1.1	0	12.1	22.0	46	Kathan, Winzler, and Johnson, 1961

[a] Glucosamine and galactosamine are expressed as free base, sialic acid as *N*-acetylneuraminic acid.

[b] Assuming *N*-acetylation of amino sugars.

chain (Murphy and Gottschalk, 1961; Tanaka, Bertolini, and Pigman, 1964). The prosthetic group of the bovine glycoprotein differs from that of the ovine only in the type of sialic acid present (Blix *et al.*, 1956; Gottschalk and Graham, 1959) (see Volume I, Chapter 2).

A prominent feature of the glycoprotein obtained from ovine submaxillary gland is its high intrinsic viscosity. This property is imparted to the molecule by the 800 negatively charged carboxyl groups ($pK_a =$ 2.6) of *N*-acetylneuraminic acid residues (one such residue per 6.4 amino acid residues) repelling each other and thus expanding and stiffening the molecular framework. The dimensions (in terms of the equivalent spheroid) of the particle are M (unhydrated mass) $= 1 \times 10^6$, J (ellipticity) $= 8.7$, and V' (effective hydrodynamic value) $= 30$ ml/g, suggesting that the particle in solution resembles a random coil with some rigidity and slight elongation (Gottschalk and Thomas, 1961; Gottschalk and McKenzie, 1961) (Table I).

No information is available on the molecular structure and shape of the blood-group specific Le^a substance which inhibits hemagglutinin.

Insofar as the chemistry of the influenza-virus receptor substance present at the surface of the red blood cell is concerned, it was already evident from the early investigations of de Burgh *et al.* (1948), Howe (1951), and McCrea (1953) that it was a glycoprotein–lipid from which the lipid could be removed without impairing appreciably the "receptor" property of the remainder. Subsequently, Howe, Rose, and Schneider (1957), using partition dialysis (chloroform–methanol, 2:1, v/v), and Klenk and Uhlenbruck (1960), using phenol–water (1:1, w/v) at 65°C, for extraction of the receptor substance from human erythrocyte stroma, showed that the material thus obtained contained considerable amounts of sialic acid (10–14%) in addition to galactose, galactosamine, and glucosamine. All these materials prepared from erythrocytes and purified to some extent inhibited hemagglutination by influenza virus and lost this property on treatment with RDE or influenza virus. Evidence for a high degree of purification of an influenza-virus receptor from human erythrocytes was advanced by Kathan, Winzler, and Johnson (1961). The method of preparation included pH adjustment of the stroma, phenol extraction of 70°C, chloroform–methanol treatment, and ultracentrifugation. The physical characteristics and carbohydrate analyses of the receptor material, shown to be a glycoprotein, are included in Tables I and II. The material inhibited hemagglutination by the virus; active influenza virus and RDE destroyed its inhibitory capacity. At pH 8.6 the glycoprotein moved as a single peak toward the anode; treatment with active influenza virus resulted in a single band with decreased

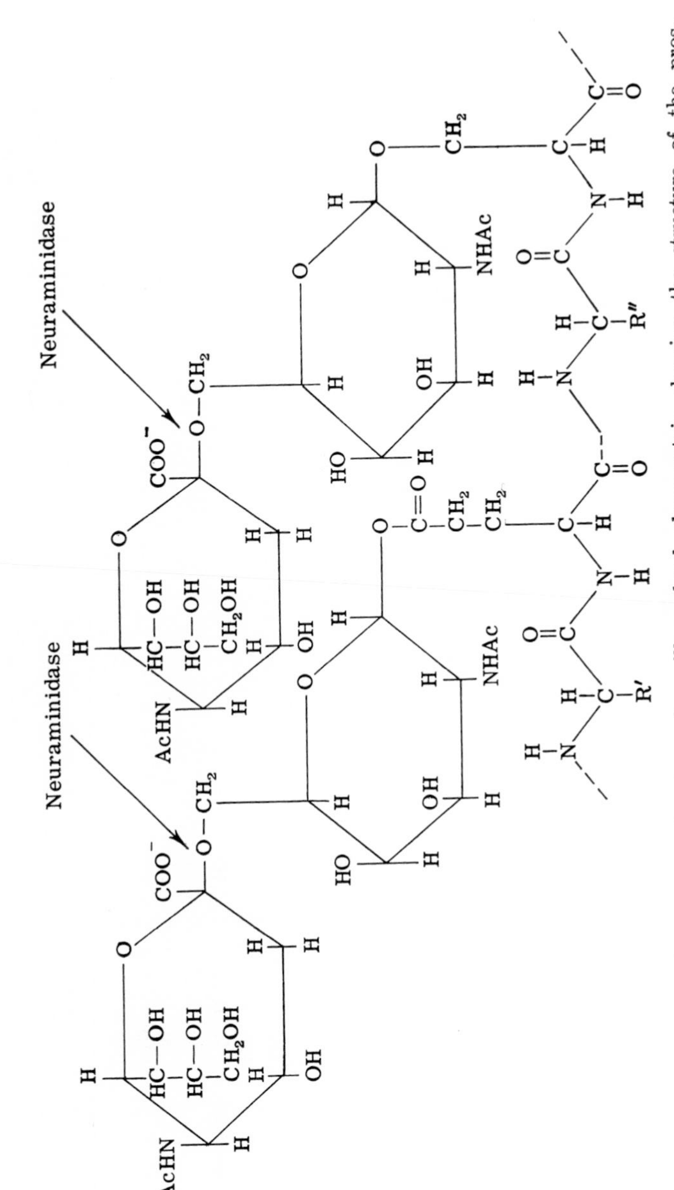

Fig. 1. Diagrammatic segment of ovine submaxillary-gland glycoprotein showing the structure of the prosthetic group, the linkage of the prosthetic group to glutamyl and seryl residues, respectively, and the neuraminidase-susceptible ketosidic linkage.

TABLE III
INHIBITORY TITERS AND ELECTROPHORETIC MOBILITIES OF SOME GLYCOPROTEINS AND THEIR REDUCTION BY ACTIVE INFLUENZA VIRUS AND BY RDE[a]

Source of glycoprotein	Inhibitory titer per mg dry weight		Electrophoretic mobility (cm^2 $volt^{-1}$ sec^{-1})	References
	Indicator virus	Titer		
Human urine	PR8	6.30×10^5	$-8.4 \times 10^{-5} \xrightarrow{\text{Lee}} -6.7 \times 10^{-5}$	Perlmann, Tamm, and Horsfall, 1952; Pye, 1955; Gottschalk and Fazekas de St. Groth, 1960a
	Lee	8.91×10^4	$-8.7 \times 10^{-5} \xrightarrow{\text{Mel,RDE}} -6.5 \times 10^{-5}$	
Bovine submaxillary glands	PR8	$8.48 \pm 3.85 \times 10^5$	$-5.4 \times 10^{-5} \xrightarrow{\text{RDE}} -2.9 \times 10^{-5}$	Pye, 1955; Gottschalk and Fazekas de St. Groth, 1960a
	Lee	$3.65 \pm 0.85 \times 10^2$		
Ovine submaxillary glands	PR8	$2.79 \pm 0.33 \times 10^6$	—	Gottschalk and Fazekas de St. Groth, 1960a
	Lee	$2.79 \pm 1.21 \times 10^5$		
Human ovarian-cyst fluid	Rob	1.43×10^4	$-7.6 \times 10^{-5} \xrightarrow{\text{RDE}} -4.2 \times 10^{-5}$	Pusztai and Morgan, 1961
Sputum	Mel	1.15×10^5	$-6.9 \times 10^{-5} \xrightarrow{\text{RDE}} -5.0 \times 10^{-5}$	Marmion, Curtain, and Pye, 1953
	Lee	8.33×10^4		
Human erythrocytes	PR301	1.0×10^4	—	Howe, Rose, and Schneider, 1957
	Lee	1.4×10^4		
	Lee	1.0×10^4	—	Klenk and Uhlenbruck, 1960
	PR8	1.2×10^4	—	Kathan, Winzler, and Johnson, 1961
	Lee	5.2×10^4		

[a] Inhibitory titer is defined as the dilution factor at which 0.25 ml of the test solution prevents three out of four hemagglutinating doses of a particular indicator virus from aggregating an equal volume of 0.5% fowl erythrocytes. Whenever the inhibitors were tested by variants of the technique, their titers were rendered comparable by rescaling. In all cases, the titer was reduced by active influenza virus or by RDE by more than 98%. The electrophoretic mobility was determined at pH values ranging from 7–8.

electrophoretic mobility toward the anode at pH 8.6. It is believed that the glycoprotein is the red-cell receptor for the influenza viruses because no other fraction obtained by the adopted procedure displayed significant inhibitory properties and because pretreatment of the intact erythrocytes with active influenza virus did not yield any inhibitor by the same procedure.

The water-soluble inhibitors of influenza-virus hemagglutinin are conjugated proteins with oligosaccharides or small polysaccharides as prosthetic groups. The feature common to all of them is the presence in the prosthetic group of sialic acid and *N*-acetylgalactosamine, either as the only components or together with other sugars, such as galactose, mannose, fucose, and glucosamine. The value of the electrophoretic mobility is high, and the boundary moves at neutral pH toward the anode. On treatment with RDE or active influenza virus, the inhibitory capacity of these substances is lost, and their electrophoretic mobility, i.e., their over-all net negative charge, is greatly reduced. Some relevant data are collected in Table III. Three lines of evidence strongly suggest that the soluble inhibitory glycoproteins are chemical analogues of the virus receptors built into the surface structure of the red blood cells: (1) chemical analysis of purified receptor substances prepared from human erythrocytes revealed them to be glycoproteins and to contain sugar components the same as are found in the soluble inhibitors; (2) the isolated receptor glycoproteins inhibited influenza-virus hemagglutination and lost this property on treatment with active influenza virus or with RDE, a behavior characteristic of the soluble inhibitory glycoproteins; (3) the electrophoretic mobility toward the anode of both the receptor material and the soluble inhibitors was reduced by active influenza virus in a similar manner. It may be remembered that the electrophoretic mobility of red blood cells toward the anode was also reduced by treatment with influenza virus or RDE, with a concomitant loss of their agglutinability by indicator virus.

III. The Mode of Action of Influenza Virus and RDE on Inhibitory and Noninhibitory Glycoproteins

A. Sialic Acid as Split Product

The chemical reaction underlying the inactivation of the glycoproteins which inhibit virus hemagglutination (receptor analogues) was first investigated by Gottschalk and Lind (1949a) and Gottschalk (1951). They isolated, from the digest of ovomucin with influenza A virus (Mel) or with RDE and from the digest of the homogeneous urinary glycoprotein with highly purified influenza B virus (Lee), the same dialyzable com-

TABLE IV

ACTION OF VIRAL AND BACTERIAL ENZYMES ON MATERIALS CONTAINING SIALIC ACID[a]

Substrate	Enzyme	Sialic acid released: Type of sialic acid	Sialic acid released: % of total	References
Urinary glycoprotein	Virus (Lee)	NANA	35	Klenk, Faillard, and Lempfrid, 1955
	RDE		60	Faillard, 1957
Bovine submaxillary-gland glycoprotein	RDE	NANA[b]	64–76	Gottschalk, 1956; Graham and Gottschalk, 1960
			53	Heimer and Meyer, 1956
			57	Faillard, 1957
			64	Mohr and Schramm, 1960
Ovine submaxillary-gland glycoprotein	RDE	NANA	76–85	Graham and Gottschalk, 1960
Porcine submaxillary-gland glycoprotein	RDE	*N*-glycolylneuraminic acid	75	Klenk and Uhlenbruck, 1957
Human ovarian-cyst glycoprotein	RDE	NANA	94	Pusztai and Morgan, 1961
α_1-Acid glycoprotein (orosomucoid)	*Clostridium perfringens*	NANA	100	Popenoe and Drew, 1957
Ba-α_2-globulins	RDE	NANA (most probably)	80	Kamiyama and Schmid, 1961
Fetuin	RDE	NANA (predominantly)	95	Graham, 1961
Meconium glycoprotein	Virus (Lee)	NANA	13	Zilliken *et al.*, 1957
	RDE		48	
Human erythrocyte glycoprotein	Virus (PR301)	NANA	27	Howe, Rose, and Schneider, 1957
	Virus (FM1)		56	Howe, Rose, and Schneider, 1957
	RDE		88	Klenk and Uhlenbruck, 1960
Bovine erythrocyte glycoprotein	RDE	*N*-glycolylneuraminic acid	79	Klenk and Uhlenbruck, 1958
Human erythrocyte stroma	Virus (PR8)	NANA	31	Howe, Rose, and Schneider, 1957
	Virus (PR301)		33	Howe, Rose, and Schneider, 1957
	RDE		58	Klenk and Lempfrid, 1957

[a] Abbreviations: NANA = *N*-acetylneuraminic acid; RDE = receptor-destroying enzyme of *Vibrio cholerae*.

[b] *O*-Acetyl groups lost on preparation of bovine submaxillary-gland glycoprotein or on isolation of released sialic acid.

pound of low molecular weight to be referred to as the split product. The compound was characterized by reducing power, nitrogen content, a positive Ehrlich reaction after alkali pretreatment according to the method of Morgan and Elson (1934), a positive resorcinol test, as given by ketosugars, and by its rapid decomposition with humin formation on very mild acid treatment. These results proved conclusively the enzymatic activity of the influenza-virus preparation and the close similarity of the modes of action of the viral enzyme and RDE. Moreover, the viral enzyme was shown to be an intrinsic component of the influenza-virus particle. No similar enzyme was found by biological tests in the host cells of the influenza virus (Gottschalk and Perry, 1951).

Odin (1952) and Klenk and Lauenstein (1952) soon drew attention to the similarity of the properties of the split product on the one hand and of sialic acid and methoxyneuraminic acid, respectively, on the other. This similarity became still more evident when pyrrole-2-carboxylic acid was isolated from the alkaline hydrolyzate of the purified inhibitory glycoproteins from bovine submaxillary glands and human urine (Gottschalk, 1953, 1955), and when both the split product and *N*-acetylneuraminic acid were converted by alkali to pyrrole-2-carboxylic acid (Gottschalk, 1954; Klenk and Faillard, 1954). Finally Klenk, Faillard, and Lempfrid (1955) crystallized the split product obtained from influenza-virus action on the urinary glycoprotein and identified it as *N*-acetylneuraminic acid. During the following years, sialic acid was shown to be released from all inhibitory glycoproteins and from many noninhibitory glycoproteins containing sialic acid by the influenza-virus enzyme and by RDE (see Table IV). Again, the same result was obtained with cellular receptors as substrate. Thus, Klenk and Lempfrid (1957) isolated *N*-acetylneuraminic acid as a product of RDE action on human erythrocytes, and the same product was obtained from the digest of the virus receptor substances, prepared from human erythrocytes and the chorioallantoic membrane, with RDE or influenza virus (Klenk and Uhlenbruck, 1960; Laučiková, 1959). In all cases tested, RDE was superior to the influenza-virus enzyme in removing sialic acid, most probably because RDE is a soluble enzyme, whereas the viral enzyme is in particulate form.

B. Characterization of the Viral and *Vibrio* Enzymes as α-Neuraminidases

From the experimental results presented in the previous section, it is evident that the influenza-virus enzyme and RDE are isodynamic enzymes and that they split off specifically sialic acid from glycoproteins containing sialic acid, whether or not these are endowed with inhibitory capacity in the hemagglutination test. Since both very mild acid treat-

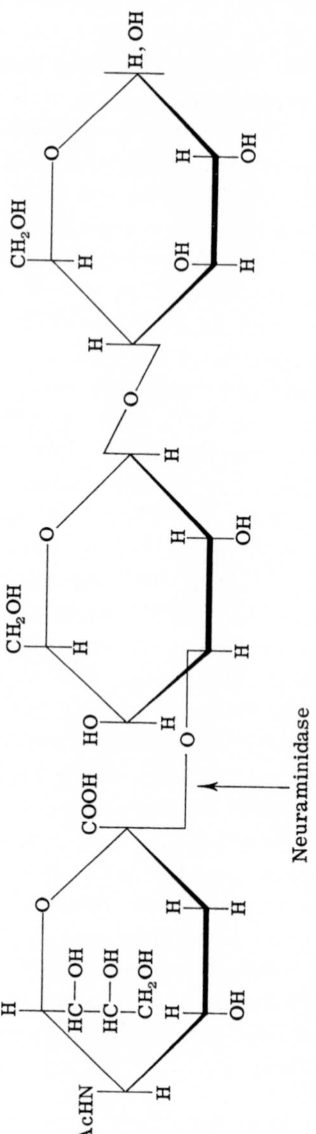

FIG. 2. Sialyllactose [O-N-acetylneuraminyl-(2 → 3)-O-β-D-galactopyranosyl-(1 → 4)-D-glucopyranose].

ment (pH 1–2, 80°C, 60 min) and RDE released only sialic acid from the glycoprotein of bovine submaxillary gland, it was concluded that sialic acid occupies a terminal position, the linkage being ketosidic (Gottschalk, 1956; Heimer and Meyer, 1956).

More detailed information concerning the susceptible ketosidic linkage was obtained when small oligosaccharides containing sialic acid became available. Trucco and Caputto (1954) and Kuhn and Brossmer (1956) prepared from rat mammary glands and from cow colostrum, respectively, a trisaccharide, sialyllactose (Fig. 2, see Gottschalk, 1957; Kuhn and Brossmer, 1958a). The sialic acid of sialyllactose is *O,N*-diacetylneuraminic acid. When it was established that sialic acid is engaged in a ketosidic linkage in sialyllactose and is quantitatively split off both by the intact influenza virus and by RDE, the enzyme was termed "neuraminidase" and defined as the agent catalyzing "the hydrolytic cleavage of the glycosidic bond joining the keto group of neuraminic acid to D-galactose or D-galactosamine and possibly to other sugars" (Gottschalk, 1957). From the specific rotation of sialyllactose ($[\alpha]_D^{21} = +16°$; $c = 2$; water) Gottschalk (1958a) and Kuhn and Brossmer (1958a) inferred an α-configuration of the ketosidic linkage (Hudson's isomutarotation rules). Neuraminidase is therefore most likely an α-ketosidase.

Disaccharides susceptible to neuraminidase were prepared from the glycoproteins obtained from bovine and ovine submaxillary glands. The ovine disaccharide is D-*N*-acetylneuraminyl-(2 → 6)-*N*-acetylgalactosamine (Graham and Gottschalk, 1960). On alkaline treatment (0.2 *N* Na_2CO_3, 80°C, 10 min), this disaccharide was converted to neuraminyl-substituted chromogens. The sialyl residue can be removed by neuraminidase.

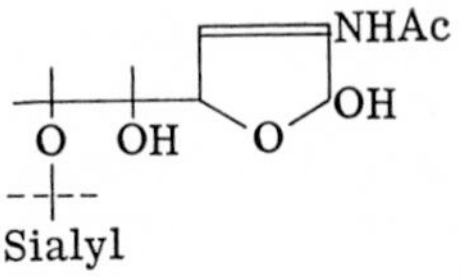

NHAc
OH
O OH O
Sialyl

NHAc
O OH O
Sialyl

Chromogen I — disaccharide 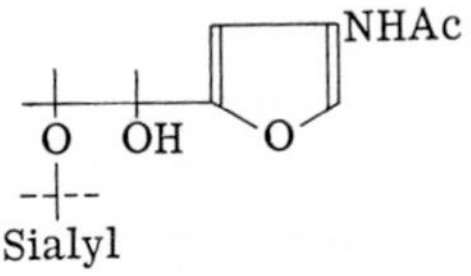 Chromogen III — disaccharide

---- bond susceptible to neuraminidase

The disaccharide from bovine submaxillary-gland glycoprotein was found to be a mixture of 85% *N*-acetylneuraminyl-(2 → 6)-*N*-acetylgalactosamine and 15% *N*-glycolylneuraminyl-(2 → 6)-*N*-acetylgalactosamine, the *O*-acetyl groups being lost by the use of alkali in the isolation procedure. Both substances were cleaved quantitatively into their components by neuraminidase (Gottschalk and Graham, 1958, 1959).

So far, only D-galactose and *N*-acetylgalactosamine have been recognized as natural partners of sialic acid in the neuraminidase-sensitive α-ketosidic linkage. In sialyllactose, in α_1-acid glycoprotein, and in the Ba-α_2-serum globulins the terminal sialic acid is linked to C-3 or C-4 of a galactose residue (Kuhn and Brossmer, 1958; Popenoe, 1959; Eylar and Jeanloz, 1962a; Kamiyama and Schmid, 1961). In the disaccharides present in the submaxillary-gland glycoproteins, sialic acid is joined to C-6 of *N*-acetylgalactosamine. Colominic acid, a polymer of *N*-acetylneuraminic acid prepared from the culture medium of *E. coli* K_{235} by Barry (1958), was found to be resistant to neuraminidase action (Gottschalk, unpublished data). Insofar as the substituents in the terminal neuraminic acid residues are concerned, activity of neuraminidase was shown toward sialosides containing *N*-acetyl, *N*-glycolyl, *O,N*-diacetyl, or *N*-acetyl-*O*-diacetyl groups, although the presence of *O*-acetyl groups decreases considerably the reaction rate (Faillard, 1959).

Vibrio cholerae neuraminidase was crystallized independently by Schramm and Mohr (1959) and by Ada and French (1959). The enzyme has a high affinity for its substrates; with erythrocyte stroma (sheep) as substrate, K_m was found to be 2×10^{-4} (expressed in moles per liter). The pH optimum is 5.5 to 6.5. The *Vibrio* enzyme requires Ca^{++} or Mn^{++} (0.01 molar) for its activity (Mohr and Schramm, 1960). Free *N*-acetylneuraminic acid is an inhibitor; the methyl ester is not. The enzyme is not sensitive to SH reagents (Mohr, 1960).

Mayron *et al.* (1961) reported the separation of neuraminidase from Asian and PR8 strains of influenza virus by treating the virus with trypsin at pH 7.0. The enzyme released specifically *N*-acetylneuraminic acid from sialyllactose and α_1-acid glycoprotein. The pH optimum was about 6.5. In contrast to *Vibrio cholerae* neuraminidase, the viral enzyme apparently did not require bivalent ions for activity; thus, addition of Ca^{++} had no effect on its performance. Ethylenediaminetetraacetate, however, greatly reduced its activity. With sialyllactose as substrate, K_m was 5×10^{-4} (moles per liter). Like the *Vibrio* enzyme, the isolated viral enzyme did not agglutinate red cells; it destroyed the receptor sites of human red cells in 2 hr at 37°.

Allowing purified, intact influenza-virus particles of the strain $A_2$1 (Singapore 1957) to act on sialyllactose, Walop, Boschman, and Jacobs (1960) estimated K_m to be 6×10^{-4} (moles per liter). Free *N*-acetylneuraminic acid inhibited competitively the viral action on its substrate, the inhibitor constant K_i being 5×10^{-3} moles per liter. Available data suggest that per virus particle and per hemagglutinating unit, respectively, the strains A_2 (Japan 305/57) and A_21 (Singapore 1957) have the highest neuraminidase activity of all A strains (A_2, FM1, PR8, PR301, NWS, swine) and B strains (Lee, Bon, 33 Johannesburg) tested (Howe, Lee, and Rose, 1960; Jacobs and Walop, 1961; Seto *et al.*, 1961).

Recently, Ada and Lind (1961) extracted and partially purified a neuraminidase from the chorioallantoic membrane of chick embryos, a host tissue for influenza viruses. The concentration of the neuraminidase in this tissue was very low, indeed. The relationship between the membrane neuraminidase and the viral enzyme is not yet clear. Although there seems to be little doubt that neuraminidase is an intrinsic component of the influenza-virus particle (Gottschalk and Perry, 1951), further work has to reveal whether the viral enzyme is fully determined by the virus genome or, as the authors discuss, is determined by the genetic material of the host, but incorporated into the virus under the influence of the virus genome.

IV. Definition in Structural Terms of a Glycoprotein Inhibiting Viral Hemagglutination

Inhibition of influenza-virus hemagglutination by glycoproteins is a phenomenon resulting from the distribution of the indicator virus between two glycoproteins—namely, the soluble glycoprotein (inhibitor) and the cell-bound glycoprotein (red-cell receptor). Actually, the test is arranged to provide conditions more favorable for the inhibitor than for the receptors in this competition. Thus, the inhibitor is allowed to interact first and on its own with the indicator virus for an hour, after which time the red cells are added; the patterns of agglutination are read 30 min later. The inhibitor is granted some advantage in the test because of the high affinity of the cell receptors for the virus, as seen when the indicator virus is added to a mixture of the competitors. Under these impartial conditions, inhibition by a glycoprotein which is very potent in the standard test may be reduced 100 times.

The interpretation of the following four observations may shed some light on the structural features required to qualify a glycoprotein as a potent inhibitor of viral hemagglutination. The phenomena are:

(1) All inhibitory glycoproteins contain sialic acid and are susceptible to, and inactivated by, neuraminidase, but many neuraminidase-susceptible glycoproteins are devoid of inhibitory capacity (Gottschalk, 1960).

(2) The glycopeptides obtained by trypsin treatment of ovine submaxillary-gland glycoprotein are devoid of any inhibitory activity against PR8 and Lee indicator viruses, although trypsin is without effect on the linkages between *N*-acetylneuraminic acid and *N*-acetyl-

galactosamine and between *N*-acetylgalactosamine and the peptide chain (Gottschalk and Fazekas de St. Groth, 1960).

(3) The cell-bound receptors are very potent competitors in the inhibitory test, yet their inhibitory capacity is relatively low when they are isolated in soluble form and tested under standard conditions (see Table III).

(4) Whereas the glycoprotein of ovine submaxillary gland is a very potent inhibitor for the PR8 (A) and Lee (B) strains of influenza virus (Table III), it scarcely inhibits hemagglutination by the Cam (A) and FM-1 (A) strains of influenza virus (Gottschalk and Fazekas de St. Groth, 1960a).

Obviously, in order to be a potent inhibitor of viral hemagglutination—to compete successfully with the red-cell receptors—the glycoprotein must have a high affinity for the indicator virus. It may be inferred from the molecular structure of the ovine submaxillary-gland glycoprotein (see Section II) that the large number of prosthetic groups terminating in sialic acid and distributed along the whole polypeptide chain is one of the factors endowing a glycoprotein with high affinity for an indicator virus. It seems reasonable to assume that such a molecule can attach itself with several hundred terminal sialic acid residues to appropriate groupings at the virus surface, even when one allows for the possibility that the spatial arrangement of a portion of the sialic acid residues prevents them from contact with the virus surface. The urinary glycoprotein, which is closest to the ovine submaxillary-gland glycoprotein in inhibitory potency (Table III), will also be able to adsorb to the virus by means of a great number of sialic acid residues representing the terminal groupings of more than 200 individual prosthetic groups. In contrast, the glycopeptides resulting from trypsin digestion of ovine submaxillary-gland glycoprotein have only a few sialic acid residues, and sialyllactose has only one such residue available for interaction with the virus surface. The reversible interaction of these molecules with the virus surface will not be strong enough to stand the competition by the red-cell receptors. This interpretation is substantiated by the demonstration that the glycopeptides of ovine submaxillary-gland glycoprotein are completely adsorbed to Lee indicator virus in the absence of red cells (Fazekas de St. Groth and Gottschalk, 1963).

The affinity of the cell-bound receptor glycoproteins for the virus is high, probably not so much because of the great number of their prosthetic groups, but rather because of the density of the individual receptor molecules at the red-cell surface (see Gottschalk, 1959). When isolated and in solution, the receptor glycoproteins are far apart, thus losing much of their capacity to bind the virus.

Another important aspect of the structural features of a potent inhibitor of hemagglutination is that, in addition to a multitude of accessible terminal sialic-acid residues, the inhibitory molecule must have in its three-dimensional structure an area complementary to an area at the virus surface. This seems to be the only plausible interpretation of the observation that the inhibitory titers of a single species of inhibitory glycoprotein against a set of ten different indicator viruses form a characteristic pattern (Stone, 1949a; Gottschalk and Fazekas de St. Groth, 1960a). As indicated by their different surface antigens, the viral strains differ in their surface structure.

Alpha$_1$-acid glycoprotein (mol. wt. 44,100) and fetuin (mol. wt. 48,400) are glycoproteins with a relatively high sialic acid content (about 11% and 9%, respectively) but are devoid of inhibitory property. Since they have only very few prosthetic groups, their sialic acid residues are closely packed at the few prosthetic sites (see Volume I, Chapter 10, and Gottschalk, 1962, 1963). They may not be inhibitors, either because a substantial proportion of the acidic groups is sterically hindered from contact with the virus surface, or because the virus surface lacks areas complementary to the densely packed sialic acid residues. In the absence of red cells, α_1-acid glycoprotein and fetuin combine with Lee indicator virus (Fazekas de St. Groth and Gottschalk, 1963).

V. Association between Some Other Viruses and Hexosamine-Containing Substances

Mandel and Racker (1953,a) isolated from the intestinal tissue of adult mice a glycoprotein which inhibits specifically the hemagglutinin and the infectivity of Theiler's GD VII strain of encephalomyelitis virus of mice through a virus–inhibitor combination. The glycoprotein in neutral solution could be heated at 115°C for 10 min without loss of biological activity. It contained 5.9% nitrogen, 31.8% hexosamine, 8.3% hexuronic acid, 2.7% methylpentose, and 19.2% galactose. The polypeptide moiety was found to be composed of aspartic and glutamic acids, serine and threonine, alanine, isoleucine, and one or two other amino acids. Treatment with 0.03 molar periodate at 20°C inactivated the inhibitory glycoprotein.

Goebel and Jesaitis (1952) showed that the type-specific somatic antigen of Phase II *Shigella sonnei* which is present at the cell surface serves as the receptor for the T phages which attack this particular dysentery bacillus. The antigen is a glycolipid–protein complex and it inhibits *in vitro* all the T-coli-dysentery phages to which this organism is susceptible. On treatment with 90% phenol, the complex dissociates into its glycolipid and protein components. The lipid fraction accounts for 33.4% of the glycolipid, the carbohydrate contributes 45.8%, and amino acids, still present, about 9%. Further analysis revealed the presence of glucose, galactose, glucosamine (probably *N*-acetylated), and an aldoheptose in the carbohydrate moiety. The antiviral properties of the Phase II antigen are a function of the carbohydrate moiety of the glycolipid–protein molecule. It is inferred that the biologically active carbohydrate group combines with and inactivates the phages *in vitro* by competing with the phage receptor at the surface of the susceptible organism. The type-specific antigen of a phage-resistant variant of Phase II *Shigella sonnei* differs markedly in its carbohydrate composition from that of the parent Phase II bacillus and fails to inhibit the phages to which it is resistant (Jesaitis and Goebel, 1952). In the H-FGS-phage–*Shigella flexneri*—FGS system the receptor was found to consist of two-thirds polysaccharide and one-third lipid. The polysaccharide moiety contained 38.5% glucose, 21.6% rhamnose, and 28.6% glucosamine. About 670 receptor molecules are present per bacterium. The biological activity of the substance is high: 0.5 μg/ml inactivates 50% of a phage suspension containing 2×10^6 particles/ml (Dirkx and Beumer, 1961).

VI. Inactivation of Hormonal Glycoproteins by Viral and Bacterial Neuraminidases

The interactions between influenza virus and cellular receptors and influenza virus and inhibitory glycoproteins were the first examples of a system illustrating the dependence of the biological activity of some glycoproteins on the presence of terminal sialic acid residues. The gonadotropic hormones provided the next instance. It has long been known that the follicle-stimulating hormone (FSH) and the interstitial-cell-stimulating hormone—both of which are gonadotropins derived from the pituitary glands—and the chorionic gonadotropins present in serum of pregnant mares and in urine of pregnant women contain carbohydrate and have a low isoelectric point (for review see Li, 1949). Recent work has shown beyond doubt that sialic acid is an essential component of the gonadotropins and that its enzymatic removal inactivates these hormones. Follicle-stimulating hormone from sheep pituitary glands was found to have a sialic acid content of 5%. The sialyl residues occupy a terminal position, and are completely removable by influenza-virus and *Vibrio cholerae* neuraminidases. Such release resulted in a reduction of the hormonal activity by 97% or more (Whitten, 1948; Gottschalk,

Whitten, and Graham, 1960). Human menopausal gonadotropin, derived from pituitary-gland tissue, contains 7.8% sialic acid; removal of 60% of the sialic acid residues decreased its biological activity by 80% (Got and Bourrillon, 1961). An electrophoretically and ultracentrifugally homogeneous chorionic gonadotropin of human origin (mol. wt. 30,000) containing sialic acid was studied in detail by Got, Bourrillon, and Michon (1960) (see Volume I, Chapter 11). Inactivation of this hormone by neuraminidase has been described by several authors (for review see Got, Bourrillon, and Michon, 1960).

An electrophoretically homogeneous glycoprotein with erythropoietic activity was obtained from plasma of rabbits with phenylhydrazine anemia; it contained 14% sialic acid (see Volume I, Chapter 10). On treatment with neuraminidase, the sialic acid residues were split off, with a concomitant loss of biological activity (Lowy, Keighley, and Borsook, 1960; Campbell *et al.*, 1961).

Addendum

Kathan and Winzler (1963) have further elucidated the properties and structure of the influenza-virus receptor previously isolated from human erythrocyte stroma (Kathan, Winzler, and Johnson, 1961). The amino acid composition of the inhibitor is shown in Table V.

TABLE V
AMINO ACID COMPOSITION OF THE VIRUS-HEMAGGLUTININ INHIBITORY GLYCOPROTEIN FROM HUMAN ERYTHROCYTE STROMA (VIRUS RECEPTOR)

Amino acid	Micromoles per milligram of protein	Moles per 31,000 g of protein	No. of residues per mole of protein (nearest integer)
Lysine	0.099	3.0	3
Histidine	0.106	3.3	3
Arginine	0.112	3.5	3
Aspartic acid	0.164	5.1	5
Threonine	0.383	11.8	12
Serine	0.377	11.6	12
Glutamic acid	0.278	8.6	9
Proline	0.183	5.7	6
Glycine	0.187	5.8	6
Alanine	0.187	5.8	6
Valine	0.213	6.6	7
Isoleucine	0.122	3.8	4
Leucine	0.126	3.9	4
Tyrosine	0.100	3.1	3
Phenylalanine	0.098	3.0	3
Methionine	0.040	1.2	1

The sialic acid present in this glycoprotein is probably *N*-acetylneuraminic acid. It occupies a terminal position since all of it can be removed, without the concomitant release of any other sugar, by the neuraminidase of Asian influenza virus. There are 23, 22, 22, and 2 moles, respectively, of *N*-acetylneuraminic acid, hexosamine, galactose, and fucose per 31,000 g of glycoprotein (mol. wt., 31,000). The hexosamine is a mixture of galactosamine and glucosamine in the ratio of 3–4 to 1. Treatment of the native glycoprotein with sodium borohydride did not result in the loss of any carbohydrate component, indicating that the carbonyl functions of the component sugars are involved in glycosidic linkages.

The stromal virus receptor, which is a potent inhibitor of influenza-virus hemagglutination, has also M and N blood-group specific activities (Klenk and Uhlenbruck, 1960; Kathan, Riff, and Real, 1963). As observed earlier by Springer and Ansell (1958), these activities were lost upon treatment with influenza virus or *Vibrio cholerae* neuraminidase.

Noll, Aoyagi, and Orlando (1962) reported the release of 90% of the virus-associated neuraminidase in 10 min at 37°C from the Lee strain of influenza virus (10^4 to 10^6 hemagglutinating particles) upon treatment with crystalline trypsin (1 mg/ml) at pH 7.2. The sedimentation coefficient (9.0S) of the soluble neuraminidase indicated a molecular weight of 190,000 for a spherical particle. When the experiment was carried out with virus labeled with leucine-H^3, the enzyme contained all the solubilized radioactivity. The influenza virus neuraminidase was estimated to account for 5–15% of the total virus protein. All the hemagglutinin was recovered in the sediment after treatment with trypsin. Laver (1963) disrupted the Lee virus particles with dodecyl sulfate and showed that the neuraminidase activity was associated with a minor protein component of 8.2S. The neuraminidase isolated from Lee virus differed markedly from the neuraminidase present in the uninfected host cells (chorioallantoic membrane) in sedimentation velocity and its stability toward dodecyl sulfate.

In preliminary experiments, antiserum prepared against soluble enzyme from Lee virus grown in eggs was shown to inhibit equally well the soluble enzyme isolated from Lee virus grown in the chick embryo and in calf kidney cells but to have no effect on purified avian neuraminidase (Ada, Lind, and Laver, 1963). These data, if confirmed, would suggest that the influenza virus neuraminidase is a virus-specific product; they would support the conclusion drawn by Gottschalk and Perry (1951) from their earlier work that the enzyme is not derived from the host cells.

Measurements in systems of enzymically inactive influenza virus (indicator virus) and glycoproteins inhibiting influenza-virus hemagglutinin disclosed the equilibrium

$$\text{indicator virus} + \text{inhibitor} \rightleftharpoons \text{virus–inhibitor complex}$$

When equilibrium constants K (rate constant of back reaction:rate constant of forward reaction) were determined (by two independent methods) in systems with inhibitors of high and low potency, the following values (expressed in molar terms) were obtained: 1×10^{-8} for ovine submaxillary glycoprotein, 9×10^{-7} for fetuin, 2×10^{-5} for α_1-acid glycoprotein of human plasma, and 4×10^{-6} for the glycopeptides obtained by controlled trypsin treatment of the ovine submaxillary glycoprotein (Fazekas de St. Groth and Gottschalk, 1963). These results suggest that the determinant for the potency of an inhibitor of virus hemagglutinin is a compound of the number of sialic acid residues available per glycoprotein molecule and of the complementariness of the contacting areas on the surface of virus and glycoprotein.

Chapter 51

INTERACTION OF AMINO SUGARS AND AMINO SUGAR-CONTAINING MACROMOLECULES WITH VIRUSES, CELLS, AND TISSUES

Endre A. Balazs and Bernard Jacobson

Introduction

The raison d'être underlying this final chapter is the attempt to summarize briefly those findings that indicate the effects of amino sugars and amino sugar-containing macromolecules on living systems. This chapter encompasses a variety of biological phenomena, such as virus propagation *in vitro*, the fertilization process of eggs, and tumor growth. The goal, however, was not to treat comprehensively all biological systems nor cover exhaustively the topics discussed, but was rather to indicate biological effects attributable specifically to amino sugars, glycosaminoglycans, and glycoproteins.

It is hoped that the biochemist, interested in the structure and metabolism of these compounds, may become fully aware of the wide spectrum of biological events in which amino sugars, glycosaminoglycans, and glycoproteins may play an important role. It is hoped also that the biologist will gain a broader understanding of the complexities that the chemical and physical structure of these compounds signify in their interaction.

I. Viral and Bacterial Growth

A. Viruses

The first indication that glycosaminoglycans may interact with viruses came from the observations of Duran-Reynals (1928), McClean (1930), and Hoffman (1931) that testicle extract considerably enhances the development of viral lesions in the skin when strains of vaccine virus, herpes vesicular stomatitis, and foot and mouth disease were injected together with the viral suspension.

Duran-Reynals and Duran-Reynals (1952) were the first to suggest that hyaluronic acid, a polyanion, interferes with the process of virus multiplication. They found that hyaluronic acid preparations obtained from human umbilical cord or bovine vitreous caused a slight decrease of virus titer or complete inactivation of the virus when added to vaccine (dermo- and Levadite neuro-) virus grown in media of the Maitland type. The variation of the effect depended on the source and concentration of hyaluronic acid, the type of culture medium, and the strain of virus. The hyaluronic acid preparations were probably of low molecular weight because they were steamed before use. When hyaluronidase and hyaluronic acid were simultaneously added to the cultures, the inactivation of virus was even more efficient.

The latter finding was extended by McCrea and Duran-Reynals (1953), who showed that the virus-inactivating substance was dialyzable through a cellophane membrane after hyaluronidase digestion and that glucuronic acid was the active material. The dermovirus could also be inhibited by glucuronic acid, but galacturonic acid had only about half of the activity, whereas mannuronic acid and *N*-acetylglucosamine were inactive.

Cohen (1942) observed that the addition of heparin to a solution of tobacco mosaic virus resulted in the production of needle-shaped paracrystals in which very little or no heparin was bound. Dissolution of the crystal showed no apparent loss of virus activity. Tomato-bushy-stunt virus was also precipitated by heparin, hyaluronic acid, and chondroitin sulfate. The author concluded that the virus precipitation is not a function of the charge density of the particular glycosaminoglycan, and the phenomenon, therefore, appears to be different from a salt-like interaction, although the precipitation of tobacco mosaic virus by heparin and hyaluronic acid was inhibited by 0.1 M phosphate.

The results obtained by Cohen (1942) may perhaps be interpreted as being at least partially due to the "excluded volume" effect (Feltz and Regelson, 1962), proposed for glycosaminoglycans by Johnston (1955), Ogston and Phelps (1961), Laurent and Pietruszkiewicz (1961), and Laurent (1963). It may be, then, that the formation of virus crystals when glycosaminoglycan is added to virus solution is due to the "exclusion" of the virus from part of the solution occupied by the glycosaminoglycan, although the charge interaction cannot be disregarded as an additional factor.

Polyanions of various chemical composition, such as polyglutamate, polyacrylate, aromatic polysulfonates, polyglucose sulfate, and ethylene maleic anhydride copolymers, prevented infections by influenza B, Newcastle-disease, tobacco mosaic and ECHO 9 viruses and bacteriophage

(T_2) (Neher and Kradolfer, 1955; Stahmann and Gothoskor, 1958; Heymann *et al.*, 1958; Young and Mowra, 1960; Feltz and Regelson, 1962). On the other hand, it was found that polycations, such as polylysine and polyvinylamine, inactivate tobacco mosaic, mumps, Type B influenza, and Newcastle-disease viruses (Burger and Stahmann, 1951; Green and Stahmann, 1953, 1954; Green, Stahmann, and Rasmussen, 1953; Tsuyuki, Tsuyuki, and Stahmann, 1956). The assumption is that the inhibiting action of the polycations lies in the coulombic interaction between the negatively charged virus and the positively charged macromolecule, whereas the inhibiting action of the polyanions was attributed to a blocking of the positively charged receptor sites of the cell surface with the negatively charged macromolecules.

Gerber *et al.* (1958) reported that insoluble compounds prepared as a suspension in 0.25% agar afforded some protection for chick embryos which had been infected with influenza B virus. Sulfated polysaccharides extracted from *Gelidium cartilaginium* (the usual source of domestic agar) and carrageenan produced inhibition of the growth of influenza B virus and mumps virus in chick embryos, but did not affect influenza A or Newcastle-disease viruses.

Takemoto and Liebhaber (1961) reported that heparin, polyglucose sulfate, and agar polysaccharide inhibited the hemagglutination of sheep erythrocytes caused by a wild type of encephalomyocarditis (EMC) virus. The same authors (1962) found that dextran sulfate was a potent inhibitor of plaque formation by viruses such as ECHO, Coxsackie A9, and herpes simplex.

In contrast to the latter finding, a type 1 polio virus showed enhancement of plaque formation after the addition of dextran sulfate (Takemoto and Liebhaber, 1962) and diminution of plaque formation after the addition of the polycation, DEAE-dextran (Liebhaber and Takemoto, 1961). Takemoto and Fabisch (1963) reported that the inhibitory effect of agar polysaccharide on plaque formation of influenza A2 and B viruses was reversed when DEAE-dextran was added—again, a result which is just the opposite of that found with polio virus type 1. The agar polysaccharide did not inhibit the adsorption of the virus to monkey kidney cells. The agar extract was found to be a polymer of D-galactose and 3,6-anhydro-L-galactose with monoesterified sulfate (O'Neill and Stewart, 1956; Araki, 1959).

Liebhaber and Takemoto (1962, 1963) also found that sulfated polysaccharides interfered with the adsorption of one virus variant to cells. Adsorption of a small-plaque EMC virus was reduced, whereas the large-plaque variant was unaffected—the effect depending both on pH and ionic strength. The small-plaque EMC variant sedimented in the ultracentrifuge with S^{35}-polyglucose sulfate, whereas the large-plaque variant did not exhibit this behavior (Liebhaber and Takemoto, 1962). It was proposed that a charge interaction between the polyanion and virus binds the virus and reduces its chances to be attached to cells.

Agol and Chumakova (1962,a, 1963) also reported the inhibition of a polio virus variant by agar polysaccharide, heparin, hyaluronic acid, and polyvinyl sulfate.

Bengtsson, Philipson, and Albertsson (1962) and Bengtsson and Philipson (1963) demonstrated that differing genetic strains of polio virus were separable via countercurrent distribution in two-phase systems containing dextran sulfate and polyethylene glycol. Bengtsson *et al.* (1964) attempted the separation of a virulent strain (E206) and an attenuated strain (Sabin vaccine LSc 2 ab) of polio virus type 1 by preparative ultracentrifugation in a dextran sulfate gradient. The process of separating macromolecules by ultracentrifugation in polymer media depends either on the molecular sieve action that various polymers exert on a sedimenting substance or on the chemical affinity that various polymers have for a sedimenting substance. The separation obtained was explained as probably being caused by an increased affinity of the more slowly sedimenting attenuated strain to dextran sulfate as a result of differences in the surface structure of the viruses. A "sieve" mechanism was not excluded, however, inasmuch as the formation of well-defined aggregates of the virus particles of one of the strains could also occur.

The potent inhibitory effect of heparin on the infectivity of herpes simplex virus (HSV) in cell cultures was reported by Vaheri and Cantell (1963) and by Nahmias and Kibrick (1964). Vaheri (1964) found that the anti-HSV action of heparin, which occurred during the early interaction of HSV and primary human amnion cells, was reversible by dilution of the heparin–HSV complex, resulting in a quantitative recovery of the virus. Heparin had no effect on the intracellular replication of the virus. The minimum effective dose of heparin in a balanced salt medium was about 0.1 μg/ml and, in 50% serum, about 2 μg/ml. The inhibition of HSV by heparin was reduced by the following substances: serum albumin, hyaluronidase, and thrombin, as well as the polycationic, anti-heparin agents, Polybrene (hexadimethrine bromide) and protamine sulfate. Since the inhibitory effect of heparin was inversely proportional to the concentration of serum used in the culture medium, it was evident that heparin required no serum cofactor in its antiviral effect, in contrast to its anti-thrombin action. The action of heparin was dependent on the ionic strength, and, therefore, the reversible inhibition of heparin on HSV was proposed to be an association–dissociation reaction determined by electrostatic forces. Dextran sulfate also exerted a potent, heparin-like effect on HSV. It is of interest that the polycations Polybrene and protamine sulfate, which inhibited the action of heparin, were themselves powerful inhibitors of HSV. The results indicated that the antiviral action of the polyionic substances stemmed from the charged groups, and, therefore, the sensitivity of a virus strain to polyanions or polycations may depend on the distribution of charged sites on the virus surface. The results just mentioned do not preclude the possibility that an interaction between heparin and the cell surface also plays an important role in the inhibition of virus propagation. (For more detail see Vaheri, 1964.)

Vaheri (1964) also found that the following viruses were not affected by heparin: one strain each of adeno 1 and 11, Coxsackie B5, ECHO 9 and 13, measles, mumps, Newcastle-disease, and polio types 1 and 3.

Salganik, Tomsons, and Protas (1963) assumed that replication of viral RNA should be preceded by its denaturation. The denaturation of RNA was inhibited by polyanions, and it was further observed that heparin, hyaluronic acid, and polyxenylphosphate inhibited the multiplication of poliovirus in tissue culture. Again, the antiviral activity was dependent on electrostatic interaction, inasmuch as the addition of polycationic histones eliminated the inhibitory actions of the polyanions.

Infection of rabbits with the Shope fibroma virus produces a rapidly growing tumor which regresses after a short period of time (Febvre, 1962). Higginbotham and Murillo (1965) reported that heparin protected rabbits against the pathogenic effects of Shope fibroma virus, as measured by a reduction in virus titer and decrease in tumor size. More marked inhibition was demonstrated by the use of polyanethol sulfonate. They proposed that the inhibitory action of the polyanions was due to depression of virus proliferation. Bengtsson (1965), on the other hand, came to the conclusion that sulfated dextran, with a high degree of polymerization (molecular weight larger than 100,000), inhibits the reversible, temperature-independent, attachment of virus to the cell, but it has little effect on the subsequent steps of viral multiplication. Using two strains of poliovirus (E 206 and L Sc 2 ab), the author could show that the virus, which is normally adsorbed by a cation exchanger (Sephadex sulfate), is not adsorbed when mixed with sulfated dextrans. For further details on the interaction between virus and polyelectrolytes, the reader is referred to the recent reviews of Vaheri (1964) and Voss (1964).

B. Bacteria

It is not the aim of this section to discuss the presence or role of amino sugars in antibiotics. The chemistry of these substances is discussed in Volume I, Chapter 7, and a table listing those antibiotics containing amino sugars, as well as their sources, is presented in Chapter 18 (for inhibition of cell-wall synthesis, see page 42).

It is of interest, however, to point out the necessity, in some cases, of the free amino groups for antibacterial activity, as illustrated by the following examples. Gentamicin (Garymycin), an antibiotic containing the amino sugar deoxystreptamine, was resolved into two closely related, active antibiotic components by alkaline hydrolysis of the microbiologically inactive *N*-acetyl derivatives (Weinstein *et al.*, 1963). Since gentamicin is a member of the same chemical family as neomycin, kanamycin, and paromomycin, Wagman and Weinstein (1964) investigated the possible conversion of the inactive *N*-acetyl derivatives of these antibiotics to compounds with antibacterial activity via hydrolysis. The *N*-acetyl derivatives at a concentration of 10 mg/ml had no antibacterial activity against *Staphylococcus aureus* ATCC 6538P or *Bacillus subtilis* ATCC 6633. Saponification with NaOH regenerated the original antibacterial activity in each case, implicating the free amino function as a necessity for bacteriostatic action.

In contrast to the bacteriostatic properties of the amino sugar-containing antibiotics, Baggi and Prodi (1954) reported that the intradermal inoculation of a mixture of the potassium salt of hyaluronic acid and staphylococci into an area on the back of albino rabbits produced an inflammatory reaction which was more intense than that produced by the staphylococci alone. Hyaluronic acid after hyaluronidase digestion also increased the inflammatory reaction, although to a lesser degree than did the undegraded macromolecule itself.

II. Pseudopodium Formation in Amoeba

Jeon and Bell (1962) found that the migration of *Amoeba proteus* toward pieces of living or heat-killed *Hydra* (*Hydra viridis* or *Tetrahymena pyriformis*) depends on the stimulation of localized pseudopodium formation. Pseudopodia form rapidly when micropipettes which contain pieces or extract of *Hydra* are placed within a 50 μ distance from the surface of the amoeba. The membrane potential of the amoeba decreases at the same time (Bingley, Bell, and Jeon, 1962). The change in the electrostatic surface charge of the amoeba seems to be the important factor in the locomotion of the cell. Bingley and Thompson (1962) found that the forward-moving part of the advancing amoeba is "depolarized" in relation to the rear portion. Heparin inhibits or stimulates the pseudopodium formation, depending on two factors: the concentration of the heparin to which the cell surface is exposed and the state of the cell surface in terms of electrostatic-charge conditions.

Heparin stimulation was observed when the amoeba had been exposed previously to cationic polyions, and the inhibiting effect of heparin was evident when the surface of the amoeba was not pretreated with polyanions or when the pretreated amoeba was exposed to a high concentration of heparin solution (Bell and Jeon, 1962). Jeon and Bell later (1965) could not confirm these results using different heparin preparations, but they were successful in separating a cationic macromolecule from *Hydra* (*H. littoralis, H. viridis,* and *H. vulgaris*) which had a pseudopod-inducing, chemotactic effect on amoebae. This cationic substance formed a water-insoluble precipitate with heparin. The authors speculated that the chemotactic agent of the *Hydra,* acting as a polycation, may "disturb the charge balance on the cell surface" by reducing its negative charge density, which in turn would trigger further changes in the cytoplasm, resulting in its oriented flow.

O'Neill (1964) isolated the surface membrane of an amoeba and found 14.1% carbohydrate in the preparation. The hexosamine content was 3.4%, and paper chromatography indicated that mannose, galactose, and glucose, but not sialic acid, were present.

III. Fertilization, Growth, and Wound Healing

A. Fertilization of Eggs

When a living cell divides, its protoplasm first undergoes a sharp increase in viscosity. This phenomenon has been called "mitotic gelation," and it precedes the appearance of the spindle. After the spindle formation, the protoplasm reverts to its original fluid state. It has been proposed that gelation during mitosis is similar to that which occurs in the protoplasm when various stimulating agents are added, and, therefore, gelation of the protoplasm is similar, in many respects, to that which occurs during the clotting of vertebrate blood (Heilbrunn, 1928). Heilbrunn and Wilson (1949) proposed that substances which inhibit blood clotting may also prevent the gelation during mitosis. The viscosity of the protoplasm of the *Chaetopterus* egg normally increases sharply just before the mitotic spindle is formed, but, in eggs treated with heparin, this gelation did not occur; therefore, it was assumed that heparin interfered with mitosis by inhibiting gelation.

Samples of a bacterial polysaccharide that caused tumors to regress (Shear and Turner, 1943; see Section V,B,2, of this chapter) were used by Heilbrunn and Wilson (1950,a) to test the effects of this substance on fertilization and cell division in *Chaetopterus pergamentaceus* eggs. Eggs placed in a solution of the polysaccharide showed neither viscosity increase in the protoplasm nor cleavage.

Harding (1951) studied the comparative actions of heparin and two other polysaccharides (fucoidin from the plant *Fucus vesiculosus* and a glycoprotein identical with blood group H substance, extracted from pig mucin) on the fertilization process and subsequent cleavage in the eggs of *Arbacia punctulata* and *Echinarachnius parma*. All three polysaccharides inhibited elevation of the fertilization membrane. Oxidation with sodium periodate caused a loss of this inhibitory power, indicating that the polysaccharide itself was the active inhibitory factor. The observed inhibition of cleavage by heparin was attributed to its prevention of normal fertilization, since the eggs were most sensitive when exposed to heparin at the time of fertilization. It was proposed that the inhibitory effect on fertilization was exerted primarily on the protoplasmic surface of the egg.

Runnström's theory (1949) on the fertilization of the sea-urchin egg proposed that the fertilization membrane is formed from the vitelline membrane, which covers the surface of the unfertilized egg, and material exuded from the cortex of the egg at the time of fertilization. The capacity of sea-urchin eggs, at various stages of ripeness, to elevate normal fertilization membranes led to the hypothesis that an inhibitor to activation is present in the unfertilized egg, and there are indications that this inhibitor may be polysaccharide in nature (Runnström and Kriszat, 1950). Normal elevation of the fertilization membrane is inhibited when eggs of *Echinocardium cordatum* are fertilized in the presence of a 0.025%-solution of jelly-coat substance (Runnström, 1950). The cortical material did not fuse in normal fashion with the vitelline membrane, and a low, thin fertilization membrane was formed instead of the normal, well-elevated, thick membrane.

The nature of this inhibitor may be better understood by Ishihara's (1964) findings. In the sea water in which freshly fertilized sea-urchin eggs (*Pseudocentrotus depressus* and *Anthocidaris crassispina* are suspended, he found a polysaccharide, which may be a glycoprotein, which has a chemical composition distinctly different from that of the polysaccharide found in the jelly-coat of the egg. This macromolecule found in the sea water is a product of the fertilization process and contains fucose, galactose (and, in one species, also glucose and mannose), hexosamine, sulfate, and, probably, amino acids. The jelly-coat polysaccharide in the same species contained fucose, galactose, and sulfate, but no hexosamine. This analysis agrees with that of other authors who found that the jelly-coat polysaccharide has no hexosamine and sialic acid, but is primarily a sulfated polyfucose with some other hexoses present (Vasseur and Immers, 1949a; Vasseur, 1952a). Ishihara (1964) suggested that this anionic polysaccharide is identical with the acid known, since Runnström's observation in 1930, to be formed during fertilization. It was suggested that the jelly-coat (Runnström and Immers, 1956) or the cortical granules (Allen and Griffin, 1958) may be the source of this acid, which is extruded to the previtelline space concomitantly with the elevation of the fertilization membrane (Immers, 1961).

From the jelly coat of the eggs of an *Echinodermata* (starfish, *Asterias amurensis*) a macromolecule was separated which contained galactose (20.2%), fucose (15.7%), hexosamine (5.6%), and sulfate (19.1%) (Muramatsu, 1965). Like all other jelly-coat substances, it has no sialic acid or uronic acid, but the amino acid content (20.3%) indicates that it is a glycoprotein rather than a pure polysaccharide.

Using eggs of *Strongylocentrotus droebachiensis* and *Arbacia lixula,* Runnström and Wicklund (1950) found that heparin acted in a manner similar to that of the jelly-coat substance, although higher concentrations were required. Harding (1949) found that when eggs of *Rana pipiens* were pricked in the presence of heparinated frog blood, the percentage of dividing eggs was lower in every case than it was when the eggs were pricked in the presence of blood and Ringer's solution. Since the most effective method of producing artificial parthenogenesis in the frog egg is by pricking it in the presence of blood, it was believed that the active principle in blood was a thrombin or thrombin-like substance which could initiate protoplasmic gelation, thus producing cell division.

Many of the more recent studies on fertilization employ materials that do not contain hexosamine, and, consequently, these studies are not discussed here. The reader is referred, therefore, to the review of Metz (1961) on the use of inhibiting agents on fertilization mechanisms and the article by Austin (1961) on fertilization of mammalian eggs *in vitro.*

B. Tissue Growth

1. Inhibition

The effect of hexosamine on the growth of cells *in vitro* was tested mostly in cultures of malignant cells. Consequently, the studies dealing with this subject are reviewed in Section V,B,1, of this chapter, where the growth-inhibiting effect of amino sugars and glycosaminoglycans is discussed. In this section, the effect of glycosaminoglycans and other polyanions on the growth of normal embryonic tissue is described.

The first report describing the growth inhibition by heparin on cultures of normal embryonic tissue was published by Zakrzewski (1932, 1933), who made a systematic investigation of the effect of heparin on the growth of various tissues *in vitro*. The growth of normal embryonic tissues, measured by the increase of the area of the culture, was suppressed by heparin. Heparin neutralized the growth-stimulating effect of embryo extract and embryo serum, and the effect of heparin on tissue growth paralleled the antithrombin activity of this glycosaminoglycan. All these observations led the author to the suggestion that heparin inactivates a growth-stimulating substance in the embryonic tissue. Fischer (1936) confirmed the inhibitory effect of heparin on fibroblast cultures and found that hydrolyzed heparin (boiled in HCl) did not inhibit fibroblast growth or blood coagulation.

Balazs (1949, cited by Balazs and Holmgren, 1949; Balazs, Högberg, and Laurent, 1951) demonstrated that not only heparin but other sulfated polysaccharides, such as agar acid and chondroitin sulfate, suppress the growth of the embryonic chicken fibroblasts *in vitro*. The suppressing effect depends on the surface charge density of the polyanions. Chondroitin sulfate was less effective than agar acid or heparin. Hyaluronic acid, which has no sulfate ester groups, did slightly stimulate tissue growth *in vitro*. A sulfated hyaluronic acid preparation, which contained the same number of sulfate ester groups per disaccharide unit as does heparin (2.9), showed a more pronounced growth-suppressing effect on cultures of chicken heart fibroblasts than did heparin itself. One must point out an important structural difference between the two preparations—viz., the amino group of sulfated hyaluronic acid is substituted with acetyl, whereas that of heparin is substituted with a sulfamate group. The growth-suppressing effect of heparan sulfate, with one sulfate ester per disaccharide unit, was considerably less (Balazs, Högberg, and Laurent, 1951).

Dialyzed extracts of the limbs of chicken embryos neutralized the effect of sulfated polysaccharides, and it was noted that, although the suppression of the growth of the fibroblasts in chicken heart cultures was completely prevented with proper concentrations of heparin or sulfated hyaluronic acid, the continuous spontaneous pulsation and growth of the heart-muscle cells were not affected at all. These sulfated polysaccharides showed no effect on the growth of embryonic epithelial or retinal cell cultures, either. These observations suggest a specific effect of the polyanions on embryonic fibroblasts (Balazs and Holmgren, 1949). Further studies (Balazs and Eckl, unpublished data) showed that other sulfated polysaccharides, such as sulfated dextran, the polysaccharide of the jelly coat of sea-urchin eggs, sulfated starch, cellulose, and pectin, also inhibited the growth of fibroblasts *in vitro*, in proportion to their sulfate ester content. Evidence that this suppression of growth was a result of inhibition of cell multiplication was demonstrated by a decreased mitotic rate and a lack of DNA and RNA synthesis in the cultures when they were treated with these anionic polysaccharides. Increasing the glucose concentration in the culture medium did not affect the growth inhibition, but when the concentration of $CaCl_2$ was raised to 0.6 mole per ml of medium, the inhibitory effect of heparin was nearly completely abolished.

The mechanism of the growth inhibition is not yet explained, but one must point out that all these experiments were carried out in systems in which the fibroblasts grow and migrate in a fibrin coagulum. When the cells, however, were cultured on a glass surface in a liquid medium, the effect was not noticeable. The increase in area of the culture is a result of multiplication and migration of the cells. The latter is achieved by the fibrolytic activity of the cells, and thus any agent which would interfere with this lytic activity would suppress the increase of the culture. The polyanions, such as glycosaminoglycans, may interact with the fibrin or with the cell surface, in both cases interfering with the fibrinolytic activity of the cells. Fischer (1936–37) was the first to show that living cells (leukocytes) may bind heparin *in vitro,* and Astrup and Piper (1946) demonstrated that polyanions, such as sulfated cellulose and starch, form insoluble complexes with plasma fibrinogen. The interaction between glycosaminoglycans and plasma proteins, including fibrinogen, is reviewed in Chapter 48 of this volume.

Another possible mechanism by which acid glycosaminoglycans inhibit the *in vitro* growth of cells could be through their interactions with lipids. It is well known that fatty degeneration appears rapidly in cell cultures which depend on the lipid content of the medium and the general metabolic condition of the cells. The total lipid content of HeLa cell and chick aorta intima cell cultures, after being "loaded" with lipids by incubation with hyperlipemic serum, decreased when chondroitin 4-sulfate or the extract of acetone-dried calf aorta was added to the culture medium (Morrison *et al.,* 1963). The dry weight of the cultures at the end of the incubation period increased significantly. Direct observation on the multiplication or growth of cells in the culture was not made, and so it is not possible to determine if the changes in lipid content are related to the growth rate or to some specific clearing effect of the added agents.

The effects of polyanions with large molecular weight on the serum lipid level and experimental atherosclerosis have been discussed in other chapters (Chapters 33, 46, 48). Here, we would like only to point out that the *in vivo* effects of sulfated polysaccharides, such as heparin or carrageenan, in clearing hyperlipemia and retarding the atherosclerotic process in the aorta walls are well documented (Besterman and Evans, 1957; Constantinides, Szasz, and Harder, 1953; Constantinides, Cairns, and Werner, 1954; Graham *et al.,* 1951; Hawkins and Leonard, 1958;

Horlick and Duff, 1954; Mookerjea and Hawkins, 1958; Gore and Larkey, 1960; Hawkins and O'Neill, 1955; Murata, 1962). The possibility of a similar mechanism *in vitro* cannot be excluded, and further investigation must shed light on the role of acidic glycosaminoglycans in this process.

2. STIMULATION

The growth-promoting effect of embryo extract is a well-known fact, and has been the objective of many investigations. Among the many macromolecular components of the embryonic tissue, two groups were implicated in this effect: nucleoproteins and glycoproteins. In this review, only the possible *in vitro* growth-stimulating effect of glycoproteins is discussed.

Fisher, Puck, and Sato (1958) prepared fetuin from calf serum by ammonium sulfate fractionation and reported that it showed a growth-stimulating effect in tissue culture of mammalian cells. Lieberman, Lamy, and Ove (1959) studied the biological effect of fetuin prepared by ammonium sulfate fractionation and then further fractionated on a DEAE-cellulose column. The most active fraction caused the cells of Appendix A1 cell culture to adhere to the glass surface and to "assume an epitheloid shape." The authors interpreted this effect as growth stimulation and found that the protein responsible for it was present in one of the fractions of the chromatographed fetuin and represented 12% of the unfractionated fetuin. Fetuin prepared by low-temperature ethanol fractionation in the presence of zinc and barium ions showed no appreciable growth-stimulating effect (Spiro, 1960; Graham, 1961), suggesting that macromolecules other than fetuin present in the impure preparation were responsible for the biological effect, or that the activity may be destroyed by certain preparation methods.

Marr, Owen, and Wilson (1962) reinvestigated this problem, using fetuin prepared by ammonium sulfate fractionation and subsequent fractionation by ultracentrifugation. A "light fraction" was found to be purified fetuin, with 5.5% sialic acid and 3.3% hexosamine, and a "heavy fraction" was identified as a macroglobulin with 0.7% sialic acid and 1.2% hexosamine. Both preparations caused an increase in the number of cells in a monolayer culture of HeLa cells incubated for 7 days in a tissue-culture system containing the synthetic medium No. 199, with 1% albumin and the test substance in a concentration of 30–960 μg/ml of medium.

The growth-stimulating effect of dialyzed embryo extracts prepared from the limbs of chick embryos 12–15 days old by extraction with 0.15 N NaCl solution, can be counteracted by heparin, sulfated hyaluronic acid, and dextran sulfate solutions. The *in vitro* growth and migration of chicken heart fibroblast in fibrin coagulum can be stimulated with appropriate concentration of this chicken embryo extract to reach a maximal growth rate. When heparin, in a concentration of 0.4 mg/ml of medium, is added to the cultures, the growth-stimulating effect of the embryo extract is completely neutralized (Balazs, unpublished data).

A unique growth-stimulating effect of heparin was observed by Holmgren (1938). When calcium salt of heparin (0.1 gram per liter) was added to the water in which tadpoles live, a significant increase in the growth rate of the animals was observed. In many cases, the appearance of the extremities occurred earlier in the animals living in the water containing heparin, indicating an acceleration in the transformation process. The sodium salt of chondroitin sulfate was much less effective.

3. Cell Adhesion and Cohesion

The adhesion of the cells to a medium and their cohesion to one another are two characteristically distinguishable phenomena (Coman, 1961; Weiss, 1961, 1963). The adhesion of growing cells *in vitro* to a supporting medium such as glass is affected by charged molecules. Cationic macromolecules are adsorbed to the cell surface and cause agglutination of red blood cells (Rubini, Stahmann, and Rasmussen, 1951; Katchalsky *et al.*, 1959; Taylor, 1961; see also Chapter 35 of Volume II-A for glycolipids and glycoproteins of erythrocytes). Cationic peptides such as salmine sulfate and poly-L-lysine induce adhesion of cells to the glass surface (Lieberman and Ove, 1958). Cells incubated with trypsin (trypsinized) do not adhere to surfaces with a negative charge (such as glass, agar, calcium alginate, and silica), but do adhere when serum is added to the medium (Weiss, 1959). L. Weiss (1963) speculated that trypsin treatment of cells liberates "mucoid material" and that the loss of this material results in a decrease in the anionic surface-charge density. Using erythrocytes, several authors indeed showed that trypsin treatment did cause a decrease of the negative charge of the cells (Ponder, 1951; Seaman and Heard, 1960), probably because of the release of glycoproteins that contain sialic acid (Cook, Heard, and Seaman, 1960; see also Section V,A, of this chapter). Further experimental work is needed before one can conclude that this mechanism offers a valid explanation for the effect of trypsin on other types of cells.

Some authors reported that serum inhibits the adhesion of cells to glass surfaces (Easty, Easty, and Ambrose, 1960; Taylor, 1961). Nordling, Penttinen, and Saxén (1963) found that individual sera had various effects on the attachment of cells to glass, and speculated that these differences were due to the β-lipoprotein concentration of the serum. Since β-lipoproteins are known to interact with heparin and other polyanions (Bernfeld, Donahue, and Berkowitz, 1957; see also Chapter 48), it is reasonable to assume that they may also interact with the anionic sites of the cell surface and thereby decrease the repulsion between the negatively charged glass and the cell.

Lieberman and Ove (1958), on the other hand, prepared a glycoprotein from the serum of adult cattle and humans which caused mammalian epithelial cells (HeLa, Lung E2, and Human Appendix A1) to adhere to glass surfaces and which stimulated their growth in an epithelial sheet pattern. Fibroblast-type cells ("altered" kidney cells) were not influenced by this glycoprotein preparation. The glycoprotein fraction, which was purified about 40-fold from bovine serum, contained hexoses, hexosamine, and sialic acid. Albumin, γ-globulin, and several glycoprotein fractions from the supernatant fluid of Cohn's Fraction V (Cohn *et al.*, 1946) had no activity.

The negative surface charge of cells, especially of tumor cells, has been studied extensively (see Section V,A, of this chapter). The chemical nature of this anionic charge was first investigated in normal (nonmalignant) cells by Weiss (1961), who found that neuraminidase (from *Vibrio cholerae*) treatment significantly weakened the cohesive strength between cells of cultures derived from fetal skin and bovine kidney. The authors concluded that sialic acid must be an important structural component of the cell surface and must be responsible for the negative surface charge of the cell.

Berwick and Coman (1962) used squamous epithelial cells from scrapings of buccal mucosa to study the adhesiveness of these cells to siliconized glass surfaces and their cohesiveness to one another. They found that the chelating agent ethylenediaminetetraacetic acid reduced the cohesiveness but did not affect the adhesion of the cells to glass. Acid and alkaline phosphatase reduced both cohesiveness and adhesiveness, but neuraminidase affected only the adhesiveness to the glass surface. The authors felt that these results supported the concept that calcium bridges are the important factors in the cohesiveness of epithelial cells (see, for review, Curtis, 1962) and that glycoproteins attached to the cell surface are responsible for the cohesion between cells (Coman, 1961).

A negative electrostatic potential, when present on the cell surface, may not be the intrinsic characteristic of the cell membrane but could be the result of interaction with polyanionic molecules from the environment. Nordling *et al.* (1965) made a systematic study of the effect of polyanions on the adhesion and growth behavior of HeLa cells. The polyanions used included heparin, Polystilbol phosphates, polyvinyl alcohols with acid esters of phthalic acid, dextran containing acid esters of phthalic acid, formaldehyde polymer of phenolsulfonic acid, and formaldehyde polymer of salicylic acid, which all had hyaluronidase-inhibiting activity. It was shown that these polymers in small concentration (0.01–0.1 mg/ml) inhibited cell adhesion to glass surfaces and altered the growth behavior of HeLa cells, forcing them to grow in dense clumps. This effect was manifest only in serum-containing media, and it was inhibited by thrombin or anti-β-lipoprotein serum, but not by anti-α_1- and anti-α_2-lipoprotein or anti-γ_1-A-globulin sera. The close relationship between the inhibition of adhesion to the glass and the facilitation of cell cohesion indicates that the HeLa cells "stick together" when their attachment to the solid glass surface is inhibited. Nordling *et al.* (1965) suggested that this effect is caused by the interaction of the polyanions with the cell surface, so that there is an increase in the negative surface charge and a decrease in the deformability of the cells. Ca^{++} or other divalent cations may act as counterions of the polyanions, with β-lipoprotein as a cofactor, forming a complex with the cell surface or with the polyanion. It is of special interest that the effect of polyanions is indistinguishable from the effect of fresh serum and that both effects can be inhibited by thrombin. The authors claimed that the differences observed in cell adhesion (attachment) and cell cohesion (clumping) in various sera may be the result of the differences in their polyanion (heparin) and cofactor (β-lipoprotein) content. This suggestion calls for further experimentation regarding the effect of serum and tissue components on the adhesion and cohesion of cells.

C. Wound Healing

There is, as yet, no consensus as to whether a wound heals outward from the center or inward from the periphery. The granulation tissue in the center of the wound had been believed to be a primary element responsible for wound closure, but Watts, Grillo, and Gross (1958) observed that excision of the tissue in the center of a wound did not interfere with wound contraction. They, therefore, believed that the cellular mass underlying the epithelium of the advancing skin edges was the dominant factor. Reynolds and co-workers (1959, 1960) confirmed these findings and attempted to interfere chemically with the healing process. Dinitrophenol (an uncoupler of oxidative phosphorylation) and adenosine monophosphate were injected into the peripheral cellular mass of open skin wounds in mice, and a second group received dinitrophenol and *N*-acetylglucosamine. In the former group, wound retraction ceased, and both fibroblastic migration and activity were arrested. Hexosamine concentrations did not fall on the 5th day after wounding, and the collagen concentration was lower in comparison with that in control animals. In the group receiving *N*-acetylglucosamine after dinitrophenol treatment, wound retraction approached that of the controls. Fibroblastic migration was evident, along with an increased deposition of collagen and higher levels of hexosamine for the first 3-½ days after wounding. The wound contraction, arrested by the injection of the phosphorylation-uncoupling agent beneath the wound edge, was continued after the injection of *N*-acetylglucosamine. Microscopic examination revealed that the tissue which had been reactivated had a highly disorganized pattern, except for the cells around the periphery of the wound.

Hoffmeister *et al.* (1964) tried to determine if the metabolic effect of mechanical trauma is comparable to the effects of uncoupling agents, in order to test the postulate of Reynolds and his associates (Reynolds *et al.*, 1959; Reynolds, Leveque, and Buxton, 1960) that mechanical trauma to a tissue has an effect similar to that of chemical trauma. If this theory is correct, then *N*-acetylglucosamine should enhance the metabolic recovery after trauma, just as it did in the case of a wound arrested chemically.

Back wounds of mice were used for the evaluation of healing, and the tensile strength—a function of the weight necessary to disrupt a wound—was selected for measurement, since it is indicative of the progress of the healing process and is simple to quantitate. The addition of *N*-acetylglucosamine to a standard diet resulted in a 16% increase in tensile strength, indicating an enhancing effect on the healing of a traumatic wound.

With mitochondrial preparations of ascites tumor cells, *N*-acetylglucosamine was found to have no effect on the uncoupling of oxidative phosphorylation caused by dinitrophenol, leaving unanswered the question of the mechanism of *N*-acetylglucosamine stimulation of wound healing.

Balazs and Holmgren (1950) endeavored to ascertain whether any regulative factor occurs in growing wound tissue which changes the tissue from undifferentiated to differentiated. It was suggested by several authors that the increase of the intensity of the metachromatic staining of growing and regenerating tissues is attributable to the accumulation of acidic glycosaminoglycans in the intercellular matrix (Holmgren, 1938a, 1939, 1940; Sandblom, 1944; Sylvén, 1945; Balazs and Holmgren, 1949). Therefore, in order to investigate the quantitative aspects of metachromatic reaction in regenerating tissues, Balazs and Holmgren (1950) measured the capacity of skin wounds to bind the cationic dye, toluidine blue. Examination of granulation tissue (1–30 days old) from rats indicated that the uptake of dye increased from the 1st through the 9th day, after which it decreased until the value for normal skin was reached on the 15th day. The variations in the capacity to take up dye were attributed to extracellular polyanions. The growth of fibroblast cultures was inhibited by dialyzed water extracts of granulation tissues; extracts of wounds 6–9 days old showed the greatest effect. This growth inhibition was not obtained with extracts of fresh wounds (less than 4 days old) or normal skin (nor was the basic-dye uptake significant in these tissues). The inhibitory effect was thought to be due to the presence of glycosaminoglycans. The authors pointed out that differentiation seemed to be possible only when growth had ceased, and, although it was not maintained that the glycosaminoglycans are the most important factors in this respect, it was proposed that they exert some effect on the tissue concerned.

Evidence has been obtained that powdered cartilage, applied topically or parenterally, enhances the healing rate of experimental wounds in normal animals. Most of the evidence has been obtained in studies on incised wounds, although Sabo, Oberlander, and Enquist (1964) found a slight but significant increase in the rate of closure of open wounds treated with powdered cartilage. This material appeared to be capable of speeding the gain in tensile strength of incised wounds in rats with alloxan diabetes. Inasmuch as many of the wound problems in diabetic patients occur during the healing of open ulcers in the skin, the authors studied the effect of local or parenteral application of powdered cartilage on the closure of open wounds in diabetic animals. Sabo, Oberlander, and Enquist (1964) treated alloxan diabetic rats with powdered, pepsin-digested bovine tracheal cartilage applied topically after a square, 2 cm $\times$ 2 cm, of skin from the right flank was excised. There was a slight increase in the healing rate in these treated animals, as evidenced by a healing time of from 14 to 25 days (mean 20.2 days) against a healing time of from 17 to 30 days (mean 22.4 days) for an untreated group. Prudden (1958) and Prudden and Allen (1965) reported that powdered cartilage accelerated the healing of wounds, and the tensile strength of the treated wounds was 42% greater than that of the untreated controls.

For a general discussion of wound healing in skin, the reader is referred to Chapter 24.

IV. Animal Metabolism

A. General Metabolic Effects

Although the main pathway of biosynthesis of glucosamine is via fructose 6-phosphate and various amino group donors to yield glucosamine 6-phosphate (Ghosh *et al.*, 1960), exogenous glucosamine can be phosphorylated by ATP and beef brain extracts (Harpur and Quastel, 1949,a) at such a rate that the phosphorylation of glucose and fructose is inhibited. *N*-Acetylglucosamine, which is not phosphorylated by the brain extracts, also inhibits the rate of phosphorylation of glucosamine and of fructose. Since acetylcholine synthesis in brain proceeds rapidly anaerobically, provided that ATP is present, the hexoses just mentioned remove ATP via the hexokinase reaction, thereby inhibiting acetylcholine biosynthesis in brain. Brain extracts were also found to deaminate glucosamine and *N*-acetylglucosamine anaerobically. The substrate for the deaminase is most probably glucosamine 6-phosphate, since a requirement for ATP and Mg ions was evident.

Spiro (1958) found that the presence of either glucosamine or *N*-acetylglucosamine incubated with rat liver slices produced a competitive inhibition of glucose conversion to glycogen and CO_2, as well as a decrease in fatty acid synthesis. The changes observed were consistent with the action of a nonspecific hexokinase phosphorylating the inhibitors.

Berencsi, Krompecher, and László (1964) reported on the pharmacological effect of thyroxine on serum hexosamine. Daily treatment of rats with 3 mg of thyroxine or 15 mg of glucosamine, or both, for a 48-day period revealed that the serum hexosamine content of those rats treated with thyroxine alone decreased 15.9% more than it did in saline-treated controls, whereas, in rats treated with hexosamine plus thyroxine, the decrease in serum hexosamine was only 9.2%. The serum hexosamine level of rats treated with hexosamine alone was 9.4% higher than it was in the controls. Mucin administration also increased the serum hexosamine content when given alone, and, when given simultaneously with thyroxine, protected against the decreases seen in those rats receiving only thyroxine.

Nakada, Morita, and Wick, in 1955, reported that insulin increased the rate of disappearance of glucosamine when incubated with a rat-diaphragm system. The uptake of glucose was inhibited by the presence of glucosamine in this system, and glucosamine exerted a greater inhibitory effect on glucose oxidation than did fructose, suggesting that it competed with glucose at the site of insulin action. Wick *et al.* (1955) found a similar effect in extra-hepatic tissues. After injection of C^{14}-glucose to eviscerated and nephrectomized rabbits, the rate of plasma glucose disappearance was decreased by the injection of glucosamine, thus producing a hyperglycemia.

Several observations have led to the suggestion that *N*-acetylglucosamine may be useful as a sugar (dextrose) substitute in postoperative subjects and in patients with diabetes and liver disease. Its removal from the blood is not significantly affected by insulin (Winzler, 1960), and *N*-acetylglucosamine supposedly is also a source of oral and parenteral nitrogen, but it does not seem to increase the blood ammonia, as do some protein hydrolysates (Roberts, 1962—personal communication to Gaulden and Keating, 1964).

N-Acetyl-D-glucosamine was administered intravenously to ten healthy subjects, and the metabolism of this compound was compared with that of glucose by the determination of glucose and total reducing substances in the blood and the 24-hour excretion of reducing substances in the urine. Intravenous administration of *N*-acetylglucosamine produced no significant change in blood glucose concentration. The data suggested that the acetylated glucosamine was metabolized into fragments, although none seemed to be converted to glucose. Thirty per cent of a 100-g dose was excreted in the urine within 1 hr after administration (Gaulden and Keating, 1964).

Pellegrini (1961) reported that when one group of rats was treated with hyaluronic acid and another group with chondroitin sulfate for 25 days, a slight increase of the total protein and a decrease of lipoprotein were observed. No modification of free and bound hexosamine was noted. The glycosaminoglycan content was increased, whereas a decrease in respiration of the hepatic tissues was noted.

Katz and Hennigar (1965) gave, to white rabbits, daily injections (0.6 g per kilogram of body weight) of D-glucosamine HCl for 14 days. In 75% of the animals, plaques (2–10 mm in diameter) developed on the wall of the ascending aorta, histologically characterized by fragmentation of elastic fibers, calcium deposition, and increases in metachromasia and PAS staining reactions. A moderate thickening of the intima and proliferation of fibrocytes, with no demonstrable lipid deposition, were also evident.

B. Effect of Hexosamines on Alligators

One of the most interesting series of studies on the pharmacological effects of hexosamines has been carried out by Coulson and Hernandez (1964). During a study of the alligator's metabolism of various carbohydrates, it was observed that glucosamine produced a hyperglycemia of such magnitude and duration that the authors believed that it might well be the most effective such compound known. The hyperglycemia was evident in both the alligator and the rat, suggesting a diabetogenic effect of this compound.

The injection of 1 gram of glucosamine per kilogram of body weight produced a rise in plasma glucose of 180 mg/100 ml or more. When larger amounts were injected (up to 2 grams per kilogram of body weight), the plasma glucose levels rose to levels as high as 450 mg/100 ml. Those alligators receiving more than 1.7 gram per kilogram of body weight died within 48 hr. If the animals were given enough $NaHCO_3$ to prevent acidosis caused by released HCl (from glucosamine hydrochloride), they still died when the injection was 1.5 grams per kilogram of body weight, which appeared to be the minimum lethal dose of glucosamine. When glucosamine was given to alligators which had previously received insulin, no significant rise in glucose occurred, and the injected hexosamine disappeared from the plasma in much less time. Insulin protected the alligators from the toxic effects of even the largest doses of glucosamine. When 1 gram of galactosamine per kilogram of body weight was injected, the plasma galactosamine level rose to approximately 150 mg/100 ml. Galactosamine did not produce hyperglycemia in doses up to 3 grams per kilogram of body weight, although it proved to be as toxic as glucosamine. *N*-Acetylglucosamine in similar amounts was neither toxic nor a hyperglycemic agent.

During a study of the effect of glucosamine on glucose tolerance, it was found that glucosamine caused a constriction of the alligator's pupils (miotic effect) similar to that produced by epinephrine, thus raising the possibility that the pharmacological effect may be sympathomimetic in character. The pupils were constricted within a few hours after injection, and by 12 hr they were almost invisible slits. The duration of this effect was similar to that of the hyperglycemic response, and the pupils remained significantly constricted for up to 5 days afterward. Less glucosamine was required for this effect than for elevation of blood sugar. Insulin delayed the miosis caused by glucosamine and decreased the degree of constriction, whereas, in contrast to this effect, the miosis caused by epinephrine was unaffected.

When rats received injections of 1 gram of glucosamine per kilogram of body weight, no change in blood glucose occurred, but, when larger amounts were administered (2.5 gram of glucosamine per kilogram of body weight), the level was elevated by approximately 300 mg/100 ml. Whereas the alligator had a slow, prolonged response to glucosamine, the response of the metabolically more active rat was of shorter duration. Insulin affected the rate of removal of glucosamine and the hyperglycemic response in the rat in much the same manner as it did in the alligator. Glucosamine did cause an inhibition of glucose utilization in the rat but had no glycogenolytic effect, nor was it utilized for glycogen synthesis.

V. Neoplastic Transformation and Growth

A. Cell Surface, Cohesion, and Mobility

Calcium, an important component in maintaining the cohesiveness of cells, was shown to have disappeared from the intercellular matrix when a carcinogenic chemical was applied to the skin of mice (Carruthers and Suntzeff, 1944). Another group of human cancers was found to be calcium deficient by Scott (1943), leading to the proposal of Coman (1946) that the loss of calcium and the decreased cellular cohesiveness may be of functional importance in malignant invasion. The findings of Boyland and McClean (1935) indicated that the amount of "spreading factor," or hyaluronidase, paralleled the degree of malignancy of various tumors, ranging from benign, non-invasive, tumors, to malignant, invasive cancers. The more malignant the tumor, the more spreading factor it contained. These results suggest that the decreased cohesiveness of cancer cells may depend on both a decreased calcium content and an excessive amount of spreading factor.

Coman (1946) also presented an interesting theory regarding the invasive character of cancer growth, to explain why malignant tumor cells infiltrate and permeate into the surrounding areas, in contrast to benign tumors, which remain localized. Earlier (1944) Coman had observed that if micro needles were inserted into an attached pair of fresh living cancer cells from a human lip, the cells were easily separable, in contrast to a pair of normal cells which were separated only with difficulty. This observation led to the proposal that the easy separability of the malignant cells from one another offers a physical basis for invasive growth, since cells easily detached would be free for mechanical displacement into the surrounding tissues. Cells from other lip cancers and cervical cancers, as well as from normal cervices and benign skin tumors, were examined. In each case, the malignant cells showed lower values of cohesiveness than did the normal or benign tumor cells.

A new approach to the problems of cell-surface changes in neoplastic transformation is represented by recent studies on the charge characteristics of cell surfaces. It was suggested that neoplastic transformation of certain cells is accompanied by an increase of their anionic surface charge that is evidenced by the increased electrophoretic mobility of the cell (Abercrombie and Ambrose, 1962; Vogt, 1963; Ambrose, James, and Lowick, 1956; Purdom, Ambrose, and Klein, 1958; Straumfjord and Hummel, 1959). Forrester, Ambrose, and Stoker (1964) found that the electrophoretic mobility of hamster kidney fibroblasts increased after transformation to neoplastic cells by polyoma virus and that this increase was diminished after incubation of the cells with neuraminidase. Cook, Heard, and Seaman (1962) also studied the electrophoretic mobility of Ehrlich ascites tumor cells before and after treatment with neuraminidase and trypsin. The electrophoretic mobility of the neuraminidase-treated cells was reduced, and free sialic acid was found in the incubation medium. Trypsin treatment of human erythrocytes (Cook, Heard, and

Seaman, 1960) produces a release of sialic acid; in the case of ascites tumor cells, however, a "mucilaginous matrix" is formed in which the tumor cells are embedded. After the cells are mechanically freed, they showed no change in their electrophoretic mobility, and the supernatant contained no sialic acid (Cook, Heard, and Seaman, 1962). Fibroblasts of mouse embryonic tissue exhibited a higher electrophoretic mobility than did fibroblasts cultured from the hearts of adult mice (Heard, Seaman, and Simon-Reuss, 1961).

Other experimental work indicates that the increase in electrophoretic mobility of cells and the assumed underlying enhancement of anionic surface charge of the cell is a quality of rapidly growing cells, rather than a sign of malignancy. Ruhenstroth-Bauer and Fuhrmann (1961) found a correlation between the electrophoretic mobility of cells and their mitotic activity. Liver cells of hepatectomized rats showed higher mobility than do normal liver cells. Ben-Or, Eisenberg, and Doljanski (1960) obtained identical results and reported (Eisenberg, Ben-Or, and Doljanski, 1962) that the mobility of the liver cells of newborn animals is higher than that in the cells of adults. The electrophoretic mobility of cells of liver, either in the resting or in the rapidly dividing state, or of cells of the solid form of Sarcoma 37 are not affected by neuraminidase treatment (Ruhenstroth-Bauer *et al.,* 1961; Fuhrmann *et al.,* 1962; Cook, Seaman, and Weiss, 1963).

These experiments suggest that the increased electrophoretic mobility of cells is a manifestation of normal growth, as well as of malignant growth; this high-charge density, however, is not affected by neuraminidase treatment in regenerating normal cell systems, but it is affected in some of the neoplastic cell systems.

Wallach and Eylar (1961) determined the sialic acid content of subcellular fractions obtained from Ehrlich ascites carcinoma cells. Sixty-nine per cent of the total sialic acid content was found in the microsomal fraction. When intact cells were treated with neuraminidase, 73% of the total sialic acid was removed, and the electrophoretic mobility of the cells was reduced by 72%. The authors assumed that the surface membrane of the cells has a large amount of sialic acid which is responsible for the high electrophoretic mobility, and that this membrane, in the fractionation procedure, separates with the microsomes. Langley and Ambrose (1964) separated, from trypsin-digested Ehrlich ascites tumor cells, a glycopeptide fraction on Sephadex G-50 which contained both sialic acid and hexosamine. Since this peptide fraction contained relatively large amounts of proline, glutamic acid, and glycine and was low in aromatic amino acid content, the authors speculated that it originated from a collagen-like protein attached to the surface of the cell. The latter assumption was based on the finding that the amount of sialic acid released by neuraminidase treatment was the same when intact viable cells or cells disrupted by ultrasonic treatment were digested.

Gasic and Gasic (1962) found that simultaneous intravenous injection of neuraminidase-treated ascites tumor cells (TA3) and neuraminidase itself (obtained from *Vibrio cholerae*) caused less frequent metastases than did the injection of untreated tumor cells. The authors interpreted this finding as an indication that the removal of the PAS-positive glycoprotein coating with the enzyme renders the cells less "sticky" which, in turn, will prevent the cells from adhering to capillary walls and each other—thus forming a nucleus of tumor growth. Since this effect can be observed only when neuraminidase is injected simultaneously with the tumor cells, the possibility remains, as the authors pointed out, that the enzyme acts on the "vascular coat."

The relationship between the sialic acid content and the electrophoretic mobility of three types of mouse tumor cells, obtained from Ehrlich ascites carcinoma, solid sarcoma (MCIM$_{SS}$, and ascites sarcoma was studied by Wallach and de Perez Esandi (1964), and no correlation was found. A gradual removal of sialic acid was achieved by incubation of the cells with *Vibrio cholerae* neuraminidase, and, again, no correlation was found between the amount of sialic acid removed and changes in electrophoretic mobility. The solid-sarcoma cells did not show a decrease in mobility, even after the sialic acid concentration dropped to 30% of the original value. On the other hand, the mobility of the Ehrlich carcinoma cells decreased parallelly with the removal of the sialic acid. The mobility of the ascites sarcoma cells dropped significantly after a decrease of the sialic acid content to 80% of the original value, but no further changes in mobility could be observed, even after nearly all of the sialic acid was removed. These results indicate that much more experimental work is needed before one can conclude that the negative surface charge of some tumor cells originates primarily from the sialic acid-containing macromolecules which are attached to the cell surface or are part of the cell membrane.

B. Effect on Growth

1. Amino Sugars

There are several reports in the literature concerning the effort to interrupt the energy metabolism of cancer cells by the use of glucosamine as a glucose antagonist. The earliest report of this nature was that of Quastel and Cantero (1953). At concentrations of glucosamine which produced no adverse effects on a normal mouse, a marked inhibition of the growth of mouse Sarcoma 37 was evident. Daily injections of neutral solutions of 2.5 to 5.0 mg of glucosamine hydrochloride produced a retardation in cell mass and extensive hemorrhagic areas in the tumors. Cytotoxic effects were evident 2 hr after administration, manifested by shrinkage of the nuclei, retraction of the cytoplasm, and a marked eosinophilia. Within 6 to 8 hr, further degeneration took place. Nuclei became pyknotic, with further cytoplasmic retraction. Later, additional pyknosis and necrosis were followed by the production of distorted mitotic figures. After 48 hr, normal proliferating cells were seen at the periphery of the tumor, whereas cellular distintegration was observed in the severely affected portion. Necrosis was followed by autolysis, and the tumor decreased in size, although regression was not complete. The survival rate of the treated animals almost doubled, whereas the activity of liver catalase, which is lowered in the presence of the tumors, was considerably increased. The combination of glucose and ammonium sulfate caused no tumor regression, nor did ammonium sulfate alone. Lettré (1953) was unable to inhibit growth when glucosamine was added to Ehrlich ascites mouse tumors.

In experiments not directly concerned with tumor growth, Ely, Tull, and Schanen (1953) were able to show a reduction of the mitotic index and a depression of the growth rate when glucosamine was added to chick heart cells in tissue culture. Rubin, Springer, and Hogue (1954) found that glucosamine, glucose, and an equimolar mixture of glucose and ammonium chloride each caused the degeneration of cells in tissue culture of mouse Sarcoma 37; *N*-acetylglucosamine showed no effect. After 24 hr of culturing in the presence of 1% glucosamine, all cells were dead in 14% of the cultures, and, after 48 hr, one-third or more of the cells had degenerated in 71% of the cultures. In contrast to the proposal that glucosamine's cytotoxic effect was due to the inhibition of glucose metabolism, it was observed that the addition of 1% glucose to the cultures produced degeneration or death in 50% of the cultures after 24 hr—a finding which is difficult to reconcile with the authors' proposal that, since a 1% equimolar mixture of glucose and ammonium chloride also produced degeneration within 24 hr, the adverse effect of glucosamine must be due to the decomposition of glucosamine hydrochloride, above pH 7, into glucose, free ammonia, and chloride ion.

Sorkin and Fjelde (1956) and Fjelde, Sorkin, and Rhodes (1956) reported the inhibition, by glucosamine, of the growth of human epidermoid carcinoma cells in tissue culture. At a concentration of 1 mg/ml, cellular death was evident within 24 hr, and depressed growth was obtained with concentrations as low as 1×10^{-3} μg/ml. Glucose produced no effect on the condition of the cells. Cytological damage appeared first at the periphery of the cultures, in the area of new, actively growing cells. Nuclear changes and granulation of the cytoplasm occurred. Dividing cells and those at the growing edge seemed more sensitive to glucosamine than did resting cells—a finding of interest in connection with the previously mentioned results of Ely, Tull, and Schanen (1953). Fjelde (1955) had found that dormant cultures which had not received renewal of the medium or transfer for several months were undamaged by glucosamine at concentrations which were toxic for actively growing cells.

Ball, Wick, and Sanders (1957) found that glucosamine and 2-deoxyglucose, both of which would interfere with glucose metabolism via the glycolytic pathway, produced a significant reduction in the growth of Walker 256 tumor which had been transplanted into rats. Upon cessation of the treatment, the tumor growth began again, but re-institution of treatment again reduced the growth.

The effects of 2-deoxyglucose were greater and more consistent than those of glucosamine, a finding which may be a reflection of their relative effectiveness as glucose anti-metabolites. The K_m of 2-deoxyglucose for hexokinase is 2.7×10^{-5} M, with a maximal rate equal to that of glucose, whereas the K_m of glucosamine is 8×10^{-5} M, with the maximal rate being only 60% of that produced with glucose.

Lindner, Schweinitz, and Becker (1960) found that glucosamine *in vivo* exerted a cytotoxic effect, but, *in vitro,* exerted an inhibition of anaerobic glycolysis on ascites tumor cells of the Yoshida sarcoma, as well as a reduction of the inhibitory effect of glucose on tumor cell respiration (reversed Pasteur effect).

Since the effect of glucosamine may have depended on the dissociation of the amino group, Becker and Lindner (1961) studied the influence of pH on the glucosamine effect. Between pH 6.5 and 8.0, the anaerobic glycolysis of the Yoshida ascites tumor cells was reduced, as was the reversed Pasteur effect of glucose. Since the two actions did not depend on pH, the authors proposed that a similar mechanism of action was involved in both cases. If glucosamine alone was added, without glucose, the O_2 uptake at pH 6.5 was intensified, but it was reduced at pH 8.0. These results are extended and discussed in greater length by Becker, Lindner, and Voss (1964).

Csaba, Horváth, and Ács (1960) administered D-glucosamine to mice bearing Ehrlich carcinoma in peritoneal or subcutaneous growth and found a slight, but statistically not proved, decrease in survival time.

The studies mentioned up to this point have dealt with 2-amino-2-deoxyhexosamines or polymers containing these compounds. An interesting study by Baker, Joseph, and Williams (1955) deals with the conversion of puromycin from an antibacterial agent, which interrupts protein synthesis, to an anti-tumor agent via a change in the substituted group on its 3-amino-3-deoxyribose moiety. The structure of puromycin, 6-dimethylamino-9-(3-*p*-methoxy-L-phenylalanylamino-3-deoxy-D-ribosyl)-purine, as illustrated below (I), contains the sequence: purine–amino-pentose–amino acid. 3-Amino-3-deoxy-D-ribose is attached to the purine

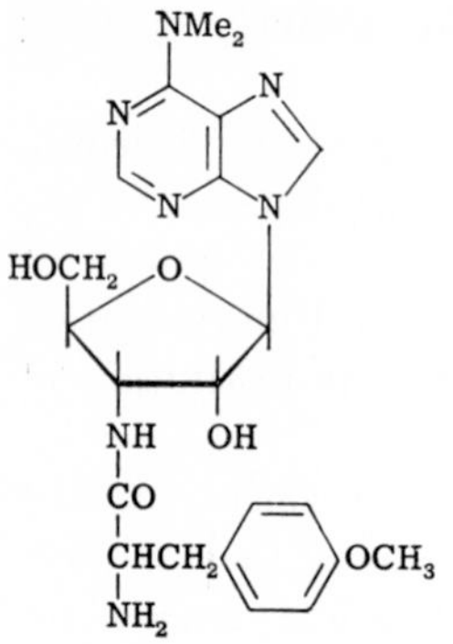

I 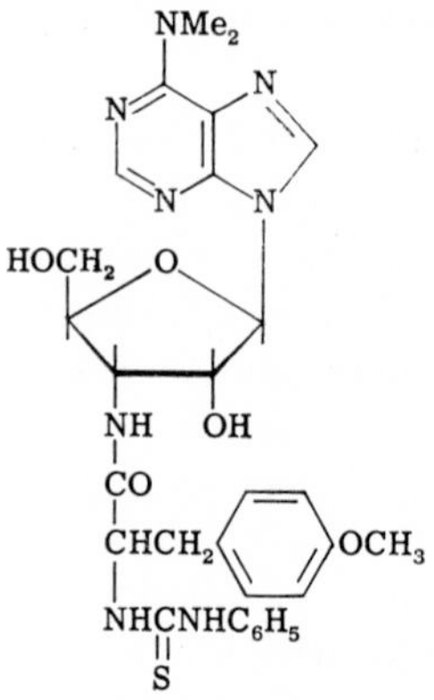 II 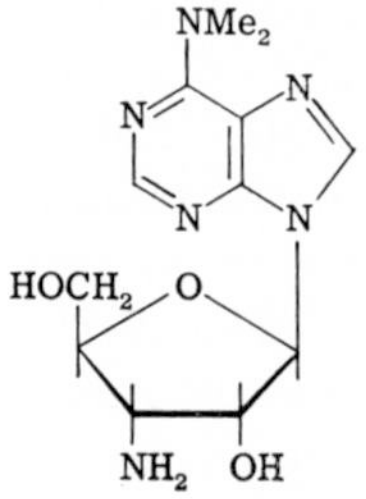 III

by a β-furanosyl linkage. If puromycin is treated with phenyl isothiocyanate and triethylamine in boiling ethanol, the *N*-phenylthiourea derivative is obtained (II). Alkaline cleavage of this derivative yields 6-dimethylamino-9-(3-amino-3-deoxy-β-D-ribofuranosyl)-purine (III). This new aminonucleoside has lost the antibacterial activity characteristic of puromycin, but possesses an enhanced growth-inhibiting action on transplanted mammary adenocarcinoma of mouse.

2. Glycosaminoglycans and Other Polyanions

The first report that heparin treatment affects the growth of a transplanted tumor came from Goerner (1930), who observed that transplants of rat carcinoma (Flexner–Jobling) grew faster in untreated control hosts than they did in hosts treated with heparin. Zakrzewski (1932) made an extensive study on the effect of heparin on the growth of tumor cells *in vitro*. The growth of Jensen sarcoma cultures could be suppressed when heparin was added to the medium, but the malignant undifferentiated character of the cells was not changed. During 112 days, the culture did not grow when heparin was present in the medium, but, when the heparin was removed on the last day, a rapid growth started that was identical in morphological appearance to a normal tumor culture never treated with heparin. Zakrzewski concluded that a basic biological difference exists between normal and tumor cells which cannot be changed by heparin treatment. Zakrzewski (1933a) also investigated the effect of heparin on the tumor growth *in vivo*, using Jensen sarcomas of rats and sarcomas from humans. The intravenously or intraperitoneally administered heparin suppressed the increase in the size of the tumor and prolonged the survival time of the animal. Hedenius and Snellman (1937) and Hedenius (1939), on the other hand, reported that the subcutaneous injection of heparin, as sodium, protamine, or benzidine salt failed to inhibit the growth or to change the macroscopic or microscopic appearance of transplanted Jensen sarcomas. Balazs and Holmgren (1949) found that subcutaneous administration of sodium salt of heparin and agar acid to mice with Ehrlich ascites carcinoma significantly prolonged the lifespan of the treated animals. The growth of cultures of sarcoma cells from methylcholanthrene tumors of rats was also significantly suppressed by these two polyanions. Cytological studies with the phase-contrast microscope and microcinematography showed no significant morphological changes in the treated cells, but indicated a general slowdown on their migratory mobility in the fibrin of coagulum. The possible explanations, suggested by the authors, for the tumor-suppressing effect of polyanions are: (1) a neutralizing effect on the toxic products of the tumor cells; (2) a general resistance-increasing effect on the tissues of the organism; and (3) a direct antagonistic effect on the growing tumor cells or on a growth-promoting agent produced by these cells.

Paff *et al.* (1952) observed that fibroblast cultures from chicken heart, when treated with heparin, showed a marked accumulation of granular material in the cytoplasm, which stained by the Giemsa technique and could be removed by ribonuclease treatment. This result was interpreted as an indication that heparin interferes with the metabolism of nucleoproteins and thereby exerts its growth-inhibiting effect.

Lippman (1957) found that a single intraperitoneal injection of heparin (0.2 mg) into a mouse with Ehrlich ascites tumor produces a significant decrease in the mitotic index of tumor cells; repeated injections, however, failed to show any increased effect. The intraperitoneal injection of heparin also caused a decrease of the volume of the tumor, but did not increase survival time.

Regelson extended these investigations to a series of synthetic polyanions of various chemical structure, using transplanted animal tumors, as well as human malignant neoplasms as testing material. The polyanions such as polyethylenesulfonate, polymethaphosphate acid, and acrylamide, sulfated pectic and sulfated alginic acid, sulfated dextran, and sulfated chitosan were among the polymers tested on subcutaneously transplanted solid tumors of mice (Ehrlich 2, Krebs 2, Leukemia 5178, Leukemia 1210, Sarcoma 180, Ca 755). Usually, 24 hr after the inoculation of the tumor, Na or K salts of the polyanions were injected subcutaneously, but not at the site of the tumor inoculation or intraperitoneally. The most efficient inhibitor, polyethylene sulfonate, used against a Carcinoma 755, resulted in a tumor that was 50% smaller than that of the control, but the survival of the animal was not prolonged (Regelson and Holland, 1958; Regelson, Tunis, and Kuhar, 1960). In another series of experiments (Regelson *et al.*, 1960), varying-molecular-weight polymers of ethylene–maleic anhydride copolymers, polyacrylic acid, and polymethacrylic acid were used on mouse Sarcoma 180 so that tumor inhibition could be correlated with the quality and density of the surface charge. The density and distribution of the charged groups on the polymer chain, but not the size of the macromolecule, were found to significantly determine the degree of tumor suppression. The monomeric components of the polyanions, however, caused no suppression. The optimal suppressive effect was shown by the polyanions in which carboxamide and carboxyl groups were interdispersed on the polymer backbone; when all carboxyl groups were converted to carboxamides, the suppressive activity was lost. Among the completely carboxylated copolymers, those with higher charge density showed the greatest suppressive activity.

Regelson, Tunis, and Kuhar (1960) also found that extracts of tumor cells exhibited deoxyribonuclease II activity and that those synthetic polyanions which supressed tumor growth *in vivo* were also capable of inhibiting the activity of this enzyme *in vitro*. Among the glycosaminoglycans and glycoproteins tested, chondroitin 4-sulfate, chondroitin 6-sulfate, α_1-acid glycoprotein, and α_2-glycoprotein did not have any inhibitory effect, whereas heparin did. Since the inhibition was abolished by increasing the ionic strength of the solution, an ionic interaction between the inhibitor and the enzyme was suggested (Tunis and Regelson, 1963).

Ozzello, Lasfargues, and Murray (1960) found that the growth of a strain of pure epithelium from human duct cell carcinoma of the breast (BT20) cultured on a glass surface was not at all affected by chondroitin 6-sulfate or *N*-acetylglucosamine, but was slightly stimulated by hyaluronic acid. This finding fully agrees with that of Balazs (Balazs and Holmgren, 1949; Balazs and Eckl, unpublished data), who used embryonic tissues (see Section III,B,1, of this chapter).

Several investigators, using the size of the tumor or the number of surviving animals as criteria for growth suppression, found that heparin had very little or no effect (Kreisler, 1952; Jolles and Greening, 1960; Csaba, Horváth, and Ács, 1960; Retik *et al.*, 1962).

Csaba *et al.* (1964) confirmed the finding that heparin treatment does not inhibit the growth of various transplanted rat tumors if this inhibition is judged by the change of the weight of the solid tumor. These authors found, however, that administration of heparin coupled with various cationic molecules, assumedly as salts, slowed down the weight increase of the tumor, but no prolonged survival time or inhibition of growth was reported. The heparin used was first "inactivated"—that is, its anticoagulant activity was reduced by an undisclosed procedure and then coupled with such cationic substances as 1,6-bis(β-chloro-ethylamino)-1,6-dideoxy-D-manitol,2-bis(β-chloro-ethylamino)-benzimidazole, or D-(-)-*threo*-1-*p*-nitrophenyl-2-amino-1,3-propanediol. Several of these substances are known to have cytotoxic, enzyme-inhibiting, or bactericidal effects, but, according to the authors, coupling with "inactivated heparin" also produced an "antitumor effect."

Lippman (1965) studied the effect of glycosaminoglycans and follicle fluid of porcine ovaries on the growth of Ehrlich ascites tumor. Three different criteria were used to measure tumor growth: the weight of the animal; the volume of the ascites fluid; and the volume of the cell sediment of the ascites fluid. Heparin was found to be the most effective "antitumor agent," whereas chondroitin sulfate, dermatan sulfate, hyaluronic acid, and heparin sulfate had little or no effect. Intraperitoneal injection of follicular fluid to tumor-bearing animals caused a decrease of the volume of ascites fluid and of the volume of cell sediment. It should be emphasized that the chemical composition of the follicular fluid is not well known. Incomplete analyses suggest, however, that this fluid is rich in glycosaminoglycans or glycoproteins (Jensen and Zachariae, 1958; Zachariae and Jensen, 1958).

Shear and Turner (1943) reported the preparation of a polysaccharide fraction, from filtrates of *Serratia marcescens* (*Bacillus prodigiosus*) cultures, possessing a highly potent hemorrhage-producing activity on mouse sarcomas. An amount of 0.1 μg of trypsin-digested material produced hemorrhage in 50% of the tumors tested. Chemical analysis of this fraction (Hartwell *et al.*, 1943) indicated that approximately two-thirds of it consisted of carbohydrate, the major portion of which was aldohexose. Firmly bound phospholipid was also present. The carbohydrate composition was made up of glucose, 44.1%; hexosamine (calculated as glucosamine, 2.7%—accounting for 10% of the total nitrogen); and methyl pentose (most probably rhamnose), 16.5%.

Further analyses of the active, trypsin-digested material indicated small amounts of phosphoric acid, a solid fatty acid, glycerol, and an unidentified nitrogenous constituent. The lipid portion, firmly combined with the polysaccharide moiety, was necessary for potency. Only 0.16% surfur was present. The active material contained approximately 6% "acetyl," not identified as such, but representing the volatile acids calculated as acetic acid. Treatment with 2 *N* HCl at 37° resulted in a 90% loss of activity in 6 hr.

Rathgeb and Sylvén (1954,a), during further studies on Shear's polysaccharide, found that the hemorrhagic material of the tumor actually contained two polysaccharides, as well as phospholipid. One of the polysaccharides was a glucan linked by alternate $1 \rightarrow 4$ and $1 \rightarrow 6$ glycosidic bonds. Quantitative estimation of the constituent sugars by paper chromatography indicated that, of the total reducing power of 77%, 52 to 55% was accounted for by glucose, 12 to 15% by glucosamine, and 6 to 9% by an unidentified material giving a weakly positive uronic acid reaction (carbazole). Digestion with a crude soybean β-amylase preparation (which probably also contained a $1 \rightarrow 6$-branch-splitting enzyme, or z-enzyme) removed the glucan portion, leaving the glucosamine concentration unchanged. Bioassays of the enzymically degraded material indicated that it had an even higher hemorrhage-inducing activity than had the starting material. The smallest active unit contained phospholipid, protein, and carbohydrate firmly linked together. The carbohydrate moiety contained all the *N*-acetylglucosamine and some of the glucose, and removal of either of these two carbohydrates led to loss of activity.

Malmgren (1954), employing ultracentrifugation, diffusion, and electrophoresis, further showed that the hemorrhage-producing activity in the tumor need not be restricted to one particle weight, since preparations with varying degrees of aggregation possessed similar degrees of potency.

An agent present in *Escherichia coli* culture filtrates was found to produce a hemorrhagic response and a regression of growth in an experimental mouse Sarcoma 180 (Ikawa *et al.*, 1952). The isolated material was found to contain polysaccharide, phospholipid, and polypeptide. Analyses showed the following values: acetyl, 5.1%; glucose equivalent, 52–55%; glucosamine equivalent, 15–17%; phosphorus, 1.5–1.7%; nitrogen, 3.2%; and bound lipid, 24–25%. Treatment with trichloroacetic acid cleaved the complex, producing an inactive polypeptide and an active lipopolysaccharide whose nitrogen content was lowered to 1.9%.

Paper chromatography of an acid hydrolysate indicated glucosamine and either, or both, glucose and galactose. Ultracentrifugal analysis indicated that the preparation was heterogeneous. A light and a heavy fraction were isolated, both of which proved to be equally active. In more than a thousand tumor-bearing, untreated mice, there were 9.7% spontaneous regressions, whereas, in approximately the same number of mice receiving varying amounts of the hemorrhage-producing agent, there were 53% permanent regressions and 12% regressions with recurrence.

Another anionic polysaccharide of plant origin, found in the gum, tragacanth, from various species of *Astragalus,* was shown (Roe, 1959) to inhibit, *in vivo,* the growth of different mouse ascites tumors. Mayhew and Roe (1964,a) were able to demonstrate that the gum has a tumor-inhibiting and mitotic effect on Landschutz ascites tumor cells. The polyanionic gum probably interacts with the cell surface and causes changes in the permeability of the cells. Such an interaction could account for the appearance of mitotic block at metaphase and, later, of the cytostasis.

3. Role of the Mast Cell and the Intercellular Matrix

The possibility of a relationship between the mast-cell population of a connective tissue area, which surrounds or penetrates a neoplasm, and the growth of the tumor was first mentioned by Ehrlich (1879) and Westphal (1891), who observed the abundance of mast cells in certain spontaneous tumors. Subsequently, a great number of investigators confirmed this observation with histological studies made on human tumors. An accumulation of mast cells was reported in the connective tissue surrounding (capsule) and penetrating (stroma) the neoplastic growth, as well as in the regional lymph nodes that contain metastases (among others see: Bergonzini, 1891; Audry, 1896; Fromme, 1906; Weill, 1919; Regaud and Lacassagne, 1922; Bierich, 1922; Brack, 1925; Fabris, 1927; Kückens, 1928; Higuchi, 1930; Quensel, 1933; Sylvén, 1941, 1945; Janes and McDonald, 1948; Kabelitz, 1949; Consolandi, 1949; Baglioni, 1952; Bruni and Caschera, 1952; De Palo and Papadia, 1955; Cazal, 1955; Blomquist, 1956; Dunn and Montgomery, 1957; Macaluso, 1960; Cawley and Hoch-Ligeti, 1961).

The second fundamental observation made by several authors was that there is an increase of mast cells in the skin of animals during application of tar or carcinogenic hydrocarbons, such as 9,10-dimethyl-1,2-benzanthracene, 3,4-benzpyrene, and 20-methylcholanthrene (see, for example, Yamagiwa and Ichikawa, 1916; Fibiger and Bang, 1921; Guldberg, 1934; Cramer and Simpson, 1944; Holmgren and Wohlfart, 1947; Wolf, 1952; Kelsall, 1952; Riley, 1958; Fiore-Donati *et al.,* 1962).

The third important observation, confirmed by several investigators, is that there is an accumulation of mast cells in the connective tissue surrounding experimentally transplanted animal tumors. This mast-cell accumulation occurs immediately after implantation, when the connective tissue around the tumor is in an inflammatory stage and when an intensive growth of blood vessels around a proliferating tumor is evident. On the other hand, no mast cells could be found in the necrotic center of the tumors (Köksal, 1953; Kelsall and Crabb, 1953; Wada *et al.*, 1955; Asobe-Hansen, Levi, and Wegelius, 1957; Holmgren and Wohlfart, 1941; Csaba *et al.*, 1960). On the other hand, when tumors are implanted in the abdominal cavity, a fragmentation or disappearance of mast cells is observed in the mesentery or peritoneal cavity (Hilliard and Nash, 1951; Scott, Scheline, and Stone, 1958; Goldie *et al.*, 1962; Scott, 1963).

All these observations led investigators to formulate two different concepts about the role of mast cells in tumor growth. The vast majority of authors regarded the "mast cell reaction" as a defence mechanism of the connective tissue against the invasive growth of the neoplastic tissue. It was theorized that heparin, the polyanionic glycosaminoglycan stored in the granules of the mast cells (see for review, Chapter 27, Volume II-A), after being released from the granules, could act as a growth inhibitor. Csaba and his co-workers (Csaba *et al.*, 1961), on the other hand, speculated that mast cells take up heparin from the extracellular space and thereby are competing with the tumor cells which need heparin or its components for their growth. This opinion is based on the observation that the metachromatic reaction of the intercellular matrix around tumors is uneven and that the histological appearance of the mast cells and their granules shows great variation (Sylvén, 1945; Panizzari and Vegeto, 1958; Csaba *et al.*, 1961). It has also been claimed that the administration of the monosaccharide components of heparin (D-glucuronic acid and D-glucosamine) to tumor-bearing animals shortens the survival time of the animal so treated (Csaba, Horváth, and Ács, 1960).

Some authors have stressed the importance of the mast cells as the source and storage place of such biological amines as histamine and serotonin (5-hydroxytryptamine) and speculated that these compounds may participate in the defence mechanism against tumor formation and growth. It was suggested that the increased fluorescence of dermal mast cells during carcinogenesis is due to the accumulation of serotonin in the granules (Riley, 1958; Coupland and Riley, 1960; Fiore-Donati *et al.*, 1962). In some experiments, the administration of serotonin or histamine increased the tumor growth (Scott, Scheline, and Stone, 1958); in others, local serotonin application inhibited the growth of Walker carcinosarcomas in rats, but histamine and heparin had no effect (Fisher and Fisher, 1965).

According to the second concept, mast cells participate in the defence against tumor growth because of their role in inflammatory processes. Some authors (see, for detail, Kelsall and Crabb, 1959, p. 339) emphasized the inflammatory character of the connective tissue around the tumor and the wound-healing reaction after tumor transplantation which involves a vascular reaction and dilatation of the capillary system. The accumulation of mast cells or their disappearance is regarded as part of the inflammatory or healing process and related to the tumor growth only indirectly. Of some importance in this connection is the observation of Prodi (1963) that the treatment of rabbit skin with the carcinogenic hydrocarbon 9,10-dimethyl-1,2-benzanthracene causes a change in the glucosamine–galactosamine ratio in the glycosaminoglycans of the dermal connective tissue. Similar treatment of the skin with a non-carcinogenic but inflammation-causing substance, croton oil, resulted, however, in the same change, thus indicating that the general tissue response to irritation is the cause of the alteration of glycosaminoglycan composition of the cutaneous connective tissue (Prodi and David, 1964).

In the opinion of the reviewers, these two concepts are complementary rather than mutually exclusive. Thus, the mast cells, as a source of biological polyanions (glycosaminoglycans) and amines, are implicated in the natural reaction of the connective tissue against the spreading of neoplastic growth, and further experimental work is warranted to clarify this potentially important biological defence mechanism.

The importance of the intercellular matrix as a barrier against migrating tumor cells was suggested by Coman (1946). Large-molecular-weight glycosaminoglycans, such as hyaluronic acid and chondroitin sulfate in protein complexes, may act as a stabilizing factor in the intercellular collagen network (Balazs, 1961; see also Chapter 37 of Volume II-A) or they may fill the intercellular space between microscopic collagen fibers, acting as a molecular sieve. In both cases, the molecular network of glycosaminoglycans, alone or in combination with collagen filaments, can form an effective barrier against cell migration. Hyaluronidase or non-enzymatic degrading agents of glycosaminoglycans (see Chapter 47) can effectively destroy this sieve, facilitating the migration of cells and thereby the spreading of tumors. It was shown that repeated local injection of testicular hyaluronidase, after transplantation of tumor, facilitated the spread of squamous-cell carcinoma in mice (Gopal-Ayengar and Simpson, 1947), Walker carcinosarcoma in rats (Russo and Terranova, 1953), and Rous sarcoma in rats (Saldeen, 1963). Other authors, using shorter, not local, application or smaller doses, found no significant effect with hyaluronidase treatment (Seifter and Warren, 1950; Ghose, 1960). Since hyaluronidase can have effects other than the degradation of the glycosaminoglycans of the intercellular matrix, the interpretation of these experiments must be regarded with caution.

The findings that some tumors contain an agent which causes degradation of hyaluronic acid or facilitates the spreading of dyes in the skin of test animals (spreading factor) indicate that malignant tumors produce hyaluronidase or a degrading substance that is not an enzyme. Thus, the invasiveness of the malignant tumor would be explained by the breakdown of the glycosaminoglycan network of the intercellular matrix in the connective tissue that surrounds the growing tumor or separates it from the capillaries. Hyaluronic acid-degrading activity was shown to be present in many human and animal tumors (Duran-Reynals and Stewart, 1931; Boyland and McClean, 1935; Gibertini, 1942; Pirie, 1942; Bergamini, 1943; McCutcheon and Coman, 1947; Dux, Guérin, and Lacour, 1948). Kiriluk, Kremen, and Glick (1950) found no activity in human benign tumors and in mouse mammary adenocarcinoma, and suggested that previous positive results were caused by bacterial hyaluronidase present in infected tumor tissues. Balazs and Euler (1952) found hyaluronidase activity in Walker carcinosarcoma of rats which was present in tumors free from bacterial contamination. Not all tumors tested showed activity, but, when present, it was highest in the necrotic part of the tissue.

4. Glycoproteins

It is a well-documented observation that the glycoproteins in the serum are elevated in humans with malignant tumors (Almquist and Lausing, 1957; Bernasconi, Buscarini, and Ezechieli, 1958; Bonomo and Bonelli, 1952; Macbeth and Bekesi, 1962; Meeroff, 1958; Seibert *et al.*, 1947; Weisbrod, 1950; Winzler and Smyth, 1948) and in the serum of animals with experimental tumors (Baldwin and Harries, 1958; Catchpole, 1950; Hokkanen, Pyörälä, and Taipale, 1956; Macbeth, Bekesi, and Tuba, 1963; Modica, 1959; Shetlar, Erwin, and Everett, 1950; Wada *et al.*, 1957; Weimer *et al.*, 1957; Macbeth and Bekesi, 1964) (see also Chapter 34). The mechanism responsible for the increased amount of glycoproteins in the circulation is not known. The various suggestions offered by investigators can be summarized in four groups: First, it was suggested that the elevated glycoprotein level in the serum represents breakdown products caused by tissue necrosis. Secondly, the explanation was offered that the rapidly metabolizing tumor cells produce these glycoproteins. Thirdly, based on the histochemical observation that the normal tissue around the malignant growth contains more glycoproteins than otherwise, it was speculated that a destruction of glycoproteins in the normal connective tissue around the tumor is the source of elevated serum glycoproteins. Fourthly, it was suggested that the tumor growth stimulates the hepatic synthesis of glycoproteins and that the serum glycoprotein level is increased through this nonspecific stimulus in a process similar to that observed in many chronic infectious diseases.

The increase of glycoproteins in subcutaneous connective tissue bordering fibrosarcoma implants in mice was noted by Catchpole (1950). Macbeth and Bekesi (1964) determined the tissue protein-bound hexosamine and *N*-acetylneuraminic acid in the tissues of rats bearing Walker 256 carcinoma after perfusion of the blood vessels to remove all serum from the tissues. The hexosamine content of the liver proteins increased significantly from the fourth day of transplantation on, but no change was found in the *N*-acetylneuraminic acid content. In the muscle adjacent to the tumor, there was also a significant increase in hexosamine, as well as in *N*-acetylneuraminic acid concentration. Neither one of these amino sugars was found to be elevated in the skeletal muscles not in the immediate vicinity of the growing tumor. The tumor proteins themselves contained approximately the same amount of hexosamine (0.7–0.9%) as did the liver proteins ($0.79 \pm 0.02\%$), but a considerably higher amount of *N*-acetylneuraminic acid (liver: $0.117 \pm 0.029\%$; tumor: 0.2–0.3%). The possibility exists, therefore, that some of the glycoproteins originate from the tumor, whereas others appear as a result of increased synthesizing activity of the liver. A more conclusive picture of the relationship between tumor growth *in vivo* and the glycoprotein content of tissues can be drawn only when the fate of the individual glycoproteins during malignant growth is carefully studied in the tumors, in adjacent tissues, and in the liver.

The possibility of preferential utilization of certain glycoproteins by tumor cells was suggested by Kent and Gey (1957, 1960). When rat tumor cell cultures—one of mesenchymal origin (Sarcoma TSAT-72) and another of epithelial origin (Walker carcinosarcoma 256)—were grown in mediums containing human adult and placental cord serum, it was found that the carbohydrate-rich α_2-globulins were utilized more rapidly than were other protein fractions. Approximately 35% of the α_2-globulin fraction was "utilized" during the incubation period by both cell strains, whereas other serum proteins did not seem to "disappear" from the medium. With the Walker carcinosarcoma, the levels of β-globulins after 29 days of culture remained almost identical to the level of the original incubation medium.

Addendum

The following papers of interest, published after this chapter was completed, are hereby added to make the survey of the literature more comprehensive. These articles are also included in the reference list.

Colter, J. S., and Campbell, J. B. (1965). The effect of polyanions and polycations on Mengo virus–L cell interaction.

Takemoto, K. K., and Spicer, S. S. (1965). Effects of natural and synthetic sulfated polysaccharides on viruses and cells.

THE AMINO SUGARS

Volume IIB

Bibliography and Author Index

Subject Index

BIBLIOGRAPHY AND AUTHOR INDEX

The references of all chapters in Volume IIB were collected and combined in one list as a convenience for the reader in locating any specific reference and to present a comprehensive picture of the publications of various authors in the field. For further convenience, the author index was combined with the reference list. The abbreviations of periodicals used in this list, with certain exceptions, conform to the style of *Chemical Abstracts*.

To provide an accurate bibliography, of the 2900 references, 2826 were verified by the editorial staff.

The following points should serve as a guide in the use of this combined reference list and author index.

(1) *Articles by one, two, or three authors.* The names of all authors are cited in the text and in the reference list, followed by the year of publication. When more than one article published by the same author or authors in the same year is cited, then, in the second and subsequent references, the year of publication is followed by the letters "a," "b," etc. (Example: Asboe-Hansen, 1950. Asboe-Hansen, 1950a. Asboe-Hansen, 1950b.) All of these articles appear in the reference list alphabetically by author.

(2) *Articles by more than three authors.* The name of the first author, followed by *"et al."* and the year of publication, is cited in text. When more than one article published by the same first author and more than two co-authors in the same year is cited in text, then in the second and subsequent references the year of publication is followed by the letters "a," "b," etc. In the reference list, the names of all authors are given, and the articles are listed in chronological order, rather than alphabetically.

(3) *The italicized numbers in parentheses after each reference* refer to the page or pages on which the article is cited.

(4) *Material enclosed within brackets* was interpolated by the editors to correct mistakes in the original source or to supply explanatory or additional data for the alphabetization and identification of names.

(5) *Author index.* Since the author index was combined with the reference list, the reference itself serves as a listing of the first author of all articles. An author's name listed without a reference, but followed by an italicized page number, indicates that the author is cited as a second or subsequent author of a reference cited on that page or as having provided unpublished information.

A

Abe, T. 1953. *Japan. J. Exptl. Med.* **23**: 197. (*34*)

Abercrombie, M., and Ambrose, E. J. 1962. *Cancer Res.* **22**:525. (*381*)

Abraham, E. P. 1939. *Biochem. J.* **33**:622. (*183*)

Abraham, E. P., and Robinson, R. 1937. *Nature* **140**:24. (*183*)

Abraham, S. (*95*)

Abrams, E., and Sandson, J. 1964. *Ann. Rheumatic Diseases* **23**:295. (*237*)

Abrams, W. B. (*187*)

Ackerman, R. F., and Zilversmit, D. B. 1953. *Circulation* **7**:581. (*216*)

Ács, T. (*385, 389, 392*)

Ada, G. L. (*177, 302, 339*)

Ada, G. L. 1963. *Biochim. Biophys. Acta* **73**:276. (*178*)

Ada, G. L., and French, E. L. 1957.

Australian J. Sci. **19**:227. (*42*) 1959. *Nature* **183**:1740. (*172, 339, 352*)
Ada, G. L., French, E. L., and Lind, P. E. 1961. *J. Gen. Microbiol.* **24**:409. (*172, 175, 176*)
Ada, G. L., and Gottschalk, A. 1956. *Biochem. J.* **62**:686. (*328*)
Ada, G. L., and Lind, P. E. 1961. *Nature* **190**:1169. (*171, 175, 353*)
Ada, G. L., Lind, P. E., and Laver, W. G. 1963. *J. Gen. Microbiol.* **32**:225. (*178, 358*)
Ada, G. L., and Stone, J. D. 1950. *Brit. J. Exptl. Pathol.* **31**:263. (*171, 339*)
Adams, E. V. (*363*)
Adams, J. B. 1959. *Nature* **184**:274. (*60*) 1959a. *Biochim. Biophys. Acta* **32**: 559. (*61*) 1960. *Biochem. J.* **76**:520. (*60*)
Adams, J. B., and Meaney, M. F. 1961. *Biochim. Biophys. Acta* **54**:592. (*72*)
Adams, J. R., Jr. (*389*)
Adams, M. H. (*317*)
Adelsberger, L. (*270, 278, 287, 329*)
Agol, V. I., and Chumakova, M. Ya. 1962. *Virology* **17**:221. (*364*) 1962a. *Acta Virol.* (*Prague*) **6**:24. (*364*) 1963. *Acta Virol.* (*Prague*) **7**:97. (*364*)
Agranoff, B. W., Radin, N., and Suomi, W. 1962. *Biochim. Biophys. Acta* **57**:194. (*122*)
Ågren, G., and de Verdier, C. H. 1958. *Acta Chem. Scand.* **12**:1927. (*23*)
Akabori, S. (*83, 84*)
Alais, C. (*85*)
Alais, C., and Jollès, P. 1961. *Biochim. Biophys. Acta* **51**:315. (*85*)
Albertsson, P. A. (*364*)
Albrieux, A. (*141*)
Alburn, H. E., and Whitley, R. W. 1951. *J. Biol. Chem.* **192**:379. (*187, 196*) 1954. *Federation Proc.* **13**:330. (*187*)
Alderton, G., Ward, W. H., and Fevold, H. L. 1945. *J. Biol. Chem.* **157**:43. (*183*)
Alessandrini, A., Schmidt, E., Zilliken, F., and György, P. 1956. *J. Biol. Chem.* **220**:71. (*82*)
Alexander, P. (*240*)
Alexander, P., Bacq, Z. M., Cousens, S. F., Fox, M., Herve, A., and Lazar, J. 1955. *Radiation Res.* **2**:392. (*235*)
Alkjaersig, N. (*224*)
Allen, E. 1927. *Contr. Embryol. Carnegie Instn.* **19**:No. 98, 1. (*142, 143*)
Allen, H. C., Jr. (*54*)
Allen, J. (*377*)
Allen, J. G., and Jacobson, L. O. 1947. *Science* **105**:388. (*245*)
Allen, J. G., Sanderson, M., Milham, M., Kirschon, A., and Jacobson, L. O. 1948. *J. Exptl. Med.* **87**:71. (*245*)
Allen, P. Z., and Kabat, E. A. 1959. *J. Immunol.* **82**:340. (*274, 286, 287, 288*) 1959a. *J. Immunol.* **82**:358. (*274, 286, 287*)
Allen, R. D., and Griffin, J. L. 1958. *Exptl. Cell Res.* **15**:163. (*369*)
Allfrey, V. G. (*19*)
Allgén, L.-G. (*52*)
Allison, A. C. (*329*)
Allison, A. C. 1958. *Proc. Roy. Soc. Med.* **51**:641. (*309*)
Almon, L. 1943. *Bacteriol. Rev.* **7**:43. (*326*)
Almquist, P. O., and Lausing, E. 1957. *Scand. J. Clin. Lab. Invest.* **9**:179. (*394*)
Alonzo, N. F. (*311*)
Altman, K. I. (*83, 102, 105, 249*)
Altshuler, C. H., Kinsman, G., and Bareta, J. 1961. *Federation Proc.* **20**: 164. (*46, 49, 68*)
Alvarado, F. 1960. *Biochim. Biophys. Acta* **41**:233. (*14*)
Amako, T. 1914. *Z. Immunitaetsforsch.* **22**:641. (*329*)
Amaral, D. (*40*)
Ambrose, E. J. (*373, 381, 382*)
Ambrose, E. J., James, A. M., and Lowick, J. H. B. 1956. *Nature* **177**: 576. (*381*)
Aminoff, D. 1961. *Biochem. J.* **81**:384. (*172*)
Aminoff, D., Dodyk, F., and Roseman, S. 1963. *J. Biol. Chem.* **238**:1177. (*44*)

Aminoff, D., Morgan, W. T. J., and Watkins, W. M. 1948. *Biochem. J.* **43**:xxxvi. (*287*) 1950. *Biochem. J.* **46**:426. (*287*)

Amprino, R. 1955. *Acta Anat.* **24**:121. (*54, 55*) 1956. *In* "Ciba Foundation Symposium, Bone Structure and Metabolism, 1955" (G. E. W. Wolstenholme and C. M. O'Connor, eds.), p. 89. Boston: Little, Brown. (*54*)

Anai, M., Ikenaka, T., and Matsushima, Y. 1963. *Seikagaku* (*J. Japan. Biochem. Soc.*) **35**:79. (*84*)

Anastassiadis, P. A. 1959. *Can. J. Biochem. Physiol.* **37**:1081. (*148*)

Anastassiadis, P. A., Maw, W. A., and Common, R. H. 1955. *Can. J. Biochem. Physiol.* **33**:627. (*135, 141, 148*)

Andersen, J. 1961. *Nature* **190**:730. (*289*)

Andersen, S. O., and Graae, J. 1955. *Acta Chem. Scand.* **9**:1431. (*194*)

Anderson, A. J. 1965. *Biochem. J.* **94**:401. (*250*)

Anderson, B. (*52*)

Anderson, B., Hoffman, P., and Meyer, K. 1963. *Biochim. Biophys. Acta* **74**: 309. (*83*)

Anderson, B., and Odell, T. T., Jr. 1960. *J. Gerontol.* **15**:249. (*79, 249*)

Anderson, B., Seno, N., Sampson, P., Riley, J. G., Hoffman, P., and Meyer, K. 1964. *J. Biol. Chem.* **239**: PC 2716. (*83*)

Anderson, D. O. (*224, 225, 227*)

Anderson, F. B., and Leaback, D. H. 1961. *Tetrahedron* **12**:236. (*157*)

Anderson, H. H. (*34*)

Anderson, J. S. (*116, 117*)

Anderson, N. G., and Fawcett, B. 1950. *Proc. Soc. Exptl. Biol. Med.* **74**:768. (*214*)

Anderson, R. J. 1941. *Chem. Rev.* **29**:225. (*322*)

Anderson, S. G. 1948. *Australian J. Exptl. Biol. Med. Sci.* **26**:347. (*340*)

Ando, K., Takeda, S., and Hamano, M. 1938. *J. Immunol.* **34**:303. (*308*)

Andreoli, A. J. (*188, 194, 195*)

Andreyeva, A. P. (*83*)

Anfinsen, C. B. (*215, 216, 222*)

Anfinsen, C. B., Boyle, E., and Brown, R. K. 1952. *Science* **115**:583. (*214, 251*)

Anfinsen, C. B., and Haber, E. 1961. *J. Biol. Chem.* **236**:1361. (*222*)

Anfinsen, C. B., Haber, E., Sela, M., and White, F. H., Jr. 1961. *Proc. Natl. Acad. Sci. U.S.* **47**:1309. (*222*)

Anker, H. S. 1960. *In* "The Plasma Proteins" (F. W. Putnam, ed.), Vol. II, p. 267. New York: Academic Press. (*92*)

Annison, E. F., and Morgan, W. T. J. 1952. *Biochem. J.* **50**:460. (*286, 334*)

Ansell, N. J. (*289, 290, 300, 358*)

Anstadt, G. L. (*101*)

Antonio, C., Federico, L., Nobile, C., and Cerutti, G. 1954. *Ricerca Sci.* **24**:769. (*34*)

Aoki, K. (*392*)

Aoyagi, T. (*175, 358*)

Åqvist, S. E. G. (*51*)

Araki, C. 1959. *Proc. Intern. Congr. Biochem., 4th, Vienna, 1958* **1**:15. (*363*)

Arata, L., and Pecora, P. 1962. *Boll. Soc. Ital. Biol. Sper.* **38**:209. (*200*)

Araujo, P., and Krause, R. M. 1963. *J. Exptl. Med.* **118**:1059. (*320*)

Archibald, A. R., Baddiley, J., and Buchanan, J. G. 1961. *Biochem. J.* **81**:124. (*113*)

Armanicu, M. (*182*)

Armstrong, F. B. (*99*)

Armstrong, J. J., Baddiley, J., and Buchanan, J. G. 1959. *Nature* **184**: 248. (*313*) 1961. *Biochem. J.* **80**:254. (*113*)

Armstrong, J. J., Baddiley, J., Buchanan, J. G., and Carss, B. 1958. *Nature* **181**:1692. (*313*)

Armstrong, J. J., Baddiley, J., Buchanan, J. G., Carss, B., and Greenberg, G. R. 1958a. *J. Chem. Soc.*, p. 4344. (*313*)

Arnon, R. (*335*)

Arons, M. S. (*389*)

Arrhenius, S. [A.] 1907. "Immunochemie," especially pp. 191–197.

Leipzig: Akademische Verlagsgesellschaft. (*267*)
Asboe-Hansen, G. 1953. *Cancer Res.* **13:**587. (*55, 74*) 1954. "Connective Tissue in Health and Disease." Copenhagen: Munksgaard. (*46*) 1954a. *Cancer Res.* **14:**94. (*55, 74*)
Asboe-Hansen, G., Levi, H., and Wegelius, O. 1957. *Cancer Res.* **17:**792. (*392*)
Asensio, C., and Amaral, D. 1961. *Federation Proc.* **20:**A-85e. (*40*)
Asensio, C., and Sols, A. 1958. *Abstr. Intern. Congr. Biochem., 4th, Vienna, 1958,* p. 125. (*16*)
Ashwell, G. (*22, 44*)
Ashworth, J. N. (*374*)
Askonas, B. A. (*307*)
Askonas, B. A., and Fahey, J. L. 1961. *Biochem. J.* **80:**261. (*336*)
Astrup, T., and Alkjaersig, N. 1950. *Nature* **166:**568. (*224*)
Astrup, T., and Piper, J. 1946. *Acta Physiol. Scand.* **11:**211. (*371*)
Athineos, E., Kukral, J. C., and Winzler, R. J. 1964. *Arch. Biochem. Biophys.* **106:**338 (*100*)
Atno, A. J. (*394*)
Attyah, A. M. (*266*)
Audry, C. 1896. *Ann. Dermatol. Syphilol.* **7:**9. (*391*)
Auer, R. (*188*)
Aurell, G., Dohlman, C.-H., and Rodén, L. 1956. *Acta Ophthalmol.* **34:**281. (*53*)
Austin, C. R. 1961. *Intern. Rev. Cytol.* **12:**337. (*369*)
Austrian, R. (*45, 48, 50*)
Avakian, S. (*197*)
Avery, O. T. (*267, 307, 313, 317, 332*)
Avery, O. T., and Goebel, W. F. 1929. *J. Exptl. Med.* **50:**533. (*267*)
Avery, O. T., Goebel, W. F., and Babers, F. H. 1932. *J. Exptl. Med.* **55:**769. (*332*)
Avery, O. T., and Heidelberger, M. 1923. *J. Exptl. Med.* **38:**81 (*267*)
Avigad, G. (*29*)
Axelrod, J. (*47*)
Aykroyd, O. E., and Zuckerman, S. 1938. *J. Physiol.* (*London*) **94:**13. (*144, 146*)

B

Baba, T., Ishii, M., and Aoki, K. 1964. *Gann* **55:**331 (*392*)
Babers, F. H. (*332*)
Bacharach, A. L., Chance, M. R. A., and Middleton, T. R. 1940. *Biochem. J.* **34:**1464. (188) 1940a. *Chem. & Ind.* (*London*) **59:**348. (*188*)
Bachhawat, B. K. (*12, 169*)
Bachman, C. (*300, 301*)
Bachman, C., Collip, J. B., and Selye, H. 1935. *Proc. Roy. Soc.* (*London*), *Ser. B* **117:**16. (*143, 144, 152*) 1936. *Proc. Soc. Exptl. Biol. Med.* **33:**549. (*142*)
Bachtold, J. G., and Gebhardt, L. P. 1952. *J. Biol. Chem.* **194:**635. (*187*)
Bacon, J. S. D. (*27*)
Bacq, Z. M. (*235*)
Baddiley, J. (*82, 113, 313, 314, 315*)
Baddiley, J. 1962. *Biochem. J.* **82:**36P. (*313, 314*)
Baddiley, J., Buchanan, J. G., and Carss, B. 1957. *J. Chem. Soc.,* p. 1869. (*82, 113*) 1958. *Biochim. Biophys. Acta* **27:**220. (*113*)
Baddiley, J., Buchanan, J. G., Mathias, A. P., and Sanderson, A. R. 1956. *J. Chem. Soc.,* p. 4186. (*113*)
Baddiley, J., Blumsom, N. L., DiGirolamo, A., and DiGirolamo, M. 1961. *Biochim. Biophys. Acta* **50:**391. (*82*)
Baddiley, J., Buchanan, J. G., Hardy, F. E., Martin, R. O., RajBhandary, U. L., and Sanderson, A. R. 1961a. *Biochim. Biophys. Acta* **52:**406. (*113*)
Baddiley, J., Buchanan, J. G., RajBhandary, U. L., and Sanderson, A. R. 1962. *Biochem. J.* **82:**439. (*168, 314*)
Baddiley, J., Buchanan, J. G., Martin, R. O., and RajBhandary, U. L. 1962a. *Biochem. J.* **85:**49. (*314*)
Badin, J., and Schubert, M. 1955. *J. Clin. Invest.* **34:**1312. (*252*)
Baeder, D. H. (*216, 224, 331*)
Baer, H. (*284, 286, 289*)

Baer, H., and Rasmussen, U. 1960. *J. Immunol.* **85**:1. (*271*)
Baer, H. H. (*29, 165, 281*)
Baggett, B. 1962. *Federation Proc.* **21**: 211. (*140*)
Baggi, G. F., and Prodi, G. 1954. *Proc. Soc. Exptl. Biol. Med.* **86**:461. (*366*)
Baglioni, T. 1952. *Tumori* **38** (Anno): 267. (*391*)
Bailey, G. H., and Shorb, M. S. 1931. *Am. J. Hyg.* **13**:831. (*285*) 1933. *Am. J. Hyg.* **17**:329. (*285*) 1933a. *Am. J. Hyg.* **17**:358. (*285*)
Bailey, R. E. 1952. *Condor* **54**:121. (*147*)
Baker, B. R., Joseph, J. P., and Williams, J. H. 1955. *J. Am. Chem. Soc.* **77**:1. (*385*)
Baker, B. R., Joseph, J. P., Schaub, R. E., and Williams, J. H. 1954. *J. Org. Chem.* **19**:1786. (*157*)
Baker, E. E. (*327*)
Baker, E. E., Whiteside, R. E., Basch, R., and Derow, M. A. 1959. *J. Immunol.* **83**:680. (*327*)
Baker, E. M., Webster, M. E., Freeman, M. E., Cary, S. G., and Sanders, A. C. 1956. *Proc. Soc. Exptl. Biol. Med.* **91**:24. (*193, 194*)
Balazs, E. A. (*134, 136–138, 147, 231, 233, 234, 236, 237, 240–244, 247, 248, 370, 373, 388*)
Balazs, E. A. 1961. *In* "The Structure of the Eye" (G. K. Smelser, ed.), p. 203. New York: Academic Press. (*246, 393*)
Balazs, E. A., and von Euler, J. 1952. *Cancer Res.* **12**:326. (*196, 394*)
Balazs, E. A., Högberg, B., and Laurent, T. C. 1951. *Acta Physiol. Scand.* **23**: 168. (*224, 266, 370*)
Balazs, [E.] A., and Holmgren, H. 1949. *Proc. Soc. Exptl. Biol. Med.* **72**:142. (*251, 370, 376, 387, 388*) 1950. *Exptl. Cell Res.* **1**:206. (*376*)
Balazs, E. A., and Laurent, T. C. 1951. *J. Polymer Sci.* **6**:665. (*238*)
Balazs, E. A., Mars, P. H., and Szirmai, J. [A.] 1955. *Abstr. 128th Meeting, Am. Chem. Soc., Minneapolis, Minn., Sept. 11–16*, p. 46c. (*65, 137, 138*)
Balazs, E. A., and Sundblad, L. 1959. *Acta Soc. Med. Upsalien.* **64**:137. (*232, 234*)
Balazs, E. A., Sundblad, L., and Dewey, K. F. 1959. *Bienn. Rept. Retina Found., 1957–1958*, p. 24. (*232*)
Balazs, E. A., Sundblad, L., and Toth, L. [Z. J.] 1958. *Federation Proc.* **17**: 184. (*65*)
Balazs, E. A., and Szirmai, J. A. 1958. *J. Histochem. Cytochem.* **6**:278. (*134*) 1958a. *J. Histochem. Cytochem.* **6**:416. (*134, 135, 137*)
Balazs, E. A., Szirmai, J. A., and Bergendahl, G. 1959. *J. Biophys. Biochem. Cytol.* **5**:319. (*65, 138, 139*)
Balazs, E. A., Laurent, T. C., Howe, A. F., and Varga, L. 1959. *Radiation Res.* **11**:149. (*239–242, 244*)
Baldinus, J. G. (*224–226*)
Baldwin, R. W., and Harries, H. J. 1958. *Brit. J. Cancer* **12**:99. (*394*)
Bale, W. F. (*92*)
Balfour, B. M., Doniach, D., Roitt, I. M., and Couchman, K. G. 1961. *Brit. J. Exptl. Pathol.* **42**:307. (*303*)
Balfour, Y. M. (*126*)
Ball, H. A., Wick, A. N., and Sanders, C. 1957. *Cancer Res.* **17**:235. (*14, 385*)
Ballantyne, M. (*183*)
Ballou, C. E. (*333*)
Baló, J. (*85*)
Bancroft, F. W. (*265*)
Bandurski, R. S. (*56*)
Bang, F. (*391*)
Banga, I., Baló, J., and Szabó, D. 1961. *Acta Physiol. Acad. Sci. Hung.* **19**: 19. (*85*)
Ban-I, K. [Katsuko, B.] (*83*)
Baranowski, T., Lisowska, E., Morawiecki, A., Romanowska, E., and Stróżecka, K. 1959. *Arch. Immunol. Terap. Doswiadczalnej* **7**:15. (*290*)
Bareta, J. (*46, 49, 68*)
Barker, A. N. (*54*)
Barker, S. A. (*312, 317, 318*)
Barker, S. A., and Bourne, E. J. 1953. *Quart. Rev. (London)* **7**:56. (*58*)

Barker, S. A., Keith, M. C., and Stacey, M. 1961. *Nature* **189**:746. (*316*)
Barker, S. A., Heidelberger, M., Stacey, M., and Tipper, D. J. 1958. *J. Chem. Soc.*, p. 3468. (*316*)
Barker, S. A., Brimacombe, J. S., How, M. J., Stacey, M., and Williams, J. M. 1961. *Nature* **189**:303. (*317*)
Barker, S. A., Pardoe, G. I., Stacey, M., and Hopton, J. W. 1963. *Nature* **197**: 231. (*89, 336*)
Barker, S. A., Bayyuk, S. I., Brimacombe, J. S., and Palmer, D. J. 1963a. *Nature* **199**:693. (*200*)
Barker, S. A., Pardoe, G. I., Stacey, M., and Hopton, J. W. 1964. *Protides Biol. Fluids, 11th, Colloq., Bruges, 1963*, p. 284. (*89*)
Barkulis, S. S. (*116*)
Barnard, R. D., Goldman, B., Kessler, L. N., and Stanton, H. T., Jr. 1954. *J. Am. Pharm. Assoc.* **43**:110. (*197*)
Barnet, H. N. (*14, 378*)
Barry, G. T. 1958. *J. Exptl. Med.* **107**: 507. (*27, 327, 352*) 1959. *Nature* **183**:117. (*327*)
Barry, G. T., and Tsai, T. 1963. *Federation* Proc. **22**:206. (*328*)
Basch, R. (*327*)
Bass, S. T. (*84*)
Bauditz, W. (*61, 69*)
Bauer, K. (*88*)
Bauer, W. (*186, 229, 230, 232, 237*)
Bauereis, R. (*187*)
Baugh, P. (*241–244*)
Baumann, E. 1876. *Arch. Ges. Physiol.* **12**:69. (*50*) 1876a. *Arch. Ges. Physiol.* **13**:285. (*50*)
Bayne, S. 1952. *Biochem. J.* **50**:xxvii. (*3*)
Bayyuk, S. I. (*200*)
Bazin, S., and Delaunay, A. 1959. *Biol. Med. (Paris)* **48**:351. (*46*)
Bean, R. C., Porter, G. G., and Steinberg, B. M. 1961. *J. Biol. Chem.* **236**:1235. (*40*)
Beaufay, H. (*166*)
Beaune, A., and Falk, R. 1936. *Compt. Rend. Soc. Biol.* **122**:721. (*148*)
Becker, C. E., and Day, H. G. 1953. *J. Biol. Chem.* **201**:795. (*3, 4, 94, 95*)
Becker, K. (*385*)
Becker, K., and Lindner, J. 1961. *Biochim. Biol. Sper.* **1**:55. (*385*)
Becker, K., Lindner, J., and Voss, H. 1964. *Biochim. Biol. Sper.* **3**:64. (*385*)
Beckfield, W. J. (*331*)
Bedford, D. (*290*)
Bednarik, T. (*100*)
Bednarik, T., Rejnek, J., and Knesslova, V. 1962. *Physiol. Bohemoslov.* **11**: 329. (*100*)
Beeby, R. (*85*)
Beeken, W. L., and Imredy, K. 1962. *Biochim. Biophys. Acta* **62**:579. (*101*)
Beeson, P. B. (*286, 316*)
Beeson, P. B., and Goebel, W. F. 1939. *J. Exptl. Med.* **70**:239. (*285*)
Begany, A. J. (*224*)
von Behring, E. [A.] 1912. "Einführung in die Lehre von der Bekämpfung der Infektionskrankheiten." Berlin. (*306*)
Beiler, J. M. (*197*)
Beiler, J. M., Brendel, R., and Martin, G. J. 1954. *J. Am. Pharm. Assoc.* **43**:480. (*197*)
Beiler, J. M., and Martin, G. J. 1947. *J. Biol. Chem.* **171**:507. (*197*) 1948. *J. Biol. Chem.* **174**:31. (*197*)
Beiser, S. M., and Kabat, E. A. 1951. *J. Am. Chem. Soc.* **73**:3501. (*275*) 1952. *J. Immunol.* **68**:19. (*274, 276, 286*)
Beiser, S. M., Kabat, E. A., and Schor, J. M. 1952. *J. Immunol.* **69**:297. (*275*)
Bekesi, J. G. (*105, 394, 395*)
Bélanger, L. F. 1953. *Nature* **172**:1150. (*54*) 1953a. *Science* **118**:520. (*55*) 1954. *Can. J. Biochem. Physiol.* **32**: 161. (*54*) 1954a. *Anat. Record* **118**: 755. (*54, 55*) 1955. *J. Dental Res.* **34**:20. (*54*) 1958. *J. Histochem. Cytochem.* **6**:146. (*54*) 1958a. *Proc. Soc. Exptl. Biol. Med.* **99**:605. (*54*)
Belenkaya, G. M., and Gladshtein, A. I. 1962. *Zh. Mikrobiol. Epidemiol. Immunobiol.* **33**:No. 8, 42. (*200*)
Belenkaya, G. M., Gladstein, A. I., Loran, I. D., and Tchertkova, F. A. 1962. *Lab. Delo* **8**:No. 4, 28. (*200*)

Bell, L. G. E. (*366, 367*)

Bell, L. G. E., and Jeon, K. W. 1962. *Nature* **195**:400. (*367*)

Bellman, S., Boström, H., Göthman, B., and Rodén, L. 1956. *Angiology* **7**: 396. (*53*)

Belyavin, G. (*303*)

Bencze, W. L. (*86*)

Bender, R. (*155*)

Bendich, A. (*264, 275, 284*)

Bendich, A., Kabat, E. A., and Bezer, A. E. 1946. *J. Exptl. Med.* **83**:485. (*276, 334*) 1947. *J. Am. Chem. Soc.* **69**:2163. (*275*)

Benditt, E. P. (*52, 137, 141*)

Benecke, W. 1905. *Botan. Z. Abt. I Orig.*, **63**:227. (*181*)

Benedek, A. L. (*245*)

Benesch, R. (*51, 52, 77*)

Benesch, R. E. (*51, 52, 77*)

Bengtsson, S. 1965. *Proc. Soc. Exptl. Biol. Med.* **118**:47. (*365*)

Bengtsson, S., and Philipson, L. 1963. *Virology* **20**:176. (*363*)

Bengtsson, S., Philipson, L., and Albertsson, P. Å. 1962. *Biochem. Biophys. Res. Commun.* **9**:318. (*364*)

Bengtsson, S., Philipson, L., Persson, H., and Laurent, T. C. 1964. *Virology* **24**:617. (*364*)

Ben-Or, S. (*382*)

Ben-Or, S., Eisenberg, S., and Doljanski, F. 1960. *Nature* **188**:1200. (*382*)

Benson, A. A., Wiser, R., Ferrari, R. A., and Miller, J. A. 1958. *J. Am. Chem. Soc.* **80**:4740. (*123*)

Benton, A. G. 1935. *J. Bacteriol.* **29**: 449. (*181*)

Berdick, M., and Morawetz, H. 1954. *J. Biol. Chem.* **206**:959. (*226, 253*)

[Berdnikoff] Berdnikow, A., and Champy, C. 1931. *Compt. Rend. Soc. Biol.* **106**:804. (*134, 135*) 1932. *Compt. Rend. Soc. Biol.* **110**:261. (*134, 135*) 1934. *Compt. Rend. Soc. Biol.* **116**:515. (*134, 135*)

Berencsi, G., Krompecher, S., and László, M. D. 1964. *Acta Anat.* **57**: 5. (*378*)

Berenson, G. S. (*118*)

Berenson, G. S., Lumpkin, W. M., and Shipp, V. G. 1958. *Anat. Record* **132**: 585. (*63*)

Berg, D. (*267, 332*)

Berg, P. 1958. *J. Biol. Chem.* **233**:601. (*27*)

Berg, P., and Newton, G. 1956. *J. Biol. Chem.* **222**:991. (*27*)

Bergamini, L. 1943. *Boll. Ist. Sieroterap. Milan.* **22**:55. (*394*) 1948. *Boll. Ist. Sieroterap. Milan.* **27**:115. (*197*)

Bergendahl, G. (*65, 138, 139*)

Bergenstal, D. M. (*52*)

Berger, A. (*220*)

Berger, L. R., and Reynolds, D. M. 1958. *Biochim. Biophys. Acta* **29**: 522. (*157, 160, 164, 182*)

Berger, L. R., and Weiser, R. S. 1957. *Biochim. Biophys. Acta* **26**:517. (*87, 164, 182*)

Bergfeld, W., and Kapfhammer, J. 1944. *Deut. Z. Verdauungs-Stoffwechselkrankh.* **8**:113. (*33*)

Berghagen, N., Ericsson, Y., and Stjernström, L. 1954. *Svensk Tandläkaretidskrift* **47**:409. (*238*)

Bergman, G. (*54*)

Bergner, P.-E. E. 1962. "The Significance of Certain Tracer Kinetical Methods, Especially with Respect to the Tracer Dynamic Definition of Metabolic Turnover. Uppsala: Almqvist and Wiksell [*Acta Radiol. Suppl.* **210**,1]. (*79*)

Bergonzini, C. 1891. *Anat. Anz.* **6**:595. (*391*)

Bergström, S. (*265*)

Bergström, S. 1936. *Z. Physiol. Chem.* **238**:163. (*265, 266*)

Berkeley, B. J. (*222, 224–226, 255, 257*)

Berkowitz, M. E. (*254, 255, 261, 374*)

Berkowitz, R. D. (*260*)

Berman, A. (*141*)

Berman, S. (*85, 193*)

de Bernard, B. (*48*)

Bernasconi, C., Buscarini, L., and Ezechieli, S. 1958. *Progresso Med.* **14**:97. (*394*)

Bernfeld, H. C. (*221–223, 225–227*)

Bernfeld, P. (*261*)

Bernfeld, P. 1954. *Federation Proc.* **13**: 183. (*255*) 1955. *Federation Proc.* **14**:182. (*255*) 1957. *Federation Proc.* **16**:153. (*254*) 1958. *In* "The Lipoproteins, Methods and Clinical Significance" (F. Homburger and P. Bernfeld, eds.), p. 24. Basel: Karger. (*254*) 1959. *Abstr. Am. Chem. Soc. Ann. Meet., 136th, Atlantic City, 1959*, p. C1. (*254*)

Bernfeld, P., Berkeley, B. J., and Bieber, R. E. 1965. *Arch. Biochem. Biophys.* **111**:31. (*222, 224–226*)

Bernfeld, P., Berkowitz, M. E., and Donahue, V. M. 1957. *J. Clin. Invest.* **36**:1363. (*254*)

Bernfeld, P., Donahue, V. M., and Berkowitz, M. E. 1957. *J. Biol. Chem.* **226**:51. (*254, 255, 261, 374*)

Bernfeld, P., Jacobson, S., and Bernfeld, H. C. 1957. *Arch. Biochem. Biophys.* **69**:198. (*223, 225–227*)

Bernfeld, P., and Kelley, T. F. 1960. *Federation Proc.* **19**:231. (*217, 224–226*) 1962. *Federation Proc.* **21**:282. (*217, 218*) 1963. *J. Biol. Chem.* **238**: 1236. (*217, 218, 224–226*)

Bernfeld, P., and Nisselbaum, J. S. 1956. *Federation Proc.* **15**:220. (*257*)

Bernfeld, P., and Stefanini, M. 1951. *Proc. Soc. Exptl. Biol. Med.* **77**:551. (*260*)

Bernfeld, P., and Tuttle, L. P. 1959. *Federation Proc.* **18**:191. (*221, 224–227*)

Bernfeld, P., Tuttle, L. P., and Hubbard, R. W. 1961. *Arch. Biochem. Biophys.* **92**:232. (*221, 222, 224–227*)

Bernfeld, P., Stefanini, M., Berkowitz, R. D., and Hennessey, F. B. 1953. *Proc. Soc. Exptl. Biol. Med.* **83**: 311. (*260*)

Bernfeld, P., Bernfeld, H. C., Nisselbaum, J. S., and Fishman, W. H. 1954. *J. Am. Chem. Soc.* **76**:4872. (*221, 222*)

Bernfeld, P., Nisselbaum, J. S., Berkeley, B. J., and Hanson, R. W. 1960. *J. Biol. Chem.* **235**:2852. (*255, 257*)

Bernhard, K., Hany, A., Hausheer, L., and Pedersen, W. 1962. *Helv. Chim. Acta* **45**:1298. (*126*)

Bernhard, W. G. (*317*)

Bernheim, F., and Bernheim, M. L. C. 1943. *J. Pharmacol. Exptl. Therap.* **78**:394. (*50*)

Bernheim, M. L. C. (*50*)

Bernheimer, H. P. (*45, 48, 50*)

Bernier, G. M. (*305*)

Bernstein, F. 1925. *Z. Induktive Abstammungs-Vererbungslehre* **37**:237. (*272*)

Bernstein, S., and McGilvery, R. W. 1952. *J. Biol. Chem.* **198**:195. (*53*) 1952a. *J. Biol. Chem.* **199**:745. (*53*)

Bersin, T. 1951. "Lehrbuch der Enzymologie." Leipzig: Akademische. (*213*)

Bertaccini, G. (*391, 392*)

Berthold [A. A.] 1849. *Arch. Anat. Physiol. Wiss. Med.* (*Müllers*) *Abt.* 2, p. 42. (*134*)

Berti, T., and Trocca, M. 1964. *Life Sci.* **3**:343. (*116*)

Bertolini, M. (*83, 344*)

Berwick, L., and Coman, D. R. 1962. *Cancer Res.* **22**:982. (*374*)

Bescol-Liversac, J. (*54*)

Best, C. H., Cowan, C., and MacLean, D. L. 1938. *J. Physiol.* **92**:20. (*264*)

Best, G. K., and Durham, N. N. 1964. *Arch. Biochem. Biophys.* **105**:120. (*116*)

Best, M. M. (*216*)

Besterman, E. M. M., and Evans, J. 1957. *Brit. Med. J.* **1**:310. (*371*)

Bettelheim-Jevons, F. R. 1958. *Advan. Protein Chem.* **13**:35. (*252, 253, 302*)

Beumer, J. (*356*)

Bezer, A. E. (*272, 275, 284–287, 315, 321, 334*)

Bhavanandan, V. P. (*341*)

Bhavanandan, V. P., Buddecke, E., Carubelli, R., and Gottschalk, A. 1964. *Biochem. Biophys. Res. Commun.* **16**:353. (*83, 87, 90, 106*)

Bianchi, A. (*141*)

Bianco, L., Castellani, A. A., De Bernard, B., and Zambotti, V. 1957. *Boll. Soc. Ital. Biol. Sper.* **33**:1271. (*70*) 1958. *Giorn. Biochim.* **7**:57. (*70*)

Bieber, R. E. (*222, 224–226*)
Bier, A. M. (*52*)
Bierich, R. 1922. *Arch. Pathol. Anat. Physiol.* **239**:1. (*391*)
Biggers, J. D. (*101*)
Biggers, J. D., Lawson, K. A., Lucy, J. A., and Webb, M. 1961. *Biochim. Biophys. Acta* **54**:236. (*101*)
Bigley, N. J. (*271, 311*)
Bigley, N. J., Chandler, R. W., and Dodd, M. C. 1958. *J. Immunol.* **80**: 85. (*271*)
Bigley, N. J., Dodd, M. C., Randles, C. I., Geyer, V. B., and Lazen, A. G. 1963. *J. Immunol.* **90**:526. (*271*)
Billingham, R. E., Brent, L., and Medawar, P. B. 1953. *Nature* **172**: 603. (*300*) 1956. *Phil. Trans. Roy. Soc. London, Ser. B* **239**:357. (*300, 303*)
Bingley, M., Bell, L. G. E., and Jeon, K. W. 1962. *Exptl. Cell Res.* **28**:208. (*365*)
Bingley, M. S., and Thompson, C. M. 1962. *J. Theoret. Biol.* **2**:16. (*366*)
Binkley, S. B. (*173*)
Birnbaum, S. M. (*33*)
Biserte, G. (*83*)
Biserte, G. 1957. *Bull. Soc. Chim. Biol.* **39**:Suppl. III, 93. (*306*)
Bister, W. (*281*)
Bitman, J. (*149*)
Björklund, B. (*318*)
Black, J. (*366*)
Blacklow, R. S. (*26, 126*)
Blanchet, H. J., Jr. (*211*)
Blasius, R., and Seitz, W. 1952. *Klin. Wochschr.* **30**:905. (*258*)
Blaškovič, D. (*171*)
Blivaiss, B. B. 1951. *Am. J. Anat.* **89**: 381. (*141*)
Blix, G. (*234*)
Blix, G., and Snellman, O. 1945. *Arkiv Kemi* **19A**:No. 32, 1. (*231*)
Blix, G., Lindberg, E., Odin, L., and Werner, I. 1956. *Acta Soc. Med. Upsalien.* **61**:1. (*344*)
Block, R. J. 1961. *Ann. N.Y. Acad. Sci.* **94**:31. (*96*)
Block, W. D. (*305*)
Blomqvist, H. E. 1956. *Acta Pathol. Microbiol. Scand.* **39**:313. (*391*)
Bloom, G. (*245*)
Bloom, G., and Ringertz, N. R. 1960. *Arkiv Kemi* **16**:51. (*245*)
Blumberg, B. S., and Ogston, A. G. 1957. *Biochem. J.* **66**:342. (231) 1958. *Biochem. J.* **68**:183. (*231*)
Blumbergs, P. (*44*)
Blumenthal, H. (*39*)
Blumenthal, H. J. (*7, 12, 40, 57, 377*)
Blumenthal, H. J., Horowitz, S. T., Hemerline, A., and Roseman, S. 1955. *Bacteriol. Proc.* **55**:137. (*7*)
Blumsom, N. L. (*82*)
Blumsom, N. L., and Baddiley, J. 1961. *Biochem. J.* **81**:114. (*82*)
Boas, N. F. (*134, 137, 138, 140*)
Boas, N. F. 1949. *J. Biol. Chem.* **181**:573. (*135*) 1953. *J. Biol. Chem.* **204**:553. (*135*) 1959. *Ann. N.Y. Acad. Sci.* **72**:1045. (*138*)
Boas, N. F., and Foley, J. B. 1955. *Endocrinology* **56**:474. (*302*)
Boas, N. F., and Ludwig, A. W. 1950. *Endocrinology* **46**:299. (*141*)
Bocher, C. A. (*387*)
Böhm, P. (*307*)
Bogdanov, V. P., Kaverzneva, E. D., and Andreyeva, A. P. 1964. *Biochim. Biophys. Acta* **83**:69. (*83*)
Bogoch, S. (*119*)
Bogoch, S. 1957. *J. Am. Chem. Soc.* **79**: 3286. (*122*)
Boissier, J. R., Gross, F., and Bonfils, S. 1954. *Therapie* **9**:512. (*197*)
Boivin, A., and Delaunay, A. 1944. *Bull. Acad. Méd. (Paris)* **128**:357 (*268*)
Bollet, A. J., Bonner, W. M., Jr., and Nance, J. L. 1963. *J. Biol. Chem.* **238**:3522. (*196*)
Bolton, W. 1953. *J. Endocrinol.* **9**:440. (*148*)
Boltralik, J. J. (*116*)
Bond, J. (*149*)
Bonde, G., and Jensen, C. E. 1956. *Bull. Soc. Chim. Belg.* **65**:50. (*35, 231*)
Bonde, G. J., Jensen, C. E., and Schmidt, A. 1957. *Acta Pharmacol. Toxicol.* **13**:194. (*231*)
Bonde, G. J., Jensen, C. E., and

Thamsen, J. 1957. *Acta Pharmacol. Toxicol.* **13**:184. (*231*)

Bonelli, M. (*390*)

Bonét-Maury, P. (*188*)

Bonfils, S. (*197*)

Boni, M., Gaetani, S., Mariani, A., and Spadoni, M. A. 1960. *Boll. Soc. Ital. Biol. Sper.* **36**:2061. (*52*)

Bonner, W. M., Jr., (*196*)

Bonomo, E., and Bonelli, M. 1952. *Tumori* **38** (Anno):351. (*394*)

Bonventre, P. F. (*34*)

Boor, A. K. (*323*)

Boor, A. K., and Miller, C. P. 1934. *J. Exptl. Med.* **59**:63. (*323*)

Boorman, K. E., and Dodd, B. E. 1957. "Introduction to Blood Group Serology." Boston: Little, Brown. (*269, 273*)

Boosfeld, E. (*183*)

Borek, E. (*112*)

Borooah, J., Leaback, D. H., and Walker, P. G. 1961. *Biochem. J.* **78**:106. (*156, 158–161, 163*)

Borrebaek, B. (*102*)

Borsook, H. (*357*)

Borsook, H., Keighley, G., Yost, D. M., and McMillan, E. 1937. *Science* **86**: 525. (*50*)

Borsook, H., Deasy, C. L., Haagen-Smit, A. J., Keighley, G., and Lowy, P. H. 1950. *J. Biol. Chem.* **187**:839. (*92*)

Boschman, T. A. C. (*352*)

Boström, H. (*44, 48, 52–56, 69, 74, 75, 78–80, 264*)

Boström, H. 1952. *J. Biol. Chem.* **196**: 477. (*51, 52, 69, 77*) 1953. *Arkiv Kemi* **6**:43. (*51, 52*) 1954. *In* "Connective Tissue in Health and Disease" (G. Asboe-Hansen, ed.), p. 97. Copenhagen: Munksgaard. (*209*)

Boström, H., and Åqvist, S. [E. G.] 1952. *Acta Chem. Scand.* **6**:1557. (*51*)

Boström, H., and Gardell, S. 1953. *Acta Chem. Scand.* **7**:216. (*52, 72, 77*)

Boström, H., Gustafsson, B. E., and Wengle, B. 1963. *Proc. Soc. Exptl. Biol. Med.* **114**:742. (*80*)

Boström, H., and Månsson, B. 1952. *J. Biol. Chem.* **196**:483. (*53, 69, 211*) 1952a. *Acta Chem. Scand.* **6**:1559. (*70*) 1953. *Arkiv Kemi* **6**:23. (*53, 69*) 1953a. *Acta Chem. Scand.* **7**: 1014. (*5, 69, 71*)

Boström, H., Moretti, A., and Whitehouse, M. 1963. *Biochim. Biophys. Acta* **74**:213. (*53*)

Boström, H., and Odeblad, E. 1952. *Acta Endocrinol.* **10**:89. (*148, 149*) 1953. *Acta Psychiat. Neurol. Scand.* **28**:5. (*54*) 1953a. *Anat. Record* **115**:505. (*55*) 1954. *Acta Physiol. Scand.* **32**: 124. (*54, 79*)

Boström, H., Odeblad, E., and Friberg, U. 1952. *Arch. Biochem. Biophys.* **38**: 283. (*54*) 1953. *Acta Pathol. Microbiol. Scand.* **32**:516. (*54*)

Boström, H., and Rodén, L. 1961. *Biochem. Pharmacol.* **6**:100. (*46*)

Boström, H., Rodén, L., and Vestermark, A. 1955. *Nature* **176**:601. (*71*)

Boström, H., Rodén, L., and Yamashina, I. 1958. *J. Biol. Chem.* **230**:381. (*96*)

Boström, H., Jorpes, [J.] E., Månsson, B., Rodén, L., and Vestermark, A. 1955. *Arkiv Kemi* **8**:469. (*5, 53*)

Bothner-By, C. T., and Balazs, E. A. 1957. *Radiation Res.* **6**:302. (*241*)

Bourne, E. J. (*58*)

Bourrillon, R. (*85, 357*)

Bourrillon, R., Got, R., and Meyer, D. 1964. *Biochim. Biophys. Acta* **83**: 178. (*83*)

Bourrillon, R., Got, R., and Michon, J. 1961. *Clin. Chim. Acta* **6**:91. (*100*)

Bourrillon, R., and Michon, J. 1960. *Biochim. Biophys. Acta* **44**:608. (*85*)

Boursnell, J. C., Coombs, R. R. A., and Rizk, V. 1953. *Biochem. J.* **55**:745. (*274*)

Boussier, G. (*309*)

Bovarnick, M. (*340, 344*)

Bowley, C. C. (*300*)

Bowman, K. (*189*)

Boyd, E. S., and Neuman, W. F. 1954. *Arch. Biochem. Biophys.* **51**:475. (*69*)

Boyd, W. 1947. "A Textbook of Pathology" (5th ed.), p. 778. Philadelphia: Lea & Febiger. (*302*)

Boyd, W. C. (*305*)

Boyd, W. C. 1954. *In* "The Proteins" (H. Neurath and K. Bailey, eds.), Vol. II, Part B, p. 755. New York: Academic Press. (*306*) 1956. "Fundamentals of Immunology," 3rd ed., p. 183. New York: Wiley (Interscience). (*287, 305, 306, 336*) 1961. *J. Immunol.* **85**:221. (*267*)

Boyd, W. C., McMaster, M. H., and Waszczenko-Zacharczenko, E. 1959. *Nature* **184**:989. (*271*)

Boyd, W. C., and Reeves, E. 1961. *Nature* **191**:511. (*327*)

Boyd, W. C., Bhatia, H. M., Diamond, M. A., and Matsubara, S. 1962. *J. Immunol.* **89**:463. (*274*)

Boyden, S. V. (*323*)

Boyden, S. V. 1951. *J. Exptl. Med.* **93**:107. (*289*)

Boyland, E., and McClean, D. 1935. *J. Pathol. Bacteriol.* **41**:553. (*381, 394*)

Boyle, E. (*214, 216, 219, 251*)

Brack, E. 1925. *Folia Haematol.* **31**:202. (*391*)

Brada, Z. 1963. *Nature* **197**:592. (*106*)

Bradford, R. H. (*97*)

Brading, I. 1956. *Australian J. Exptl. Biol.* **34**:157. (*289*)

Bradley, D. (*117*)

Brady, R. O. (*120–122, 126, 311*)

Braganca, B. (*49*)

Bragdon, J. H. (*216*)

Bragdon, J. H., and Havel, R. J. 1954. *Science* **120**:113. (*216, 266*)

Brambell, F. W. R., Hemmings, W. A., and Rowlands, W. T. 1948. *Proc. Roy. Soc. (London), Ser. B* **135**:390. (*307*)

Brand, E., Kassell, B., and Heidelberger, M. 1939. *J. Biol. Chem.* **128**:xi. (*302*)

Brandes, D. (*54, 137, 138*)

Brandes, W. C. (*271, 272, 290, 297, 299, 311, 325, 327, 333*)

Braun, G. A. (*28, 157, 167*)

Bray, H. G., Henry, H., and Stacey, M. 1946. *Biochem. J.* **40**:124. (*311, 329*)

Breinl, F. (*267*)

Bremner, J. M. 1958. *J. Sci. Food Agr.* **9**:528. (*35*)

Brendel, R. (*197*)

Breneman, W. R. 1942. *Endocrinology* **30**:609. (*141*)

Brener, J. L. (*303*)

van den Brenk, H. A. S. 1959. *Brit. J. Exptl. Pathol.* **39**:356. (*246*)

Brent, L. (*300, 303*)

Brice, B. A. (*183*)

Brimacombe, J. S. (*200, 317*)

Brinkhous, K. M., Smith, H. P., Warner, E. D., and Seegers, W. H. 1939. *Am. J. Physiol.* **125**:683. (*263*)

Brinkman, R. (*249*)

Brinkman, R., and Lamberts, H. B. 1958. *Nature* **181**:774. (*248*) 1958a. *Koninkl. Nederl. Akademie van Wetenschappen-Amsterdam* (Reprinted from *Proceedings, Ser. C* **61**:No. 1, 1958). (*248*)

Brinkman, R., Lamberts, H. B., and Zuideveld, J. 1961. *Intern. J. Radiation Biol.* **3**:509. (*248, 249*) 1961a. *Intern. J. Radiation Biol.* **3**:279. (*232, 240, 248, 249*)

Brinkman, R., and Veninga, T. S. 1962. *Intern. J. Radiation Biol.* **4**:249. (*249*)

Brinkman, R., Lamberts, H. B., Wadel, J., and Zuideveld, J. 1961. *Intern. J. Radiation Biol.* **3**:205. (*248*)

Briody, B. A. 1948. *J. Immunol.* **59**:115. (*338*)

Britton, B. B. (*37*)

Brockman, J. A., Jr. (*266*)

Brody, S., and Carlström, G. 1960. *Lancet* **2**:99. (*301*) 1961. *Nature* **189**:841. (*301*) 1962. *In* "Ciba Foundation Colloquia on Endocrinology," Vol. 14: "Immunoassay of Hormones" (G. E. W. Wolstenholme and M. P. Cameron, eds.), p. 329. Boston: Little, Brown. (*301*)

Bronner, F. (*52, 54*)

Bronner, F. 1960. *Am. J. Physiol.* **198**:605. (*52*)

Brookes, P., Crathorn, A. R., and Hunter, G. D. 1959. *Biochem. J.* **73**:396. (*109*)

Brooks, R. E. (*192, 238*)

Broser, W. (*266*)

Brossmer, R. (*24, 42, 171, 281, 351, 352*)

Brossmer, R., and Walter, K. 1958. *Klin. Wochschr.* **36**:925. (*301*)

Brown, A. D. 1961. *Biochim. Biophys. Acta* **48**:352. (*88*)

Brown, D. H. (*19, 20, 45, 59, 66, 67, 76, 97*)

Brown, D. H. 1951. *Biochim. Biophys. Acta* **7**:487. (*14, 19*) 1953. *J. Biol. Chem.* **204**:877. (*17*) 1955. *Biochim. Biophys. Acta* **16**:429. (*12, 57*) 1957. *Proc. Natl. Acad. Sci. U.S.* **43**:783. (*56*)

Brown, D. M. (*182*)

Brown, J. G. (*84*)

Brown, J. R. (*52, 119–121, 125*)

Brown, R. 1939. *J. Immunol.* **37**:445. (*317*)

Brown, R., and Robinson, L. K. 1943. *J. Immunol.* **47**:7. (*317*)

Brown, R. K. (*214, 251*)

Brown, R. K., Boyle, E., and Anfinsen, C. B. 1953. *J. Biol. Chem.* **204**:423. (*215*)

Brown, W. D. 1952. *Quart. J. Exptl. Physiol.* **37**:119. (*216*)

Brug, J., Esser, R. J. E., and Paerels, G. B. 1959. *Biochim. Biophys. Acta* **33**:241. (*42*)

Bruni, C., and Caschera, F. 1952. *Lavoro Ist. Anat. Univ. Perugia* **12**:5. (*391*)

Brunish, R., and Mozersky, S. M. 1958. *J. Biol. Chem.* **231**:291. (*194*)

Brunius, [F.] E. 1936. "Chemical Studies on the True Forssman Hapten, the Corresponding Antibody and Their Interaction." Stockholm: Fahlcranz. (*287*)

Brunk, Re. (*292*)

Brunk, Ru. (*292*)

Buchanan, J. G. (*82, 113, 313, 314*)

Buchanan, J. M. (*4, 5, 102, 103*)

Bucherer, H. (*182*)

Bucherer, H. 1935. *Zentr. Bakteriol. Parasitenk. Abt. II* **93**:12. (*181, 182*)

Buck, R. C. 1955. *J. Histochem. Cytochem.* **3**:435. (*54*)

Buck, R. C., and Heagy, F. C. 1958. *Can. J. Biochem. Physiol.* **36**:63. (*52*)

Buckingham, J. C., Selden, R., and Danforth, D. N. 1962. *Ann. N.Y. Acad. Sci.* **97**:733. (*149*)

Buckner, G. D., Insko, W. M., Jr., Henry, A. H., and Wachs, E. F. 1951. *Poultry Sci.* **30**:267. (*141*)

Buddecke, E. (*83, 87, 90, 106*)

Bueding, E. (*47*)

Bueding, E., Ruppender, H., and MacKinnon, J. A. 1954. *Proc. Natl. Acad. Sci. U.S.* **40**:773. (*15*)

Buehler, H. J., Katzman, P. A., and Doisy, E. A. 1951. *Proc. Soc. Exptl. Biol. Med.* **78**:3. (*202*)

Bürgel, E. (*266*)

Bugher, J. C. (*342*)

Bulliard, H. (*147, 151*)

Bulman, N. (*305*)

Bunim, J. J. (*65*)

Bunting, H. (*143, 145, 146, 152*)

Bunnell, W. W. (*295*)

Burger, M. 1950. "Bacterial Polysaccharides." Springfield, Ill.: Thomas. (*312*)

Burger, M., Glaser, L., and Burton, R. M. 1962. *Biochim. Biophys. Acta* **56**:172. (*123*) 1963. *J. Biol. Chem.* **238**:2595. (*127*)

Burger, W. C., and Stahmann, M. A. 1951. *J. Biol. Chem.* **193**:13. (*363*)

de Burgh, P. M., Yu, P.-C., Howe, C., and Bovarnick, M. 1948. *J. Exptl. Med.* **87**:1. (*340, 344*)

Burghartz, N., and Boosfeld, E. 1954. *Klin. Wochschr.* **32**:181. (*183*)

Burk, D. (*161*)

Burke, D. C. 1961. *Biochem. J.* **78**:556. (*335*)

Burnet, F. M. 1948. *Australian J. Exptl. Biol. Med. Sci.* **26**:71. (*187*)

Burnet, F. M., McCrea, J. F., and Stone, J. D. 1946. *Brit. J. Exptl. Pathol.* **27**:228. (*171, 338*)

Burnet, F. M., and Stone, J. D. 1947. *Australian J. Exptl. Biol. Med. Sci.* **25**:227. (*339*)

Burnett, G. W. (*193, 203*)

Burnett, W. T., Jr. (*235*)

Burns, R. K. 1961. *In* "Sex and Internal Secretions" (W. C. Young, ed.), 3rd.

ed., Vol. I, p. 76. Baltimore: Williams & Wilkins. (*151*)
Burón, F. A. (*274*)
Burrows, H. 1935. *Proc. Roy. Soc. (London), Ser. B* **118**:485. (*149*) 1949. "Biological Actions of Sex Hormones," 2nd edition, revised. London: Cambridge University Press. (*134, 148, 149*)
Burns, J. J. (*49*)
Burton, A. J., and Carter, H. E. 1964. *Biochemistry* **3**:411. (*125*)
Burton, R. M. (*122, 123, 127*)
Burton, R. M. 1963. *J. Neurochem.* **10**:503. (*178*)
Burton, R. M., Sodd, M. A., and Brady, R. O. 1958. *J. Biol. Chem.* **233**:1053. (*120–122*)
Burton, R. M., Garcia-Bunuel, L., Golden, M., and Balfour, Y. M. 1963. *Biochemistry* **2**:580. (*126*)
Buruiana, L. M. 1957. *Naturwissenschaften* **44**:306. (*224*)
Buruiana, L. M., and Hadarag, E. 1958. *Naturwissenschaften* **45**:293. (*224*)
Buscarini, L. (*394*)
Bussard, A. (*301*)
Bussard, A., and Eyquem, A. 1947. *Ann. Inst. Pasteur* **73**:1194. (*301*)
Butenandt, A., Günther, H., and Turba, F. 1960. *Z. Physiol. Chem.* **322**:28. (*140*)
Butler, G. C. (*47*)
Butt, W. R., Crooke, A. C., and Cunningham, F. J. 1962. *In* "Ciba Foundation Colloquia on Endocrinology," Vol. 14: "Immunoassay of Hormones" (G. E. W. Wolstenholme and M. P. Cameron, eds.), p. 310. Boston: Little, Brown. (*301*)
Buxton, C. L. (*307*)
Buxton, R. W. (*376*)
Bywaters, H. W. 1909. *Biochem. Z.* **15**:322. (*305*)

C

Cabib, E. (*45, 57, 58*)
Cabib, S., Leloir, L. F., and Cardini, C. E. 1953. *J. Biol. Chem.* **203**:1055. (*18, 45*)
Cachera, J. P. (*188*)
Caesar, R. (*309*)
Cahan, A. (*300*)
Cahill, W. (*201*)
Cahill, W. M. (*201, 209*)
Cairns, A. (*216, 265*)
Cairns, S. (*371*)
Calkins, E. (*310*)
Calkins, E., Cohen, A. S., and Gitlin, D. 1958. *Federation Proc.* **17**:431. (*310*)
Calkins, E., Cohen, A. S., and Larsen, B. 1960. *Ann. N.Y. Acad. Sci.* **86**(Art. 4):1033. (*309, 310*)
Callahan, H. J. (*280, 296, 297, 299*)
Calvin, J. R. 1952. *Can. J. Chem.* **30**:831. (*183*)
Cameron, C., Graham, F., Dunsford, I., Sickles, G., MacPherson, C. R., Cahan, A., Sanger, R., and Race, R. R. 1959. *Brit. Med. J.* **2**:29. (*300*)
Cameron, G. L., and Staveley, J. M. 1957. *Nature* **179**:147. (*292*)
Cameron, J. A. (*118*)
Campani, M. 1948. *Boll. Soc. Med.-Chir. Modena* **48**:3. (*246*)
Campbell, B. J., Schlueter, R. J., Weber, G. F., and White, W. F. 1961. *Biochim. Biophys. Acta* **46**:279. (*357*)
Campbell, D., and Persson, B. H. 1951. *Experientia* **7**:304. (*54*)
Campbell, D. H. (*267, 333, 335*)
Campbell, D. H., and Bulman, N. 1952. *Fortschr. Chem. Org. Naturstoffe* **9**:443. (*306*)
Campbell, H. W. (*394*)
Campbell, J. B. (*396*)
Campbell, L. L., Jr., and Williams, O. B. 1951. *J. Gen. Microbiol.* **5**:894. (*181*)
Campbell, P. N. (*302, 303*)
Campo, R. D., and Dziewiatkowski, D. D. 1961. *J. Biophys. Biochem. Cytol.* **9**:401. (*54*)
Candeli, A., and Tronieri, A. 1951. *Boll. Soc. Ital. Biol. Sper.* **27**:651. (*202*)
von Caneghem, P., Marx, R., and Spier, H. W. 1956. *Arch. Exptl. Pathol. Pharmacol.* **227**:149. (*197*)
von Caneghem, P., and Spier, H. W. 1954. *Biochem. Z.* **325**:366. (*197*)

Canfield, R. E. 1963. *J. Biol. Chem.* **238**: 2698. (*184*)

Cantell, K. (*271, 290, 364*)

Cantero, A. (*224, 383*)

Cantino, E. C., Lovett, J., and Horenstein, E. A. 1957. *Am. J. Botany* **44**: 498. (*182*)

Canu, P. (*199*)

Capps, J. C. (*100*)

Cappuccino, J. G. (*199*)

Caputo, A. 1957. *Nature* **179**:1133. (*239, 240*)

Caputto, R. (*27, 105, 171, 351*)

Cardini, C. E. (*6, 11, 16, 18, 37, 45, 57–59, 66, 76, 84*)

Cardini, C. E., and Leloir, L. F. 1953. *Arch. Biochem. Biophys.* **45**:55. (*14*) 1957. *J. Biol. Chem.* **225**:317. (*21, 24*)

Carey, C. L. (*181*)

Caridroit, F. 1942. *Rev. Sci.* **80**:230. (*141*)

Caridroit, F., and Moszkowska, A. 1947. *Compt. Rend.* **224**:1735. (*142*) 1948. *J. Physiol. (Paris)* **40**:134-A. (*142*)

Caridroit [F.], and Pézard [A.] 1926. *Compt. Rend. Soc. Biol.* **95**:296. (*140*)

Caridroit, F., and Régnier, V. 1941. *Rev. Sci.* **79**:309. (*141, 142*) 1944. *Compt. Rend. Soc. Biol.* **138**:157. (*142*)

Carlsöö, S. (*55*)

Carlson, D. M. (*44, 126*)

Carlson, L. A., and Wadström, L. B. 1957. *Clin. Chim. Acta* **2**:9. (*215*)

Carlström, G. (*301*)

Carminatti, H. (*59*)

Carpenter, C. M. (*323*)

Carr, J. J. (*206*)

Carroll, P. M., and Cornforth, J. W. 1960. *Biochim. Biophys. Acta* **39**:161. (*24*)

Carroll, W. R. 1945. *Endocrinology* **36**: 266. (*149*)

Carruthers, C., and Suntzeff, V. 1944. *Science* **99**:245. (*381*)

Carss, B. (*82, 113, 313*)

Carter, H. E. (*125, 163*)

Carter, H. E., Gigg, R. H., Law, J. H., Nakayama, T., and Weber, E. 1958. *J. Biol. Chem.* **233**:1309. (*123*)

Carter, M. K., and Peters, L. 1958. *Arch. Intern. Pharmacodyn.* **113**:406. (*15*)

Carubelli, R. (*83, 87, 90, 106*)

Carubelli, R., Bhavanandan, V. P., and Gottschalk, A. 1965. *Biochim. Biophys. Acta* **101**:67. (*341*)

Carubelli, R., Trucco, R. E., and Caputto, R. 1962. *Biochim. Biophys. Acta* **60**:196. (*171*)

Carubelli, R., Taha, B., Trucco, R. E., and Caputto, R. 1964. *Biochim. Biophys. Acta* **83**:224. (*105*)

Cary, S. G. (*193, 194*)

Caschera, F. (*391*)

Casper, W. (*267*)

Casper, W. A. 1930. *Klin. Wochschr.* **9**: 2154. (*323*) 1937. *J. Immunol.* **32**: 421. (*323*)

Cassidy, J. T., Jourdian, G. W., and Roseman, S. 1962. *Bacteriol. Proc.* **62**:63. (*173, 175*)

Castaigne, A. 1959. *Anesthes. Analges. Reanim.* **16**:567. (*185*)

Castellani, A[mleto]. 1954. *Giorn. Biochim.* **3**:19. (*232*)

Castellani, A., Perri, G. C., and Zambotti, V. 1955. *Boll. Soc. Ital. Biol. Sper.* **31**:1305. (*8*)

Castellani, A., and Torlone, V. 1956. *J. Pathol. Bacteriol.* **72**:505. (*232, 237*)

Castellani, A. A. (*8, 70*)

Castellani, A. A., and Zambotti, V. 1956. *Nature* **178**:313. (*8, 70*)

Castellani, A. A., de Bernard, B., and Zambotti, V. 1957. *Nature* **180**:859. (*48*)

Castellani, A. A., Ferri, G., Ronchi, S., and Zambotti, V. 1961. *Abstr. Proc. Intern. Congr. Biochem. 5th, Moscow, 1961,* p. 376. (*52*)

Castle, W. B. 1953. *New Engl. J. Med.* **249**:603. (*293*)

Castor, C. W. 1957. *Proc. Soc. Exptl. Biol. Med.* **94**:51. (*63*) 1959. *Arthritis Rheumat.* **2**:259. (*64*)

Catchpole, H. R. 1950. *Proc. Soc. Exptl. Biol. Med.* **75**:221. (*394, 395*)

Cathcart, P. 1903. *Z. Physiol. Chem.* **39**:423. (*32*)

Cawley, E. P., and Hoch-Ligeti, C. 1961. *A.M.A. Arch. Dermatol.* **83**:92. (*391*)
Caygill, J. C., and Jevons, F. R. 1965. *Clin. Chim. Acta* **11**:233. (*179*)
Cazal, P. 1955. *Sang* **26**:585. (*391*)
Ceccaldi, P. F. (*54*)
Cecil, H. C. (*149*)
Celano, M. (*289, 293*)
Celano, N. J. (*291*)
Ceppellini, R., and De Gregorio, M. 1953. *Boll. Ist. Sieroterap. Milan.* **32**:429. (*326*)
Ceppellini, R., and Siniscalco, M. 1955. *Riv. Ist. Sieroterap. Ital.* **30**:431. (*108*)
Cerroni, R. (*331*)
Cerutti, G. (*34*)
Chaikoff, I. L. (*96*)
Chain, E., and Duthie, E. S. 1939. *Nature* **144**:977. (*229*) 1940. *Brit. J. Exptl. Pathol.* **21**:324. (*145, 195*)
Chaloupka, J., Říhová, L., and Křečková, P. 1964. *Folia Microbiol.* **9**:9. (*117*)
Champy, C. (*134, 135*)
Champy, C. 1926. *Compt. Rend. Soc. Biol.* **94**:311. (*134, 137, 147*)
Champy, C., and Kritch, N. 1925. *Compt. Rend. Soc. Biol.* **92**:683. (*134, 137, 139*) 1926. *Arch. Morphol. Gen. Exptl.* **25**:1. (*147, 148*)
Champy, C., Kritch, N., and Llombart, A. 1929. *Compt. Rend. Assoc. Anat.* **24**:120. (*134, 147, 148, 151*)
Champy, C., Bulliard, H., Kritch, N., and Demay, M.-L. 1931. *Arch. Anat. Microscop. Morphol. Exptl.* **27**:301. (*147, 151*)
Chance, M. R. A. (*188*)
Chandler, H. L., Lawry, E. Y., Potee, K. G., and Mann, G. V. 1953. *Circulation* **8**:723. (*216*)
Chandler, R. W. (*271*)
Chandrasekhar, N., Osbahr, A., and Laki, K. 1964. *Biochem. Biophys. Res. Commun.* **15**:182. (*89*)
Chargaff, E. (*122, 126, 127, 263, 264*)
Chargaff, E. 1945. *Advan. Enzymol.* **5**:31. (*262, 263*)
Chargaff, E., Bancroft, F. W., and Stanley-Brown, M. 1936. *J. Biol. Chem.* **115**:155. (*265, 266*)
Chargaff, E., Bendich, A., and Cohen, S. S. 1944. *J. Biol. Chem.* **156**:161. (*264*)
Chargaff, E., Ziff, M., and Cohen, S. S. 1940. *J. Biol. Chem.* **136**:257. (*264*)
Chargaff, E., Ziff, M., and Moore, D. H. 1941. *J. Biol. Chem.* **139**:383. (*252, 253, 258, 263*)
Charlemagne, D. (*199*)
Charlwood, P. A. (*306*)
Charney, W. (*366*)
de Charpal, O. (*54*)
Chase, M. W., and Landsteiner, K. 1939. *Ann. Rev. Biochem.* **8**:579. (*287*)
Chatterjee, A. N., and Park, J. T. 1964. *Proc. Natl. Acad. Sci. U.S.* **51**:9. (*116*)
Cheburkina, N. V. (*329*)
Cheese, I. A. F. L., and Morgan, W. T. J. 1961. *Nature* **191**:149. (*278, 279, 287*)
Cheeseman, G. C. (*85*)
Cheftel, R. I., Cloarec, L., Moretti, J., Rafelson, M., and Jayle, M.-F. 1960. *Bull. Soc. Chim. Biol.* **42**:993. (*309*)
Cheng, H. F. (*94*)
Chieco-Bianchi, L. (*391, 392*)
Chien, S. (*106*)
Cho, M. H., and Jaques, L. B. 1956. *Can. J. Biochem. Physiol.* **34**:799. (*198*)
Chosson, A. (*83, 99*)
Chou, T. C., and Soodak, M. 1952. *J. Biol. Chem.* **196**:105. (*57*)
Chowdhury, A. (*100*)
Christensen, H. E. (*310*)
Christenson, W. N. (*284*)
Christman, J. F., and Doherty, D. G. 1956. *J. Bacteriol.* **72**:429. (*198*)
Chu, C. M. 1948. *Nature* **161**:606. (*171*)
Chumakova, M. Ya. (*364*)
Cifonelli, J. A. (*4, 45, 48, 49, 52, 59, 60, 65, 67, 69, 70, 72, 77*)
Cifonelli, J. A., and Dorfman, A. 1957. *J. Biol. Chem.* **228**:547. (*19*) 1960. *J. Biol. Chem.* **235**:3283. (*56*) 1962. *Biochem. Biophys. Res. Commun.* **7**:41. (*73*)
Cizek, L. J. (*106*)

Clamp, J. R., Bernier, G. M., and Putnam, F. W. 1964. *Biochim. Biophys. Acta* **86**:149. (*305*)

Clark, G. 1946. *Endocrinology* **39**:155. (*143*)

Clark, W. R., McLaughlin, J., and Webster, M. E. 1958. *J. Biol. Chem.* **230**:81. (*163, 326*)

Clarke, F. H. (*306*)

Clarke, J. S., and Pasternak, C. A. 1962. *Biochem. J.* **84**:185. (*7, 9*)

Clarke, P. H., and Tracey, M. V. 1956. *J. Gen. Microbiol.* **14**:188. (*181*)

Claude, A. 1940. *Proc. Soc. Exptl. Biol. Med.* **43**:684. (*195*)

Clausen, J., and Christensen, H. E. 1964. *Acta Pathol. Microbiol. Scand.* **60**:493. (*310*)

Clauser, H. (*83*)

Clay, M. M., and Sinai, C. R. 1965. *J. Pharmaceut. Sci.* **54**:469. (*200*)

Cleland, W. W., and Kennedy, E. P. 1958. *Federation Proc.* **17**:202. (*121, 122*)

Cloarec, L. (*309*)

Cobbin, L. B., and Dicker, S. E. 1962. *J. Physiol.* **163**:168. (*195*)

Codington, J. F. (*376*)

Cohen, A. S. (*309, 310*)

Cohen, L. (*291, 292*)

Cohen, S. 1955. *J. Endocrinol.* **12**:196. (*147*) 1956. *Biochem. J.* **64**:286. (*147*)

Cohen, S. S. (*264*)

Cohen, S. S. 1942. *J. Biol. Chem.* **144**:353. (*362*)

Cohen, S. S., and Chargaff, E. 1940. *J. Biol. Chem.* **136**:243. (*264*) 1941. *J. Biol. Chem.* **139**:741. (*264*) 1941a. *J. Biol. Chem.* **140**:689. (*264*)

Cohn, E. J. 1953. *In* "Blood Cells and Plasma Proteins: Their State in Nature" (J. L. Tullis, ed.), p. 52. New York: Academic Press. (*277*)

Cohn, E. J., Strong, L. E., Hughes, W. L., Jr., Mulford, D. J., Ashworth, J. N., Melin, M., and Taylor, H. L. 1946. *J. Am. Chem. Soc.* **68**:459. (*374*)

Cohn, M. (*333*)

Cohn, M., Wetter, L. R., and Deutsch, H. F. 1949. *J. Immunol.* **61**:283. (*333*)

Cole, J. W. (*245*)

Cole, R. M. (*196*)

Coleby, B. 1957. *Chem. Ind.* (*London*), p. 111. (*241*)

Collings, M. R. 1926. *Anat. Record* **33**:271. (*144, 146*)

Collins, D. H., and Meachim, G. 1961. *Ann. Rheumatic Diseases* **20**:117. (*53*)

Collip, J. B. (*142–144, 152*)

Colobert, L., and Dirheimer, G. 1961. *Biochim. Biophys. Acta* **54**:455. (*183, 184*)

Colter, J. S., and Campbell, J. B. 1965. *Ann. N.Y. Acad. Sci.* **130**:383. (*396*)

Colvin, J. R., Smith, D. B., and Cook, W. H. 1954. *Chem. Rev.* **54**:687. (*333*)

Coman, D. R. (*374, 394*)

Coman, D. R. 1944. *Cancer Res.* **4**:625. (*381*) 1946. *Am. J. Med. Sci.* **211**:257. (*381, 393*) 1961. *Cancer Res.* **21**:1436. (*373, 374*)

Comar, C. L. (*55*)

Comb, D. G., and Roseman, S. 1956. *Biochim. Biophys. Acta* **21**:193. (*37*) 1958. *J. Am. Chem. Soc.* **80**:497. (*24, 38*) 1958a. *Biochim. Biophys. Acta* **29**:653. (*21, 24, 42, 163*) 1958b. *J. Biol. Chem.* **232**:807. (*38, 39*) 1960. *J. Biol. Chem.* **235**:2529. (*42*)

Comb, D. G., Shimizu, F., and Roseman, S. 1959. *J. Am. Chem. Soc.* **81**:5513. (*26*)

Comb, D. G., Jourdian, G. W., Watson, D. R., and Roseman, S. 1960. *Abstr. Am. Chem. Soc. 137th Meeting, Cleveland, 1960,* p. 15c. (*27*)

Common, R. H. (*135, 141, 148*)

Conchie, J., and Findlay, J. 1959. *J. Endocrinol.* **18**:132. (*166*)

Conchie, J., Findlay, J., and Levvy, G. A. 1959. *Biochem. J.* **71**:318. (*157, 165*)

Conchie, J., and Hay, A. J. 1963. *Biochem. J.* **87**:354. (*91, 169*)

Conchie, J., and Levvy, G. A. 1957.

Biochem. J. **65**:389. (*161*) 1957a. *Brit. J. Cancer* **11**:487. (*157, 166, 167*)
Conchie, J., and Mann, T. 1957. *Nature* **179**:1190. (*157*)
Coniglio, C. T. (*366*)
Connell, G. E. (*308*)
Conney, A. H. (*49*)
Consden, R. (*149*)
Consolandi, G. 1949. *Lavoro Ist. Anat. Univ. Perugia* **8**:5. (*391*)
Constantinides, P., Cairns, A., and Werner, A. 1954. *Arch. Intern. Pharmacodyn.* **99**:334. (*216, 265, 371*)
Constantinides, P., Szasz, G., and Harder, F. 1953. *Arch. Pathol.* **56**:36. (*371*)
Cook, G. M. W., and Eylar, E. H. 1964. *Federation Proc.* **23**:No. 1039. (*291*)
Cook, G. M. W., Heard, D. H., and Seaman, G. V. F. 1960. *Nature* **188**: 1011. (*373, 381*) 1962. *Exptl. Cell* Res. **28**:27. (*381, 382*)
Cook, G. M. W., Seaman, G. V. F., and Weiss, L. 1963. *Cancer Res.* **23**:1813. (*381*)
Cook, W. H. (*333*)
Coombs, R. R. A. (*274, 290*)
Coombs, R. R. A., Bedford, D., and Rouillard, L. M. 1956. *Lancet* **I**:461. (*289*)
Coombs, R. R. A., Mourant, A. E., and Race, R. R. 1945. *Brit. J. Exptl. Pathol.* **26**:255. (*308*)
Coons, A. H., and Kaplan, M. H. 1950. *J. Exptl. Med.* **91**:1. (*289*)
Copenhaver, W. M. 1958. *Anat. Record* **131**:669. (*54, 55*)
Cordova, M. S. (*271*)
Cori, C. F. (*122*)
Cori, C. F., and Cori, G. T. 1945. *J. Biol. Chem.* **158**:341. (*16*)
Cori, G. T. (*16, 122*)
Corner, G. W. 1923. *Contr. Embryol. Carnegie Instn.* **15,** No. 75 (Publ. No. 332):73. (*143*)
Cornforth, J. W. (*24*)
Cornwell, D. G. (*254*)
Coss, J. A., Jr. (*238, 239*)
Coste, F., and Delbarre, F. 1956. *Compt. Rend. Soc. Biol.* **150**:876. (*197*)
Côté, R. H., and Morgan, W. T. J. 1956. *Nature* **178**:1171. (*277, 316*)
Couchman, K. G. (*303*)
Coulson, R. A., and Hernandez, T. 1964. "Biochemistry of the Alligator," Chapt. 5, p. 36. Baton Rouge: Louisiana State Univ. Press. (*379*)
Coupland, R. E., and Riley, J. F. 1960. *Nature* **187**:1128. (*392*)
Courcon, J. (*102*)
Cousens, S. F. (*235*)
Cowan, C. (*264*)
Crabb, E. D. (*392, 393*)
Cramer, F. B. (*14*)
Cramer, W., and Simpson, W. L. 1944. *Cancer Res.* **4**:601. (*391*)
Crane, R. K. (*13*)
Crane, R. K. 1955. *Congr. Intern. Biochim., 3ᵉ, Bruxelles, 1955, Résumés des Communications,* p. 108. (*14*)
Crane, W. A. J. 1962. *J. Pathol. Bacteriol.* **84**:113. (*52–54*)
Crathorn, A. R. (*109*)
Crathorn, A. R., and Hunter, G. D. 1958. *Biochem. J.* **69**:47P. (*110*)
Crawther, W. G., and Lennox, F. G. 1953. *Australian J. Biol. Sci.* **6**:410. (*86*)
Cremer, H. D., and Dittmann, G. 1956. *Biochem. Z.* **327**:377. (*51, 52*)
Cresseri, A. 1954. *Boll. Soc. Ital. Biol. Sper.* **30**:718. (*294*)
Cronkite, E. P. (*54*)
Cronkite, E. P. 1950. *Blood* **5**:32. (*245*)
Crooke, A. C. (*301*)
Crookston, J. H. (*284*)
Crowle, A. J. 1961. "Immunodiffusion." New York: Academic Press. (*267*)
Crumpton, M. J. 1957. *Nature* **180**:605. (*163*)
Csaba, G., Horváth, C., and Ács, T. 1960. *Brit. J. Cancer* **14**:362. (*385, 389, 392*)
Csaba, G., Ács, T., Horváth, C., and Kapa, E. 1960. *Brit. J. Cancer* **14**: 367. (*388*)
Csaba, G., Ács, T., Horváth, C., and Mold, K. 1961. *Brit. J. Cancer* **15**: 327. (*392*)

Csaba, G., Kórösi, J., Horváth, C., Mold, K., and Ács, T. 1964. *Neoplasma* **11**: 137. (*389*)

Cummins, C. S. 1962. *Ann. Inst. Pasteur* **103**:385. (*323*)

Cummins, C. S., and Harris, H. 1956. *J. Gen. Microbiol.* **14**:583. (*111*) 1956a. *Intern. Bull. Bacteriol. Nomenclature and Taxonomy* **6**:111 (see also p. 139). (*111*) 1958. *J. Gen. Microbiol.* **18**:173. (*313*)

Cunningham, F. J. (*301*)

Cunningham, L. W. (*86*)

Curnen, E. C. (*285, 316*)

Curran, R. C., and Kennedy, J. S. 1955. *J. Pathol. Bacteriol.* **70**:449. (*54*)

Curtain, C. C. (*176, 346*)

Curtis, A. S. G. 1962. *Biol. Rev.* **37**:82. (*374*)

Custer, J. H. (*253*)

Cutolo, E. (*49*)

D

D'Abramo, F., and Lipmann, F. 1957. *Biochim. Biophys. Acta* **25**:211. (*60*) 1958. *Abstr. Intern. Congr. Biochem., 4th, Vienna, 1958,* p. 75, Section 6–41. (*60*)

Dacie, J. V. 1960. "The Haemolytic Anaemias, Congenital and Acquired: Part 1: The Congenital Anaemias," 2d ed. New York: Grune. (*273*)

Dacie, J. V., Crookston, J. H., and Christenson, W. N. 1957. *Brit. J. Haematol.* **3**:77. (*284*)

Dahlberg, J. E. (*89*)

Dain, J. A. (*311*)

Dameshek, W. (*261, 262*)

Danforth, D. N. (*149*)

Daniels, E. E. (*163*)

Daniher, F. A. (*44*)

Danishefsky, I. (*52, 74, 260*)

Danishefsky, I., and Eiber, H. B. 1959. *Arch. Biochem. Biophys.* **85**:53. (*210*)

Danishefsky, I., Eiber, H. B., and Carr, J. J. 1960. *Arch. Biochem. Biophys.* **90**:114. (*206*)

Dankert, M., Gonçalves, I. R. J., and Recondo, E. 1964a. *Biochim. Biophys. Acta* **81**:78. (*84*)

Dankert, M., Passeron, S., Recondo, E., and Leloir, L. F. 1964. *Biochem. Biophys. Res. Commun.* **14**:358. (*84*)

Danon, D. (*373*)

D'Ari, L. (*124*)

Dark, F. A. (*88, 115, 163*)

Dasté, P. 1956. *Ann. Biol.* **60**:473. (*182*)

Dau, P. (*237*)

Daubenmerkl, W. 1951. *Acta Pharmacol. Toxicol.* **7**:153. (*230, 237*) 1953. *Acta Pharmacol. Toxicol.* **9**:1. (*230, 237*) 1953a. *Acta Pharmacol. Toxicol.* **9**: 362. (*230*)

David, K. 1938. *Acta Brev. Neerl. Physiol. Pharmacol. Microbiol.* **8**:133. (*142*)

David, R. (*393*)

Davidson, C. S. (*32*)

Davidson, E. A. (*7, 14, 21, 48, 49, 73, 377*)

Davidson, E. A. 1960. *J. Biol. Chem.* **235**: 23. (*15*)

Davidson, E. A., Blumenthal, H. J., and Roseman, S. 1957. *J. Biol. Chem.* **226**:125. (*12, 57*)

Davidson, E. A., and Meyer, K. 1954. *J. Biol. Chem.* **211**:605. (*60, 189*)

Davidson, E. A., and Riley, J. G. 1960. *J. Biol. Chem.* **235**:3367. (*62, 72, 210*) 1960a. *Biochim. Biophys. Acta* **42**: 566. (*72, 77*)

Davidson, E. A., and Small, W. 1963. *Biochim. Biophys. Acta* **69**:445. (*78*) 1963a. *Biochim. Biophys. Acta* **69**: 453. (*78*) 1963b. *Biochim. Biophys. Acta* **69**:459. (*78*)

Davidson, E. A., and Wheat, R. W. 1963. *Biochim. Biophys. Acta* **72**:112. (*14*)

Davies, D. A. L. 1960. *Advan. Carbohydrate Chem.* **15**:271. (*29, 312, 325*)

Davies, D. A. L., Staub, A. M., Fromme, I., Lüderitz, O., and Westphal, O. 1958. *Nature* **181**:822. (*333*)

Davies, D. V., and Young, L. 1954. *Nature* **173**:448. (*54*)

Davies, K. W. (*244*)

Davies, R. E. (*53*)

Davis, A. (*388*)

Davison, A. N. 1964. *Biochem. J.* **91**:3P. (*125*)

Davison, A. N., and Gregson, N. A. 1962. *Biochem. J.* **85**:558. (*125*)
Dawson, M. H. (*64, 319, 330, 332*)
Day, H. G. (*3, 4, 94, 95*)
Day, M., Green, J. P., and Robinson, J. D., Jr. 1962. *Brit. J. Pharmacol. Chemotherap.* **18**:625. (*211*)
Day, S. M., and Green, J. P. 1959. *Federation Proc.* **18**:381. (*74*)
Day, T. D. 1952. *J. Physiol.* **117**:1. (*249*)
Deal, W. C., Jr., and Van Holde, K. E. 1962. *Federation Proc.* **21**:254. (*222*)
Deasy, C. L. (*92*)
De Benedictis, G. (*391, 392*)
De Bernard, B. (*70*)
De Boer, C. J. (*363*)
Debro, J. R. (*99*)
DeCarli, L. (*32*)
Dedonder, R. A. 1961. *Ann. Rev. Biochem.* **30**:347. (*58*)
De Gregorio, M. (*326*)
Dehne, R. (*308*)
DeLamirande, G., Weber, G., and Cantero, A. 1956. *Am. J. Physiol.* **184**: 415. (*224*)
Delaunay, A. (*46, 268*)
Delbarre, F. (*197*)
Delbrück, A. (*72*)
Delbrück, A., and Lipmann, F. 1959. Report to the Gesellschaft für Physiologische Chemie, Berlin, 23–26 September, 1959. (*60*) 1960. Cited by Delbruck, A., *in Struk. Stoffwechsel Bindegewebes, Symp. Med. Univ.-Klin. 2, Muenster, 1959,* p. 38. (*60, 69*)
DelGiacco, R., and Maley, F. 1964. *J. Biol. Chem.* **239**:PC2400. (*104*)
DellaMonica, E. S. (*253*)
Dellert, E. E., and Stahmann, M. A. 1955. *Nature* **176**:1028. (*225*)
Demay, M.-L. (*147, 151*)
De Meio, R. H., and Tkacz, L. 1950. *Arch. Biochem. Biophys.* **27**:242. (*53*)
De Meio, R. H., Wizerkaniuk, M., and Schreibman, I. 1955. *J. Biol. Chem.* **213**:439. (*53, 55*)
Denamur, R., Fauconneau, G., and Guntz, G. 1958. *Compt. Rend.* **246**: 2820. (*82*)
De Nie, I. (*106*)
Denko, C. W. 1958. *J. Lab. Clin. Invest.* **51**:174. (*52*)
Denko, C. W., and Bergenstal, D. M. 1955. *Endocrinology* **57**:76. (*52*)
Denko, C. W., and Priest, R. E. 1957. *J. Lab. Clin. Med.* **50**:107. (*52*)
Denko, C. W., and Stoughton, R. B. 1958. *Arthritis Rheumat.* **1**:77. (*52*)
De Palo, A., and Papadia, S. 1955. *Quaderni Clin. Ostet. Ginecol.* **10**:29. (*391*)
Derache, R., and Mariel, J. P. 1962. *Compt. Rend. Soc. Biol.* **156**:1158. (*100*)
Derevitskaya, V. A. (*83, 87*)
Derow, M. A. (*327*)
Desai, P. (*298, 333*)
Desai, P. R. (*275, 281, 299, 333*)
Desbordes, J. (*188*)
Dessert, A. M. (*197*)
Deutsch, H. F. (*307, 309, 333*)
Deutsch, H. F. 1954. *J. Biol. Chem.* **208**: 669. (*308*)
Deutsch, H. F., and Morton, J. I. 1957. *Science* **125**:600. (*306*)
Deutsch, H. F., Kratochvil, C. H., and Reif, A. E. 1955. *J. Biol. Chem.* **216**: 103. (*307*)
Deutsch, H. F., Thorpe, N. O., and Fudenberg, H. H. 1963. *Immunology* **6**:539. (*306, 307*)
Devigne, J., and Jeuniaux, C. 1961. *Arch. Intern. Physiol. Biochim.* **69**:223. (*181, 182*)
Devlin, H. B. (*322*)
DeVries, A. (*373*)
Dewey, K. F. (*233*)
Diaz, T. (*117*)
Di Caprio, J. M., Rantz, L. A., and Randall, E. 1952. *A.M.A. Arch. Internal Med.* **89**:374. (*187*)
Di Carlo, F. J., and Fiore, J. V. 1958. *Science* **127**:756. (*329*)
Dicker, S. E. (*195*)
Dicker, S. E., and Eggleton, M. G. 1960. *J. Physiol.* **151**:44P. (*195*)
Dickman, S. R. 1958. *Science* **127**:1392. (*224, 225*)
Dickman, S. R., and Proctor, C. M. 1952.

Arch. Biochem. Biophys. **40**:364. (*183*)

Diczfalusy, E., Fernö, O., Fex, H., Högberg, B., Linderot, T., and Rosenberg, T. 1953. *Acta Chem. Scand.* **7**:913. (*197, 226*)

Diczfalusy, E., Fernö, O., Fex, H., Högberg, B., and Kneip, P. 1959. *Acta Chem. Scand.* **13**:1011. (*197*)

Dierickx, L. (*90*)

Di Ferrante, N. (*52, 54*)

Di Ferrante, N. 1954. *J. Biol. Chem.* **209**:579. (*187*) 1956. *J. Biol. Chem.* **220**:303. (*187*) 1964. *Science* **143**:250. (*331*)

Di Ferrante, N., Meyers, A. L., and Miller, L. L. 1964. *Circulation Res.* **15**:451. (*80*)

Di Girolamo, A. (*82*)

DiLapi, M. M. (*268, 317, 326*)

Dirheimer, G. (*183, 184*)

Dirscherl, W., and Krüskemper, H.-L. 1952. *Biochem. Z.* **323**:1. (*197*)

Dirkx, J., and Beumer, J. 1961. *Biochem. J.* **79**:37P. (*356*)

Dische, Z. (*332*)

Dische, Z., Pallavicini, C., Kavasaki, H., Smirnow, N., Cizek, L. J., and Chien, S. 1962. *Arch. Biochem. Biophys.* **97**:459. (*106*)

Disraely, M. N. (*39*)

Di Stefano, V., Neuman, W. F., and Rouser, G. 1953. *Arch. Biochem. Biophys.* **47**:218. (*13*)

Distler, J., and Roseman, S. 1960. *J. Biol. Chem.* **235**:2538. (*21*) 1964. *Proc. Natl. Acad. Sci. U.S.* **51**:897. (*124*)

Dittmann, G. (*51, 52*)

Dixon, F. J. (*310*)

Dixon, F. J., Weigle, W. O., and Vazquez, J. J. 1961. *Lab. Invest.* **10**:216. (*99*)

Dochez, A. R., and Avery, O. T. 1917. *J. Exptl. Med.* **26**:477. (*267*)

Dockrill, M. (*7*)

Doczi, J., Fischman, A., and King, J. A. 1953. *J. Am. Chem. Soc.* **75**:1512. (*264*)

Dodd, B. E. (*269, 273*)

Dodd, M. C. (*271*)

Dodd, M. C., Bigley, N. J., and Geyer, V. B. 1960. *Science* **132**:1398. (*271*) 1963. *J. Immunol.* **90**:518. (*271, 311*)

Dodgson, K. S. (*209*)

Dodgson, K. S. 1959. *Biochim. Biophys. Acta* **35**:532. (*157*) 1961. *Biochem. J.* **78**:324. (*207, 208*)

Dodgson, K. S., and Lloyd, A. G. 1957. *Biochem. J.* **66**:532. (*193, 202–204*) 1958. *Biochem. J.* **68**:88. (*193, 204*) 1961. *Biochem. J.* **78**:319. (*208, 210*)

Dodgson, K. S., Lloyd, A. G., and Spencer, B. 1957. *Biochem. J.* **65**:131. (*202, 205*)

Dodgson, K. S., and Spencer, B. 1953. *Biochem. J.* **55**:436. (*210*) 1954. *Biochem. J.* **57**:310. (*208*)

Dodgson, K. S., Spencer, B., and Thomas, J. 1955. *Biochem. J.* **59**:29. (*207*)

Dodyk, F. (*44*)

Doerr, R. (Ed.) 1948. "Die Immunitaetsforschung," Vol. III: "Die Antigene." Wien: Springer. (*267*)

Doerschuk, A. P. 1952. *J. Biol. Chem.* **195**:855. (*47*)

Dohan, F. C. (*141*)

Doherty, D. G. (*198*)

Doherty, D. G., Burnett, W. T., Jr., and Shapira, R. 1957. *Radiation Res.* **7**:13. (*235*)

Dohlman, C.-H. (*53*)

Dohlman, C.-H. 1956. *Acta Physiol. Scand.* **37**:220. (*52, 209, 210*) 1957. "Chemical and Metabolic Studies on the Cornea." Lund: Berlingska Boktryckeriet. (*51*) 1957a. *Acta Ophthalmol.* **35**:115. (*51, 55*)

Dohlman, C.-H., and Boström, H. 1955. *Acta Ophthalmol.* **33**:455. (*52, 78*)

Dohlman, C.-H., and Friedenwald, J. S. 1955. *J. Histochem. Cytochem.* **3**:492. (*209*)

Doisy, E. A. (*202*)

Doljanski, F. (*382*)

Donahue, V. M. (*254, 255, 261, 374*)

Doniach, D. (*302, 303*)

Doniach, D., and Roitt, I. M. 1957. *J. Clin. Endocrinol. Metabol.* **17**:1293. (*302*)

Donlan, C. P. (*238, 239*)
Donohoe, W. T. A. (*283*)
Donskikh, N. V., and Ivanova, L. N. 1963. *Akusherstvo Ginekol.* **39**:No.4, 79. (*154*)
Dorfman, A. (*4, 19, 45, 46, 48, 49, 52, 56, 59, 60, 65, 67–70, 72, 73, 77–80, 101, 135, 137, 141, 157, 158, 162, 167, 168, 189, 192, 196, 197, 245, 331*)
Dorfman, A. 1948. *J. Biol. Chem.* **172**: 377. (*187, 193*) 1955. *Pharmacol. Rev.* **7**:1. (*46*) 1960. *In* "Studies on Connective Tissue and Its Diseases," Mucopolysaccharide Research Group, Japan. [Private circulation.] (*46*) 1960a. *In* Springer, 1960a. (*335*)
Dorfman, A., and Ott, M. L. 1948. *J. Biol. Chem.* **172**:367. (*187*)
Dorfman, A., Reimers, E. J., and Ott, M. L. 1947. *Proc. Soc. Exptl. Biol. Med.* **64**:357. (*197*)
Dorfman, A., Roseman, S., Ludowieg, J., Mayeda, M., Moses, F. E., and Cifonelli, J. A. 1955. *J. Biol. Chem.* **216**:549. (*4*)
Dorfman, A., Roseman, S., Moses, F. E., Ludowieg, J., and Mayeda, M. 1955a. *J. Biol. Chem.* **212**:583. (*4, 65, 95*)
Dorfman, R. I. (Ed.) 1962. "Methods in Hormone Research," Vol. 2. New York: Academic Press. (*134*)
Dorfman, R. I., and Shipley, R. A. 1956. "Androgens." New York: Wiley. (*134, 140, 142*)
Dorwart, W. V., Jr. (*89*)
Doudoroff, M. (*16, 41*)
Douglas, J. F., and King, C. G. 1953. *J. Biol. Chem.* **202**:865. (*47*)
Doyen, A. (*166*)
Doyle, B. (*192, 239*)
Doyle, J. (*139*)
Doyle, J., and Szirmai, J. A. 1961. *Biochim. Biophys. Acta* **50**:582. (*135, 138*)
Doyle, J., Szirmai, J. A., and de Tyssonsk, E. R. 1964. *Acta Endocrinol.* **45**:457. (*138, 140*)
Draper, P., and Kent, P. W. 1963. *Biochem. J.* **86**:248. (*105*)
Dravis, F. (*181, 182*)
Dray, S., and Young, G. O. 1959. *Science* **129**:1023. (*308*)
Drenckhahn, F.-O., and Meissner, J. 1956. *Arch. Exptl. Pathol. Pharmakol.* **227**:444. (*54*)
Drew, R. M. (*348*)
Dreyer, W. J. (*184, 199*)
Droz, B. (*54*)
Drury, D. R. (*14, 378*)
Dubin, A. (*106*)
Dubos, R. (*229*)
Dubos, R. J. (*323*)
Dudley, H. W. (*322*)
Duff, G. L. (*372*)
Dukes, P. P., Takaku, F., and Goldwasser, E. 1963. *Biochem. Biophys. Res. Commun.* **13**:223. (*43, 106*)
Duncan, C. H., Best, M. M., and McGaff, C. J. 1959. *Lancet* **I**:1014. (*216*)
von Dungern [E.] 1900. *Münch. Med. Wochschr.* **47**:677. (*329*)
Dunn, M. R., and Montgomery, P. O. 1957. *Lab. Invest.* **6**:542. (391)
Dunn, T. B., and Potter, M. 1957. *J. Natl. Cancer. Inst.* **18**:587. (*74*)
Dunsford, I. (*300*)
Dunsford, I., Bowley, C. C., Hutchison, A. M., Thompson, J. S., Sanger, R., and Race, R. R. 1953. *Brit. Med. J.* **2**:81. (*330*)
Du Pan, R. M. (*307*)
Dupont, M. 1934. *Arch. Intern. Med. Exptl.* **9**:133. (*272*)
Duran-Reynals, F. (*362*)
Duran-Reynals, F. 1928. *Compt. Rend. Soc. Biol.* **99**:6. (*361*) 1954. *In* "Connective Tissue in Health and Disease" (G. Asboe-Hansen, ed.), p. 103. Copenhagen: Munksgaard. (*188*)
Duran-Reynals, F., Bunting, H., and van Wagenen, G. 1950. *Ann. N.Y. Acad. Sci.* **52**:1006. (*143–146, 152*)
Duran-Reynals, F., and Duran-Reynals, M. L. 1952. *Science* **115**:40. (*362*)
Duran-Reynals, F., and Stewart, F. W., 1931. *Am. J. Cancer* **15**:2790. (*394*)
Duran-Reynals, M. L. (*361*)
Durant, G. J., Hendrickson, H. R., and

Montgomery, R. 1962. *Arch. Biochem. Biophys.* **99**:418. (*206*)
Durham, N. N. (*116*)
Durieux, J., and Kaminski, M. 1956. *Bull. Soc. Chim. Biol.* **38**:1445. (*312*)
Durso, J. G. (*187*)
Dussaussoy, C. (*188*)
Dussaussoy, C. 1954. Thèse méd. Lille (*188*)
Dutcher, J. D. (*363*)
Duthie, E. S. (*145, 195, 229*)
Duthie, R. B., and Barker, A. N. 1955. *J. Bone Joint Surg.* **37B**:304. (*54*)
Dutton, G. J. (*45, 47*)
Dutton, G. J., and Storey, I. D. E. 1953. *Biochem. J.* **53**:xxxvii. (*45, 47*) 1954. *Biochem. J.* **57**:275. (*47*)
de Duve, C. (*166*)
Dux, C., Guérin, M., and Lacour, F. 1948. *Bull. Assoc. Franc. Etude Cancer* **35**:427. (*394*)
Dyer, J. R. (*163*)
Dyrbye, M. O. 1959. *J. Gerontol.* **14**:32. (*53*)
Dzawachiszwili, N. (*329*)
Dzelzkalns, M. (*141*)
Dziewiatkowski, D. D. (*54*)
Dziewiatkowski, D. D. 1949. *J. Biol. Chem.* **178**:197. (*50, 52*) 1949a. *J. Biol. Chem.* **178**:389. (*50, 69*) 1951. *J. Biol. Chem.* **189**:187. (*51, 52, 69, 77*) 1951a. *J. Exptl. Med.* **93**:451. (*54*) 1952. *J. Exptl. Med.* **95**:489. (*54*) 1953. *J. Exptl. Med.* **98**:119. (*52, 55*) 1954. *J. Exptl. Med.* **100**:11. (*52*) 1956. *J. Biophys. Biochem. Cytol.* **2**:29. (*54, 79*) 1956a. *J. Biol. Chem.* **223**:239. (*210*) 1958. *Intern. Rev. Cytol.* **7**:159. (*51*)
Dziewiatkowski, D. D., Benesch, R. E., and Benesch, R. 1949. *J. Biol. Chem.* **178**:931. (*51, 52, 77*)
Dziewiatkowski, D. D., and Woodard, H. Q. 1959. *Lab. Invest.* **8**:205. (*249*)
Dziewiatkowski, D. D., Di Ferrante, N., Bronner, F., and Okinaka, G. 1957. *J. Exptl. Med.* **106**:509. (*52, 54*)

E

Eadie, G. S. (*224*)
East, M. E., Madinaveitia, J., and Todd, A. R. 1941. *Biochem. J.* **35**:872. (*157, 162*)
Easty, D. M. (*373*)
Easty, G. C., Easty, D. M., and Ambrose, E. J. 1960. *Exptl. Cell Res.* **19**:539. (*373*)
Eberhard, T. (*188, 194*)
Eckl, E. A. (*370, 388*)
Eckstein, P., and Zuckerman, S. 1956. *In* "Marshall's Physiology of Reproduction," 3rd edition (A. S. Parkes, ed.), Vol. I, Part 1, pp. 43–155 and 226–396. London: Longmans. (*143*)
Edmondson, P. R. (*187*)
Edstrom, R. D., and Heath, E. C. 1964. *Biochem. Biophys. Res. Commun.* **16**:576. (*84, 124*)
Edwards, J., and Panos, C. 1962. *J. Bacteriol.* **84**:1202. (*115*)
Edwards, K. W. (*101*)
Eeg-Larsen, N. (*101*)
Eeg-Larsen, N., and Laland, S. G. 1954. *Acta Physiol. Scand.* **30**:295. (*3*)
Egami, F. (*202–204, 207, 208, 266*)
Egami, F., and Takahashi, N. 1955. *J. Chem. Soc. Japan* **59**:1202. (*208*)
Egan, R. W. (*302*)
Eggleton, M. G. (*195*)
Ehrenberg, A., Ehrenberg, L., and Löfroth, G. 1963. *Acta Chem. Scand.* **17**:53. (*243*)
Ehrenberg, L. (*243*)
Ehrich, W. E. 1952. *Am. Heart J.* **43**:121. (*310*)
Ehrlich [P.]. 1879. *Arch. Anat. Physiol.*, p. 166. (*391*)
Ehrlich, P. 1900. *Proc. Roy. Soc.* (*London*) **66**:424. (*272*)
Ehrlich, P. 1904, 1957. "Collected Papers," Vol. 2, Immunology and Cancer Research. Berlin: Springer; London: Pergamon Press. (*267*)
Eiber, H. B. (*206, 210*)
Eiber, H. B., and Danishefsky, I. 1957. *J. Biol. Chem.* **226**:721. (*52, 74*) 1959. *Proc. Soc. Exptl. Biol. Med.* **102**:18. (*260*)
Eichberg, J., Jr., and Karnovsky, M. L.

1963. *J. Biol. Chem.* **238**:3827. (*43, 105*)
Eichel, H. (*269*)
Eisele, J. (*89*)
Eisen, H. N., and Karush, F. 1949. *J. Am. Chem. Soc.* **71**:363. (*306*)
Eisenberg, F., Jr., and Gurin, S. 1952. *J. Biol. Chem.* **195**:317. (*47*)
Eisenberg, S. (*382*)
Eisenberg, S., Ben-Or, S., and Doljanski, F. 1962. *Exptl. Cell Res.* **26**:451. (*382*)
Eisler, M. 1920. *Zentr. Bakteriol. Parasitenk.* **84**:46. (*308*)
Elkner, A., and Slonimski, P. 1927. *Bull. Histol. Appl. Tech. Microscop.* **4**:263. (*139*)
Ellis, F. (*54*)
Ellis, S., Hublé, J., and Simpson, M. E. 1953. *Proc. Soc. Exptl. Biol. Med.* **84**:603. (*52*)
Elliott, H. A. (*215*)
Ellwood, D. C. (*314, 315*)
Elsner, H., Broser, W., and Bürgel, E. 1937. *Z. Physiol. Chem.* **246**:244. (*266*)
Elson, L. A. (*349*)
Elson, L. A., and Morgan, W. T. J. 1933. *Biochem. J.* **27**:1824. (*240*)
Ely, J. O., Tull, F. A., and Schanen, J. M. 1953. *J. Franklin Inst.* **255**:561. (*33, 384, 385*)
Emmart, E. W., and Longley, J. E. 1953. *J. Gen. Physiol.* **37**:361. (*192*)
Emmart, E. W., and Turner, W. A., Jr. 1960. *J. Histochem. Cytochem.* **8**:273. (*196*)
Emmart, E. W., Cole, R. M., May, E. L., and Longley, J. B. 1958. *J. Histochem. Cytochem.* **6**:161. (*196*)
Emmens, C. W. (*134, 148, 187, 193*)
Endecott, B. (*97*)
Enders, J. F. 1929. *J. Exptl. Med.* **50**:777. (*322*)
Endo, H. (*53*)
Engelberg, H. 1958. *Proc. Soc. Exptl. Biol. Med.* **97**:304. (*219*) 1958a. *Proc. Soc. Exptl. Biol. Med.* **99**:489. (*219*)
Engelberg, R. (*227, 266*)
Engfeldt, B., Bergman, G., and Hammarlund-Essler, E. 1954. *Exptl. Cell Res.* **7**:381. (*54*)
Engfeldt, B., Engström, A., and Boström, H. 1954. *Exptl. Cell Res.* **6**:251. (*52, 54*)
Engfeldt, B., and Hammarlund-Essler, E. 1956. *Acta Odontol. Scand.* **14**:293. (*55*)
Engfeldt, B., and Hjertquist, S.-O. 1954. *Acta Pathol. Microbiol. Scand.* **35**:205. (*54*)
Engfeldt, B., and Westerborn, O. 1960. *Acta Pathol. Microbiol. Scand.* **49**:73. (*54*)
Engström, A. (*52, 54*)
Enquist, I. F. (*377*)
Entenman, C. (*96*)
Entner, N., and Doudoroff, M. 1952. *J. Biol. Chem.* **196**:853. (*41*)
Epstein, C. J., and Goldberger, R. F. 1963. *J. Biol. Chem.* **238**:1380. (*184, 199*)
Epstein, F. H., and Block, W. D. 1959. *Proc. Soc. Exptl. Biol. Med.* **101**:740. (*305*)
Erickson, D. 1941. *J. Bacteriol.* **41**:277. (*182*)
Ericsson, Y. (*238*)
Ericsson, Y. 1954. *Acta Pathol. Microbiol. Scand.* **35**:573. (*238*)
Ericsson, Y., and Lundbeck, H. 1955. *Acta Pathol. Microbiol. Scand.* **37**:493. (*238*) 1955a. *Acta Pathol. Microbiol. Scand.* **37**:507. (*238*)
Ericsson, Y., and Stjernström, L. 1951. *Oral Surg. Oral Med. Oral Pathol.* **4**:1465. (*237*)
Erlandson, A. L. (*322*)
Erwin, C. P. (*394*)
Esser, R. J. E. (*42*)
Estrada-Parra, S., Heidelberger, M., and Rebers, P. A. 1963. *J. Biol. Chem.* **238**:510. (*319*)
von Euler, J. (*196, 394*)
Evans, A. S. 1953. *Exptl. Parasitol.* **2**:417. (*189*)
Evans, C., Conney, A. H., Trousof, N., and Burns, J. J. 1959. *Federation Proc.* **18**:223. (*49*)

Evans, D. A. P[rice-]., McConnell, R. B., and Donohoe, W. T. A. 1963. *Abstr. Proc. 11th Intern. Congr. Genet., The Hague, 1963,* p. 293, 15.72. (*283*)

Evans, D. G., Perkins, F. T., and Gaisford, W. 1951. *Lancet* **1**:1253. (*187*)

Evans, H. M. (*85*)

Evans, J. (*371*)

Everall, P. H. (*99, 304*)

Everett, M. R. (*394*)

Eylar, E. H. (*128, 291, 382*)

Eylar, E. H. 1962. *Biochem. Biophys. Res. Commun.* **8**:195. (*83*)

Eylar, E. H., and Jeanloz, R. W. 1962. *J. Biol. Chem.* **237**:622. (*89*). 1962a. *J. Biol. Chem.* **237**:1021. (*352*)

Eyquem, A. (*301*)

Eyquem, A., and Bussard, A. 1949. *Ann. Inst. Pasteur* **77**:160. (*301*)

Ezechieli, S. (*394*)

F

Faarvang, H. J. 1962. *Acta Pharmacol. Toxicol.* **19**:293. (*200*)

Faber, M. 1948. *Acta Med. Scand.* **130**: *Suppl.* 206, p. 351. (*310*)

Faber, V. (*187*)

Fabian, E. 1899. *Z. Physiol. Chem.* **27**: 167. (*32*)

Fabianek, J., Herp, A., Dau, P., and Pigman, W. 1962. *Arthritis Rheumatism* **5**:107. (*237*)

Fabisch, P. (*363*)

Fabris, A. 1927. *Pathologica* **19** (Anno): 157. (*391*)

Fahey, J. L. (*336*)

Fahey, J. L. 1963. *J. Immunol.* **91**:438. (*305*)

Fahey, J. L., and Askonas, B. A. 1962. *J. Exptl. Med.* **115**:623. (*307*)

Fahrenbach, M. J. (*266*)

Faillard, H. (*308, 310, 348, 349*)

Faillard, H. 1957. *Z. Physiol. Chem.* **307**: 62. (*348*) 1959. *Z. Physiol. Chem.* **317**:257. (*352*)

Faillard, H., and Pribilla, W. 1964. *Klin. Wochschr.* **42**:686. (*294*)

Falk, R. (*148*)

Falkowski, F. (*293*)

Fasquelle, R. (*236*)

Fauconneau, G. (*82*)

Faulk, M. (*199*)

Faulkner, P., and Quastel, J. H. 1956. *Nature* **177**:1216. (*36*)

Faustina, C. (*388*)

Favilli, G. 1940. *Nature* **145**:866. (*195, 230*)

Fawcett, B. (*214*)

Fazekas de St. Groth, S. (*85, 86, 346, 354, 355*)

Fazekas de St. Groth, S. 1948. *Australian J. Exptl. Biol. Med. Sci.* **26**:29. (*339*) 1948a. *Australian J. Exptl. Biol. Med. Sci.* **26**:271. (*339*) 1949. *Australian J. Exptl. Biol. Med. Sci.* **27**:65. (*339*)

Fazekas de St. Groth, S., and Gottschalk, A. 1963. *Biochim. Biophys. Acta* **78**: 248. (*354, 355, 359*)

Febvre, H. 1962. *In* "Ultrastructure in Biological Systems" (A. J. Dalton and F. Haguenau, eds.), Vol. I, p. 79. New York: Academic Press. (*365*)

Federico, L. (*34*)

Feigenbaum, A. S. (*94*)

Feinberg, J. G., and Morgan, W. T. J. 1953. *Brit. J. Exptl. Pathol.* **34**: 104. (*330*)

Fekete, J. (*197, 226*)

Feldman, J. (*291, 292*)

Felix, A., and Pitt, R. M. 1934. *Lancet* **2**:186. (*325, 326*) 1934a. *J. Pathol. Bacteriol.* **38**:409. (*325, 326*) 1935. *J. Hyg.* **35**:428. (*325, 326*)

Fell, H. B. (*53*)

Fellig, J. (*224, 227*)

Fellig, J., and Wiley, C. E. 1959. *Arch. Biochem. Biophys.* **85**:313. (*224–226*)

Fellowes, O. N., and Routh, J. I. 1944. *J. Lab. Clin. Med.* **29**:1054. (*321*)

Felsenfeld, H. (*24, 25*)

Felton, L. D. 1932. *J. Immunol.* **23**:405. (*267*)

Felton, L. D., Sutliff, W. D., and Steele, B. F. 1935. *J. Infect. Diseases* **56**:101. (*267*)

Feltz, E. T., and Regelson, W. 1962. *Nature* **196**:642. (*363*)

Ferguson, L. C. (*295*)
Fernö, O. (*197, 226*)
Fernö, O., Fex, H., Högberg, B., Linderot, T., and Rosenberg, T. 1953. *Acta Chem. Scand.* **7**:921. (*197, 226*)
Ferrari, R. A. (*123*)
Ferri, G. (*52*)
Fetherolf, K. (*222*)
Fevold, H. L. (*183*)
Fex, H. (*197, 226*)
Fibiger, J., and Bang, F. 1921. *Kong. Danske Vidensk. Selskabs Biol. Med.* **3**:1. (*391*)
Field, J. B. (*216, 245*)
Field, J. B., Ramsay, G. D., Attyah, A. M., and Starr, P. 1953. *J. Lab. Clin. Med.* **41**:208. (*266*)
Fields, J. (*388*)
Fierke, S. S. (*32*)
Findlay, J. (*157, 165, 166*)
Findlay, J., and Levvy, G. A. 1960. *Biochem. J.* **77**:170. (*157–160, 166*)
Findlay, J., Levvy, G. A., and Marsh, C. A. 1958. *Biochem. J.* **69**:467. (*157, 158, 161, 162, 167*)
Finestone, A. J. (*188*)
Finland, M., and Curnen, E. C. 1938. *Science* **87**:417. (*285, 316*)
Finland, M., and Sutliff, W. D. 1931. *J. Exptl. Med.* **54**:637. (*267*) 1931a. *J. Exptl. Med.* **54**:653 (*267*) 1932. *J. Exptl. Med.* **55**:853. (*267*)
Fiore, M. 1952. *Tumori* **38**:285. (*196*)
Fiore-Donati, L., De Benedictis, G., Chieco-Bianchi, L., and Bertaccini, G. 1962. *Nature* **193**:287. (*391, 392*)
Fiorini, H. (*54*)
Fischer, A. 1936. *Protoplasma* **26**:344. (*370*) 1936–37. *Skand. Arch. Physiol.* **75**:121. (*371*)
Fischer, A., and Herrmann, H. 1937. *Enzymologia* **3**:180. (*224, 225*)
Fischer, E., and Piloty, O. 1891. *Ber. Deut. Chem. Ges.* **24**:521. (*46*)
Fischer, E. H., and Stein, E. A. 1960. *In* "The Enzymes" (P. D. Boyer, H. Lardy, and K. Myrbäck, eds.), Vol. 4, 2nd ed., p. 301. New York: Academic Press. (*181*)
Fischer, H. O. L. (*333*)
Fischman, A. (*264*)
Fisher, B. (*392*)
Fisher, E. R., and Fisher, B. 1965. *Arch. Pathol.* **79**:185. (*392*)
Fisher, H. (*94*)
Fisher, H. W., Puck, T. T., and Sato, G. 1958. *Proc. Natl. Acad. Sci. U.S.* **44**:4. (*372*)
Fisher, M. W., Devlin, H. B., and Erlandson, A. L. 1963. *Nature* **199**:1074. (*322*)
Fisher, R. B., and Zuckerman, S. 1937. *J. Physiol. (London)* **89**:15P. (*146*)
Fishman, W. H. (*195, 221, 222*)
Fitting, C., and Doudoroff, M. 1952. *J. Biol. Chem.* **199**:153. (*16*)
Fitzgerald, J. B. (*101*)
Fjelde, A. (*384*)
Fjelde, A. 1955. *Nature* **175**:434. (*385*)
Fjelde, A., Sorkin, E., and Rhodes, J. M. 1956. *Exptl. Cell Res.* **10**:88. (*384*)
Fleischer, S. (*94, 100*)
Fleming, A. 1922. *Proc. Roy. Soc. (London) Ser. B* **93**:306. (*182*)
Flores, M. (*227*)
Florey, H. W. (*52, 54*)
Földi, M., Papp, N., Kisfaludy, A., and Stekker, K. 1960. *Clin. Chim. Acta* **5**:839. (*188*)
Fogelson, S. J. (*183*)
Folch-Pi, J. 1955. *Biochem. Develop. Nervous Systems, Proc. Intern. Neurochem. Symp., 1st, Oxford, 1954*, p. 121. (*121*)
Folch[-Pi], J., and Le Baron, F. N. 1953. *Federation Proc.* **12**:203. (*120*)
Folch[-Pi], J., Meath, J. A., and Bogoch, S. 1956. *Federation Proc.* **15**:254. (*119*)
Foley, J. B. (*302*)
Folkes, B. F., Grant, R. A., and Jones, J. K. N. 1950. *J. Chem. Soc.*, p. 2136. (*294*)
Forbes, M. (*272, 300*)
Formijne, P., Van der Schoot, J. B., and De Nie, I. 1964. *Biochim. Biophys. Acta* **83**:239. (*106*)
Forrest, J., Overell, B. G., Petrow, V.,

and Stephenson, O. 1952. *J. Pharm. Pharmacol.* **4**:231. (*197*)
Forrester, J. A., Ambrose, E. J., and Stoker, M. G. P. 1964. *Nature* **201**: 945. (*381*)
Forssman, J. 1911. *Biochem. Z.* **37**:78. (*287*)
Foster, A. B., Martlew, E. F., and Stacey, M. 1953. *Chem. Ind.* (*London*), p. 899. (*264*)
Foster, A. B., Martlew, E. F., and Stacey, M. 1954. *Abstr. Am. Chem. Soc., 126th Meeting, New York City, Sept.*, p. 6D. (*56*)
Foster, D. W., and Ginsburg, V. 1961. *Biochim. Biophys. Acta* **54**:376. (*82*)
Foster, J. F., and Yang, J. T. 1953. *J. Am. Chem. Soc.* **75**:5743. (*253*)
Foter, M. J. (*268*)
Fox, H. (*302*)
Fox, M. (*235*)
Fraenkel-Conrat, H. (*183*)
Francis, T., Jr. (*267, 268, 307, 317*)
Francis, T., Jr. 1947. *J. Exptl. Med.* **85**:1. (*340*)
Francis, T., Jr., and Tillett, W. S. 1930. *J. Exptl. Med.* **52**:573. (*268, 307, 317*)
Frank, E. (*197, 226*)
Frank, H. (*114, 313*)
Frank, S. M. (*296*)
Frankel, D. R. (*52, 53*)
Franklin, E. C. (*306, 307*)
Franklin, E. C. 1962. *Nature* **195**:393. (*305*)
Franklin, E. C., and Kunkel, H. G. 1957. *J. Immunol.* **78**:11. (*307, 308*)
Franklin, E. C., and Stanworth, D. R. 1961. *J. Exptl. Med.* **114**:521. (*307*)
Franks, J. J., Mosser, E. L., and Anstadt, G. L. 1963. *J. Gen. Physiol.* **46**:415. (*101*)
Franks, J. J., Edwards, K. W., Lackey, W. W., and Fitzgerald, J. B. 1963. *J. Gen. Physiol.* **46**:427. (*101*)
Fraser, K. B. 1951. *Brit. J. Exptl. Pathol.* **32**:552. (*304*)
Freeman, L. (*371*)
Freeman, M. E. (*193, 194*)
Freeman, N. K. (*215, 259*)
French, E. L. (*42, 172, 175–177, 339, 352*)
French, J. E. (*214, 215*)
Freudenberg, K., and Eichel, H. 1934. *Ann. Chem.* **510**:240. (*269*)
Freudenberg, K., and Molter, H. 1939. *Sitzber. Heidelberg. Akad. Wiss., Math.-Naturw. Kl., Abhandl.*, Part 9, p. 1 (*287*)
Freund, J. 1947. *Ann. Rev. Microbiol.* **1**:291. (*336*)
Freund, L. 1926. *Zool. Anz., Suppl.* (31st Jahrvsmlng.), p. 153. (*147*)
Friberg, U. (*54, 55*)
Friberg, U. 1958. *Arkiv Kemi* **12**:501. (*53, 70*) 1958a. *Arkiv Kemi* **12**:481. (*52, 70*)
Friberg, U., and Ringertz, N. R. 1956. *J. Embryol. Exptl. Morphol.* **4**:313. (*55*)
Frick, E., and Scheid-Seydel, L. 1960. *Klin. Wochschr.* **38**:1240. (*102*)
Friedberg, W. (*94*)
Frieden, E. H., and Hisaw, F. L. 1951. *Endocrinology* **48**:88. (*151*)
Friedenreich, V. 1928. *Acta Pathol. Microbiol. Scand.* **5**:59. (*293*)
Friedenwald, J. S. (*209*)
Friedman, S. (*149*)
Friedmann, R. 1949. *Nature* **164**:626. (*301*)
Friedreich, N., and Kekulé, A. 1859. *Arch. Pathol. Anat. Physiol.* **16**:50. (*310*)
Fromageot, C. (*183*)
Fromme. 1906. *Zentr. Gynaekol.* **30**: 1146. (*391*)
Fromme, I. (*333*)
Frommhagen, L. H., Fahrenbach, M. J., Brockman, J. A., Jr., and Stokstad, E. L. R. 1953. *Proc. Soc. Exptl. Biol. Med.* **82**:280. (*266*)
Frouin, A., and Lisbonne, M. 1911. *Compt. Rend. Soc. Biol.* **70**:26. (*287*)
Frydman, R. B., and Cardini, C. E. 1964. *Biochem. Biophys. Res. Commun.* **14**:353. (*84*)
Fudenberg, H. (*307*)
Fudenberg, H. H. (*306*)
Fudenberg, H. H., and Kunkel, H. G.

1957. *J. Exptl. Med.* **106**:689. (*306*) 1961. *J. Exptl. Med.* **114**:257. (*307*)
Fünfhausen, G. (*292*)
Fuhrmann, G. F. (*382*)
Fuhrmann, G. F., Granzer, E., Kübler, W., Rueff, F., and Ruhenstroth-Bauer, G. 1962. *Z. Naturforsch.* **17b**: 610. (*382*)
Fujisawa, K., Furukawa, K., and Iseki, S. 1963. *Proc. Japan Acad.* **39**:319. (*274*)
Fujiwara, A. (*329*)
Fukasawa, T., and Nikaido, H. 1961. *Biochim. Biophys. Acta* **48**:470. (*123*)
Fukumoto, J. (*88, 90*)
Fukuyama, T. (*53, 74*)
Fulton, G. P. (*246*)
Fulton, J. K., Marcus, S., and Robinson, W. D. 1948. *Proc. Soc. Exptl. Biol. Med.* **69**:258. (*189*)
Funaki, T. (*202*)
Funatsu, M. (*87, 182, 199*)
Furth, J., Hagen, P., and Hirsch, E. I. 1957. *Proc. Soc. Exptl. Biol. Med.* **95**:824. (*74*)
Furuhata, T. 1927. *Jap. Med. World* **7**: 197. (*272*)
Furukawa, K. (*274*)

G

Gabriel, O., and Ashwell, G. 1962. *J. Biol. Chem.* **237**:1400. (*22*)
Gaetani, S. (*52*)
Gagnon, A. (*197*)
Gaines, S. (*336*)
Gaisford, W. (*187*)
Galatch'iants, O. P. (*200*)
Galgano, M. 1950. *Monit. Zool. Ital.* (*Suppl.*) **58**:122; *Biol. Abstr.* **25**: 17474, 1956. (*148*)
Galvin, J. A. (*183*)
Galzinga, L., and Reggiani, A. 1965. *Boll. Soc. Ital. Biol. Sper.* **41**:54. (*250*)
Ganguli, N. C. 1958. *J. Biol. Chem.* **232**:337. (*49*)
Garcia-Bunuel, L. (*126*)
Gardell, S. (*52, 56, 72, 77*)
Gardiner, R. H. (*142, 143*)
Gardner, B. (*274*)
Gargill, S. L. (*192*)
Garner, H. R. (*34*)
Garrault, H. 1933. *Compt. Rend. Soc. Biol.* **113**:158. (*135*) 1933a. *Compt. Rend. Soc. Biol.* **113**:384. (*149*) 1934. *Arch. Anat. Microscop. Morphol. Exptl.* **30**:5. (*134, 135, 139, 149*)
Garrigan, O. W., and Chargaff, E. 1963. *Biochim. Biophys. Acta* **70**:452. (*126*)
Gasic, G., and Gasic, T. 1962. *Proc. Natl. Acad. Sci. U.S.* **48**:1172. (*383*)
Gasic, T. (*383*)
Gauhe, A. (*29, 165, 281–284*)
Gaulden, E. C., and Keating, W. C. 1964. *Metabolism* **13**:466. (*379*)
Gavrilesco, K., Courcon, J., Hillion, P., Uriel, J., Lewin, J., and Grabar, P. 1955. *Nature* **176**:976. (*102*)
Gebhardt, L. P. (*187*)
Gemzell, C. A. (*301*)
Gerber, G. (*105, 249*)
Gerber, G. B., Gerber, G., Altman, K. I., and Hempelmann, L. H. 1962. *Intern. J. Radiation Biol.* **5**:427. (*105, 249*)
Gerber, P., Dutcher, J. D., Adams, E. V., and Sherman, J. H. 1958. *Proc. Soc. Exptl. Biol. Med.* **99**:590. (*363*)
Gey, G. O. (*395*)
Geyer, V. B. (*271, 311*)
Ghose, T. 1960. *Indian J. Med. Sci.* **14**: 190. (*393*)
Ghosh, S. (*24*)
Ghosh, S., and Roseman, S. 1962. *Federation Proc.* **21**:89. (*24*)
Ghosh, S., Blumenthal, H. J., Davidson, E. A., and Roseman, S. 1960. *J. Biol. Chem.* **235**:1265. (*7, 377*)
Ghuysen, J.-M. (*85, 88, 164, 182, 184*)
Ghuysen, J.-M. 1954. *Compt. Rend. Soc. Biol.* **148**:729. (*88*) 1960. *Biochim. Biophys. Acta* **40**:473. (*88, 184*)
Ghuysen, J.-M., and Strominger, J. L. 1963. *Biochemistry* **2**:1110. (*90*) 1963a. *Biochemistry* **2**:1119. (*169*)
Ghuysen, J.-M., Leyh-Bouille, M., and Dierickx, L. 1962. *Biochim. Biophys. Acta* **63**:286. (*90*)
Gibbons, R. A. (*217*)
Gibbons, R. A., and Cheeseman, G. C.

1962. *Biochim. Biophys. Acta* **56**:354. (*85*)

Gibbons, R. A., and Morgan, W. T. J. 1954. *Biochem. J.* **57**:283. (*286*)

Gibertini, G. 1942. *Tumori* (Anno 28) **16**(Ser. 2):317. (*393*)

Gibian, H. (*185, 196*)

Gibian, H. 1951. *Z. Physiol. Chem.* **289**: 1. (*192*) 1952. *Z. Physiol. Chem.* **289**:165. (*187, 192*) 1952a. *Z. Physiol.* **289**:257. (*187, 192*) 1959. "Mucopolysaccharide und Mucopolysaccharidasen" (Vol. IV of "Einzeldarstellungen aus dem Gesamtgebiet der Biochemie") (O. Hoffmann-Ostenhof, ed.). Wien: F. Deuticke. (*46, 185, 186, 188, 194–196, 332*)

Gielen, W. (*311*)

Gigg, R. H. (*123*)

Gilbert, C. (*142–144, 146*)

Gilbert, C. 1944. *S. African J. Med. Sci., Biol. Suppl.* **9**:125. (*143*)

Gilbert, C., and Gillman, J. 1953. *S. African J. Med. Sci., Biol. Suppl.* **18**: 86. (*142*)

Gilbert, H. S. (*284*)

Giles, C. M., Mourant, A. E., Parkin, D. M., Horley, J. F., and Tapson, K. J. 1959. *Brit. Med. J.* **2**:32. (*300*)

Giles, R. B., Jr., and Calkins, E. 1955. *J. Clin. Invest.* **34**:1476. (*310*) 1958. *J. Clin. Invest.* **37**:846. (*310*)

Gillman, J. (*142*)

Gillman, J., and Gilbert, C. 1946. *S. African J. Med. Sci., Biol. Suppl.* **11**:1. (*142–144, 146*) 1953. *J. Obstet. Gynaecol. Brit. Empire* **60**:445. (*142*)

Gillman, T., Pillay, R. A., and Naidoo, S. S. 1960. *J. Endocrinol.* **19**:303. (*147*)

Gilmore, T. E., and Howe, C. 1959. *J. Bacteriol.* **78**:805. (*198*)

Ginsberg, T. (*226*)

Ginsburg, V. (*82, 128*)

Ginsburg, V. 1958. *J. Biol. Chem.* **232**: 55. (*49*) 1958a. *J. Am. Chem. Soc.* **80**:4426. (*82*) 1961. *J. Biol. Chem.* **236**:2389. (*82*)

Ginsburg, V., and Kirkman, H. N. 1958. *J. Am. Chem. Soc.* **80**:3481. (*82*)

Ginsburg, V., Neufeld, E. F., and Hassid, W. Z. 1956. *Proc. Natl. Acad. Sci. U.S.* **42**:333. (*49*)

Ginsburg, V., Stumpf, P. K., and Hassid, W. Z. 1956. *J. Biol. Chem.* **223**:977. (*123*)

Ginsburg, V., Weissbach, A., and Maxwell, E. S. 1958. *Biochim. Biophys. Acta* **28**:649. (*49*)

Giro, S. (*54*)

Gitlin, D. (*310*)

Gladshtein, A. I. (*200*)

Gladstein, A. I. (*200*)

Glaser, E., and Wulwek, W. 1924. *Biochem. Z.* **145**:514. (*157*)

Glaser, L. (*21, 82, 123, 127*)

Glaser, L. 1956. Thesis. Washington University. (*67*) 1958. *J. Biol. Chem.* **232**:627. (*45, 59*) 1959. *Biochim. Biophys. Acta* **31**:575. (*21*) 1959a. *J. Biol. Chem.* **234**:2801. (*21*) 1961. *Biochim. Biophys. Acta* **51**: 169. (*82*)

Glaser, L., and Brown, D. H. 1955. *Proc. Natl. Acad. Sci. U.S.* **41**:253. (*19, 66, 67*) 1957. *J. Biol. Chem.* **228**: 729. (*20, 45, 59, 76*)

Glassman, J. M. (*197*)

Glegg, R. E. (*302*)

Glick, D. (*196, 197, 394*)

Glick, D., and Gollan, F. 1948. *J. Infect. Diseases* **83**:200. (*187*)

Glick, D., Ottoson, R., and Edmondson, P. R. 1958. *J. Biol. Chem.* **233**: 1241. (*187*)

Glick, M. C. (*16, 23*)

Glick, M. C., Sall, T., Zilliken, F., and Mudd, S. 1960. *Biochim. Biophys. Acta* **37**:361. (*28, 29*)

Glücksmann, A. (*54*)

Gluesenkamp, E. (*388*)

Glynn, L. E., and Holborow, E. J. 1952. *Lancet* **2**:449. (*331*) 1959. *Brit. Med. Bull.* **15**:150. (*289*)

Glynn, L. E., Holborow, E. J., and Johnson, G. D. 1956. *J. Immunol.* **76**:357. (*331*) 1957. *Lancet* **2**:1083. (*289*)

Godman, G. (*63*)

Godman, G. C. (*64*)

Goebel, W. F. (*267, 285, 313, 317, 325, 332, 356*)

Goebel, W. F. 1938. *J. Exptl. Med.* **68**: 221. (*269, 285*) 1939. *J. Exptl. Med.* **69**:353. (*335*) 1940. *J. Exptl. Med.* **72**:33. (*335*)

Goebel, W. F., and Adams, M. H. 1943. *J. Exptl. Med.* **77**:435. (*317*)

Goebel, W. F., and Avery, O. T. 1929. *J. Exptl. Med.* **50**:521. (*267, 332*)

Goebel, W. F., Beeson, P. B., and Hoagland, C. L. 1939. *J. Biol. Chem.* **129**: 455. (*286, 316*)

Goebel, W. F., and Jesaitis, M. A. 1952. *J. Exptl. Med.* **96**:425. (*355*)

Goerner, A. 1930–31. *J. Lab. Clin. Med.* **16**:369. (*386*)

Göthman, B. (*53*)

Götz, H. (*308*)

Gofman, J. W. (*215, 259, 371*)

Goldberger, R. F. (*184, 199*)

Goldemberg, S. H. (*59*)

Golden, M. (*126*)

Golden, S. (*99*)

Goldfaber, L. (*72, 77*)

Goldie, H., Turner, T., Faustina, G., Davis, A., and Greene, E. 1962. *Federation Proc.* **21**:165. (*392*)

Goldman, B. (*197*)

Goldwasser, E. (*43, 106*)

Gollan, F. (*187*)

Gonçalves, I. R. J. (*84*)

Goodman, M. (*309*)

Goodner, K. 1925. *J. Infect. Diseases* **37**:285. (*303, 305*)

Gopal-Ayengar, A. R., and Simpson, W. L. 1947. *Cancer Res.* **7**:727. (*393*)

Gordon, A. H. 1961. *Biochem. J.* **80**: 10P. (*99*)

Gordon, A. S. (*85*)

Gordon, E. B. (*273*)

Gordon, R. S., Jr. 1953. *J. Immunol.* **71**:220. (*307*) 1955. *J. Clin. Invest.* **34**:477. (*215, 259*)

Gore, I., and Larkey, B. J. 1960. *J. Lab. Clin. Med.* **56**:839. (*372*)

Gorter, E., and Nanninga, L. 1952. *Koninkl. Ned. Akad. Wetenschap. Proc. Ser. C* **55**:341, 351. (*252*) 1953. *Discussions Faraday Soc.* **No.** 13, p. 205. (*252*)

Got, R. (*83, 100*)

Got, R., and Bourrillon, R. 1960. *Experientia* **16**:495. (*85*) 1961. *Nature* **189**:234. (*357*)

Got, R., Bourrillon, R., and Michon, J. 1960. *Bull. Soc. Chim. Biol.* **42**:41. (*357*)

Gothié, S. (*54*)

Gothié, S. 1961. *Pathol. Biol. Semaine Hop.* **9**:655. (*54, 149*)

Gothoskor, S. S. (*363*)

Gottschalk, A. (*83, 87, 90, 106, 328, 341, 343, 344, 348, 351, 352, 354, 355, 359*)

Gottschalk, A. 1951. *Nature* **167**:845. (*347*) 1952. *Nature* **170**:662. (*341, 343*) 1953. *Nature* **172**:808. (*349*) 1954. *Nature* **174**:652. (*349*) 1955. *Biochem. J.* **61**:298. (*349*) 1956. *Biochim. Biophys. Acta* **20**:560. (*348, 351*) 1957. *Biochim. Biophys. Acta* **23**:645. (*42, 351*) 1958. *In* "Ciba Foundation Symposium, Chemistry and Biology of Mucopolysaccharides, 1957" (G. E. W. Wolstenholme and M. O'Connor, eds.), p. 287. Boston: Little, Brown. (*341*) 1958a. *Advan. Enzymol.* **20**:135. (*171, 351*) 1959. *Ergeb. Hyg. Bakteriol. Immunitaetsforsch. Exptl. Therap.* **32**: 1. (*337, 359*) 1960. "The Chemistry and Biology of Sialic Acids and Related Substances." London: Cambridge Univ. Press. (*173, 290, 293, 353*) 1962. *Perspectives Biol. Med.* **5**:327. (*355*) 1963. *In* "Comprehensive Biochemistry" (M. Florkin and E. H. Stotz, eds.), Sect. 2 (Vol. **8**), p. 17. Amsterdam: Elsevier. (*341, 355*)

Gottschalk, A., and Ada, G. L. 1956. *Biochem. J.* **62**:681. (*302*)

Gottschalk, A., and Fazekas de St. Groth, S. 1960. *Biochim. Biophys. Acta* **43**:513. (*85, 86, 354*) 1960a. *J. Gen. Microbiol.* **22**:690. (*346, 354, 355*)

Gottschalk, A., and Graham, E. R. B. 1958. *Z. Naturforsch.* **13b**:821. (*352*)

1959. *Biochim. Biophys. Acta* **34**: 380. (*344*)
Gottschalk, A., and Lind, P. E. 1949. *Brit. J. Exptl. Pathol.* **30**:85. (*340*) 1949a. *Nature* **164**:232. (*347*)
Gottschalk, A., and McKenzie, H. A. 1961. *Biochim. Biophys. Acta* **54**: 226. (*341, 342, 344*)
Gottschalk, A., and Murphy, W. H. 1961. *Biochim. Biophys. Acta* **46**:81. (*86, 341*)
Gottschalk, A., Murphy, W. H., and Graham, E. R. B. 1962. *Nature* **194**:1051. (*84*)
Gottschalk, A., and Perry, B. T. 1951. *Brit. J. Exptl. Pathol.* **32**:408. (*349, 353, 358*)
Gottschalk, A., and Simmonds, D. H. 1960. *Biochim. Biophys. Acta* **42**: 141. (*341, 342*)
Gottschalk, A., and Thomas, M. A. W. 1961. *Biochim. Biophys. Acta* **46**:91. (*86, 238, 344*)
Gottschalk, A., Whitten, W. K., and Graham, E. R. B. 1960. *Biochim. Biophys. Acta* **38**:183. (*356*)
Gottschalk, R. G. 1960. *J. Bone Joint Surg.* **42**:1239. (*54*)
Gottschalk, R. G., and Allen, H. C., Jr. 1952. *Proc. Soc. Exptl. Biol. Med.* **80**:334. (*54*)
Gouws, F. (*52*)
Graae, J. (*194*)
Graae, J., and Jensen, C. E. 1956. *Acta Chem. Scand.* **10**:643. (*194*)
Grabar, P. (*102*)
Grabar, P., and Williams, C. A. 1953. *Biochim. Biophys. Acta* **10**:193. (*267*)
Grässlin, D. (*106*)
Graf, L. (*311*)
Graham, D. M., Lyon, T. P., Gofman, J. W., Jones, H. B., Yankley, A., Simonton, J., and White, S. 1951. *Circulation* **4**:666. (*259, 371*)
Graham, E. R. B. (*84, 344, 352, 357*)
Graham, E. R. B. 1961. *Australian J. Sci.* **24**:140. (*348, 372*)
Graham, E. R. B., and Gottschalk, A. 1960. *Biochim. Biophys. Acta* **38**: 513. (*341, 343, 348, 351*)
Graham, F. (*300*)
Gramling, E. (*232*)
Grant, G. H., and Everall, P. H. 1957. *J. Clin. Pathol.* **10**:360. (*99, 304*)
Grant, P. T., and Long, C. 1952. *Biochem. J.* **50**:xx. (*14*)
Grant, R. A. (*294*)
Granzer, E. (*382*)
Grassmann, W., Zechmeister, L., Bender, R., and Tóth, G. 1934. *Ber. Deut. Chem. Ges.* **67**:*I, Abt. B,* 1. (*155*)
Graves, J. H. (*141*)
Green, J. 1952. *Nature* **169**:546. (*263*)
Green, J. P. (*74, 211*)
Green, J. P., and Robinson, J. D., Jr. 1959. *Federation Proc.* **18**:398. (*52*) 1960. *J. Biol. Chem.* **235**:1621. (*52, 120*)
Green, M., and Stahmann, M. A. 1953. *Proc. Soc. Exptl. Biol. Med.* **83**:852. (*363*) 1954. *Proc. Soc. Exptl. Biol. Med.* **87**:507. (*363*)
Green, M., Stahmann, M. A., and Rasmussen, A. F., Jr. 1953. *Proc. Soc. Exptl. Biol. Med.* **83**:641. (*362*)
Greenberg, B. E. (*192*)
Greenberg, G. R. (*313*)
Greenberg, J., Taylor, D. J., and Bond, H. W. 1956. *Am. J. Trop. Med. Hyg.* **5**:62. (*34*)
Greene, E. (*388*)
Greene, R. R., and Harris, S. C. 1940. *Proc. Soc. Exptl. Biol. Med.* **45**:34. (*149*)
Greening, S. G. (*389*)
Greenspan, E. M. 1954. *A.M.A. Arch. Internal Med.* **93**:863. (*92*)
Greenstein, J. P. (*33*)
Greenstein, J. P., and Jenrette, W. V. 1941. *Cold Spring Harbor Symp. Quant. Biol.* **9**:236. (*252*)
Gregory, J. (*83*)
Gregory, J. D., and Nose, Y. 1957. *Federation Proc.* **16**:189. (*56*)
Gregory, J. D., and Robbins, P. W. 1960. *Ann. Rev. Biochem.* **29**:347. (*53*)
Gregson, N. A. (*125*)
Greif, R. L. 1952. *J. Biol. Chem.* **194**: 619. (*187*)

Greig, C. G. 1960. Ph.D. Thesis: University of London. *(157, 160–162)*

Greig, C. G., Leaback, D. H., and Walker, P. G. 1961. *J. Chem. Soc.*, p. 879. *(162)*

Greiling, H. *(14, 194)*

Greiling, H. 1957. *Z. Physiol. Chem.* **309**:239. *(188, 194)*

Greiling, H., and Bauditz, W. 1959. *Naturwissenschaften* **46**:355. *(61, 69)*

Greiling, H., Günther, T., and Eberhard, T. 1960. *Z. Physiol. Chem.* **319**: 161. *(188, 194)*

Greulich, R. C. 1956. *Exptl. Cell Res.* **11**:225. *(54)*

Greulich, R. C., and Friberg, U. 1957. *Exptl. Cell Res.* **12**:685. *(55)*

Griffin, G. E. *(86)*

Griffin, J. L. *(369)*

Griffith, G. C. *(216)*

Grillo, H. C. *(373)*

Gross, F. *(197)*

Gross, J. *(200, 373)*

Gross, J. I., Mathews, M. B., and Dorfman, A. 1960. *J. Biol. Chem.* **235**: 2889. *(78, 79, 101)*

Grossfeld, H., Meyer, K., and Godman, G. 1955. *Proc. Soc. Exptl. Biol. Med.* **88**:31. *(63)*

Grossfeld, H., Meyer, K., Godman, G., and Linker, A. 1957. *J. Biophys. Biochem. Cytol.* **3**:391. *(63)*

Grubb, R. 1959. *In* "Ciba Foundation Symposium, Biochemistry of Human Genetics, 1959" (G. E. W. Wolstenholme and C. M. O'Connor, eds.), p. 264. Boston: Little, Brown. *(306, 308, 336)*

Grubb, R., and Laurell, A.-B. 1956. *Acta Pathol. Microbiol. Scand.* **39**: 390. *(308)*

Grubin, A. F. *(238, 239)*

Grula, E. A. *(118)*

Gryder, R. M. *(7)*

Gude, W. D. *(54)*

Günther, H. *(140)*

Günther, T. *(188, 194)*

Günther, T., and Greiling, H. 1960. *Z. Physiol. Chem.* **318**:234. *(14)*

Guérin, M. *(394)*

Guidotti, G. 1957. *Exptl. Cell Res.* **12**: 659. *(55)*

Guldberg, G. 1934. *Bull. Assoc. Franc. Etude Cancer* **23**:155. *(391)*

Gulick, Z. R. *(226)*

Guntz, G. *(82)*

Gurin, S. *(47, 301)*

Gurin, S. 1942. *Proc. Soc. Exptl. Biol. Med.* **49**:48. *(301)*

Gurin, S., Bachman, C., and Wilson, D. W. 1939. *J. Biol. Chem.* **128**:525. *(301)* 1940. *J. Biol. Chem.* **133**:477. *(301)*

Gurner, B. W. *(290)*

Gustafsson, B. E. *(80)*

György, P. *(28, 82, 157, 167, 181, 269, 286, 293, 294, 348)*

György, P., Norris, R. F., and Rose, C. S. 1954. *Arch. Biochem. Biophys.* **48**:193. *(28)*

H

Haagen-Smit, A. J. *(92)*

Haas, H. J. *(281)*

Haase, H. *(188)*

Haber, E. *(222)*

Haber, E., and Anfinsen, C. B. 1961. *J. Biol. Chem.* **236**:422. *(222)*

Haber, F. *(281)*

Haber, G. V. *(284)*

Habermann, E. 1957. *Biochem. Z.* **329**:1. *(193)* 1958–59. *Arch. Exptl. Pathol. Pharmakol.* **235**:513. *(194)*

Habich, H. 1953. *Schweiz. Med. Wochschr.* **83**:1253. *(307)*

Hackman, R. H. 1954. *Australian J. Biol. Sci.* **7**:168. *(35, 182)*

Hadarag, E. *(224)*

Hadhazy, C. *(105)*

Hadidian, Z., and Pirie, N. W. 1948. *Biochem. J.* **42**:266. *(187)*

Hadjiioannou, S. *(91)*

Häkkinen, I. P. T. 1960. *Acta Physiol. Scand. Suppl.* **177**, p. 51. *(52)*

Hässig, A. *(307)*

Hässig, A. 1961. *Ergeb. Mikrobiol.* **34**: 180. *(307)*

Hagen, P. *(74)*

Hahn, L. 1943. *Biochem. Z.* **315**:83. *(187)* 1945. *Arkiv Kemi* **21A**:No.

1, p. 1. (*157, 192*) 1945a. *Arkiv Kemi* **A19**:33. (*195*) 1946. *Arkiv Kemi* **22A**:1. (*192*) 1947. *Biochem. Z.* **318**:123. (*192*) 1947a. *Biochem. Z.* **318**:138. (*192*) 1952. *Nature* **170**: 282. (*226*)

Hahn, L., and Fekete, J. 1953. *Acta Chem. Scand.* **7**:798. (*197, 226*)

Hahn, L., and Frank, E. 1953. *Acta Chem. Scand.* **7**:806. (*197, 226*)

Hahn, N. J. Ansell (*289, 300*)

Hahn, P. F. 1943. *Science* **98**:19. (*214, 251*)

Hajra, A. K., and Radin, N. S. 1963. *Biochim. Biophys. Acta* **70**:97. (*126*)

Hakomori, S. (*106*)

Hakomori, S., and Ishimoda, T. 1962. *J. Biochem.* (*Tokyo*) **52**:250. (*106*)

Hakomori, S., and Jeanloz, R. W. 1961. *J. Biol. Chem.* **236**:2827. (*270*)

Hakomori, S., Kawauchi, H., and Ishimoda, T. 1962. *Biochim. Biophys. Acta* **65**:546. (*106*)

Hale, C. W. (*187, 188, 229, 230, 236*)

Hale, C. W. 1944. *Biochem. J.* **38**:362. (*230, 234*)

Hall, J. J. (*192, 238*)

Hall, K. 1938. *J. Pathol. Bacteriol.* **47**:19. (*148*) 1947. *J. Endocrinol.* **5**:174. (*151*) 1950. *J. Endocrinol.* **7**:54. (*151*) 1956. *J. Endocrinol.* **13**: 384. (*151*)

Hallauer, C. 1934. *Z. Immunitaetsforsch.* **83**:114. (*270*)

Halwer, M., Nutting, G. C., and Brice, B. A. 1951. *J. Am. Chem. Soc.* **73**: 2786. (*183*)

Hamagami, L. T. (*307*)

Hamaguchi, K., and Funatsu, M. 1959. *J. Biochem.* (*Tokyo*) **46**:1659. (*87, 182*)

Hamaguchi, K., and Kurono, A. 1963. *J. Biochem.* (*Tokyo*) **54**:497. (*199*)

Hamaguchi, K., Hayashi, K., Imoto, T., and Funatsu, M. 1964. *J. Biochem.* (*Tokyo*) **55**:24. (*199*)

Hamano, M. (*308*)

Hambraeus, L., Rodén, L., and Boström, H. 1959. *Acta Soc. Med. Upsalien.* **64**:247. (*48, 75*)

Hamburger, F., and Dehne [R.]. 1904. *Wien. Klin. Wochschr.* **17**:457. (*308*)

Hamilton, J. B. 1936. *Proc. Soc. Exptl. Biol. Med.* **35**:386. (*148*)

Hammarlund-Essler, E. (*54, 55*)

Hanavan, H. R. (*100*)

Hancock, R., and Park, J. T. 1958. *Nature* **181**:1050. (*110*)

Handa, N. (*311*)

Hanessian, S. (*322*)

Hansen, R. G. (*84*)

Hanson, R. W. (*255, 257*)

Hany, A. (*126*)

Harbon, S. (*83*)

Harder, F. (*371*)

Hardesty, M. 1931. *Am. J. Anat.* **47**: 277. (*134, 137, 140*)

Harding, C. V. 1951. *Exptl. Cell Res.* **2**:403. (*368, 369*)

Harding, D. 1949. *Proc. Soc. Exptl. Biol. Med.* **71**:14. (*368*)

Hardy, F. E. (*113*)

Hare, R. (*337*)

Harlow, C. (*149*)

Harpur, R. P., and Quastel, J. H. 1949. *Nature* **164**:693. (*13, 377*) 1949a. *Nature* **164**:779. (*13, 377*)

Harries, H. J. (*394*)

Harris, A. (*94*)

Harris, H. (*111, 313*)

Harris, P. M. (*216*)

Harris, R., Harrison, G. A., and Rondle, C. J. M. 1963. *Acta Genet. Statist. Med.* **13**:44. (*329*)

Harris, S. (*187*)

Harris, S. C. (*149*)

Harris, T. N., and Harris, S. 1950. *J. Immunol.* **65**:255. (*186, 187*)

Harris, T. N., Abrams, W. B., and Harris, S. 1950. *J. Infect. Diseases* **86**:122. (*187*)

Harrison, G. A. (*329*)

Harte, R. A. (*287*)

Hartles, R. L., and McLean, N. D. 1952. *Brit. Dental J.* **93**:147. (*202*)

Hartman, C. G. 1932. *Contr. Embryol. Carnegie Instn.* **23**, No. 134 (Publ. No. 433): 1. (*143*)

Hartmann, A. F. (*314, 321*)

Hartree, E. F. (*200*)

Hartsell, S. E. (*183*)
Hartwell, J. L., Shear, M. J., Adams, J. R., Jr., and Perrault, A. 1943. *J. Natl. Cancer Inst.* **4**:107. (*389*)
Hasegawa, E., Delbrück, A., and Lipmann, F. 1961. *Federation Proc.* **20**:86. (*72*)
Hashimoto, Y. (*295*)
Haskell, T. H., and Hanessian, S. 1963. *Nature* **199**:1075. (*322*)
Hassid, W. Z. (*19, 49, 84, 123*)
Hassid, W. Z., Neufeld, E. F., and Feingold, D. S. 1959. *Proc. Natl. Acad. Sci. U.S.* **45**:905. (*82*)
Hatheway, C. L., Ludwick, T. M., and Weseli, D. F. 1964. *J. Dairy Sci.* **47**:693. (*295*)
Hattori, C. (*208*)
Hauk, R., and Brown, D. H. 1959. *Biochim. Biophys. Acta* **33**:556. (*59*)
Haukenes, G. 1962. *Acta Pathol. Microbiol. Scand.* **55**:450. (*314, 315*)
Haukenes, G., Ellwood, D. C., Baddiley, J., and Oeding, P. 1961. *Biochim. Biophys. Acta* **53**:425. (*314, 315*)
Haurowitz, F. (*94*)
Haurowitz, F. 1952. *Biol. Rev. Cambridge Phil. Soc.* **27**:247. (*336*)
Haurowitz, F., and Breinl, F. 1933. *Z. Physiol. Chem.* **214**:111. (*267*)
Haurowitz, F., Fleischer, S., Walter, H., and Leitze, A. 1958-1959. *Proc. U.N. Intern. Conf. Peaceful Uses Atomic Energy, 2nd, Geneva* **25**:111. (*100*)
Hauser, G. 1964. *Biochim. Biophys. Acta* **84**:212. (*125*)
Hauser, G., and Karnovsky, M. L. 1957. *J. Biol. Chem.* **224**:91. (*123*)
Hausheer, L. (*126*)
Hauss, W. H. (*52*)
Hauss, W. H., Junge-Hülsing, G., and Holländer, H. J. 1962. *J. Atheroscler. Res.* **2**:50. (*52*)
Hauss, W. H., Junge-Hülsing, G., and Schulze, W. 1960. *Z. Alternsforsch.* **14**:259. (*52*)
Havel, R. J. (*216, 266*)
Havel, R. J., and Boyle, E. 1954. *Proc. Soc. Exptl. Biol. Med.* **85**:468. (*219*)
Havel, R. J., and Bragdon, J. H. 1954. *Circulation* **10**:591. (*216*)
Havez, R. (*99*)
Hawk, H. W., Bitman, J., Cecil, H. C., Wiltbank, J. N., Bond, J., and Sykes, J. F. 1961. *Am. J. Physiol.* **200**:345. (*149*)
Hawkins, J. D. 1961. *Biochem. J.* **80**:210. (*99*)
Hawkins, W. (*232*)
Hawkins, W. W. (*372*)
Hawkins, W. W., and Leonard, V. G. 1958. *Can. J. Biochem. Physiol.* **36**:161. (*371*)
Hawkins, W. W., and O'Neill, A. N. 1955. *Can. J. Biochem. Physiol.* **33**:545. (*372*)
Haworth, N., Kent, P. W., and Stacey, M. 1948. *J. Chem. Soc.*, p. 1211. (*322*) 1948a. *J. Chem. Soc.*, p. 1220. (*322*)
Hawthorne, E. W. (*142*)
Hawthorne, J. R. 1950. *Biochim. Biophys. Acta* **6**:94. (*322*)
Hay, A. J. (*91, 169*)
Hayano, S., and Tobimatsu, G. 1956. *Japan. J. Exptl. Med.* **26**:57. (*34*)
Hayashi, H., Funaki, T., Udaka, K., and Kato, Y. 1955. *Mie Med. J.* **4**:Suppl. 2, p. 143. (*202*)
Hayashi, J. A., Stone, W. H., Link, K. P., and Irwin, M. R. 1958. *J. Immunol.* **81**:82. (*295*)
Hayashi, K. (*128, 199*)
Hayes, F. (*24*)
Heagy, F. C. (*52*)
Heard, D. H. (*373, 381, 382*)
Heard, D. H., Seaman, G. V. F., and Simon-Reuss, I. 1961. *Nature* **190**:1009. (*382*)
Heath, E. C. (*84, 124*)
Hedberg, H., and Moritz, U. 1958. *Proc. Soc. Exptl. Biol. Med.* **98**:80. (*63*)
Hedenius, P. 1939. *Acta Med. Scand.* **100**:130. (*387*)
Hedenius, P., and Snellman, B. 1937. *Nord. Med. Tidskr.* **13**:914. (*387*)
Heide, K. (*305*)
Heidelberger, M. (*64, 267, 302, 303, 306, 308, 314, 316, 317, 319, 330, 332, 336*)

Heidelberger, M. 1927. *Physiol. Rev.* **7**:107. (*269*) 1938. *J. Am. Chem. Soc.* **60**:242. (*303*) 1953. *In* "The Nature and Significance of the Antibody Response" (A. M. Pappenheimer, Jr., ed.), p. 90. New York: Columbia Univ. Press. (*268*) 1955. *J. Am. Chem. Soc.* **77**:4308. (*286*) 1956. "Lectures in Immunochemistry." New York: Academic Press. (*267, 315, 332, 333, 336*) 1959. *Proc. Intern. Congr. Biochem., 4th, Vienna, 1958* **1**:52. (*312, 315*)

Heidelberger, M., and Avery, O. T. 1923. *J. Exptl. Med.* **38**:73. (*267, 313*) 1924. *J. Exptl. Med.* **40**:301. (*313*)

Heidelberger, M., Barker, S. A., and Björklund, B. 1958. *J. Am. Chem. Soc.* **80**:113. (*318*)

Heidelberger, M., Barker, S. A., and Stacey, M. 1954. *Science* **120**:781. (*317*)

Heidelberger, M., Goebel, W. F., and Avery, O. T. 1925. *J. Exptl. Med.* **42**:727. (*313*)

Heidelberger, M., and Kabat, E. A. 1936. *J. Exptl. Med.* **63**:737. (*305*) 1937. *J. Exptl. Med.* **65**:885. (*290*)

Heidelberger, M., and Kendall, F. E. 1931. *J. Exptl. Med.* **53**:625. (*269, 317*) 1932. *J. Biol. Chem.* **95**:127. (*269, 317*) 1933. *J. Exptl. Med.* **57**:373. (*315, 316, 318*) 1937. *J. Exptl. Med.* **65**:647. (*318*)

Heidelberger, M., Kendall, F. E., and Scherp, H. W. 1936. *J. Exptl. Med.* **64**:559. (*317*)

Heidelberger, M., MacLeod, C. M., and DiLapi, M. M. 1948. *J. Exptl. Med.* **88**:369. (*317*) 1951. *J. Immunol.* **66**:145. (*326*)

Heidelberger, M., and MacPherson, C. F. C. 1943. *Science* **97**:405. (*275*) 1943a. *Science* **98**:63. (*275*)

Heidelberger, M., and Menzel, A. E. O. 1937. *J. Biol. Chem.* **118**:79. (*322*)

Heidelberger, M., and Pedersen, K. O. 1937. *J. Exptl. Med.* **65**:393. (*306, 318*)

Heidelberger, M., Pedersen, K. O., and Tiselius, A. 1936. *Nature* **138**:165. (*306*)

Heidelberger, M., Treffers, H. P., and Mayer, M. 1940. *J. Exptl. Med.* **71**:271. (*267*)

Heidelberger, M., Treffers, H. P., Schoenheimer, R., Ratner, S., and Rittenberg, D. 1942. *J. Biol. Chem.* **144**:555. (*336*)

Heidelberger, M., MacLeod, C. M., Kaiser, S. J., and Robinson, B. 1946. *J. Exptl. Med.* **83**:303. (*268, 317*)

Heidelberger, M., MacLeod, C. M., Hodges, R. G., Bernhard, W. G., and DiLapi, M. M. 1947. *J. Exptl. Med.* **85**:227. (*317*)

Heidelberger, M., DiLapi, M. M., Siegel, M., and Walter, A. W. 1950. *J. Immunol.* **65**:535. (*268, 317*)

Heidelberger, M., Dische, Z., Neely, W. B., and Wolfrom, M. L. 1955. *J. Am. Chem. Soc.* **77**:3511. (*332*)

Heilbrunn, L. V. 1928. "The Colloid Chemistry of Protoplasm." Berlin: Borntraeger. (*367*)

Heilbrunn, L. V., and Wilson, W. L. 1949. *Proc. Soc. Exptl. Biol. Med.* **70**:179. (*251, 367*) 1950. *Science* **112**:56. (*367*) 1950a. *Protoplasma* **39**:28. (*367*)

Heimer, R., and Meyer, K. 1956. *Proc. Natl. Acad. Sci. U.S.* **42**:728. (*23, 41, 171, 348, 351*) 1958. *Biochim. Biophys. Acta* **27**:490. (*27*)

Heinle, R. W. (*294*)

Hektoen, L., Fox, H., and Schulhof, K. 1927. *J. Infect. Diseases* **40**:641. (*302*)

Hektoen, L., and Schulhof, K. 1925. *Proc. Natl. Acad. Sci. U.S.* **11**:481. (*302*)

Hele, T. S. 1924. *Biochem. J.* **18**:110. (*50*) 1931. *Biochem. J.* **25**:1736. (*50*)

Helferich, B., and Iloff, A. 1933. *Z. Physiol. Chem.* **221**:252. (*155, 157, 158, 162*)

Hemerline, A. (*7*)

Hemmings, W. A. (*307*)

Hempelmann, L. H. (*105, 249*)

Hendrickson, H. R. (*206*)
Hennessey, F. B. (*260*)
Hennigar, G. R. (*379*)
Henry, A. H. (*141*)
Henry, H. (*311, 329*)
Herbst, F. S. M., Lever, W. F., and Hurley, N. A. 1955. *J. Invest. Dermatol.* **24**:507. (*260*)
Herbst, F. S. M., Lever, W. F., Lyons, M. E., and Hurley, N. A. 1955. *J. Clin. Invest.* **34**:581. (*260*)
Heremans, J. F. (*304*)
Heremans, J. F. 1960. "Les globulines sériques du système gamma; leur nature et leur pathologie." Paris: Masson; Bruxelles: Arscia. (*306*)
Heremans, J. F., Heremans, M.-T., and Schultze, H. E. 1959. *Clin. Chim. Acta* **4**:96. (*307*)
Heremans, M.-T. (*307*)
Heringa, G. C. 1948. *Verhandel. Koninkl. Vlaam. Acad. Geneeskunde Belg.* **10**: 7. (*139, 151*)
Heringa, G. C., and de Jongh, S. E. 1934. *Z. Zellforsch. Mikroskop. Anat.* **21**:629. (*149, 150*)
Heringa, G. C., and Weidinger, A. 1940. *Ned. Tijdschr. Geneesk.* **84**:4907. (*139*)
Herman, G., Harbon, S., Rossignol, B., and Clauser, H. 1964. *Abstr. Proc. Intern. Congr. Biochem., 6th, New York, 1964,* Sect. VI, p. 510. (*83*)
Herman, M. (*290*)
Hermann, G. 1963. *Verhandl. Deut. Ges. Inn. Med.* **69**:178. (*106*)
Hern, D. (*97*)
Hern, D. L. (*100*)
Hernandez, T. (*379*)
Herp, A. (*237*)
Herrick, E. H., and Torstveit, O. 1938. *Endocrinology* **22**:469. (*141*)
Herring, P. T., and Hynd, A. 1928. *J. Physiol. (London)* **66**:267. (*3*)
Herriott, R. M. 1941. *J. Gen. Physiol.* **24**:325. (*220*)
Herrmann, H. (*224, 225*)
Hertz, R., and Tullner, W. 1947. *J. Natl. Cancer Inst.* **8**:121. (*142*)
Herve, A. (*235*)
Herzog, H. L. (*366*)
Hestrin, S., and Avigad, G. 1958. *Biochem. J.* **69**:388. (*29*)
Hewitt, W. F., Jr. 1947. *Anat. Record* **98**:159. (*141*)
Heymann, H. (*116*)
Heymann, H., Ovlick, Z. R., De Boer, C. J., Stevens, G. D., and Mayer, P. L. 1958. *Arch. Biochem. Biophys.* **73**:366. (*363*)
Heymann, H., Ginsberg, T., Gulick, Z. R., and Mayer, R. L. 1959. *Proc. Soc. Exptl. Biol. Med.* **100**:279. (*226*)
Heyns, K., Koch, C.-M., and Koch, W. 1954. *Z. Physiol. Chem.* **296**:121. (*11*)
Heyns, K., and Meinecke, K.-H. 1953. *Chem. Ber.* **86**:1453. (*11*)
Heyns, K., Kiessling, G., Lindenberg, W., Paulsen, H., and Webster, M. E. 1959. *Chem. Ber.* **92**:2435. (*22, 326*)
Heyworth, R. (*17, 88, 156–163*)
Heyworth, R., and Bacon, J. S. D. 1957. *Biochem. J.* **66**:41. (*27*)
Heyworth, R., Leaback, D. H., and Walker, P. G. 1959. *J. Chem. Soc.,* p. 4121. (*155, 158*)
Heyworth, R., Perkins, H. R., and Walker, P. G. 1961. *Nature* **190**: 261. (*30, 163*)
Higginbotham, R. D., and Murillo, G. J. 1965. *J. Immunol.* **94**:228. (*365*)
Higuchi, K. 1930. *Folia Haematol.* **41**: 401. (*391*)
Hill, C. R. (*54*)
Hill-Cottingham, D. G. 1955. *Nature* **175**:347. (*234*)
Hilliard, G. W., and Nash, H. E. 1951. *J. Lab. Clin. Med.* **38**:846. (*392*)
Hillion, P. (*102*)
Hilz, H., and Lipmann, F. 1955. *Proc. Natl. Acad. Sci. U.S.* **41**:880. (*55*)
Hirs, C. H. W. (*83*)
Hirsch, E. I. (*74*)
Hirschfeld, J. 1959. *Acta Pathol. Microbiol. Scand.* **46**:229. (*308*) 1960. *Sci. Tools* **7**:18. (*309*)
Hirschman, A. 1961. *Abstr. Proc. Intern.*

Congr. Biochem., 5th, Moscow, 1961, Abstr. no. 17.61.2087. (*52, 79*)
Hirschmann, D. J. (*183*)
Hirst, G. K. 1941. *Science* **94**:22. (*337*) 1941a. *J. Exptl. Med.* **73**:493. (*195*) 1942. *J. Exptl. Med.* **75**:49. (*338*) 1942a. *J. Exptl. Med.* **76**:195. (*171, 338*) 1943. *J. Exptl. Med.* **78**:99. (*338*) 1945. *Ann. Rept. Intern. Health Div. Rockefeller Found.*, p. 50. (*339*)
Hirszfeld, L. 1926. *Ergeb. Hyg.* **8**:367. (*272*)
Hisatsune, K. (*323*)
Hisaw, F. L. (*151*)
Hisaw, F. L. 1925. *J. Exptl. Zool.* **42**: 411. (*151*)
Hiyama, N. 1949. *Tohoku J. Exptl. Med.* **50**:373. (*294*) 1949a. *Tohoku J. Exptl. Med.* **50**:379. (*294*) 1949b. *Tohoku J. Exptl. Med.* **50**:385. (*294*)
Hjertquist, S.-O. (*54*)
Hjertquist, S.-O. 1961. *Biochim. Biol. Sper.* **1**:126. (*52*) 1962. *Acta Pathol. Microbiol. Scand. Suppl.* **154**:99. (*54*)
Hjertquist, S.-O., and Westerborn, O. 1962. *Arch. Pathol. Anat. Physiol.* **335**:143. (*54*)
Hoagland, C. L. (*286, 316*)
Hoare, D. S., and Work, E. 1955. *Biochem. J.* **61**:562. (*110*) 1957. *Biochem. J.* **65**:441. (*109, 110*)
Hoch-Ligeti, C. (*391*)
Hochstein, L. I. (*188, 194, 195*)
Hock, C. W. 1940. *Biol. Bull.* **79**:199. (*181*)
Hockenhull, D. J. D. (*30*)
Hodge, H. C. (*211*)
Hodges, R. G. (*317*)
Hodgson, W. G. (*234*)
Högberg, B. (*197, 224, 226, 266, 370*)
Högberg, B. 1954. *Acta Chem. Scand.* **8**:1098. (*192*)
Högman, C. F. 1959. *Vox Sanguinis* **4**: 319. (*290*)
Hoffman, D. C. 1931. *J. Exptl. Med.* **53**:43. (*361*)
Hoffman, P. (*56, 83, 164, 186, 193–195, 198, 199, 203–207*)
Hoffman, P., Linker, A., and Meyer, K. 1958. *Biochim. Biophys. Acta* **30**: 184. (*192*)
Hoffman, P., Meyer, K., and Linker, A. 1956. *J. Biol. Chem.* **219**:653. (*189, 199*)
Hoffman, P., Linker, A., Sampson, P., Meyer, K., and Korn, E. D. 1957. *Biochim. Biophys. Acta* **25**:658. (*195, 198, 206*)
Hoffman, P., Linker, A., Lippman, V., and Meyer, K. 1960. *J. Biol. Chem.* **235**:3066. (*198, 207*)
Hoffmann, E. G. (*211*)
Hoffmann, R. C. (*97, 102*)
Hoffmeister, F. S., Wenner, C., Wilkens, H. J., and Mukhtar, F. 1964. *Surgery* **56**:1129. (*376*)
Hofmann, A. (*155*)
Hofmann, E. (*201*)
Hogue, M. J. (*384*)
Hohorst, H.-J. 1954. *Z. Hyg. Infektionskrankh.* **139**:561. (*290*) 1954a. *Z. Hyg. Infektionskrankh.* **140**:390. (*297*)
Hokkanen, E., Pyörälä, K., and Taipale, E. 1956. *Acta Pathol. Microbiol. Scand.* **39**:15. (*394*)
Holborow, E. J. (*289, 331*)
Holborow, E. J., and Loewi, G. 1962. *Immunology* **5**:278. (*273*)
Holden, D. M. (*329*)
Holden, W. D., Cole, J. W., Portmann, A. F., and Storaasli, J. P. 1949. *Proc. Soc. Exptl. Biol. Med.* **70**: 553. (*245*)
Holdsworth, E. S., and Otteson, M. 1955. *Congr. Intern. Biochim., 3e, Bruxelles, 1955, Résumés des Communications,* p. 116. (*294*)
Holeman, R. (*371*)
Holländer, H. J. (*52*)
Holland, J. F. (*388*)
Holley, H. L. (*232, 235–237*)
Hollmann, S. 1960. "Nicht-glykolytische Stoffweckselwege der Glucose." Stuttgart: Thieme. (*46*)
Holmgård, Å. 1955. *Acta Chem. Scand.* **9**:1038. (*52*)

Holmgren, H. (*73, 251, 370, 376, 387, 388*)
Holmgren, H. 1938. *Z. Anat. Entwicklungs.* **109**:293. (*373*) 1938a. *Z. Wiss. Mikroskop.* **55**:419. (*376*) 1939. *Anat. Anz.* **88**:246. (*376*) 1940. *Z. Mikroskop.-Anat. Forsch. (Abt. 2, Jahrb. Morphol. Mikroskop. Anat.)* **47**:489. (*149, 295, 300–302, 376, 436*)
Holmgren, H., and Wilander, O. 1937. *Z. Mikroskop.-Anat. Forsch. (Abt. 2, Jahrb. Morphol. Mikroskop. Anat.)* **42**:242. (*73*)
Holmgren, H., and Wohlfart, G. 1941. *Nord. Med.* **11**:2771. (*392*) 1947. *Cancer Res.* **7**:686. (*391*)
Holt, E. (*251, 263*)
Holt, M. W., and Warren, S. 1953. *Lab. Invest.* **2**:264. (*54*)
Holtman, D. F. (*34*)
Holtzer, H. (*53*)
Holzer, H. 1959. *Ann. Rev. Biochem.* **28**:171. (*46*)
Hommes, F. A., Van Leeuwen, G., and Zilliken, F. 1962. *Biochim. Biophys. Acta* **56**:320. (*102*)
Hopton, J. W. (*89, 336*)
Horecker, B. L. (*128*)
Horenstein, E. A. (*182*)
Horiguchi, Y., and Mikaya, M. 1954. *Bull. Japan. Soc. Sci. Fisheries* **19**: 957. (*202*)
Horikoshi, K., and Iida, S. 1964. *Biochim. Biophys. Acta* **83**:197. (*90, 118*)
Horley, J. F. (*300*)
Horlick, L., and Duff, G. L. 1954. *Arch. Pathol.* **57**:417. (*371, 372*)
Horne, R. W. (*329*)
Horowitz, M. I., Hashimoto, Y., and Pigman, W. 1963. *Abstr. 145th Meeting Am. Chem. Soc.*, p. 17D. (*295*) 1964. *Biochim. Biophys. Acta* **83**: 209. (*295*)
Hornung, M., and Baer, H. 1958. *Proc. Soc. Exptl. Biol. Med.* **98**:744. (*289*)
Hornung, M. O., and Berenson, G. S. 1963. *Proc. Soc. Exptl. Biol. Med.* **114**:31. (*118*)
Horowitz, S. T. (*7*)
Horsfall, F. L., Jr. (*99, 304, 342, 346*)
Horton, R. E. (*289, 300*)
Horvâth, C. (*385, 389, 392*)
Horwitt, M. K. 1940. *Science* **92**:89. (*224*)
Hosoda, J. (*88*)
Hotchkiss, M. (*181*)
Hotta, K. (*272, 290, 291*)
Houck, J. C. 1957. *Arch. Biochem. Biophys.* **71**:336. (*196*)
Houck, J. C., and Pearce, R. H. 1957. *Biochim. Biophys. Acta* **25**:555. (*189, 192, 203*) 1957a. *Biochim. Biophys. Acta* **25**:607. (*189, 192*)
How, M. J. (*317*)
Howe, A. F. (*239–242, 244, 247*)
Howe, A. F. 1955. *Concilium Ophthalmol., Acta, 17th, Montreal and New York, 1954,* Vol. II, p. 1032. (*247*)
Howe, C. (*198, 316, 340, 344*)
Howe, C. 1951. *J. Immunol.* **66**:9. (*344*)
Howe, C., and Kabat, E. A. 1953. *J. Am. Chem. Soc.* **75**:5542. (*167, 287*) 1956. *Arch. Biochem. Biophys.* **60**: 244. (*275*)
Howe, C., Lee, L. T., and Rose, H. M. 1960. *Nature* **188**:251. (*353*)
Howe, C., Rose, H. M., and Schneider, L. 1957. *Proc. Soc. Exptl. Biol. Med.* **96**:88. (*344, 346, 348*)
Howe, C., MacLennan, J. D., Mandl, I., and Kabat, E. A. 1957. *J. Bacteriol.* **74**:365. (*171, 274*)
Howe, C., Schiffman, G., Bezer, A. E., and Kabat, E. A. 1959. *J. Am. Chem. Soc.* **80**:6656. (*287*)
Howell, W. H., and Holt, E. 1918. *Am. J. Physiol.* **47**:328. (*251, 263*)
Hoyle, L. 1957. *In* "Ciba Foundation Symposium, The Nature of Viruses, 1957" (G. E. W. Wolstenholme and E. C. P. Millar, eds.), p. 211. Boston: Little, Brown. (*328*)
Hu, A. S. L., Wolfe, R. G., and Reithel, F. J. 1959. *Arch. Biochem. Biophys.* **81**:500. (*89*)
Huang, N. N. 1959. *Am. J. Hyg.* **70**: 275. (*326*)
Hubbard, R. W. (*221, 222, 224–227*)

Hublé, J. (*52*)
Hudson, M. T. (*14*)
Hudson, R. V. (*302*)
Hugentobler, F. (*307*)
Huggard, A. J. (*217*)
Hughes, R. C., and Jeanloz, R. W. 1964. *Biochemistry* **3**:1535. (*179*) 1964a. *Biochemistry* **3**:1543. (*179*)
Hughes, W. L. (*253, 374*)
Hughes-Jones, N. C., Gardner, B., and Telford, R. 1963. *Biochem. J.* **88**: 435. (*274*)
Huhnstock, K. (*106*)
Hultin, E. 1946. *Svensk Kem. Tidskr.* **58**:281. (*193*) 1948. *Svensk Kem. Tidskr.* **60**:131. (*193*)
Hummel, J. P., Jr. (*381*)
Hummel, J. P., Anderson, D. O., and Patel, C. 1958. *J. Biol. Chem.* **233**: 712. (*224, 225, 227*)
Hummel, J. P., Flores, M., and Nelson, G. 1958. *J. Biol. Chem.* **233**:717. (*227*)
Hummel, K. 1961. *Z. Immunitätsforsch.* **122**:179. (*274*)
Humphrey, J. H. 1943. *Biochem. J.* **37**: 460. (*331*) 1946. *Biochem. J.* **40**: 442. (*157*) 1957. *Bull. World Health Organ.* **16**:291. (*187*)
Hunter, G. D. (*109, 110*)
Hunter, G. D., and Hockenhull, D. J. D. 1955. *Biochem. J.* **59**:268. (*30*)
Hurley, N. A. (*259, 260*)
Husemann, E., Hoffmann, E. G., Lötterle, R., and Wiedersheim, M. 1952. *Experientia* **8**:153. (*211*)
Hutchison, A. M. (*330*)
Huttenen, J. K. (*106*)
Hynd, A. (*3*)

I

Ichikawa, H. (*298*)
Ichikawa, K. (*391*)
Iida, S. (*90, 118*)
Iida, T. (*270*)
Ikawa, M. (*113*)
Ikawa, M., and Snell, E. E. 1956. *Biochim. Biophys. Acta* **19**:576. (*322*)
Ikawa, M., Koepfli, J. B., Mudd, S. G., and Niemann, C. 1952. *J. Natl. Cancer Inst.* **13**:157. (*390*)
Ikeda, C. (*333*)
Ikeda, T. (*107*)
Ikenaka, T. (*84*)
Iloff, A. (*155, 157, 158, 162*)
Imai, K. (*222*)
Imai, K., Takagi, T., and Isemura, T. 1963. *J. Biochem. (Tokyo)* **53**:1. (*184, 199*)
Imaizumi, M. 1937. *J. Biochem. (Tokyo)* **26**:197. (*41*)
Imanaga, Y. 1957. *Kiso Kagaku Shinpojiumu* **12**:195. (*37*) 1957a. *J. Biochem. (Tokyo)* **44**:69. (*37*) 1957b. *J. Biochem. (Tokyo)* **44**:397. (*40*) 1958. *J. Biochem. (Tokyo)* **45**:647. (*41*)
Immers, J. (*312, 369*)
Immers, J. 1961. *Exptl. Cell Res.* **24**:356. (*367*)
Imoto, T. (*199*)
Imredy, K. (*101*)
Ingram, D. J. E., Hodgson, W. G., Parker, C. A., and Rees, W. T. 1955. *Nature* **176**:1228. (*234*)
Inoue, T. (*323*)
Inoue, Y. (*323*)
Insko, W. M., Jr. (*141*)
Ionescu-Stoian, F. (*200*)
Irie, R. (*270, 288*)
Irwin, M. R. (*294*)
Isaacs, A., and Lindenmann, J. 1957. *Proc. Roy. Soc. (London) Ser. B* **147**:258. (*335*)
Isacson, P., and Holden, D. M. 1962. *Virology* **17**:494. (*329*)
Iseki, S. (*274, 298*)
Iseki, S. 1952. *Gunma J. Med. Sci. (Japan)* **1**:1. (*297*)
Iseki, S., and Ikeda, T. 1956. *Proc. Japan Acad.* **32**:201. (*107*)
Iseki, S., and Masaki, S. 1953. *Proc. Japan Acad.* **29**:460. (*107, 280*)
Iseki, S., and Okada, S. 1951. *Proc. Japan Acad.* **27**:455. (*274*)
Isemura, T. (*184, 199*)
Isemura, T., Takagi, T., Maeda, Y., and Imai, K. 1961. *Biochem. Biophys. Res. Commun.* **5**:373. (*222*)

Ishihara, K. 1964. *Exptl. Cell Res.* **36**: 354. (*368*)
Ishii, M. (*392*)
Ishimoda, T. (*106*)
Ishimoto, N. (*19*)
Ishizaka, K. (*335*)
Ishizaka, R., Campbell, D. H., and Ishizaka, K. 1960. *Proc. Soc. Exptl. Biol. Med.* **103**:5. (*335*)
Isliker, H. C. 1957. *Advan. Protein Chem.* **12**:387. (*306*)
Ispolatovskya, M. V., Levdikova, G. A., and Larina, I. A. 1962. *Biochemistry* (*Biokhimiya*) **27**:65. (*200*)
Issandou-Carles, R. (*197*)
Isselbacher, K. J. 1958. *J. Biol. Chem.* **232**:429. (*49*)
Ito, E., Ishimoto, N., and Saito, M. 1958. *Nature* **181**:906. (*19*)
Ito, E., and Saito, M. 1963. *Biochim. Biophys. Acta* **78**:237. (*116*)
Ito, E., and Strominger, J. L. 1960. *J. Biol. Chem.* **235**:PC 5. (*112*) 1960a. *J. Biol. Chem.* **235**:PC 7. (*112*) 1964. *J. Biol. Chem.* **239**:210. (*117*)
Ito, Y., Takamura, K., and Endo, H. 1960. *Endocrinol. Japon.* **7**:327. (*53*)
Ivanova, L. N. (*154*)
Ivánovics, G. (*319*)
Ivánovics, G. 1940. *Z. Immunitätsforsch.* **97**:402. (*318*) 1940a. *Z. Immunitätsforsch.* **98**:373. (*318*) 1940b. *Z. Immunitätsforsch.* **98**:420. (*318*)
Iversen, O. H. 1960. *Acta Pathol. Microbiol. Scand.* **50**:25. (*149*)
Iversen, O. H., and Marcker, K. 1961. *Acta Pharmacol. Toxicol.* **18**:101. (*149*)
Iwanaga, M. (*270, 287*)
Izquierdo, I. (*137, 138*)
Izume, S. (*323*)
Izumi, K. (*128*)
Izumi, K., Makino, M., and Yamashina, I. 1961. *Biochim. Biophys. Acta* **50**: 196. (*83, 86*) 1962. *J. Biochem.* (*Tokyo*) **51**:365. (*83, 86*)
Izumi, K., Sato, M., Hayashi, K., Tamura, M., and Yamashina, I. 1963. *J. Biochem.* (*Tokyo*) **54**:530. (*128*)

J

Jacobs, J. (*352*)
Jacobs, J., and Walop, J. N. 1960. *Nature* **184**:334. (*172*) 1961. *Nature* **189**:334. (*353*)
Jacobson, B., and Boström, H. 1963. *Federation Proc.* **22**:239. (*44*)
Jacobson, B., and Davidson, E. A. 1962. *J. Biol. Chem.* **237**:635. (*48*) 1962a. *J. Biol. Chem.* **237**:638. (*49, 73*) 1963. *Biochim. Biophys. Acta* **73**: 145. (*21*)
Jacobson, L. O. (*245*)
Jacobson, S. (*223, 225–227*)
Jacques, P. (*166*)
Jänne, J. (*250*)
James, A. M. (*381*)
Janczura, E., Perkins, H. R., and Rogers, H. J. 1961. *Biochem. J.* **80**:82. (*113, 313*)
Janes, J., and McDonald, J. R. 1948. *Arch. Pathol.* **45**:622. (*391*)
Janeway, T. C., Richardson, H. B., and Park, E. A. 1918. *A.M.A. Arch. Internal Med.* **21**:565. (*264*)
Janković, B. D., and Waksman, B. H. 1962. *J. Immunol.* **89**:598. (*273*)
Jann, B. (*328*)
Jann, K. (*328*)
Jaques, L. B. (*198, 332*)
Jaques, L. B. 1940. *J. Biol. Chem.* **133**: 445. (*198*) 1943. *Biochem. J.* **37**:189. (*252*)
Jaques, L. B., and Keeri-Szanto, E. 1952. *Can. J. Med. Sci.* **30**:353. (*198*)
Jaques, R. 1953. *Biochem. J.* **53**:56. (*188*)
Jatzkewitz, H. (*212*)
Jatzkewitz, H. 1960. *Z. Physiol. Chem.* **318**:265. (*125*)
Jauregui-Adell, J. (*184, 199*)
Jay, A. R. (*189*)
Jayle, M.-F. (*309*)
Jayle, M.-F., and Boussier, G. 1954. *Presse Méd.* **62**:1752. (*309*)
Jeanloz, R. W. (*89, 157, 179, 270, 319, 352*)
Jeffay, H., and Winzler, R. J. 1958. *J.*

Biol. Chem. **231**:101. (*93, 96*) 1958a. *J. Biol. Chem.* **231**:111. (*93, 94*)
Jeffree, G. M. 1955. *Nature* **175**:509. (*222*) 1956. *Biochim. Biophys. Acta* **20**:503. (*222, 223*)
Jeljaszewicz, J. (*111*)
Jenkin, C. R. 1963. *Advan. Immunol.* **3**:351. (*287*)
Jenkins, W. J. (*300*)
Jennings, M. A. (*52*)
Jennings, M. A., and Florey, H. W. 1956. *Quart. J. Exptl. Physiol.* **41**: 131. (*54*)
Jenrette, W. V. (*252*)
Jensen, C. E. (*194, 231, 386*)
Jensen, C. E. 1949. *Acta Chem. Scand.* **3**:584. (*230*)
Jensen, C. E., and Zachariae, F. 1958. *Acta Endocrinol.* **27**:356. (*389*)
Jeon, K. W. (*366, 367*)
Jeon, K. W., and Bell, L. G. E. 1962. *Exptl. Cell Res.* **27**:350. (*366*) 1965. *Exptl. Cell Res.* **38**:536. (*367*)
Jesaitis, M. A. (*355*)
Jesaitis, M. A., and Goebel, W. F. 1952. *J. Exptl. Med.* **96**:409. (*356*)
Jeuniaux, C. (*181, 182*)
Jeuniaux, C. 1950. *Arch. Intern. Physiol. Biochim.* **58**:350. (*182*) 1950a. *Arch. Intern. Physiol. Biochim.* **58**: 352. (*35, 182*) 1950b. *Arch. Intern. Physiol. Biochim.* **58**:354. (*182*) 1955. *Arch. Intern. Physiol. Biochim.* **63**:114. (*182*) 1956. *Arch. Intern. Physiol. Biochim.* **64**:522. (*182*) 1957. *Arch. Intern. Physiol. Biochim.* **65**:135. (*182*) 1959. *Arch. Intern. Physiol. Biochim.* **67**:597. (*182*) 1959a. *Arch. Intern. Physiol. Biochim.* **67**:115. (*182*) 1961. *Nature* **192**:135. (*182*) 1961a. *Arch. Intern. Physiol. Biochim.* **69**:384. (*182*)
Jeuniaux, C., and Armanicu, M. 1955. *Arch. Intern. Physiol. Biochim.* **63**: 94. (*182*)
Jevons, F. R. (*179*)
Jevons, F. R. 1958. *Nature* **181**:1346. (*83, 86*)
Johansen, P. [G.], Marshall, R. D., and Neuberger, A. 1958. *Nature* **181**: 1345. (*86*) 1961. *Biochem. J.* **78**: 518. (*83, 86, 311*)
Johns, R. G. S., and Marrack, J. R. 1953. *J. Hyg.* **51**:55. (*276*)
Johnson, A. G. (*326*)
Johnson, A. G., Gaines, S., and Landy, M. 1956. *J. Exptl. Med.* **103**:225. (*336*)
Johnson, C. A. (*290, 342–344, 346, 357*)
Johnson, G. A., and McCluer, R. H. 1961. *Proc. Soc. Exptl. Biol. Med.* **107**:692. (*271*)
Johnson, G. D. (*289, 331*)
Johnson, J. (*388*)
Johnston, J. P. 1955. *Biochem. J.* **59**: 620. (*362*)
Johnston, P. M., and Comar, C. L. 1957. *J. Biophys. Biochem. Cytol.* **3**:231. (*55*)
Jolles, B., and Greening, S. G. 1960. *Acta Unio Intern. Contra Cancrum* **16**:682. (*389*)
Jollès, G., and Fromageot, C. 1953. *Biochim. Biophys. Acta* **11**:95. (*183*) 1954. *Biochim. Biophys. Acta* **14**: 219. (*183*)
Jollès, J. (*85, 183, 199*)
Jollès, J., Jauregui-Adell, J., and Jollès, P. 1963. *Biochim. Biophys. Acta* **71**:488. (*184, 199*)
Jollès, J., and Jollès, P. 1960. *Biochim. Biophys. Acta* **45**:407. (*183*)
Jollès, P. (*85, 183, 184, 199*)
Jollès, P. 1960. *In* "The Enzymes" (P. D. Boyer, H. Lardy, and K. Myrbäck, eds.), Vol. 4, 2nd ed. p. 431. New York: Academic Press. (*182*) 1963. *Biochim. Biophys. Acta* **69**: 505. (*184*) 1964. *Med. Hyg.* **22**: 965. (*199*)
Jollès, P., Alais, C., and Jollès, J. 1961. *Biochim. Biophys. Acta* **51**:309. (*85*)
Jollès, P., Jollès, J., and Jauregui, J. 1959. *Biochim. Biophys. Acta* **31**: 96. (*183*)
Jollès, P., Jollès-Thaureaux, J., and Fromageot, C. 1958. *Biochim. Biophys. Acta* **27**:439. (*183*)
Jollès, P., and Ledieu, M. 1959. *Biochim. Biophys. Acta* **31**:100. (*183*) 1959a.

Biochim. Biophys. Acta **36**:284. (*183*)
Jollès, P., Sternberg, M., and Mathé, G. 1964. *Proc. Symp. Intern., 3d, Lisozima di Fleming, Milano, Aprile 3–5, 1964.* (*199*)
Jollès, P., and Zuili, S. 1960. *Biochim. Biophys. Acta* **39**:212. (*182, 183*)
Jollès, P., Petit, J. F., Charlemagne, D., Salmon, S., and Jollès, J. 1964. *Proc. Symp. Intern., 3rd, Lisozima di Fleming, Milano, Aprile 3–5, 1964.* (*199*)
Jollès-Thaureaux, J. (*183*)
Jollès-Thaureaux, J., Jollès, P., and Fromageot, C. 1958. *Biochim. Biophys. Acta* **27**:298. (*183*)
Jones, H. B. (*259, 371*)
Jones, J. K. N. (*294*)
Jones, S. S., and Long, F. A. 1952. *J. Phys. Chem.* **56**:25. (*234*)
de Jongh, S. E. (*149, 150*)
Jorpes, J. E. (*5, 53*)
Jorpes, [J.] E., and Bergström, S. 1939. *Biochem. J.* **33**:47. (*265*)
Jorpes, J. E., Boström, H., and Mutt, V. 1950. *J. Biol. Chem.* **183**:607. (*56, 264*)
Jorpes, J. E., and Gardell, S. 1948. *J. Biol. Chem.* **176**:267. (*56*)
Jorpes, [J.] E., Holmgren, H., and Wilander, O. 1937. *Z. Mikroskop.-Anat. Forsch.* (*Abt. 2 Jahrb. Morphol. Mikroskop. Anat.*) **42**:279. (*73*)
Jorpes, [J.] E. Odeblad, E., and Boström, H. 1953. *Acta Haematol.* **9**:273. (*54, 55, 74, 79*)
Jorpes, [J.] E., and Yamashina, I. 1956. *Colloq. Ges. Physiol. Chem. 7th, 1956,* p. 25. (*91*)
Joseph, J. P. (*157, 385*)
Joubert, [G.]. (*366*)
Jourdian, G. W. (*25, 27, 173, 175*)
Jourdian, G. W., Carlson, D. M., and Roseman, S. 1963. *Biochem. Biophys. Res. Commun.* **10**:352. (*44, 126*)
Jourdian, G. W., Koffler, H., and Garner, H. R. 1958. *Bacteriol. Proc.* **58**:97. (*34*)
Jourdian, G. W., and Roseman, S. 1960. *Abstr. Am. Chem. Soc. 137th Meeting,* p. 47C. (*15, 27*)
Jourdian, G. W., Shimizu, F., and Roseman, S. 1961. *Federation Proc.* **20**: 161. (*27, 82*)
Jowsey, J. (*52*)
Juergens, W. G. (*314*)
Juergens, W. G., Sanderson, A. R., and Strominger, J. L. 1960. *Bull. Soc. Chim. Biol.* **42**:1669. (*314*) 1963. *J. Exptl. Med.* **117**:925. (*314*)
Juhlin, L. 1960. *Acta Dermato-Venereol.* **39**:461. (*188*)
Julén, C. (*263*)
Julianelle, L. A. (*314, 321*)
Julianelle, L. A. 1939. *Ann. Internal Med.* **13**:308. (*314, 321*)
Julianelle, L. A., and Hartmann, A. F. 1936. *J. Exptl. Med.* **64**:149. (*314, 321*)
Julianelle, L. A., and Wieghard, C. W. 1935. *J. Exptl. Med.* **62**:11. (*314, 321*) 1935a. *J. Exptl. Med.* **62**:31. (*314, 321*)
Junge-Hülsing, G. (*52*)
Junge-Hülsing, G. 1959. *Z. Rheumaforsch.* **18**:355. (*52*)
Junge-Hülsing, G., and Hauss, W. H. 1960. *In* "Struktur und Stoffwechsel des Bindegewebes" (W. H. Hauss and H. Losse, eds.), p. 83. Stuttgart: Thieme. (*52*)
Juva, K. (*9*)

K

Kabat, E. A. (*167, 171, 272, 274, 275, 278–281, 284, 286–288, 290, 292, 299, 305, 315, 316, 321, 324, 331, 334, 335*)
Kabat, E. A. 1939. *J. Exptl. Med.* **69**: 103. (*306*) 1954. *J. Am. Chem. Soc.* **76**:3709. (*333*) 1956. "Blood Group Substances—Their Chemistry and Immunochemistry." New York: Academic Press. (*268, 271, 272, 275, 284, 285, 293, 300, 316, 332, 334*) 1956a. *J. Immunol.* **77**:377. (*272, 275, 332*) 1956b. *In* Springer, 1956b. (*333*) 1958. *In* "Ciba Foundation Symposium, Chemistry and Biology

of Mucopolysaccharides" (G. E. W. Wolstenholme and M. O'Connor, eds.), p. 42. Boston: Little, Brown. (*278, 321, 334*) 1960. *In* Springer, 1960a. (*321, 324, 334*) 1961. *In* "Kabat and Mayer's Experimental Immunochemistry" (E. A. Kabat and M. M. Mayer, eds.), 2nd ed. p. 241. Springfield, Ill.: Thomas. (*306, 334*) 1962. *Arch. Biochem. Biophys. Suppl.* **1**:181. (*317*)

Kabat, E. A., Baer, H., and Knaub, V. 1949. *J. Exptl. Med.* **89**:1. (*334*)

Kabat, E. A., Bendich, A., and Bezer, A. E. 1946. *J. Exptl. Med.* **83**:477. (*275*)

Kabat, E. A., and Berg, D. 1953. *J. Immunol.* **70**:514. (*267, 332*)

Kabat, E. A., and Bezer, A. E. 1945. *J. Exptl. Med.* **82**:207. (*272, 275*)

Kabat, E. A., and Leskowitz, S. 1955. *J. Am. Chem. Soc.* **77**:5159. (*278–280*)

Kabat, E. A., and Mayer, M. M. 1961. "Experimental Immunochemistry" (2nd ed.). Springfield, Ill.: Thomas, (*306, 311, 333, 334*)

Kabat, E. A., and Pedersen, K. O. 1938. *Science* **87**:372. (*306*)

Kabat, E. A., and Stern, K. G. 1956. *In* Springer, 1956b. (*333*)

Kabat, E. A., Miller, C. P., Kaiser, H., and Foster, A. Z. 1945. *J. Exptl. Med.* **81**:1. (*324*)

Kabat, E. A., Baer, H., Bezer, A. E., and Knaub, V. 1948. *J. Exptl. Med.* **88**:43. (*284, 286*)

Kabat, E. A., Bendich, A., Bezer, A. E., and Knaub, V. 1948a. *J. Exptl. Med.* **87**:295. (*284, 286*)

Kabat, E. A., MacDonald, D. L., Ballou, C. E., and Fischer, H. O. L. 1953. *J. Am. Chem. Soc.* **75**:4507. (*333*)

Kabelitz, H. J. 1949. *Deut. Arch. Klin. Med.* **194**:499. (*391*)

Kaffka, A. 1957. *Zentr. Bakteriol. Parasitenk. Abt. I. Orig.* **168**:381. (*189*)

Kagan, R. (*246*)

Kaiser, E. 1953. *Mem. Inst. Butantan (São Paulo)* **25**:35. (*193*) 1953a. *Monatsh. Chem.* **84**:482. (*193*)

Kaiser, S. J. (*268, 317*)

Kalckar, H. M. (*47, 49, 122*)

Kalckar, H. M., Braganca, B., and Munch-Petersen, A. 1953. *Nature* **172**:1038. (*49*)

Kalckar, H. M., and Maxwell, E. S. 1958. *Physiol. Rev.* **38**:77. (*45*)

Kaminski, M. (*312*)

Kamiyama, S., and Schmid, K. 1961. *Biochim. Biophys. Acta* **49**:250. (*348, 352*) 1962. *Biochim. Biophys. Acta* **58**:80. (*86*) 1962a. *Biochim. Biophys. Acta* **63**:266. (*83*)

Kanfer, J. N., Blacklow, R. S., Warren, L., and Brady, R. O. 1964. *Biochem. Biophys. Res. Commun.* **14**:287. (*126*)

Kanzow, U., Böhm, P., and Kuhn, F. 1961. *Klin. Wochschr.* **39**:1236. (*307*)

Kapa, E. (*392*)

Kapfhammer, J. (*33*)

Kaplan, D., and Meyer, K. 1962. *J. Clin. Invest.* **41**:743. (*211*)

Kaplan, M. H. (*289*)

Karabinos, J. V. (*264*)

Kara-Murza, S. G. (*83, 87*)

Karling, J. S. 1945. *Am. J. Botany* **32**:362. (*182*)

Karnovsky, M. L. (*43, 105, 120, 123*)

Karnovsky, M. L., Moser, H., and Majno, G. 1959. *Progr. Neurobiol.* **4**:138. (*125*)

Karrer, P., and Hofmann, A. 1929. *Helv. Chim. Acta* **12**:616. (*155, 182*)

Karush, F. (*306*)

Karush, F. 1958. *In* "Serological and Biochemical Comparisons of Proteins" (W. H. Cole, ed.). New Brunswick, N.J.: Rutgers. (*306*) 1959. *In* "Mechanisms of Hypersensitivity: Henry Ford Hospital International Symposium, 1958" (J. H. Shaffer, G. A. LoGrippo, and M. W. Chase, eds.), p. 19. Boston: Little, Brown. (*334*)

Kass, E. H., and Seastone, C. V. 1944. *J. Exptl. Med.* **79**:319. (*187*)

Kassell, B. (*302*)

Katayama, H. 1957. *Annot. Zool. Japon.* **30**:71. (*33*)

Katchalski, E., Berger, A., and Neumann, H. 1954. *Nature* **173**:998. (*220*)
Katchalsky, A., Danon, D., Nevo, A., and DeVries, A. 1959. *Biochim. Biophys. Acta* **33**:120. (*373*)
Kathan, R. (*173*)
Kathan, R. H., and Winzler, R. J. 1963. *J. Biol. Chem.* **238**:21. (*357*)
Kathan, R. H., Winzler, R. J., and Johnson, C. A. 1961. *J. Exptl. Med.* **113**:37. (*290, 342–344, 346, 357*)
Kathan, R. H., Riff, L. J. M., and Real, M. 1963. *Proc. Soc. Exptl. Biol. Med.* **114**:90. (*358*)
Kato, K. (*88*)
Kato, Y. (*202*)
Katsuko, B. (*83*)
Katsura, T. (*202, 208*)
Katz, H. P., and Hennigar, G. R. 1965. *Arch. Pathol.* **79**:27. (*379*)
Katz, J., Sellers, A. L., and Golden, S. 1960. *Proc. Soc. Exptl. Biol. Med.* **103**:807. (*99*)
Katz, W. (*182*)
Katz, W., and Weidel, W. 1961. *Z. Naturforsch.* **16b**:363. (*182*)
Katzman, P. A. (*202*)
Kauffmann, F. 1941. *Acta Pathol. Microbiol. Scand.* **18**:225. (*325*) 1954. "Enterobacteriaceae," 2d revised ed. Copenhagen: Munksgaard. (*323*)
Kauffmann, F., and Møller, E. 1940. *J. Hyg.* **40**:246. (*325*)
Kaufmann, W., and Bauer, K. 1958. *J. Gen. Microbiol.* **18**:xi. (*88*)
Kavasaki, H. (*106*)
Kaverzneva, E. D. (*83*)
Kawabe, K. 1934. *J. Biochem.* (*Tokyo*) **20**:233. (*32*) 1934a. *J. Biochem.* (*Tokyo*) **20**:243. (*32, 35*) 1934b. *J. Biochem.* (*Tokyo*) **20**:293. (*32*)
Kawakami, I. 1934. *J. Biochem.* (*Tokyo*) **20**:423. (*35*) 1936. *Fukuoka Igaku Zassi* **29**:958. (*35*)
Kawauchi, H. (*106*)
Keating, W. C. (*379*)
Keeri-Szanto, E. (*198*)
Kefalides, N. A. (*309*)
Keighley, G. (*50, 92, 357*)
Keith, M. C. (*316*)
Kekulé, A. (*310*)
Kekwick, R. A. 1950. *Biochem. J.* **46**: 438. (*287*)
Kelemen, M. V., and Baddiley, J. 1961. *Biochem. J.* **80**:246. (*113*)
Kelényi, G. 1953. *Acta Morphol. Acad. Sci. Hung.* **3**:377. (*246*)
Kelley, M. B. (*94*)
Kelley, T. F. (*217, 218, 224–226*)
Kelsall, M. A. 1952. *Acta Unio Contra Cancrum* **7**:776. (*391*)
Kelsall, M. A., and Crabb, E. D. 1953. *Anat. Record* **115**:331. (*392*) 1959. "Lymphocytes and Mast Cells." Baltimore: Williams & Wilkins. (*392*)
Kelus, A., Gurner, B. W., and Combs, R. R. A. 1959. *Immunology* **2**:262. (*290*)
Kendall, F. E. (*269, 315–318*)
Kendall, F. E. 1937. *J. Clin. Invest.* **16**: 921. (*333*)
Kendall, F. E., Heidelberger, M., and Dawson, M. H. 1937. *J. Biol. Chem.* **118**:61. (*64, 319, 330, 332*)
Kenkel, H. (*307*)
Kennedy, E. P. (*122*)
Kennedy, G. D. C. (*55*)
Kennedy, J. S. (*54*)
Kennedy, J. S., and Kennedy, G. D. C. 1959. *J. Dent. Belge* **40**:63. (*55*)
Kent, H. N., and Gey, G. O. 1957. *Proc. Soc. Exptl. Biol. Med.* **94**:205. (*395*) 1960. *Science* **131**:666. (*395*)
Kent, L. H. (*23*)
Kent, P. W. (*53, 105, 323*)
Kent, P. W. 1957. *Scand. J. Clin. Lab. Invest.* **10**: Suppl. 31, p. 165. (*46*)
Kent, P. W., and Lunt, M. R. 1958. *Biochim. Biophys. Acta* **28**:657. (*76*)
Kent, P. W., and Whitehouse, M. W. 1955. "Biochemistry of the Aminosugars." London: Butterworth. (*46*)
Kent, P. W., Jowsey, J., Steddon, L. M., Oliver, R., and Vaughan, J. 1956. *Biochem. J.* **62**:470. (*52*)
Kent, P. W., Whitehouse, M. W., Jennings, M. A., and Florey, H. W.

1956a. *Quart. J. Exptl. Physiol.* **41**: 230. (*52*)
Keogh, E. V., North, E. A., and Warburton, M. F. 1947. *Nature* **160**:63. (*289*) 1948. *Nature* **161**:687. (*289*)
Kerby, G. P., and Eadie, G. S. 1953. *Proc. Soc. Exptl. Biol. Med.* **83**:111. (*224*)
Kerde, C., Fünfhausen, G., Brunk, Re., and Brunk, Ru. 1960. *Z. Immunitaetsforsch.* **119**:216. (*292*)
Kesner, L., Muntwyler, E., and Griffin, G. E. 1964. *Biochim. Biophys. Acta* **85**:435. (*86*)
Kessler, L. N. (*197*)
Ketcham, A. S. (*389*)
Kibrick, S. (*364*)
Kieber, R. J. (*34*)
Kiessling, G. (*22, 326*)
Kihara, H., Ikawa, M., and Snell, E. E. 1961. *J. Biol. Chem.* **236**:172. (*113*)
Kimmel, J. R. (*182*)
King, C. G. (*47*)
King, H. K. (*274*)
King, J. A. (*264*)
Kinsman, G. (*46, 49, 68*)
Kiriluk, L. B., Kremen, A. J., and Glick, D. 1949–50. *J. Natl. Cancer Inst.* **10**:993. (*196, 394*)
Kirkman, H. N. (*82*)
Kirkwood, J. G. (*252*)
Kirschbaum, P. (*137, 138*)
Kirschenlohr, W. (*157*)
Kirschon, A. (*245*)
Kisfaludy, A. (*188*)
Klein, G. (*381*)
Klein, H. P. 1953. *J. Bacteriol.* **66**:650. (*15*)
Klenerman, N. 1955. *S. African J. Med. Sci.* **20**:39. (*145, 146*)
Klenk, E. 1960. *Angew. Chem.* **72**:482. (*270*)
Klenk, E., and Faillard, H. 1954. *Z. Physiol. Chem.* **298**:230. (*349*) 1955. *Z. Physiol. Chem.* **299**:191. (*310*) 1957. *Deut. Z. Verdauungs-Stoffwechselkrankh.* **17**:51. (*308*)
Klenk, E., Faillard, H., and Lempfrid, H. 1955. *Z. Physiol. Chem.* **301**:235. (*348, 349*)
Klenk, E., and Gielen, W. 1960. *Z. Physiol. Chem.* **319**:283. (*310*) 1961. *Z. Physiol. Chem.* **326**:144. (*311*)
Klenk, E., and Lauenstein, K. 1952. *Z. Physiol. Chem.* **291**:147. (*349*)
Klenk, E., and Lempfrid, H. 1957. *Z. Physiol. Chem.* **307**:278. (*348, 349*)
Klenk, E., and Stoffel, W. 1955. *Z. Physiol. Chem.* **302**:286. (*308*)
Klenk, E., and Uhlenbruck, G. 1957. *Z. Physiol. Chem.* **307**:266. (*348*) 1958. *Z. Physiol. Chem.* **311**:227. (*348*) 1960. *Z. Physiol. Chem.* **319**:151. (*290, 293, 344, 346, 348, 349, 358*)
Klieneberger-Nobel, E. 1960. *In* "The Bacteria" (I. C. Gunsalus and R. Y. Stanier, eds.), Vol. 1, p. 361. New York: Academic Press. (*109*)
Kling, D. H., Levine, M. G., and Wise, S. 1955. *Proc. Soc. Exptl. Biol. Med.* **89**:261. (*63*)
Klopstock, F. 1932. *Z. Immunitaetsforsch.* **75**:348. (*332*)
Klotz, I. M. 1953. *In* "The Proteins" (H. Neurath and K. Bailey, eds.), Vol. 1, p. **727**. New York: Academic Press. (*253*)
Knacke, F. E. D. (*34*)
Knaub, V. (*284, 286*)
Kneip, P. (*197*)
Knesslova, V. (*100*)
Knight, C. A. 1946. *J. Exptl. Med.* **83**: 281. (*328*) 1947. *J. Exptl. Med.* **85**: 99. (*328*)
Knudsen, P. J., and Koefoed, J. 1961. *Nature* **191**:1306. (*195*)
Kobata, A. 1962. *Biochem. Biophys. Res. Commun.* **7**:346. (*82*)
Koch, C.-M. (*11*)
Koch, F. E., and Haase, H. 1952. *Arzneimittel-Forsch.* **2**:464. (*188*)
Koch, W. (*11*)
Kochem, H.-G. (*309, 310*)
Kochetkov, N. K., Derevitskaya, V. A., Kara-Murza, S. G., and Zharov, V. G. 1964. *Biochim. Biophys. Acta* **83**: 52. (*83, 87*)
Kodicek, E., and Loewi, G. 1955. *Proc. Roy. Soc. (London), Ser. B* **144**:100. (*52, 53*)

Koefed, J. (*195*)
Köksal, M. 1953. *Acta Med. Turci* **5**:85. (*392*)
Koenig, D. F. (*70, 71*)
Koepfli, J. B. (*390*)
Koffler, H. (*34*)
Kogure, T. (*298*)
Kohn, P., Winzler, R. J., and Hoffmann, R. C. 1962. *J. Biol. Chem.* **237**:304. (*97, 102*)
Kolb, J. J. (*114*)
Kolecki, B. (*275, 281, 284, 298, 299, 325, 333*)
Konetzka, W. A., Pelczar, M. J., Jr., and Burnett, G. W. 1954. *Bacteriol. Proc.* p. 106. (*193, 203*)
Konno, K., and Altman, K. I. 1958. *Nature* **181**:994. (*83*)
Koplitz, R. M. (*52*)
Koransky, W. 1958. *Arch. Exptl. Pathol. Pharmakol.* **234**:46. (*122*)
Korey, S. P. (*126*)
Korn, E. D. (*195, 198, 199, 203–207, 215*)
Korn, E. D. 1955. *J. Biol. Chem.* **215**:1. (*214, 215*) 1955a. *J. Biol. Chem.* **215**:15. (*215*) 1957. *J. Biol. Chem.* **226**:827. (*205, 215*) 1957a. *J. Biol. Chem.* **226**:841. (*205, 206*) 1959. *J. Biol. Chem.* **234**:1325. (*74, 75*) 1959a. *J. Biol. Chem.* **234**:1647. (*61, 74*) 1959b. *In* "Methods of Biochemical Analysis" (D. Glick, ed.), Vol. 7, p. 145. New York: Interscience. (*214, 219*)
Korn, E. D., and Payza, A. N. 1956. *Biochim. Biophys. Acta* **20**:596. (*205*)
Korn, E. D., and Quigley, T. W., Jr. 1955. *Biochim. Biophys. Acta* **18**:143. (*215*) 1957. *J. Biol. Chem.* **226**:833. (*215*)
Kornfeld, R. (*104, 128*)
Kornfeld, S., and Glaser, L. 1962. *Biochim. Biophys. Acta* **56**:184. (*21, 82*)
Kornfeld, S., Kornfeld, R., and Ginsburg, V. 1965. *Arch. Biochem. Biophys.* **110**:1. (*128*)
Kornfeld, S., Kornfeld, R., Neufeld, E. F., and O'Brien, P. J. 1964. *Proc. Natl. Acad. Sci. U.S.* **52**:371. (*104*)
Korngold, L., and Lipari, R. 1956. *Cancer* **9**:183. (*307, 336*) 1956a. *Cancer* **9**: 262. (*307, 336*)
Korngold, L., and Van Leeuwen, G. 1957. *J. Exptl. Med.* **106**:467. (*307*) 1957a. *J. Exptl. Med.* **106**:477. (*307*)
Korngold, L., Van Leeuwen, G., and Brener, J. L. 1959. *J. Lab. Clin. Med* **53**:517. (*303*)
Körösi, J. (*389*)
Kościelak, J. (*270*)
Kościelak, J. 1962. *Nature* **194**:751. (*270*) 1963. *Biochim. Biophys. Acta* **78**:313. (*270, 288*)
Kościelak, J., and Zakrzewski, K. 1960. *Nature* **187**:516. (*270*)
Koshland, D. E., Jr. 1954. *In* "The Mechanism of Enzyme Action" (W. D. McElroy and B. Glass, eds.), p. 608. Baltimore: Johns Hopkins. (*58*) 1959. *In* "The Enzymes" (P. D. Boyer, H. Lardy, and K. Myrbäck, eds.), 2nd ed., Vol. I, p. 305. New York: Academic Press.
Kosin, I. L., and Munro, S. S. 1942. *Endocrinology* **30**:102. (*138, 141*)
Kout, M., and Kubickova, Z. 1959. *Nature* **184**:639. (*271*)
Kowalewski, K. 1959. *Proc. Soc. Exptl. Biol. Med.* **101**:536. (*52*)
Kowalewski, K., and Gouws, F. 1957. *Surg. Gynecol. Obstet.* **105**:1. (*52*)
Kowalewski, K., and Williams, H. T. G. 1958. *Can. J. Biochem. Physiol.* **36**: 847. (*52*)
Kozelka, A. W. 1929. *J. Heredity* **20**:3. (*140*)
Kradolfer, F. Z. (*363*)
Krasnyanskaya, V. G. (*199*)
Kratochvil, C. H. (*307*)
Kratochvil, C. H., and Deutsch, H. F. 1956. *J. Biol. Chem.* **222**:31. (*307*)
Krause, R. M. (*320*)
Křečková, P. (*117*)
Kreisler, L. 1952. *Science* **115**:145. (*389*)
Kremen, A. J. (*196, 394*)
Krisch, K. (*87*)
Kristiansen, T. (*102*)
Kriszat, G. (*367*)
Kritch, N. (*134, 137, 139, 147, 148, 151*)
Križanová, O. (*171*)

Krohn, P. L., and Zuckerman, S. 1937. *J. Physiol.* (*London*) **88**:369. (*145, 146*)
Krompecher, S. (*378*)
Krüger, G. (*281*)
Krüpe, M. (*291*)
Krüskemper, H.-L. (*197*)
Krukenberg, C. F. W. 1884. *Z. Biol.* **20**: 307. (*45*)
Kubickova, Z. (*271*)
Kübler, W. (*382*)
Kückens, H. 1928. *Beitr. Pathol. Anat.* **80**:40. (*391*)
Kuhar, S. (*388*)
Kuhn, F. (*307*)
Kuhn, R. (*157*)
Kuhn, R. 1958. *Bull. Soc. Chim. Biol.* **40**:297. (*173*)
Kuhn, R., and Brossmer, R. 1956. *Chem. Ber.* **89**:2013. (*351*) 1958. *Ann. Chem.* **616**:221. (*24, 42, 352*) 1958a. *Angew. Chem.* **70**:25. (*171, 351*)
Kuhn, R., and Gauhe, A. 1960. *Chem. Ber.* **93**:647. (*283–284*)
Kuhn, R., Gauhe, A., and Baer, H. H. 1954. *Chem. Ber.* **87**:289. (*29*) 1956. *Chem. Ber.* **89**:1027. (*165*)
Kuhn, R., and Kirschenlohr, W. 1953. *Chem. Ber.* **86**:1331. (*157*)
Kuhn, R., and Osman, H. G. 1956. *Z. Physiol. Chem.* **303**:1. (*333*)
Kuhn, R., and Tiedemann, H. 1954. *Chem. Ber.* **87**:1141. (*157, 160*)
Kuhn, R., and Wiegandt, H. 1963. *Chem. Ber.* **96**:866. (*311*) 1963a. *Z. Naturforsch.* **18b**:541. (*311*)
Kuhn, R., Baer, H. H., Bister, W., Brossmer, R., Gauhe, A., Haas, H. J., Haber, F., Krüger, G., Tiedemann, H., and Weiser, D. 1957. *Angew. Chem.* **69**:23. (*281*)
Kujomoto, A. (*44*)
Kukral, J. C. (*100*)
Kukral, J. C., Sporn, J., Louch, J., and Winzler, R. J. 1963. *Am. J. Physiol.* **204**:262. (*100*)
Kulkarni, M. V. (*44*)
Kulonen, E. 1949. *Acta Physiol. Scand.* **17**:170. (*192*) 1952. *Ann. Med. Exptl. Biol. Fenniae* (*Helsinki*) **30**:267. (*187*)
Kulonen, E., Juva, K., Mikkonen, L., Nikkari, T., Salmi, A., and Tuominen, T. 1961. *Biochim. Pharmacol.* **6**:56. (*9*)
Kunin, C. M. 1963. *J. Exptl. Med.* **118**: 565. (*325*)
Kunkel, H. G. (*305–307*)
Kunkel, H. G. 1960. *In* "The Plasma Proteins" (F. W. Putnam, ed.) Vol. 1, 279. New York: Academic Press. (*306*)
Kunkel, H. G., Franklin, E. C., and Müller-Eberhard, H. J. 1959. *J. Clin. Invest.* **38**:424. (*307*)
Kuo, M.-H., and Blumenthal, H. J. 1961. *Biochim. Biophys. Acta* **54**:101. (*40*)
Kuriki, Y. (*82*)
Kurono, A. (*199*)
Kurose, M. (*34*)
Kuroya, M., and Kurose, M. 1940. *Tohoku J. Exptl. Med.* **38**:590. (*34*)
Kurzrok, R. (*187*)

L

Laborde, C. (*199*)
Lacassagne, A. (*391*)
Lack, C. H. (*89*)
Lackey, W. W. (*101*)
Lacour, F. (*394*)
Lacroix, P. 1956. *In* "Ciba Foundation Symposium, Bone Structure and Metabolism, 1955" (G. E. Wolstenholme and M. O'Connor, eds.), p. 36. (*54*)
Lagercrantz, C. 1964. *Acta Chem. Scand.* **18**:562. (*235*)
Laidlaw, J. C., and Young, L. 1948. *Biochem. J.* **42**[Proc.]:*l.* (*50, 69*)
Laidlaw, P. P., and Dudley, H. W. 1925. *Brit. J. Exptl. Pathol.* **6**:197. (*322*)
Lajtha, L. G., Ellis, F., and Oliver, R. 1953. *Brit. J. Cancer* **7**:401. (*54*)
Laki, K. (*89*)
Laland, S. G. (*3*)
Lamberg, B.-A. (*55*)
Lamberts, H. B. (*232, 240, 248, 249*)
Lamberts, H. B., and Alexander, P. 1964. *Biochim. Biophys. Acta* **88**:642 (*240*)
Lampl, H. (*267, 335*)

Lamy, F. (*372*)
Lancefield, R. C. (*319*)
Lancefield, R. C. 1941. *Harvey Lectures, Ser.* **36** (*1940–1941*): 251. (*319*)
Landau, J. W., Fujiwara, A., and Dzawachiszwili, N. 1964. *J. Invest. Dermatol.* **43**:59. (*329*)
Landsteiner, K. (*287*)
Landsteiner, K. 1900. *Centr. Bakteriol. Parasitenk.* **27**:357. (*269*) 1901. *Wien. Klin. Wochschr.* **14**:1132. (*269*) 1920. *Biochem. Z.* **104**:280. (*274*) 1921. *Biochem. Z.* **119**:294. (*267*) 1945. "The Specificity of Serological Reactions," 2d revised ed. Cambridge, Mass.: Harvard. (*267, 320, 334, 335*)
Landsteiner, K., and Harte, R. A. 1940. *J. Exptl. Med.* **71**:551. (*287*)
Landsteiner, K., and Lampl, H. 1918. *Biochem. Z.* **86**:343. (*267, 335*)
Landsteiner, K., and Levine, P. 1927. *Proc. Soc. Exptl. Biol. Med.* **24**:941. (*273, 292*)
Landsteiner, K., and Prašek, E. 1911. *Z. Immunitätsforsch.* **10**(T.1, Orig.):68. (*308*)
Landsteiner, K., and van der Scheer, J. 1932. *J. Exptl. Med.* **56**:399. (*318*)
Landsteiner, K., van der Scheer, J., and Witt, D. H. 1925. *Proc. Soc. Exptl. Biol. Med.* **22**:289. (*270*)
Landy, M. (*336*)
Landy, M. 1953. *Am. J. Hyg.* **58**:148. (*326*) 1954. *Am. J. Hyg.* **60**:52. (*326*) 1957. *Am. J. Hyg.* **65**:81. (*326*)
Landy, M., Johnson, A. G., and Webster, M. E. 1961. *Am. J. Hyg.* **73**:55. (*326*)
Landy, M., Webster, M. E., and Sagin, J. F. 1954. *J. Immunol.* **73**:23. (*327*)
Lange, B. 1928. *Jahrb. Morphol. Mikroskop. Anat., Abt. I (Gegenbaur)* **59**:601. (*147*)
Lange, C. F., and Dubin, A. 1964. *Biochem. Biophys. Res. Commun.* **15**:453. (*106*)
Langley, J. N., and Sherrington, C. S. 1891. *J. Physiol. (London)* **12**:278. (*142*)
Langley, O. K., and Ambrose, E. J. 1964. *Nature* **204**:53. (*382*)
Langstein, L. 1900. *Z. Physiol. Chem.* **31**:49. (*311*)
Lardy, H. A. (*19, 49*)
Larina, I. A. (*200*)
Lark, C., Bradley, D., and Lark, K. G. 1963. *Biochim. Biophys. Acta* **78**:278. (*117*)
Lark, C., and Lark, K. G. 1961. *Biochim. Biophys. Acta* **49**:308. (*114*)
Lark, K. G. (*114, 117*)
Larkey, B. Y. (*372*)
Larsen, B. (*309*)
Larsen, G. 1959. *Am. J. Ophthalmol.* **47**(Pt. 2):519. (*55*)
Larsson, B. (*52, 69, 74*)
Larsson, B. 1956. *Nord. Veterinarmed.* **8**:581. (*55, 74*)
Larsson, K. S. 1960. *Exptl. Cell Res.* **21**:498. (*52*) 1962. *Acta Odontol. Scand.* **20**:Suppl. 31. (*55*)
Larsson, K. S., and Boström, H. 1965. *Acta Paediat. Scand.* **54**:43. (*80*)
Larsson, K. S., Boström, H., and Carlsöö, S. 1959. *Exptl. Cell Res.* **16**:379. (*55*)
Lasfargues, E. Y. (*388*)
Lash, J. W., Holtzer, H., and Whitehouse, M. W. 1960. *Develop. Biol.* **2**:76. (*53*)
László, M. D. (*378*)
Latner, A. L., Merrills, R. J., and Raine, L. C. D. P. 1954. *Biochem. J.* **57**:xix. (*294*)
Laučiková, O. 1959. *Acta Virol.* **3**:139. (*349*)
Lauenstein, K. (*349*)
Lauenstein, K., and Altman, K. I. 1956. *Nature* **178**:917. (*102*)
Laufer, A. (*309*)
Laufer, A. L. (*238, 239*)
Laurell, A.-B. (*308*)
Laurent, T. (*83*)
Laurent, T. C. (*224, 238–242, 244, 266, 364, 370*)
Laurent, T. C. 1956. *J. Am. Chem. Soc.* **78**:1875. (*241*) 1957. *Arkiv Kemi* **11**:487. (*135*) 1963. *Biochem. J.* **89**:253. (*362*) 1963a. *Acta Chem. Scand.* **17**:2664. (*362*)

Laurent, T. C., and Pietruszkiewicz, A. 1961. *Biochim. Biophys. Acta* **49**: 258. (*362*)
Laurent, T. C., and Wertheim, E. M. 1952. *Acta Chem. Scand.* **6**:678. (*241*)
Lausing, E. A. (*394*)
Lavenda, N. (*142*)
Laver, W. G. (*178, 358*)
Laver, W. G. 1963. *Virology* **20**:251. (*358*)
Lavin, F. B. (*120*)
Law, J. H. (*123*)
Lawrence, J. C., and Ricketts, C. R. 1957. *Exptl. Cell Res.* **12**:633. (*53*)
Lawry, E. Y. (*216*)
Lawson, K. A. (*101*)
Lawton, V., McLoughlin, J. V., and Morgan, W. T. J. 1956. *Nature* **178**: 740. (*85*)
Layton, L. L. 1949. *Cancer* **2**:1089. (*53*) 1950. *Cancer* **3**:725. (*50, 53*) 1951. *Cancer* **4**:198. (*52, 69*)
Layton, L. L., Frankel, D. R., and Scapa, S. 1950. *Arch. Biochem. Biophys.* **28**:142. (*52*) 1950a. *Proc. Soc. Exptl. Biol. Med.* **73**:570. (*53*)
Lazar, J. (*235*)
Lazen, A. G. (*271*)
Leaback, D. H. (*155–163, 167*)
Leaback, D. H. 1963. *Biochem. Prep.* **10**: 118. (*168*)
Leaback, D. H., and Walker, P. G. 1957. *J. Chem. Soc.*, p. 4754. (*155, 157*) 1961. *Biochem. J.* **78**:151. (*158–160*)
Leatherwood, J., Rollins, E., Kulkarni, M. V., and Wheat, R. W. 1963. *Federation Proc.* **22**:239. (*44*)
LeBaron, F. N. (*120*)
Ledderhose, G. 1878. *Z. Physiol. Chem.* **2**:213. (*1*)
Lederberg, J. 1957. *J. Bacteriol.* **73**:144. (*109, 110*) 1959. *Science* **129**:1649. (*272*)
Ledieu, M. (*183*)
Lee, L. T. (*353*)
Lee, Y. C., Wu, Y.-C., and Montgomery, R. 1964. *Biochem. J.* **91**:9c. (*89*)
Le Goffe, M. 1939. *Bull. Soc. Sci. Bretagne* **16**:35. (*76*)
Lehane, D. (*274*)
Leitze, A. (*100*)
Leloir, L. F. (*14, 18, 21, 24, 45, 84*)
Leloir, L. F. 1953. *Advan. Enzymol.* **14**:193. (*122*) 1956. *In* "Currents in Biochemical Research" (D. E. Green, ed.), p. 585. New York: Wiley (Interscience). (*20*)
Leloir, L. F., and Cardini, C. E. 1953. *Biochim. Biophys. Acta* **12**:15. (*6, 11, 18, 57, 66, 76*) 1956. *Biochim. Biophys. Acta* **20**:33. (*37*) 1957. *J. Am. Chem. Soc.* **79**:6340. (*59*)
Leloir, L. F., Cardini, C. E., and Cabib, E. 1960. *In* "Comparative Biochemistry" (M. Florkin and H. S. Mason, eds.), Vol. 2, p. 97. New York: Academic Press. (*45, 57, 58*)
Leloir, L. F., Cardini, C. E., and Olavarría, J. M. 1958. *Arch. Biochem. Biophys.* **74**:84. (*16*)
Leloir, L. F., Olavarría, J. M., Goldemberg, S. H., and Carminatti, H. 1959. *Arch. Biochem. Biophys.* **81**:508. (*59*)
Leloir, L. F., and Goldemberg, S. H. 1960. *J. Biol. Chem.* **235**:919. (*59*)
Lempfrid, H. (*348, 349*)
Lenk, H.-P. (*182*)
Lenk, H. P., Wenzel, M., and Schütte, E. 1960. *Naturwissenschaften* **47**:516. (*87, 182*)
Lennox, F. G. (*86*)
Lenstrup, J. 1951. *Acta Pharmacol. Toxicol.* **7**:143. (*188*)
Leonard, S. L., Perlman, P. L., and Kurzrok, R. 1946. *Endocrinology* **39**: 261. (*187*)
Leonard, V. C. (*371*)
Leone, C. A. 1960. *J. Immunol.* **85**:268. (*312*)
Lerman, J. 1942. *Endocrinology* **31**:558. (*302*)
Lerner, L. J., Bianchi, A., Dzelzkalns, M., and Borman, A. 1962. *Federation Proc.* **21**:210. (*141*)
Leskowitz, S. (*278–280*)
Letterer, E., Caesar, R., and Vogt, A. 1960. *German Med. Monthly* **5**:401. (*309*)
Lettré, H. 1953. *Naturwissenschaften* **40**: 513. (*384*)

Leuterer, W. (*272*)
Levdikova, G. A. (*200*)
Leveille, G. A., Fisher, H., and Feigenbaum, A. S. 1961. *Ann. N.Y. Acad. Sci.* **94**:265. (*94*)
Levene, P. A. 1925. "Hexosamines and Mucoproteins." London: Longmans, Green. (*1, 135, 148, 155*) 1941. *J. Biol. Chem.* **140**:279. (*311*)
Levene, P. A., and López-Suárez, J. 1918. *J. Biol. Chem.* **36**:105. (*202*)
Leveque, T. F. (*376*)
Lever, W. F. (*260*)
Lever, W. F., Smith, P. A. J., and Hurley, N. A. 1953. *Science* **118**:653. (*259*)
Levey, S. (*224*)
Levey, S., and Sheinfeld, S. 1954. *Gastroenterology* **27**:625. (*224, 225*)
Levi, H. (*392*)
Levin, N. R. (*187*)
Levine, M. G. (*63*)
Levine, P. (*273, 292*)
Levine, P., and Celano, M. 1960. *Vox Sanguinis* **5**(n.s.):53. (*289*)
Levine, P., Celano, M. J., and Falkowski, F. 1963. *Transfusion* **3**:278. (*293*)
Levine, P., Celano, M. J., and Staveley, J. M. 1958. *Vox Sanguinis* **3**:434. (*289, 292*)
Levine, P., Ottensooser, F., Celano, N. J., and Pollitzer, W. 1955. *Am. J. Phys. Anthropol.* **13**:29. (*291*)
Levinthal, C., Signer, E. R., and Fetherolf, K. 1962. *Proc. Natl. Acad. Sci. U.S.* **48**:1230. (*222*)
Levvy, G. A. (*157–163, 165–167*)
Levvy, G. A. 1952. *Biochem. J.* **52**:464. (*161*)
Levvy, G. A., and McAllan, A. 1961. *Biochem. J.* **80**:435. (*89*) 1963. *Biochem. J.* **87**:206. (*91*) 1963a. *Biochem. J.* **87**:361. (*91*)
Levvy, G. A., and Marsh, C. A. 1959. *Advan. Carbohydrate Chem.* **14**:381. (*199*) 1960. *In* "The Enzymes" (P. D. Boyer, H. Lardy, and K. Myrbäck, eds.), Vol. 4, p. 397. New York: Academic Press. (*199*)
Levy, L., and Petracek, F. J. 1962. *Proc. Soc. Exptl. Biol. Med.* **109**:901. (*211*)
Lewin, J. (*102*)
Lewis, J. C., Snell, N. S. Hirschmann, D. J., and Fraenkel-Conrat, H. 1950. *J. Biol. Chem.* **186**:23. (*183*)
Lewis, J. H., and Wells, H. G. 1927. *J. Infect. Diseases* **40**:316. (*305, 311*)
Lewis, R. F. 1964. *Biochim. Biophys. Acta* **83**:237. (*118*)
Lewis, Y. S. (*246*)
Leyh-Bouille, M. (*90*)
Li, C. H. 1949. *Vitamins Hormones* **7**:223. (*356*)
Li, C. H., Simpson, M. E., and Evans, H. M. 1949. *Science* **109**:445. (*85*)
Li, Y.-T., and Shetlar, M. R. 1961. *Proc. Soc. Exptl. Biol. Med.* **106**:398. (*85*)
Lieben, F., and Löwe, L. 1932. *Biochem. Z.* **252**:70. (*34*)
Lieberman, I., Lamy, F., and Ove, P. 1959. *Science* **129**:43. (*372*)
Lieberman, I., and Ove, P. 1958. *J. Biol. Chem.* **233**:637. (*373, 374*)
Liebhaber, H. (*363*)
Liebhaber, H., and Takemoto, K. K. 1961. *Virology* **14**:502. (*363*) 1962. *Bacteriol. Proc.*, p. 139. (*363, 364*) 1963. *Virology* **20**:559. (*363*)
Lienert, E., and Thorsell, W. 1954. *Acta Chem. Scand.* **8**:574. (*197*)
Lietze, A. (*94*)
Likar, I. N., and Likar, L. J. 1964. *Acta Endocrinol.* **46**:493. (*154*)
Likar, I. N., Likar, L. J., and Robinson, R. W. 1964. *Nature* **203**:730. (*154*)
Likar, I. N., Likar, L. J., and Taylor, H. E. 1961. *Nature* **190**:1118. (*149*)
Likar, L. J. (*149, 154*)
Lillie, F. R. 1913. *J. Exptl. Zool.* **14**:515. (*312*)
Lin, T.-Y., and Hassid, W. Z. 1964. *J. Biol. Chem.* **239**:PC944. (*84*)
Lincicome, D. R. 1953. *Exptl. Parasitol.* **2**:333. (*189*)
Lind, P. E. (*171, 172, 175–178, 340, 347, 353, 358*)
Lindberg, E. (*344*)
Lindenberg, W. (*22, 326*)
Lindenmann, J. (*335*)

Linderot, T. (*197, 226*)
Lindgren, F. T., Elliott, H. A., and Gofman, J. W. 1951. *J. Phys. Chem.* **55**:80. (*215*)
Lindner, J. (*385*)
Lindner, J., v. Schweinitz, H. A., and Becker, K. 1960. *Klin. Wochschr.* **38**:763. (*385*)
Lineweaver, H., and Burk, D. 1934. *J. Am. Chem. Soc.* **56**:658. (*161*)
Ling, N. R. (*303*)
Link, K. P. (*294*)
Linker, A. (*17, 63, 155, 186–189, 192, 193, 195, 198, 199, 206, 207*)
Linker, A., Hoffman, P., and Meyer, K. 1957. *Nature* **180**:810. (*195*)
Linker, A., and Meyer, K. 1954. *Nature* **174**:1192. (*194*)
Linker, A., Meyer, K., and Hoffman, P. 1956. *J. Biol. Chem.* **219**:13. (*193, 194*) 1960. *J. Biol. Chem.* **235**:924. (*164, 195*)
Linker, A., Meyer, K., and Weissmann, B. 1955. *J. Biol. Chem.* **213**:237. (*164, 198*)
Linker, A., and Sampson, P. 1960. *Biochim. Biophys. Acta* **43**:366. (*73, 198, 206*)
Linker, A., Weissmann, B., and Meyer, K. 1954. *Federation Proc.* **13**:253. (*194*)
Linker, A., Hoffman, P., Sampson, P., and Meyer, K. 1958. *Biochim. Biophys. Acta* **29**:443. (*56, 198, 206*)
Linker, A., Hoffman, P., Meyer, K., Sampson, P., and Korn, E. D. 1960. *J. Biol. Chem.* **235**:3061. (*195, 199, 203–205, 207*)
Linko, P. 1958. *Acta Chem. Scand.* **12**: 129. (*118*)
Lipari, R. (*307, 336*)
Lipmann, F. (*55, 56, 60, 69, 72*)
Lipmann, F. 1958. *Science* **128**:575. (*53, 56*)
Lippman, M. 1957. *Cancer Res.* **17**:1. (*387*) 1965. *Trans. N.Y. Acad. Sci.* **27**(Ser. II): 342. (*389*)
Lippman, V. (*198, 207*)
Lipschitz, W. L., and Bueding, E. 1939. *J. Biol. Chem.* **129**:333. (*47*)
Lipton, M. M. (*3, 4, 65, 70, 142*)
Lisbonne, M. (*287*)
Lisowska, E. (*290*)
Lisowska, E. 1963. *Nature* **198**:865. (*291*)
Litwack, G. (*87*)
Litwack, G. 1958. *Proc. Soc. Exptl. Biol. Med.* **98**:408. (*183*)
Llombart, A. (*134, 147, 148, 151*)
Lloyd, A. G. (*193, 202–205, 208–210*)
Lloyd, A. G. 1960. *Biochem. J.* **75**: 478. (*205*) 1961. *Biochem. J.* **80**:572. (*209–211*) 1962. *Biochim. Biophys. Acta* **58**:1. (*209–211*)
Lloyd, K. O., and Kabat, E. A. 1964. *Biochem. Biophys. Res. Commun.* **16**:385. (*281*)
Lobstein, O. E., and Fogelson, S. J. 1951. *Am. J. Digest. Diseases* **18**:298. (*183*)
Loeb, J. 1956. *Arch. Sci. Physiol.* **10**: 129. (*263*)
Löfroth, G. (*243*)
Loeschcke, H. 1927. *Beitr. Pathol. Anat. Allgem. Pathol.* **77**:231. (*309*)
Lötterle, R. (*211*)
Löwe, L. (*34*)
Löwenthal, J., and Gagnon, A. 1948. *Can. J. Res.* **26E**:200. (*197*)
Loewi, G. (*52, 273*)
Loewi, G., and Consden, R. 1962. *Nature* **195**:148. (*149*)
Loewi, G., and Kent, P. W. 1957. *Biochem. J.* **65**:550. (*53*)
Loewy, A. G., Dahlberg, J. E., Dorwart, W. V., Jr., Weber, M. J., and Eisele, J. 1964. *Biochem. Biophys. Res. Commun.* **15**:177. (*89*)
Loftfield, R. B., and Harris, A. 1956. *J. Biol. Chem.* **219**:151. (*94*)
Long, C. (*14*)
Long, F. A. (*234*)
Longley, J. B. (*192, 196*)
Loomis, T. A. 1961. *Proc. Soc. Exptl. Biol. Med.* **106**:490. (*211*)
Loran, I. D. (*200*)
López-Suárez, J. (*201*)
Loran, I. D., and Galatch'iants, O. P. 1962. *Lab. Delo* **8**:No. 8, 47.
Loran, M. R., Kerner, M. W., and Anderson, H. H. 1956. *Exptl. Cell Res.* **10**:241.

Lormand, C. H., Desbordes, J., and Bonét-Maury, P. 1952. *Ann. Pharm. Franc.* **10**:173. (*188*)
Losnegard, N., and Oeding, P. 1963. *Acta Pathol. Microbiol. Scand.* **58**: 482. (*321*)
Lospalluto, J., and Ziff, M. 1959. *J. Exptl. Med.* **110**:169. (*307*)
Lotmar, R. 1960. *Z. Rheumaforsch.* **19**: 61. (*200*)
Louch, J. (*100*)
Lovett, J. (*182*)
Lowenthal, J. P., and Berman, S. 1959. *J. Bacteriol.* **77**:516. (*85*)
Lowick, J. H. B. (*381*)
Lowy, P. H. (*92*)
Lowy, P. H., Keighley, G., and Borsook, H. 1960. *Nature* **185**:102. (*357*)
Lowther, D. A., and Rogers, H. J. 1955. *Congr. Intern. Biochim., 3e, Bruxelles, 1955, Résumés des Communications,* p. 96. (*5*) 1955a. *Nature* **175**:435. (*66*) 1956. *Biochem. J.* **62**:304. (*5, 66*)
Lucy, J. A. (*101*)
Lucy, J. A., Webb, M., and Biggers, J. D. 1961. *Biochim. Biophys. Acta* **54**:259. (*101*)
Ludányi, G., Orbán, T., and Vajda, J. 1952. *Arch. Intern. Pharmacodyn.* **88**:496. (*332*)
Ludowieg, J. (*4, 49, 65, 70, 72, 77, 95*)
Ludwick, T. M. (*295*)
Ludwig, A. W. (*141*)
Ludwig, A. W., and Boas, N. F. 1950. *Endocrinology* **46**:291. (*134, 137, 140*)
Ludwig, K. A. (*268*)
Luedemann, G. M. (*366*)
Lüderitz, O. (*325, 333*)
Lumpkin, W. M. (*63*)
Lund, E. (*200*)
Lundbeck, H. (*238*)
Lundgren, H. P., Gurin, S., Bachman, C., and Wilson, D. W. 1947. *J. Biol. Chem.* **142**:367. (*301*)
Lundquist, F. 1949. *Acta Physiol. Scand.* **17**:44. (*193, 231*)
Lunt, M. R. (*76*)
Luria, S. E. (*334*)
de Lustig, E. S. (*55*)
Lutwak-Mann, C. 1941. *Biochem. J.* **35**:610. (*35, 36*)
Lyampert, I. M., and Yarenshko, N. T. 1961. *J. Microbiol. Epidemiol. Immunobiol.* **32**:1977. (*200*)
Lycke, E., Lund, E., and Strannegard, O. 1965. *Brit. J. Exptl. Pathol.* **46**: 189. (*200*)
Lynch, J. L. (*118*)
Lyon, T. D. (*371*)
Lyon, T. P. (*259*)
Lyons, M. E. (*260*)
Lysenko, M. G. (*196*)

M

Maass, D. (*88*)
Maass, D., and Weidel, W. 1963. *Biochim. Biophys. Acta* **78**:369. (*90*)
Maass, D., Pelzer, H., and Weidel, W. 1964. *Z. Naturforsch.* **19b**:413. (*90*)
McAllan, A. (*89, 91*)
Macaluso, M. P. 1960. *Arch. "de Vecchi" Anat. Patol.* **33**:193. (*391*)
Macbeth, R. A. L., and Bekesi, J. G. 1962. *Cancer Res.* **22**:1170. (*394*) 1964. *Cancer Res.* **24**:614. (*105, 394*) 1964a. *Arch. Surg.* **88**:633. (*105*)
Macbeth, R. A. L., Bekesi, J. G., and Tuba, J. 1963. *Cancer Res.* **23**:938. (*394, 395*)
McCann, M. P. (*39*)
McCarter, A. (*52*)
McCarty, M. 1952. *J. Exptl. Med.* **96**: 555. (*88*) 1952a. *J. Exptl. Med.* **96**: 569. (*88*) 1956. *J. Exptl. Med.* **104**: 629. (*319*) 1958. *J. Exptl. Med.* **108**: 311. (*164, 320, 333*) 1959. *J. Exptl. Med.* **109**:361. (*313, 314, 319*) 1960. *In* Springer, 1960a. (*320*)
McCarty, M., and Lancefield, R. C. 1955. *J. Exptl. Med.* **102**:11. (*319*)
McClean, D. (*381, 394*)
McClean, D. 1941. *Chem. Ind. (London)* **60**:219. (*187*) 1942. *J. Pathol. Bacteriol.* **54**:284. (*189, 224*) 1943. *Biochem. J.* **37**:169. (*186, 187, 192*)
McClean, D., and Hale, C. W. 1940. *Nature* **145**:867. (*229, 236*) 1941. *Biochem. J.* **35**:159. (*187, 188, 229,*

230, 236)
McClean, D. J. 1930. *J. Pathol. Bacteriol.* **33**:1045. (*361*)
McClelland, L., and Hare, R. 1941. *Can. Public Health J.* **32**:530. (*337*)
McCluer, R. H. (*271*)
McCluskey, R. T. 1959. *In* Springer, 1959. (*332*)
McConnell, R. B. (*283*)
McCrea, J. F. (*171, 338*)
McCrea, J. F. 1947. *Australian J. Exptl. Biol. Med. Sci.* **25**:127. (*171*) 1948. *Australian J. Exptl. Biol. Med. Sci.* **26**:355. (*340*) 1953. *Yale J. Biol. Med.* **26**:191. (*344*)
McCrea, J. F., and Duran-Reynals, F. 1953. *Science* **118**:93. (*362*)
McCready, M. H. (*187*)
McCullagh, D. R. (*187*)
McCutcheon, M., and Coman, D. R. 1947. *Cancer Res.* **7**:379. (*394*)
McDermott, D. A. (*272, 326*)
MacDonald, D. L. (*333*)
McDonald, J. R. (*391*)
McDuffie, F. C., and Kabat, E. A. 1956. *J. Immunol.* **77**:61. (*272*)
Macfarlane, R. G. 1960. *In* "The Plasma Proteins" (F. W. Putnam, ed.), Vol. 2, p. 137. New York: Academic Press. (*262, 264*)
McGaff, C. J. (*216*)
McGarrahan, J. F., and Maley, F. 1962. *J. Biol. Chem.* **237**:2458. (*104*)
McGilvery, R. W. (*53*)
McGuire, E., and Binkley, S. B. 1962. *Federation Proc.* **21**:172. (*173*)
McKay, D. G. 1950. *Am. J. Obstet. Gynecol.* **59**:875. (*149*)
McKean, C. M. 1960. *Am. J. Obstet. Gynecol.* **80**:596. (*301*)
McKenzie, H. A. (*341, 342, 344*)
McKeown, T. (*149*)
MacKinnon, J. A. (*15*)
McLaughlin, J. (*163, 326*)
McLaughlin, J. V. (*85, 163*)
MacLean, D. L. (*264*)
McLean, J. 1916. *Am. J. Physiol.* **41**: 250. (*251*)
McLean, N. D. (*202*)
MacLennan, A. P. 1963. *Biochem. J.* **89**:99P. (*294*)
MacLennan, J. D. (*171, 274*)
MacLeod, C. M. (*268, 317, 326*)
MacLeod, C. M., and Avery, O. T. 1941. *J. Exptl. Med.* **73**:191. (*307*)
MacLeod, C. M., Hodges, R. G., Heidelberger, M., and Bernhard, W. G. 1945. *J. Exptl. Med.* **82**:445. (*317*)
McLimans, W. (*290*)
McMaster, M. H. (*271*)
McMeekin, T. L., Polis, B. D., Della Monica, E. S., and Custer, J. H. 1949. *J. Am. Chem. Soc.* **71**:3606. (*253*)
McMillan, E. (*50*)
McNeely, W. H. (*217, 264*)
MacPherson, C. R. (*275, 300*)
McQuillen, K. 1955. *Biochim. Biophys. Acta* **17**:382. (*88, 109, 113*) 1956. *Bacterial Anat., 6th Symp. Soc. Gen. Microbiol., London, 1956.*, p. 127. (*109*) 1958. *J. Gen. Microbiol.* **18**: 498. (*110*) 1960. *In* Springer, 1960a. (*313*)
McShan, W. H. (*141*)
Madinaveitia, J. (*157, 162*)
Madinaveitia, J. 1938. *Biochem. J.* **32**: 1806. (*188*)
Madinaveitia, J., and Quibell, T. H. H. 1940. *Biochem. J.* **34**:625. (*187*) 1941. *Biochem. J.* **35**:453. (*229, 230*) 1941a. *Biochem. J.* **35**:456. (*187, 193*)
Maeda, Y. (*222*)
Magnusson, S., and Larsson, B. 1955. *Acta Chem. Scand.* **9**:534. (*52, 69, 74*)
Majewski, C., Siwiński, S., and Majewska, H. 1963. *Gynaecologia* **156**: 359. (*154*)
Majewska, H. (*154*)
Majno, G. (*125*)
Mäkelä, O., and Cantell, K. 1958. *Ann. Med. Exptl. Biol. Fenniae (Helsinki)* **36**:366. (*290*)
Mäkelä, O., Cantell, K., and Penttinen, K. 1959. *J. Immunol.* **83**:127. (*271*)
Makino, M. (*83, 86*)
Málek, P., and Trávníček, R. 1955. *Cesk.*

Fysiol. **4**:216. (*188*) 1957. *Chem. Zentr.*, **128**(Jahrg):159. (*188*)
Maley, F. (*104*)
Maley, F., and Maley, G. F. 1959. *Biochim. Biophys. Acta* **31**:577. (*21*)
Maley, F., Maley, G. F., and Lardy, H. A. 1956. *J. Am. Chem. Soc.* **78**: 5303. (*19, 49*)
Maley, G. F. (*19, 21, 49*)
Mallette, M. F. (*288*)
Malmgren, H. 1953. *Biochim. Biophys. Acta* **11**:524. (*192*) 1954. *J. Natl. Cancer Inst.* **14**:1119. (*390*)
Mancini, R. E., and Brandes, D. 1956. *Rev. Soc. Arg. Biol.* **32**:185. (*137*)
Mancini, R. E., and de Lustig, E. S. 1954. *Rev. Soc. Arg. Biol.* **30**:67. (*55*)
Mancini, R. E., Izquierdo, I., and Kirschbaum, P. 1957. *Rev. Soc. Arg. Biol.* **33**:262. (*138*)
Mancini, R. E., Brandes, D., Portela, A., Izquierdo, I., and Kirschbaum, P. 1960. *Endocrinology* **67**:430. (*137, 138*)
Mancini, R. E., Vilar, O., Stein, E., and Fiorini, H. 1961. *J. Histochem. Cytochem.* **9**:278. (*54*)
Mandel, B., and Racker, E. 1953. *J. Exptl. Med.* **98**:399. (*355*) 1953a. *J. Exptl. Med.* **98**:417. (*355*)
Mandelstam, J. 1962. *Biochem. J.* **82**:489. (*9*)
Mandl, I. (*171, 274*)
Mangieri, C. N., Engelberg, R., and Randall, L. O. 1951. *J. Pharmacol. Exptl. Therap.* **102**:156. (*227, 266*)
Mann, G. V. (*216*)
Mann, T. (*157*)
Mannheim, W. 1961. *Zentr. Bakteriol. Parisitenk. Abt. I. Orig.* **183**:180. (*189*)
Mannik, M., and Kunkel, H. G. 1962. *J. Exptl. Med.* **116**:859. (*305*) 1963. *J. Exptl. Med.* **117**:213. (*305*)
Mansberger, A. R. (*376*)
Månsson, B. (*5, 53, 69–71, 211*)
Mantel, N. (*389*)
Mapson, L. W. (*48*)
Marbet, R., and Winterstein, A. 1951. *Helv. Chim. Acta* **34**:2311. (*266*)
Marcker, K. (*149*)
Marcus, D. M., Kabat, E. A., and Rosenfield, R. E. 1963. *J. Exptl. Med.* **118**:175. (*292*)
Marcus, S. (*189*)
Margen, S. (*99*)
Mariani, A. (*52*)
Mariel, J. P. (*100*)
Marinelli, L. (*50, 52*)
Marinetti, G. V. (*324*)
Marini, M., and Levey, S. 1955. *Proc. Soc. Exptl. Biol. Med.* **88**:611. (*224*)
Markovitz, A. 1964. *J. Biol. Chem.* **239**: 2091. (*84*)
Markovitz, A., and Dorfman, A. 1962. *J. Biol. Chem.* **237**:273. (*68*)
Markovitz, A., Cifonelli, J. A., and Dorfman, A. 1959. *J. Biol. Chem.* **234**:2343. (*45, 48, 49, 60, 67*)
Markowitz, J. (*332*)
Marlow, H. W. 1950. *Endocrinology* **47**: 300. (*141*)
Marmion, B. P., Curtain, C. C., and Pye, J. 1953. *Australian J. Exptl. Biol. Med. Sci.* **31**:505. (*346*)
Marquez, J. A. (*366*)
Marr, A. G. M., Owen, J. A., and Wilson, G. S. 1962. *Biochim. Biophys. Acta* **63**:276. (*372*)
Marrack, J. (*308*)
Marrack, J. R. (*276*)
Marrack, J. R. 1938. *Med. Res. Council (Brit.) Mem. Spec. Rept. Ser.* **No.** 230. (*267*)
Marrack, J. [R.], and Smith, F. C. 1932. *Brit. J. Exptl. Pathol.* **13**:394. (*267*)
Mars, P. H. (*65, 136–138, 147*)
Marsh, C. A. (*157, 158, 161, 162, 167, 199*)
Marsh, C. A., and Levvy, G. A. 1957. *Biochem. J.* **66**:4P. (*163*)
Marsh, W. L. 1960. *Vox Sanguinis* **5** (n.s.):387. (*300*)
Marsh, W. L., Jenkins, W. J., and Walther, W. W. 1959. *Brit. Med. J.* **2**:63. (*300*)
Marshall, R. D. (*83, 86, 311*)
Martin, F. B. (*52, 119, 121, 125*)

Martin, G. J. (*197*)
Martin, G. J. 1953. *Science* **117**:363. (*197*)
Martin, G. R. (*324*)
Martin, H. H. (*114, 313*)
Martin, J. E., Graves, J. H., and Dohan, F. C. 1955. *Am. J. Vet. Res.* **16**:141. (*141*)
Martin, R. O. (*113*)
Martinez, A. (*117*)
Martinez, R. J., Wolfe, J. B., and Nakada, H. I. 1959. *J. Bacteriol.* **78**: 217. (*193, 203, 204*) 1959a. *J. Biol. Chem.* **234**:2236. (*193*)
Martlew, E. F. (*56, 264*)
Marx, R. (*197*)
Marx, W. (*61, 74, 75, 80*)
Masaki, J., and Hartree, E. F. 1962. *Biochem. J.* **84**:347. (*200*)
Masaki, S. (*107, 280*)
Masamune, H. 1953. *Tohoku J. Exptl. Med.* **57**:310. (*300*) 1956. *Proc. Intern. Congr. Biochem., 3rd, Brussels, 1955,* p. 72. (*83*)
Masamune, H., Hakomori, S., and Sugo, T. 1959. *Tohoku J. Exptl. Med.* **69**:383. (*106*)
Mason, H. S. (*235*)
Masouredis, S. P. 1960. *Science* **131**: 1442. (*274*) 1960a. *J. Clin. Invest.* **39**:1450. (*274*)
Mastroianni, E. (*149*)
Mathé, G. (*199*)
Mathews, M. B. (*52, 65, 69, 70, 72, 77–79, 101, 331*)
Mathews, M. B. 1954. *J. Am. Chem. Soc.* **76**:2948. (*197*) 1960. *Biochim. Biophys. Acta* **37**:288. (*252*)
Mathews, M. B., and Dorfman, A. 1954. *J. Biol. Chem.* **206**:143. (*192*) 1955. *Physiol. Rev.* **35**:381. (*196*)
Mathews, M. B., Roseman, S., and Dorfman, A. 1951. *J. Biol. Chem.* **188**: 327. (*189*)
Mathias, A. P. (*113*)
Matsubara, S. (*88*)
Matsubara, S., and Boyd, W. C. 1963. *J. Immunol.* **91**:641. (*305*)
Matsuhashi, M. (*84*)
Matsuhashi, M. 1963. *Federation Proc.* **22**:465. (*44*)
Matsuhashi, M., and Strominger, J. L. 1964. *J. Biol. Chem.* **239**:2454. (*84*)
Matsuhashi, S., Matsuhashi, M., Brown, J. G., and Strominger, J. L. 1964. *Biochem. Biophys. Res. Commun.* **15**:60. (*84*)
Matsumura, G., and Pigman, W. 1965. *Arch. Biochem. Biophys.* **110**:526. (*250*)
Matsushima, Y. (*84*)
Matsushima, Y. 1948. *Nippon Kagaku Zasshi* **69**:8. (*34*) 1951. *Sci. Papers Coll. Gen. Educ., Univ. Tokyo* **34**: 11. (*34*)
Matsushima, Y., and Shimazu, Y. 1952. *Science* **115**:499. (*34*)
Maurer, P. H. 1953. *Proc. Soc. Exptl. Biol. Med.* **83**:879. (*332*)
Maurer, W. (*93*)
Maurer, W., and Müller, E. R. 1955. *Biochem. Z.* **326**:474. (*93*)
Maw, W. A. (*135, 141, 148*)
Maxwell, E. S. (*45, 47, 49*)
Maxwell, E. S. 1957. *J. Biol. Chem.* **229**: 139. (*50*)
Maxwell, E. S., Kalckar, H. M., and Burton, R. M. 1955. *Biochim. Biophys. Acta* **18**:444. (*122*)
Maxwell, E. S., Kalckar, H. M., and Strominger, J. L. 1956. *Arch. Biochem. Biophys.* **65**:2. (*47*)
May, E. L. (*196*)
Mayeda, M. (*4, 65, 95*)
Mayer, G. 1955. *Brit. J. Ophthalmol.* **39**: 747. (*189*)
Mayer, M. (*267*)
Mayer, M. M. (*267, 306, 311, 333, 334*)
Mayer, M. M. 1958. *Progr. Allergy* **5**: 215. (*267*)
Mayer, P. L. (*363*)
Mayer, R. L. (*226*)
Mayhew, E., and Roe, E. M. F. 1964. *Brit. J. Cancer* **18**:528. (*391*) 1964a. *Brit. J. Cancer* **18**:537. (*391*)
Maynard, E. A. (*211*)
Maynard, F. L., West, G. B., Kagan, R., and Fulton, G. P. 1955. *Anat. Record* **121**:336. (*246*)

Mayron, L. W., Robert, B., Winzler, R. J., and Rafelson, M. E., Jr. 1961. *Arch. Biochem. Biophys.* **92**:475. (*172, 175, 177, 352*)
Mazur, M. L. (*224–226*)
Meacham, G. C. (*294*)
Meachim, G. (*53*)
Meadow, P. M., Anderson, J. S., and Strominger, J. L. 1964. *Biochem. Biophys. Res. Commun.* **14**:382. (*117*)
Meaney, M. F. (*72*)
Meath, J. A. (*119*)
Medawar, P. B. (*300, 303*)
Medina, A., and Nicholas, D. J. D. 1957. *Biochem. J.* **66**:573. (*14*)
Meeroff, M. 1958. *Semana Med.* (*Buenos Aires*) **113**:60. (*394*)
Mehl, E., and Jatzkewitz, H. 1963. *Z. Physiol. Chem.* **331**:292. (*212*)
Mehl, J. W. (*308*)
Mehler, A. H. (*12, 57*)
Meinecke, K.-H. (*11*)
Meissner, J. (*54*)
Mèlica, F. 1963. *Boll. Soc. Ital. Biol. Sper.* **39**:1655. (*154*)
Melin, M. (*374*)
Mellanby, J. 1934. *Proc. Roy. Soc.* (*London*) *Ser. B* **116**:1. (*263*)
Mellors, J. (*199*)
Mellors, R. C., and Ortega, L. G. 1956. *Am. J. Pathol.* **32**:455. (*310*)
Meltzer, H. L. 1955. *Federation Proc.* **14**:100. (*119*)
Menkes, J. (*127*)
Menzel, A. E. O. (*322*)
Mergenhagen, S. E., Martin, G. R., and Schiffmann, E. 1963. *J. Immunol.* **90**:312. (*324*)
Merigan, T. C., and Dreyer, W. J. 1963. *Ann. N.Y. Acad. Sci.* **103**:765. (*184, 199*)
Merlen, J. F., Cachera, J. P., and Dussaussoy, C. 1954. *Ann. Biol. Clin.* (*Paris*) **12**:H.5. (*188*)
Merrick, J. M., and Roseman, S. 1960. *J. Biol. Chem.* **235**:1274. (*41*)
Merrills, R. J. (*294*)
Messinger, W. J., and Porosowska, Y. 1953. *J. Appl. Physiol.* **6**:173. (*216*)
Mester, L., and Ivánovics, G. 1957. *Chem. Ind.* (*London*), p. 493. (*319*)
Metz, C. B. 1961. *Intern. Rev. Cytol.* **11**:219. (*369*)
Meyer, D. (*83*)
Meyer, K[arl]. (*23, 27, 41, 56, 60, 63, 83, 155, 164, 171, 187–189, 192–195, 198, 199, 203–207, 211, 332, 348, 351*)
Meyer, K[arl]. 1947. *Physiol. Rev.* **27**:335. (*192*) 1953. *Discussions Faraday Soc.*, **No.** 13, p. 271. (*252*) 1958. *Federation Proc.* **17**:1075. (*199*) 1959. *In* Springer, 1959, p. 140. (*310*)
Meyer, K., Dubos, R., and Smyth, E. M. 1937. *J. Biol. Chem.* **118**:71. (*229*)
Meyer, K., and Hoffman, P. 1960. *Arzneimittel-Forsch.* **10**:379. (*198*)
Meyer, K., Hoffman, P., and Linker, A. 1960. *In* "The Enzymes" (P. D. Boyer, H. Lardy, and K. Myrbäck, eds.), Vol. 4, 2nd ed., p. 447. New York: Academic Press. (*186, 193*)
Meyer, K., Linker, A., and Rapport, M. M. 1951. *J. Biol. Chem.* **192**:275. (*17*)
Meyer, K., Linker, A., and Weissmann, B. 1952. *Abstr. Intern. Congr. Biochim. 2e, Paris, 1952,* p. 242. (*189*)
Meyer, K., and Palmer, J. W. 1936. *J. Biol. Chem.* **114**:689. (*135*) 1936a. *Am. J. Ophthalmol.* **19**:859. (*155*)
Meyer, K., and Rapport, M. M. 1950. *Arch. Biochem.* **27**:287. (*189*) 1951. *J. Biol. Chem.* **188**:485. (*197*) 1952. *Advan. Enzymol.* **13**:199. (*192*)
Meyer, K., Smyth, E. M., and Dawson, M. H. 1939. *J. Biol. Chem.* **128**:319. (*330*) 1939a. *J. Biol. Chem.* **128**:lxx. (*330*)
Meyer, K[urt]. 1907. *Beitr. Chem. Physiol. Pathol.* **9**:134. (*32*)
Meyer, K. H., and Schwartz, D. E. 1950. *Helv. Chim. Acta* **33**:1651. (*264*)
Meyer, R. K. (*141*)
Meyers, A. L. (*80*)
Meyers, W. M., and Deutsch, H. F. 1955. *Arch. Biochem. Biophys.* **54**:39. (*309*)
Michel, M. F. (*321*)
Michon, J. (*85, 100, 357*)

Middlebrook, G., and Dubos, R. J. 1948. *J. Exptl. Med.* **88**:521. (*323*)
Middleton, T. R. (*188*)
Midgley, A. R., Jr., and Pierce, G. B., Jr. 1962. *J. Exptl. Med.* **115**:289. (*302*)
Miettinen, T. A. 1963. *Clin. Chim. Acta* **8**:693. (*106*)
Miettinen, T. A., and Huttunen, J. K. 1964. *Acta Chem. Scand.* **18**:579. (*106*)
Migita, S., and Putnam, F. W. 1963. *J. Exptl. Med.* **117**:81. (*305, 336*)
Mikaya, M. (*202*)
Miki, T. (*277*)
Mikkonen, L. (*9*)
Miles, A. A. (*272*)
Milham, M. (*245*)
Milhaud, G. (*88*)
Miller, C. P. (*323*)
Miller, C. P., and Boor, A. K. 1934. *J. Exptl. Med.* **59**:75. (*323*)
Miller, J. A. (*123*)
Miller, L. L. (*80*)
Miller, L. L., and Bale, W. F. 1954. *J. Exptl. Med.* **99**:125. (*92*)
Miller, L. L., Hanavan, H. R., Titthasiri, N., and Chowdhury, A. 1964. *Advan. Chem. Ser.* **44**:17. (*100*)
Miller, W. H., and Dessert, A. M. 1949. *Ann. N.Y. Acad. Sci.* **52**:167. (*197*)
Mills, G. T. (*19, 45, 47–50*)
Mirsky, A. E. (*19*)
Mitchell, P., and Moyle, J. 1951. *J. Gen. Microbiol.* **5**:966. (*113*) 1951a. *J. Gen. Microbiol.* **5**:981. (*313*) 1956. *J. Gen. Microbiol.* **15**:512. (*113*)
Miyano, T. 1958. *Ann. Tuberc.* (*Tenri, Japan*) **8**:77. (*323*)
Miyashita, C. (*83*)
Miyazaki, T. 1934. *J. Biochem.* (*Tokyo*) **20**:287. (*35*)
Modica, F. 1959. *Tumori* **45**:54. (*390*)
Møller, E. (*325*)
Mörner, C. T. 1889. *Skand. Arch. Physiol.* **1**:210. (*45, 78*)
Mogilevskiĭ, M. SH. 1963. *Vopr. Med. Khim.* **9**:No. 3, 288. (*200*)
Mogilevskiĭ, M. SH., and Laufer, A. L. 1951. *Doklady Akad. Nauk. S.S.S.R.* **76**:239; *Chem. Abstr.* **45**:4278g, 1951. (*238, 239*)
Mohr, E. (*172, 177, 339, 352*)
Mohr, E. 1960. *Z. Naturforsch.* **15b**:575. (*176, 352*)
Mohr, E., and Schramm, G. 1960. *Z. Naturforsch.* **15B**:568. (*172, 174, 176, 348, 352*)
Mold, K. (*389, 392*)
Mollison, P. L. 1951. "Blood Transfusion in Clinical Medicine." Oxford: Blackwell. (*273*)
Molnar, J. (*100*)
Molnar, J., Robinson, G. B., and Winzler, R. J. 1965. *J. Biol. Chem.* **240**:1882. (*128*)
Molter, H. (*287*)
Monkhouse, F. C. 1956. *Can. J. Biochem. Physiol.* **34**:757. (*52*)
Montagna, W., and Hill, C. R. 1957. *Anat. Record* **127**:163. (*54*)
Montague, M. D. 1963. *Biochim. Biophys. Acta* **78**:373. (*90*)
Montfort, I., and Pérez-Tamayo, R. 1961. *Lab. Invest.* **10**:1240. (*149*)
Montgomery, P. O. (*391*)
Montgomery, R. (*89, 206, 264*)
Montgomery, R., and Wu, Y.-C. 1963. *J. Biol. Chem.* **238**:3547. (*83*)
Montreuil, J. 1957. *Bull. Soc. Chim. Biol.* **39**: *Suppl. III,* p. 3. (*306*)
Montreuil, J., Biserte, G., and Chosson, A. 1963. *Compt. Rend.* **256**:3372. (*83*)
Montreuil, J., Chosson, A., Havez, R., and Mullet, S. 1960. *Compt. Rend. Soc. Biol.* **154**:732. (*99*)
Montreuil, J., Spik, G., Chosson, A., Segard, E., and Scheppler, N. 1962. *Chromatographie Symp. II, Brussels, 1962,* p. 47. (*83*)
Mookerjea, S., and Hawkins, W. W. 1958. *Can. J. Biochem. Physiol.* **36**: 261. (*372*)
Moore, D. H. (*252, 253, 258, 263, 306, 308*)
Moore, D. H., Du Pan, R. M., and Buxton, C. L. 1949. *Am. J. Obstet. Gynecol.* **57**:312. (*307*)
Mora, P. T. (*363*)

Mora, P. T., and Young, B. G. 1958. *Nature* **181**:1402. (*225*) 1959. *Arch. Biochem. Biophys.* **82**:6. (*225*)

Morató-Manaro, J., and Albrieux, A. 1939. *Endocrinology* **24**:518. (*141*)

Morawetz, H. (*226, 253*)

Morawetz, H., and Hughes, W. L. 1952. *J. Phys. Chem.* **56**:64. (*253*)

Morawiecki, A. (*290*)

Moreschi, C. 1908. *Z. Bakteriol. Parasitenk.* **46**(Orig.):49. (*308*) 1908a. *Z. Bakteriol. Parasitenk.* **46**(Orig.):456. (*308*)

Moretti, J. (*53, 309*)

Morgan, W. T. J. (*85, 107, 168, 240, 270, 275–281, 284, 286, 287, 289, 292, 304, 316, 317, 325, 330, 333, 334, 340, 341, 343, 346, 348*)

Morgan, W. T. J. 1936. *Biochem. J.* **30**: 909. (*325*) 1950. *Nature* **166**:300. (*312*) 1959. *Naturwissenschaften* **46**: 181. (*325*) 1960. *Proc. Roy. Soc. (London) Ser. B* **151**:308. (*107, 275, 276, 282, 283, 286, 316, 334*) 1961. Lectures on Blood Groups, Rockefeller Institute. (*283*)

Morgan, W. T. J., and Elson, L. A. 1934. *Biochem. J.* **28**:988. (*349*)

Morgan, W. T. J., and King, H. K. 1943. *Biochem. J.* **37**:640. (*274*)

Morgan, W. T. J., Painter, T. J., and Watkins, W. M. 1964. *Proc. 9th Intern. Congr. Soc. Blood Transfusion, 9th, Mexico City, 1962,* p. 220. (*279*)

Morgan, W. T. J., and Pusztai, A. 1961. *Biochem. J.* **81**:648. (*85*)

Morgan, W. T. J., and Van Heyningen, R. 1944. *Brit. J. Exptl. Pathol.* **25**:5. (*274*)

Morgan, W. T. J., and Watkins, W. M. 1951. *Brit. J. Exptl. Pathol.* **32**:34. (*274*) 1953. *Brit. J. Exptl. Pathol.* **34**:94. (*168, 277, 279*) 1958. *Nature* **177**:521. (*275, 276*) 1959. *Brit. Med. Bull.* **15**:109. (*276, 280, 281, 283*) 1964. *Proc. Intern. Congr. Soc. Blood Transfusion, 9th, Mexico City, 1962,* p. 225. (*292*)

Mori, Y., Kato, K., Matsubara, T., and Kotani, S. 1960. *Biken's J.* **3**:139. (*88*)

Moricard, R., and Giro, C. 1957. *Bull. Federation Soc. Gynecol. Obstet. Langue Franc.* **9**:519. (*54*)

Moricard, R., Gothie, S., and Rodríguez-Galindo, M. 1959. *Rev. Latinoam. Anat. Pathol.* **3**:47. (*54*)

Morita, N. T. (*378*)

Morita, T. N. (*14*)

Moritz, U. (*63*)

Morris, C. C. 1960. *Ann. N.Y. Acad. Sci.* **86**:878. (*6, 64, 66*)

Morris, C. C., and Godman, G. C. 1960. *Nature* **188**:407. (*64*)

Morris, D. M. 1951. *Endocrinology* **48**: 257. (*141*)

Morrison, L. M., Schjeide, O. A., Quilligan, J. J., Jr., Freeman, L., and Holeman, R. 1963. *Proc. Soc. Exptl. Biol. Med.* **113**:362. (*371*)

Morrow, P. E., Hodge, H. C., Neuman, W. F., Maynard, E. A., Blanchet, H. J., Jr., Fassett, D. W., Birk, R. E., and Manrodt, S. 1952. *J. Pharmacol.* **105**:273. (*211*)

Morse, S. I. 1962. *J. Exptl. Med.* **115**:295. (*321*) 1962a. *J. Exptl. Med.* **116**: 229. (*314, 321*)

Morton, J. I. (*306*)

Morton, J. I., and Deutsch, H. F. 1958. *J. Biol. Chem.* **231**:1119. (*307*)

Mosbach, E. H., and King, C. G. 1950. *J. Biol. Chem.* **185**:491. (*47*)

Moschini, A. 1924. *Arch. Ital. Biol.* **74**: 117. (*32*)

Moser, H. (*125*)

Moser, H. W., and Karnovsky, M. L. 1959. *J. Biol. Chem.* **234**:1990. (*120*)

Moses, F. E. (*4, 49, 65, 70, 95*)

Moskowitz, M., and Treffers, H. P. 1950. *Science* **111**:717. (*274*)

Moss, J. N. (*197*)

Moss, S. 1952. *Science* **115**:69. (*225*)

Mosser, E. L. (*101*)

Moszkowska, A. (*142*)

Mourant, A. E. (*300, 308*)

Mourant, A. E. 1954. "The Distribution of the Human Blood Groups." Oxford: Blackwell. (*273*)

Moyle, J. (*113, 313*)
Mozersky, S. M. (*194*)
Mudd, S. (*28, 29*)
Mudd, S. G. (*390*)
Mühlbock, O. 1938. *Acta Brevia Neerl. Physiol. Pharmacol. Microbiol.* **8**:50. (*141*) 1938a. *Acta Brevia Neerl. Physiol. Pharmacol. Microbiol.* **8**:142. (*141*)
Müller, E. R. (*93*)
Müller-Eberhard, H. J. (*307*)
Müller-Eberhard, H. J., Kunkel, H. G., and Franklin, E. C. 1956. *Proc. Soc. Exptl. Biol. Med.* **93**:146. (*306*)
Münich, W. 1962. *Arch. f. Ophthalmol.* **164**:457. (*249*)
Muir, H. 1958. *Biochem. J.* **69**:195. (*83*)
Mukhtar, F. (*376*)
Mulford, D. J. (*374*)
Mullet, S. (*99*)
Munch-Petersen, A. (*49*)
Munch-Petersen, A., Kalckar, H. M., Cutolo, E., and Smith, E. E. B. 1953. *Nature* **172**:1036. (*49*)
Municio, A. M., Diaz, T., and Martinez, A. 1963. *Biochem. Biophys. Res. Commun.* **11**:195. (*117*)
Munro, S. S. (*138, 141*)
Muntwyler, E. (*86*)
Murachi, T. (*34*)
Muramatsu, T. 1965. *J. Biochem.* **57**:223. (*369*)
Murata, K. 1962. *J. Gerontol.* **17**:30. (*372*)
Murillo, G. J. (*365*)
Murphy, W. H. (*84, 86, 341*)
Murphy, W. H., and Gottschalk, A. 1961. *Biochim. Biophys. Acta* **52**:349. (*344*)
Murray, F. J., Ludwig, K. A., and Foter, M. J. 1950. *J. Immunol.* **64**:421. (*268*)
Murray, M. R. (*388*)
Murray, R. G. E., and Pearce, R. H. 1949. *Can. J. Res.* **27E**:254. (*189*)
Muschel, L. H., Osawa, E., and McDermott, D. A. 1958. *Am. J. Clin. Pathol.* **29**:418. (*272, 326*)
Muth, R. O. 1959. *Deut. Zahnaerztl. Z.* **14**:347. (*238*)
Mutt, V. (*56, 264*)
Myrbäck, K., and Persson, B. 1953. *Arkiv Kemi* **5**:177. (*224*)

N

Nagai, Y. (*200*)
Nagai, Y., and Springer, G. F. 1962. *Federation Proc.* **21**:A-67d. (*290, 291*)
Nagao, S., Izume, S., Toda, Y., and Inoue, T. 1958. *Ann. Tuberc.* (*Tenri, Japan*) **8**:57. (*323*)
Nahmias, A. J., and Kibrick, S. 1964. *J. Bacteriol.* **87**:1060. (*364*)
Naidoo, S. S. (*147*)
Naka, H. (*128*)
Nakada, H. I. (*14, 37, 193, 203, 204, 378*)
Nakada, H. I., Morita, T. N., and Wick, A. N. 1955. *J. Biol. Chem.* **215**:803. (*378*)
Nakada, H. I., and Wolfe, J. B. 1961. *Arch. Biochem. Biophys.* **94**:244. (*193, 194, 204*)
Nakada, H. I., Wolfe, J. B., Hochstein, L. I., and Andreoli, A. J. 1960. *Anal. Biochem.* **2**:168. (*188, 194, 195*)
Nakajima, J. (*394*)
Nakamura, T. 1927. *Compt. Rend. Soc. Biol.* **96**:524. (*148*)
Nakayama, T. (*123*)
Nalbandov, A. V., Meyer, R. K., and McShan, W. H. 1951. *Anat. Record* **110**:475. (*141*)
Nance, J. L. (*196*)
Nanninga, L. (*252*)
Nash, H. E. (*392*)
Nathenson, S. G. (*168, 314*)
Nathenson, S. G., and Strominger, J. L. 1962. *J. Biol. Chem.* **237**:PC3839. (*91, 117, 314*)
Neely, W. B. (*332*)
Neher, R., and Kradolfer, F. 1955. *Z. Naturforsch.* **10b**:191. (*363*)
Neidhardt, F. C. 1960. *J. Bacteriol.* **80**:536. (*9*)
Nelson, G. (*227*)
Neter, E. 1956. *Bacteriol. Rev.* **20**:166. (*273, 289*)

Neuberg, C., and Cahill, W. 1934. *Biochem. Z.* **275**:328. (*201*) 1936. *Enzymologia* **1**:22. (*201, 209*)

Neuberg, C., and Hofmann, E. 1931. *Naturwissenschaften* **19**:484. (*201*) 1931a. *Biochem. Z.* **234**:345. (*201*)

Neuberg, C., and Rubin, O. 1914. *Biochem. Z.* **67**:82. (*201*)

Neuberger, A. (*83, 86, 311*)

Neuberger, A. 1938. *Biochem. J.* **32**:1435. (*311*) 1964. *Abstr. Proc. Intern. Congr. Biochem., 6th, New York, 1964*, Section **2**, p. 105. (*83*)

Neuberger, A., and Pitt[-]Rivers, R. V. 1939. *Biochem. J.* **33**:1580. (*155, 158, 162*)

Neufeld, E. F. (*49, 82, 104*)

Neuhaus, F. C., and Lynch, J. L. 1964. *Biochemistry* **3**:471. (*118*)

Neuman, W. F. (*13, 69, 211*)

Neumann, H. (*220*)

Neurath, H., and Putnam, F. W. 1945. *J. Biol. Chem.* **160**:397. (*253*)

Nevo, A. (*373*)

Newcomer, V. D. (*329*)

Newton, G. (*27*)

Nicholas, D. J. D. (*14*)

Nichols, A. V. (*215, 259*)

Nichols, J. H. (*280, 284, 298, 299, 325*)

Nicot, G. (*199*)

Niemann, C. (*390*)

Nikaido, H. (*123*)

Nikaido, H. 1961. *Biochim. Biophys. Acta* **48**:460. (*123*) 1962. *Proc. Natl. Acad. Sci. U.S.* **48**:1542. (*123*) 1962a. *Proc. Natl. Acad. Sci. U.S.* **48**:1337. (*123, 124*)

Nikkari, T. (*9*)

Nikkilä, E. A. 1952. *Scand. J. Clin. Lab. Invest.* **4**:369. (*258*)

Niklas, A., and Maurer, W. 1952. *Biochem. Z.* **323**:89. (*93*)

Nikolskaya, I. N. (*329*)

Nishi, Y. (*353*)

Nishihara, H. (*394*)

Nisman, B. (*322*)

Nisselbaum, J. S. (*221, 222, 255, 257*)

Nitschmann, H., and Beeby, R. 1960. *Chimia (Aarau)* **14**:318. (*85*)

Nobile, C. (*34*)

Noble, W. C., and Knacke, F. E. D. 1928. *J. Bacteriol.* **15**:55. (*34*)

Nolan, C., and Smith, E. L. 1962. *J. Biol. Chem.* **237**:446. (*83*) 1962a. *J. Biol. Chem.* **237**:453. (*83*)

Noll, H., Aoyagi, T., and Orlando, J. 1961. *Virology* **14**:141. (*175*) 1962. *Virology* **18**:154. (*358*)

Nomura, M., and Hosoda, J. 1956. *Nature* **177**:1037. (*88*)

Nordling, S., Penttinen, K., and Saxén, E. 1963. *Exptl. Cell Res.* **31**:586. (*373*)

Nordling, S., Vaheri, A., Saxén, E., and Penttinen, K. 1965. *Exptl. Cell Res.* **37**:406. (*374, 375*)

Norhagen, Å., and Odeblad, E. 1955. *Acta Pathol. Microbiol. Scand.* **36**:224. (*54*)

Norris, R. F. (*28*)

North, E. A. (*289*)

Northcote, D. H., and Horne, R. W. 1952. *Biochem. J.* **51**:232. (*329*)

Nose, Y. (*56*)

Nose, Y., and Lipmann, F. 1958. *J. Biol. Chem.* **233**:1348. (*56*)

Novaes, M., and Villanueva, J. R. 1963. *Biochim. Biophys. Acta* **78**:797. (*90*)

Nuenke, R. H., and Cunningham, L. W. 1961. *J. Biol. Chem.* **236**:2452. (*86*)

Nussbaumer, T. (*86*)

Nutting, G. C. (*183*)

O

Oakley, C. L., and Warrack, G. H. 1951. *J. Pathol.* **63**:45. (*187*)

Oberlander, L. (*377*)

O'Brien, P. J. (*104*)

O'Brien, P. J., Glick, M. C., and Zilliken, F. 1960. *Biochim. Biophys. Acta* **37**:357. (*16, 23*) 1960a. *Federation Proc.* **19**:85. (*16*)

O'Brien, P. J., and Zilliken, F. 1959. *Biochim. Biophys. Acta* **31**:543. (*27, 82*)

Odeblad, E. (*52, 54, 55, 74, 79, 148, 149*)

Odeblad, E. 1952. *Acta Endocrinol.* **11**:306. (*54*)

Odeblad, E., and Boström, H. 1952. *Acta Pathol. Microbiol. Scand.* **31**:339.

(*54, 55*) 1953. *Acta Pathol. Microbiol. Scand.* **32**:448. (*54*) 1953a. *Acta Chem. Scand.* **7**:233. (*54*)
Odell, T. T., Jr. (*79, 249*)
Odell, T. T., Jr., and Anderson, B. 1957. *Proc. Soc. Exptl. Biol. Med.* **94**: 151. (*52*)
Odell, T. T., Jr., Tausche, F. G., and Gude, W. D. 1955. *Am. J. Physiol.* **180**:491. (*54*)
Oden, E. M. (*366*)
Odin, L. (*344*)
Odin, L. 1952. *Nature* **170**:663. (*343*)
Oeding, P. (*314, 315, 321*)
Ørskov, F. (*328*)
Ørskov, I., Ørskov, F., Jann, B., and Jann, K. 1963. *Nature* **200**:144. (*328*)
Oesterle, P. (*292*)
Ogston, A. G. (*231*)
Ogston, A. G., and Phelps, C. F. 1961. *Biochem. J.* **78**:827. (*362*)
Ogston, A. G. Philpot, J. St. L., and Zuckerman, S. 1939. *J. Endocrinol.* **1**:231. (*145, 146*)
Ogston, A. G., and Sherman, T. F. 1959. *Biochem. J.* **72**:301. (*232, 234*)
Ogston, A. G., and Stanier, J. E. 1950. *Biochem. J.* **46**:364. (*232*) 1952. *Biochem. J.* **52**:149. (*232*)
Ohara, H. (*394*)
Oka, Y., and Murachi, T. 1954. *J. Biochem.* (*Tokyo*) **41**:107. (*34*)
Okada, S. (*88, 274*)
Okada, S., and Fukumoto, J. 1960. *Nippon Nogeikagaku Kaishi* **34**: 128. (*90*) 1960a. *Nippon Nogeikagaku Kaishi* **34**:132. (*90*)
Okazaki, R., Okazaki, T., and Kuriki, Y. 1960. *Biochim. Biophys. Acta* **38**: 384. (*82*)
Okazaki, T. (*82*)
Okinaka, G. (*52, 54*)
Olah, E., and Hadhazy, C. 1962. *Acta Biol. Acad. Sci. Hung.* **13**:(No. 2) 127; *Chem. Abstr.* **58**:10570a, 1963. (*105*)
Olavarría, J. M. (*16, 59*)
Oliver, R. (*52, 54*)
Olivier, L. (*54*)
Oncley, J. L., Walton, K. W., and Cornwell, D. G. 1957. *J. Am. Chem. Soc.* **79**:4666. (*254*)
O'Neill, A. N. (*372*)
O'Neill, A. N., and Stewart, D. K. R. 1956. *Can. J. Chem.* **34**:1700. (*363*)
O'Neill, C. H. 1964. *Exptl. Cell Res.* **35**: 477. (*367*)
Opsahl, J. C. 1951. *In* "Adrenal Cortex, Transactions of the Second Conference, 1950" (E. P. Ralli, ed.), p. 115. New York: Josiah Macy, Jr. Foundation. (*197*)
Orbán, T. (*332*)
Orlando, J. (*175, 358*)
Ortega, L. G. (*310*)
Osawa, E. (*272, 326*)
Osawa, S., Allfrey, V. G., and Mirsky, A. E. 1957. *J. Gen. Physiol.* **40**:491. (*19*)
Osbahr, A. (*89*)
Osborn, M. J. (*125, 128*)
Osborn, M. J. 1963. *Proc. Natl. Acad. Sci. U.S.* **50**:499. (*123*)
Osborn, M. J., and D'Ari, L. 1964. *Biochem. Biophys. Res. Commun.* **16**: 568. (*124*)
Osman, H. G. (*333*)
Oster, G. (*234*)
Oster, G. 1954. *Nature* **173**:300. (*234*) 1957. *Res. Photosynthesis, Gatlinburg Conf. Oct. 25–29, 1955*, p. 50. (*234*)
Oster, G., and Wotherspoon, N. 1954. *J. Chem. Phys.* **22**:157. (*234*)
Oster, G. K., and Oster, G. 1959. *J. Am. Chem. Soc.* **81**:5543. (*234*)
Oster, G. K., Oster, G., and Prati, G. 1957. *J. Am. Chem. Soc.* **79**:595. (*234*)
Otsuji, N., and Takagi, Y. 1959. *J. Biochem.* (*Tokyo*) **46**:791. (*112*)
Ott, M. L. (*187, 197*)
Ottensooser, F. (*291*)
Otteson, M. (*294*)
Ottoson, R. (*187*)
Ouchterlony, Ö. 1948. *Arkiv Kemi* **26B** (No. 14). (*267*)
Oudin, J. 1946. *Compt. Rend.* **222**:115. (*267*) 1956. *Compt. Rend.* **242**:2489. (*308, 336*) 1956a. *Compt. Rend.* **242**: 2606. (*308, 336*) 1960. *Compt. Rend.*

250:770. (*308, 336*) 1962. *Compt. Rend.* **254**:2877. (*306*)

Ovary, Z., Fudenberg, H., and Kunkel, H. G. 1960. *J. Exptl. Med.* **112**:953. (*307*)

Ove, P. (*372–374*)

Overell, B. G. (*197*)

Overman, R. S. 1949. *In* "Blood Clotting and Allied Problems, Transactions of the Second Conference, 1949" (J. E. Flynn, ed.), p. 29. New York: Josiah Macy, Jr. Foundation. (*264*)

Ovlick, Z. R. (*363*)

Owen, J. A. (*372*)

Owen, R. D. 1945. *Science* **102**:400. (*300, 303*)

Ozanics, V. (*55*)

Ozzello, L., Lasfargues, E. Y., and Murray, M. R. 1960. *Cancer Res.* **20**: 600. (*388*)

P

Pabst, H. W., and Auer, R. 1959. *Verhandl. Deut. Ges. Inn. Med.* **65**:442. (*188*)

Pacca, M. L. 1951. *Boll. Soc. Ital. Biol. Sper.* **27**:4. (*197*)

Packham, M. A., and Butler, G. C. 1952. *J. Biol. Chem.* **194**:349. (*47*)

Paerels, G. B. (*42*)

Paff, G., Sugiura, H. T., Bocher, C. A., and Roth, J. S. 1952. *Anat. Record* **114**:499. (*387*)

Paine, J. R. (*302*)

Painter, T. J. (*277, 279–281, 284, 286, 316*)

Painter, T. J., Rege, V. P., and Morgan, W. T. J. 1963. *Nature* **199**:569. (*280*)

Painter, T. J., Watkins, W. M., and Morgan, W. T. J. 1962. *Nature* **193**: 1042. (*280*) 1963. *Nature* **199**:282. (*280, 284*)

Pallavicini, C. (*106*)

Palmer, D. J. (*200*)

Palmer, J. W. (*135, 155*)

Palmer, K. J., Ballantyne, M., and Galvin, J. A. 1948. *J. Am. Chem. Soc.* **70**:906. (*183*)

Palmer, K. N. V. 1961. *Lancet* **2**:802. (*238*)

Panigel, M. (*199*)

Panizzari, G. P., and Vegeto, A. 1958. *Arch. Ital. Patol. Clin. Tumori* **2**: 1219. (*392*)

Panos, C. (*115*)

Papadia, S. (*391*)

Papirmeister ["Papirmesiter" in title], B., and Mallette, M. F. 1955. *Arch. Biochem. Biophys.* **57**:94. (*287*) 1955a. *Arch. Biochem. Biophys.* **57**: 106. (*288*)

Papp, N. (*188*)

Pappenheimer, A. M., Jr. (*306*)

Paraventi, H., da Silva Sasso, W., and Mastroianni, E. 1960. *Rev. Paulista Med.* **57**:73. (*149*)

Pardee, A. B. (*110, 111*)

Pardoe, G. I. (*89, 336*)

Park, E. A. (*264*)

Park, J. T. (*110, 116*)

Park, J. T. 1952. *J. Biol. Chem.* **194**:877. (*22, 43, 111, 113*) 1952a. *J. Biol. Chem.* **194**:885. (*22, 43, 111, 113*) 1952b. *J. Biol. Chem.* **194**:897. (*111, 113*) 1961. *In* "Immunochemical Approaches to Problems in Microbiology" (M. Heidelberger and O. J. Plescia, eds.) pp. 123–134. New Brunswick, N.J.: Rutgers Univ. Press. (*313*)

Park, J. T., and Strominger, J. L. 1957. *Science* **125**:99. (*111*)

Parker, C. A. (*234*)

Parker, J. T. (*267, 322*)

Parkes, A. S. (*144*)

Parkes, A. S., and Emmens, C. W. 1944. *Vitamins Hormones* **2**:361. (*134, 148*)

Parkin, D. M. (*300*)

Parrot, J.-L., and Fasquelle, R. 1949. *Compt. Rend. Soc. Biol.* **143**:931. (*236*)

Parrot, J.-L., Nicot, G., Laborde, C., and Canu, P. 1962. *J. Physiol. (Paris)* **54**:739. (*199*)

Partridge, S. M., and Morgan, W. T. J. 1940. *Brit. J. Exptl. Pathol.* **21**:180. (*325*)

Passeron, S. (*84*)

Passynsky, A., and Plaskeyev, V. 1945 *Compt. Rend. Acad. Sci. U.R.S.S.* **48**: 579. (*183*)

Pasternak, C. A. (*7, 9*)
Pasternak, C. A. 1960. *J. Biol. Chem.* **235**:438. (*74*)
Pasternak, C. A., and Kent, P. W. 1958. *Biochem. J.* **68**:452. (*53*)
Pasternak, C. A., Kent, P. W., and Davies, R. E. 1958. *Biochem. J.* **68**: 212. (*53*)
Pasteur, [L.] and Joubert, [G.]. 1877. *Compt. Rend.* **85**:101. (*336*)
Patel, C. (*224, 225, 227*)
Pattabiraman, T. N., and Bachhawat, B. K. 1961. *Biochim. Biophys. Acta* **54**: 273. (*12*)
Pattabiraman, T. N., Sekhara Varma, T. N., and Bachhawat, B. K. 1964. *Biochim. Biophys. Acta* **83**:74. (*169*)
Patterson, M. K., Jr., and Touster, O. 1962. *Biochim. Biophys. Acta* **56**:626. (*128*)
Paul, J. R., and Bunnell, W. W. 1932. *Am. J. Med. Sci.* **183**:90. (*295*)
Pauling, L., Pressman, D., Campbell, D. H., and Ikeda, C. 1942. *J. Am. Chem. Soc.* **64**:3003. (*333*)
Paulsen, H. (*22, 326*)
Pavlik, J. G. (*87*)
Payne, W. J., Kieber, R. J., Bonventre, P. F., and Holtman, D. F. 1955. *J. Bacteriol.* **70**:622. (*34*)
Payza, A. N. (*205*)
Payza, A. N., and Korn, E. D. 1956. *J. Biol. Chem.* **223**:853. (*198, 205, 215*)
Pazur, J. H., and Anderson, J. S. 1963. *Biochim. Biophys. Acta* **74**:788. (*116*)
Pazur, J. H., and Shuey, E. W. 1961. *J. Biol. Chem.* **236**:1780. (*82*)
Peabody, R. B. (*232*)
Pearce, R. H. (*189, 192, 203*)
Pearce, R. H. 1953. *Biochem. J.* **55**:467. (*187*)
Pearson, F. (*197*)
Pechan, Z. 1963. *J. Chromatog.* **10**:104. (*106*)
Pecora, P. (*200*)
Pedersen, K. O. (*306, 318*)
Pedersen, K. O. 1944. *Nature* **154**:575. (*309*)
Pedersen, W. (*126*)
Pedrini, V., and Pedrini-Mille, A. 1959. *Proc. Soc. Exptl. Biol. Med.* **101**:358. (*9*)
Pedrini-Mille, A. (*9*)
Pelc, S. R., and Fell, H. B. 1960. *Exptl. Cell Res.* **19**:99. (*53*)
Pelc, S. R., and Glücksmann, A. 1955. *Exptl. Cell Res.* **8**:336. (*54*)
Pelczar, M. J., Jr. (*193, 203*)
Pellegrini, G. 1961. *Atti. Accad. Med. Lombarda* **16**:339. (*379*)
Pelzer, H. (*88, 90*)
Pelzer, H. 1962. *Biochim. Biophys. Acta* **63**:229. (*184*) 1963. *Z. Naturforsch.* **18b**:950. (*90*)
Penttinen, K. (*271, 373, 374*)
Pérez, J.-J., and Sergent, C. 1958. *Compt. Rend.* **246**:3550. (*311*)
de Perez Esandi, M. V. (*380*)
Pérez-Tamayo, R. (*149*)
Perkins, F. T. (*187*)
Perkins, H. R. (*30, 112, 113, 163, 313*)
Perkins, H. R. 1960. *Biochem. J.* **74**:182. (*164, 184*) 1963. *Biochem. J.* **86**:475. (*44, 118, 322*)
Perkins, H. R., and Allison, A. C. 1963. *J. Gen. Microbiol.* **30**:469. (*322, 329*)
Perlman, P. L. (*187*)
Perlman, R. L. 1963. "The Biosynthesis of Chondroitin Sulfuric Acid" (Thesis). The University of Chicago. (*79*)
Perlman, R. L., Telser, A., and Dorfman, A. 1964. *J. Biol. Chem.* **239**:3623. (*80*)
Perlmann, G. E., Tamm, I., and Horsfall, F. L., Jr. 1952. *J. Exptl. Med.* **95**:99. (*342, 346*)
Perlmann, P. 1954. *Exptl. Cell Res.* **6**: 485. (*312*) 1956. *Exptl. Cell Res.* **10**: 324. (*312*) 1959. *Experientia* **15**:41. (*312*)
Perlzweig, W. A., and Steffen, G. L. 1923. *J. Exptl. Med.* **38**:163. (*313*)
Perrault, A. (*389*)
Perri, G. C. (*8*)
Perri, G. C., Cappuccino, J. G., Faulk, M., Mellors, J., and Stock, C. C. 1963. *Cancer Res.* **23**:431. (*199*)
Perry, B. T. (*349, 353, 358*)
Persson, B. (*224*)
Persson, B. H. (*54*)

Persson, H. (*364*)
Pesonen, S. (*301*)
Petermann, M. L. 1946. *J. Am. Chem. Soc.* **68**:106. (*306*)
Petermann, M. L., and Pappenheimer, A. M., Jr. 1941. *J. Phys. Chem.* **45**:1. (*306*)
Peters, L. (*15*)
Peters, T., Jr. 1957. *J. Biol. Chem.* **229**: 659. (*92*) 1962. *J. Biol. Chem.* **237**: 1186. (*101*)
Petit, J.-F. (*199*)
Petit, J.-F., Panigel, M., and Jollès, P. 1963. *Bull. Soc. Chim. Biol.* **45**:211. (*200*)
Petracek, F. J. (*211*)
Petrow, V. (*197*)
Pettersson, T. 1954. *Acta Pathol. Microbiol. Scand.*, Suppl. 102. (*246*)
Pézard, [A.] (*140*)
Pézard, A. 1928. *Ergeb. Physiol.* **27**:552. (*134*)
Phelps, C. F. (*362*)
Philippart, M., and Menkes, J. 1964. *Biochem. Biophys. Res. Commun.* **15**:551. (*127*)
Philipson, L. (*364*)
Phillips, G. O. (*241–244*)
Phillips, G. O. 1961. *Advan. Carbohydrate Chem.* **16**:13. (*244*) 1963. *Radiation Res.* **18**:446. (*244*)
Phillips, G. O., and Baugh, P. 1963. *Nature* **198**:282. (*243*)
Phillips, G. O., and Davies, K. W. 1964. *J. Chem. Soc.*, p. 205. (*244*)
Philpot, J. St. L. (*145, 146*)
Picard, J. 1959. *Compt. Rend. Soc. Biol.* **153**:2069. (*52*)
Pick, E. P. 1902. *Beitr. Chem. Physiol. Pathol.* **1**:393. (*313*)
Pierce, G. B., Jr. (*302*)
Pierce, J. V. (*163*)
Pietruszkiewicz, A. (*362*)
Piette, L. H., Yamazaki, I., and Mason, H. S. 1961. *In* "Free Radicals in Biological Systems" (M. S. Blois, H. W. Brown, R. M. Lemmon, R. O. Lindblom, and M. Weissbluth, eds.), p. 195. New York: Academic Press. (*235*)
Pigman, W. (*83, 237, 250, 295, 344*)
Pigman, W., and Rizvi, S. 1959. *Biochem. Biophys. Res. Commun.* **1**:39. (*231, 232, 234–236*)
Pigman, W., Rizvi, S., and Holley, H. L. 1961. *Arthritis Rheumat.* **4**:240. (*232, 235, 236*)
Pigman, W., Hawkins, W., Gramling, E., Rizvi, S., and Holley, H. L. 1960. *Arch. Biochem. Biophys.* **89**:184. (*232*)
Pilcher, K. S., Soike, K. F., and Trosper, F. 1961. *Antibiot. Chemotherapy* **11**:381. (*176*)
Pillay, R. A. (*147*)
Pillemer, L. 1943. *Chem. Rev.* **33**:1. (*284*)
Piloty, O. (*46*)
Pincus, P. 1950. *Nature* **166**:187. (*202*)
Piper, J. (*371*)
Pirie, A. 1942. *Brit. J. Exptl. Pathol.* **23**: 277. (*230, 394*)
Pirie, N. W. (*187*)
Pirofsky, B., and Cordova, M. S. 1964. *Brit. J. Haematol.* **10**:320. (*271*)
Pitt, R. M. (*325*)
Pitt[-]Rivers, R. V. (*155, 158, 162*)
Plack, J. (*323*)
Plaskeyev, V. (*183*)
Pletsityi, D. F., and Krasnyanskaya, V. G. 1963. *Dokladi Akad. Nauk. SSSR* **149**:381. (*200*)
Plummer, T. H., Jr., and Hirs, C. H. W. 1964. *J. Biol. Chem.* **239**:2530. (*83*)
Pogell, B. M. 1956. *Biochim. Biophys. Acta* **21**:205. (*7*)
Pogell, B. M., and Gryder, R. M. 1957. *J. Biol. Chem.* **228**:701. (*7*)
Pogell, B. M., and Koenig, D. F. 1959. *J. Biol. Chem.* **234**:2504. (*70, 71*)
Polis, B. D. (*253*)
Pollitzer, W. (*291*)
Ponder, E. 1951. *Blood* **6**:350. (*373*)
Pontis, H. G. 1955. *J. Biol. Chem.* **216**: 195. (*20*)
Pope, C. G. 1939. *Brit. J. Exptl. Pathol.* **20**:132. (*306*) 1939a. *Brit. J. Exptl. Pathol.* **20**:201. (*306*)
Pope, C. G., and Stevens, M. F. 1951. *Brit. J. Exptl. Pathol.* **32**:314. (*306*)
Popenoe, E. A. 1955. *J. Biol. Chem.* **217**:

61. (*100*) 1959. *Biochim. Biophys. Acta* **32**:584. (*352*)
Popenoe, E. A., and Drew, R. M. 1957. *J. Biol. Chem.* **228**:673. (*348*)
Porosowska, Y. (*216*)
Portela, A. (*137, 138*)
Porter, G. G. (*40*)
Porter, R. R. 1950. *Biochem. J.* **46**:479. (*306*) 1958. *Nature* **182**:670. (*306*) 1960. *In* "The Plasma Proteins" (F. W. Putnam, ed.), Vol. 1, p. 241. New York: Academic Press. (*306*)
Porter, R. R., and Charlwood, P. A. 1959. *Biochem. J.* **73**:119. (*306*)
Portmann, A. F. (*245*)
Potee, K. G. (*216*)
Potter, M. (*74*)
Poznanskaya, A. A. (*329*)
Prasad, A. L. N., and Litwack, G. 1961. *Biochim. Biophys. Acta* **46**:452. (*87*)
Prašek, E. (*308*)
Prati, G. (*234*)
Pressman, D. (*333*)
Preston, R. K., Avakian, S., Beiler, J. M., Moss, J. N., and Martin, G. J. 1953. *Exptl. Med. Surg.* **11**:1. (*197*)
Preto Parvis, V., and Ugo, A. 1960. *Giorn. Ital. Dermatol.* **101**:290. (*145, 146*)
Pribilla, W. (*294*)
Priest, R. E. (*52*)
Priest, R. E. 1960. *Federation Proc.* **19**: 148. (*8*)
Priest, R. E., Koplitz, R. M., and Benditt, E. P. 1960. *J. Exptl. Med.* **112**: 225. (*52*)
Primosigh, J. (*42, 88*)
Primosigh, J., Pelzer, H., Maass, D., and Weidel, W. 1961. *Biochim. Biophys. Acta* **46**:68. (*88*)
Proctor, C. M. (*183*)
Prodi, G. (*366*)
Prodi, G. 1963. *Brit. J. Cancer* **17**:504. (*393*)
Prodi, G., and David, R. 1964. *Ital. J. Biochem.* **13**:157. (*393*)
Prokhorova, M. I., and Taranova, N. P. 1962. *Uglevody i Uglevodn. Obmen, Materialy 2-oi* (Vtoroi) *Vses. Konf., Moscow, 1961,* p. 165. (*126*)
Prokop, O., and Oesterle, P. 1958. *Blut* **4**:157. (*292*)
Prokop, O., and Uhlenbruck, G. 1963. "Lehrbuch der menschlichen Blut-und Serumgruppen." Leipzig: Thieme. (*273*)
Protas, L. K. (*365*)
Prudden, J. 1958. *Transplant. Bull.* **5**:14. (*377*)
Prudden, J. F., and Allen, J. 1965. *J. Am. Med. Assoc.* **192**:352. (*377*)
Prusoff, W. H., Welch, A. D., Heinle, R. W., and Meacham, G. C. 1953. *Blood* **8**:491. (*294*)
Puck, T. T. (*372*)
Pugh, D. (*157, 160, 166*)
Pugh, D., Leaback, D. H., and Walker, P. G. 1957. *Biochem. J.* **65**:464. (*156, 158–160, 162*) 1957a. *Biochem. J.* **65**: 16P. (*158, 159*)
Pugh, D., and Walker, P. G. 1961. *J. Histochem. Cytochem.* **9**:242. (*91, 157, 166*)
Pulvertaft, R. J. V., Doniach, D., and Roitt, I. M. 1961. *Brit. J. Exptl. Pathol.* **42**:496. (*303*)
Purdom, L., Ambrose, E. J., and Klein, G. 1958. *Nature* **181**:1586. (*381*)
Pusztai, A. (*85*)
Pusztai, A. 1964. *Nature* **201**:1328. (*118*)
Pusztai, A., and Morgan, W. T. J. 1958. *Nature* **182**:648. (*288*) 1961. *Biochem. J.* **78**:135. (*286, 304, 341–343, 346, 348*) 1961a. *Biochem. J.* **81**:639. (*85, 286, 289*)
Putnam, F. W. (*253, 305, 336*)
Putnam, F. W. 1948. *Advan. Protein Chem.* **4**:79. (*253*) 1960. *In* "The Plasma Proteins." (F. W. Putnam, ed.), Vol. 2, pp. 345–406. New York: Academic Press. (*336*) 1965. *In* "The Proteins." (H. Neurath, ed.), Vol. 3, p. 153. New York: Academic Press, (*306*)
Pye, J. (*346*)
Pye, J. 1955. *Australian J. Exptl. Biol. Med. Sci.* **33**:323. (*346*)
Pye, J., and Curtain, C. C. 1961. *J. Gen. Microbiol.* **24**:423. (*176*)
Pyörälä, K. (*394*)

Q

Quastel, J. H. (*13, 29, 36, 377*)
Quastel, J. H., and Cantero, A. 1953. *Nature* **171**:252. (*383*)
Quensel, U. 1933. *Acta Pathol. Microbiol. Scand.* Suppl. 11, p. 74. (*391*)
Quibell, T. H. H. (*187, 193, 229, 230*)
Quick, A. J. 1936. *Proc. Soc. Exptl. Biol. Med.* **35**:391. (*263*) 1954. *Sang* **25**: 726. (*262*)
Quigley, T. W., Jr. (*215*)
Quilligan, J. J., Jr. (*371*)
Quinn, F. A. (*394*)
Quinn, R. W., and Cerroni, R. 1957. *Proc. Soc. Exptl. Biol. Med.* **96**:268. (*331*)
Quinn, R. W., and Singh, K. P. 1957. *Proc. Soc. Exptl. Biol. Med.* **95**:290. (*331*)

R

Race, R. R. (*300, 308*)
Race, R. R. 1944. *Nature* **153**:771. (*267*)
Race, R. R., and Sanger, R. 1962. "Blood Groups in Man," 4th ed. Philadelphia: Davis. (*269, 273, 292*)
Race, R. R., Sanger, R., and Lehane, D. 1953. *Ann. Eugen.* **17**:255. (*274*)
Racker, E. (*355*)
Radim, N. (*122*)
Radin, N. S. (*126*)
Radin, N. S. 1957. *Federation Proc.* **16**: 825. (*270*)
Radin, N. S., Lavin, F. B., and Brown, J. R. 1955. *J. Biol. Chem.* **217**:789. (*120*)
Radin, N. S., Martin, F. B., and Brown, J. R. 1957. *J. Biol. Chem.* **224**:499. (*52, 119, 121, 125*)
Rafelson, M. (*175, 179, 309*)
Rafelson, M. E., Jr. (*171, 172, 175–177, 352*)
Rafelson, M. E., Jr. 1963. *Exposes Ann. Chem. Med.,* p. 121. (*172–174*)
Rafelson, M. E. [Jr.], Schneir, M., and Wilson, V. W. [Jr.]. 1963. *Arch. Biochem. Biophys.* **103**:424. (*178*)
Rafelson, M. E., Jr., Wilson, V. W., Jr., and Schneir, M. 1962. *Presbyterian-St. Luke's Hosp. Med. Bull.* **1**:34. (*173*)
Raffel, S. 1961. "Immunity," 2nd ed. New York: Appleton. (*267, 300*)
Ragan, C., Donlan, C. P., Coss, J. A., Jr., and Grubin, A. F. 1947. *Proc. Soc. Exptl. Biol. Med.* **66**:170. (*238, 239*)
Raine, L. C. D. P. (*294*)
RajBhandary, U. L. (*113, 168, 314*)
Rake, G. (*324*)
Rake, G. 1933. *J. Exptl. Med.* **57**:561. (*324*) 1937. *Can. J. Public Health* **28**:265. (*324*)
Rake, G., and Scherp, H. W. 1933. *J. Exptl. Med.* **58**:341. (*324*)
Ralston, D. J. 1963. *J. Bacteriol.* **85**:1185. (*91*)
Ramsay, G. D. (*266*)
Randall, L. O. (*187, 227, 266*)
Randles, C. I. (*271*)
Ranson, M. (*188*)
Rantz, L. A. (*187*)
Ranzenhofer, E. R., Steigman, A. J., and Lipton, M. M. 1958. *Federation Proc.* **17**:531. (*142*)
Rapaport, M. (*296*)
Rapport, M. M. (*17, 189, 192, 197*)
Rapport, M. M., Graf, L., and Schneider, H. 1964. *Arch. Biochem. Biophys.* **105**:431. (*311*)
Rapport, M. M., Graf, L., and Yariv, J. 1961. *Arch. Biochem. Biophys.* **92**: 438. (*311*)
Rapport, M. M., Linker, A., and Meyer, K. 1951. *J. Biol. Chem.* **192**:283. (*192*)
Rapport, M. M., Meyer, K., and Linker, A. 1950. *J. Biol. Chem.* **186**:615. (*187, 188, 192, 193*) 1951. *J. Am. Chem. Soc.* **73**:2416. (*155, 188, 189*)
Rapport, M. M., Graf, L., Skipski, V. P., and Alonzo, N. F. 1959. *Cancer* **12**: 438. (*311*)
Rasmussen, A. F., Jr. (*271, 363, 373*)
Rasmussen, P. S. 1954. *Acta Chem. Scand.* **8**:633. (*223*)
Rasmussen, U. (*353*)
Rathgeb, P. (*264*)
Rathgeb, P., and Sylvén, B. 1954. *J. Natl. Cancer Inst.* **14**:1099. (*390*)

1954a. *J. Natl. Cancer Inst.* **14**:1109. (*390*)
Ratner, S. (*336*)
Ravin, L. J., Baldinus, J. G., and Mazur, M. L. 1962. *J. Pharm. Sci.* **51**:857. (*224–226*)
Readler, B. [L.] (*273, 276, 296–298*)
Readler, B. L. (*276, 298, 299*)
Real, M. (*358*)
Rebers, P. A. (*319*)
Rebers, P. A., and Heidelberger, M. 1959. *J. Am. Chem. Soc.* **81**:2415. (*314*)
Recondo, E. (*84*)
Redlich-Moshin, J. (*394*)
Rees, W. T. (*234*)
Reese, F. E. (*184*)
Reeves, E. (*271, 328*)
Regaud, C., and Lacassagne, A. 1922. *Compt. Rend. Soc. Biol.* **87**:1084. (*391*)
Rege, V. P., Painter, T. J., Watkins, W. M., and Morgan, W. T. J. 1963. *Nature* **200**:532. (*277, 284, 286, 316*) 1964. *Nature* **203**:360. (*281*)
Regelson, W. (*363, 387, 388*)
Regelson, W., and Holland, J. F. 1958. *Nature* **181**:46. (*388*)
Regelson, W., Tunis, M., and Kuhar, S. 1960. *Acta Unio Intern. Contra Cancrum* **16**:729. (*388*)
Regelson, W., Kuhar, S., Tunis, M., Fields, J., Johnson, J., and Gluesenkamp, E. 1960. *Nature* **186**:778. (*388*)
Reggiani, A. (*250*)
Reggianini, O. 1950. *Boll. Soc. Ital. Biol. Sper.* **26**:866. (*193, 195*) 1950a. *Boll. Soc. Ital. Biol. Sper.* **26**:1117. (*202*) 1951. *Boll. Ist. Sieroterap. Milan.* **29**: 456. (*195*) 1953. *Boll. Soc. Ital. Biol. Sper.* **29**:329. (*196*)
Régnier, V. (*141, 142*)
Reif, A. E. (*307*)
Reimers, E. J. (*197*)
Reisner, C. A., and Franklin, E. C. 1961. *J. Immunol.* **87**:654. (*306*)
Reissig, J. L. 1956. *J. Biol. Chem.* **219**: 753. (*18*)
Reithel, F. J. (*89*)
Rejnek, J. (*100*)
Rejnek, J., Bednarik, T., and Knesslova, V. 1962. *Physiol. Bohemoslov.* **11**: 336. (*100*)
Rekers, R. E., and Field, J. B. 1948. *Science* **107**:16. (*245*)
Rendel, J. (*294, 295*)
Renn, C. E. (*181*)
Renton, P. H. (*269, 273, 300*)
Retik, A. B., Arons, M. S., Ketcham, A. S., and Mantel, N. 1962. *J. Surg. Res.* **2**:49. (*389*)
Reuszer, H. W. (*181*)
Reyniers, J. A. (Chairman), *et al.* 1959. *Ann. New York Acad. Sci.* **78**:1. (*305*)
Reynolds, B. L., Leveque, T. F., and Buxton, R. W. 1960. *Am. Surg.* **26**: 113. (*376*)
Reynolds, B. L., Leveque, T. F., Codington, J. B., Mansberger, A. R., and Buxton, R. W. 1959. *Am. Surg.* **25**: 540. (*376*)
Reynolds, D. M. (*157, 160, 164, 182*)
Reynolds, D. M. 1954. *J. Gen. Microbiol.* **11**:150. (*35, 182*)
Reynolds, P. E. 1961. *Biochim. Biophys. Acta* **52**:403. (*111*)
Rhodes, J. M. (*323, 384*)
Rhodes, J. M., Sorkin, E., and Boyden, S. V. 1957. *Biochim. Biophys. Acta* **25**:405. (*323*)
Rice, L. I. (*80*)
Richards, R. K. (*266*)
Richardson, H. B. (*264*)
Richmond, J. E. 1963. *Biochemistry* **2**: 676. (*100, 104*)
Richmond, M. H. 1959. *Biochim. Biophys. Acta* **33**:78. (*88, 182–184*) 1959a. *Biochim. Biophys. Acta* **34**: 325. (*88*) 1959b. *Biochim. Biophys. Acta* **33**:92. (*182, 184*)
Ricketts, C. R. (*53, 216*)
Ricketts, C. R. 1952. *Chem. Ind.* (*London*), p. 982. (*265*) 1954. *Brit. J. Pharmacol.* **9**:224. (*265*)
Ricketts, C. R., and Walton, K. W. 1952. *Chem. Ind.* (*London*), p. 869. (*265*)
Ricketts, C. R., Walton, K. W., and Saddington, S. M. 1954. *Biochem. J.* **58**:532. (*211*)

Rieder, S. V. 1953. *Dissertation Abstr.* **13**:634. (*4, 5*)

Rieder, S. V., and Buchanan, J. M. 1958. *J. Biol. Chem.* **232**:951. (*4*) 1958a. *J. Biol. Chem.* **232**:959. (*5, 102, 103*)

Rienits, K. G. 1951. *Biochem. J.* **48**:lviii. (*145*) 1960. *Biochem. J.* **74**:27. (*145*)

Riff, L. J. M. (*358*)

Říhová, L. (*117*)

Riley, J. F. (*392*)

Riley, J. F. 1953. *J. Pathol. Bacteriol.* **65**:471. (*246*) 1958. *Experientia* **14**: 141. (*391, 392*)

Riley, J. G. (*62, 72, 77, 83, 210*)

Rimington, C. 1940. *Biochem. J.* **34**:931. (*340*)

Ringertz, N. R. (*55, 245*)

Ringertz, N. R. 1955. *Exptl. Cell Res.* **10**:230. (*52–54*) 1960. *Arkiv Kemi* **16**:67. (*52, 61, 62, 74, 245*) 1960a. "Acid Polysaccharides of Mast Cell Tumours." Uppsala: Almqvist & Wiksell. (*61, 62, 74*) 1963. *Ann. N.Y. Acad. Sci.* **103**:209. (*74, 75*)

Ringertz, N. R., and Bloom, G. 1960. *Arkiv Kemi* **16**:57. (*245*)

Rittenberg, D. (*336*)

Rittenberg, S. C. (*181*)

Rizk, V. (*274*)

Rizvi, S. (*231, 232, 234–237*)

Rizzoli, C., and Rondinini, R. 1950. *Arch. Sci. Biol.* (*Bologna*) **34**:213. (*134*)

Robbins, P. W. (*53, 334*)

Robbins, P. W., and Lipmann, F. 1956. *J. Am. Chem. Soc.* **78**:6409. (*56*) 1957. *J. Biol. Chem.* **229**:837. (*56*) 1958. *J. Biol. Chem.* **233**:681. (*56*)

Robert, B. (*172, 175, 177, 352*)

Roberts, K. E. (*379*)

Roberts, S., and Kelley, M. B. 1956. *J. Biol. Chem.* **222**:555. (*94*)

Robertson, W. van B. (*232*)

Robertson, W. van B., Ropes, M. W., and Bauer, W. 1939. *Am. J. Physiol.* **126**:609. (*229, 230, 237*) 1940. *J. Biol. Chem.* **133**:261. (*186*) 1941. *Biochem. J.* **35**:903. (*229, 230, 237*)

de Robichon-Szulmajster, H. 1961. *J. Mol. Biol.* **3**:253. (*21*)

Robinson, B. (*268, 317*)

Robinson, D. S., and French, J. E. 1953. *Quart. J. Exptl. Physiol.* **38**:233. (*215*) 1957. *Quart. J. Exptl. Physiol.* **42**:151. (*214*)

Robinson, D. S., Harris, P. M., and Ricketts, C. R. 1958. *Biochem. J.* **69**:11P. (*216*)

Robinson, G. A., Bier, A. M., and McCarter, A. 1961. *Brit. J. Haematol.* **7**:271. (*52*)

Robinson, G. B. (*128*)

Robinson, G. B., Molnar, J., and Winzler, R. J. 1964. *J. Biol. Chem.* **239**: 1134. (*100*)

Robinson, J. D., Jr. (*52, 120, 211*)

Robinson, L. K. (*317*)

Robinson, R. (*183*)

Robinson, R. W. (*154*)

Robinson, W. D. (*189*)

Rodén, L. (*5, 46, 48, 53, 71, 75, 96*)

Rodén, L. 1956. *Arkiv Kemi* **10**:325. (*5, 51, 53, 71*) 1956a. *Arkiv Kemi* **10**:383. (*5, 53, 69, 75*) 1956b. *Arkiv Kemi* **10**: 345. (*6, 53, 71*) 1956c. *Arkiv Kemi* **10**:333. (*53, 70, 71*) 1956d. "On the Biosynthesis of Sulpho-mucopolysaccharides with Special Reference to the Role of Glutamine. Uppsala: Almqvist & Wiksell. (*69*)

Rodén, L., and Dorfman, A. 1958. *J. Biol. Chem.* **233**:1030. (*49, 65, 70*)

Rodén, L., Gregory, J., and Laurent, T. 1964. *Biochem. J.* **91**:2P. (*83*)

Rodney, G., Swanson, A. L., Wheeler, L. M., Smith, G. N., and Worrel, C. S. 1950. *J. Biol. Chem.* **183**:739. (*197*)

Rodríguez-Galindo, M. (*54*)

Roe, E. M. F. (*388*)

Roe, E. M. F. 1959. *Nature* **184**:1891 (*391*)

Rogers, H. J. (*5, 66, 113, 220, 223, 225, 226, 313*)

Rogers, H. J. 1946. *Biochem. J.* **40**:583. (*224*) 1949. *Biochem. J.* **45**:87. (*65*)

Rogers, H. J., and Jeljaszewicz, J. 1961. *Biochem. J.* **81**:576. (*111*)

Rogers, H. J., and Perkins, H. R. 1960. *Biochem. J.* **77**:448. (*112*)

Rogers, H. J., and Spensley, P. C. 1954.

Biochim. Biophys. Acta **13**:293. (*197, 226*)
Roitt, I. M. (*302, 303*)
Roitt, I. M., Campbell, P. N., and Doniach, D. 1958. *Biochem. J.* **69**: 248. (*302, 303*)
Roitt, I. M., Doniach, D., Campbell, P. N., and Hudson, R. V. 1956. *Lancet* **2**:820. (*302*)
Roitt, I. M., Ling, N. R., Doniach, D., and Couchman, K. G. 1964. *Immunology* **7**:375. (*303*)
Rollins, E. (*23, 30, 44*)
Rollins, E. L. (*44*)
Romanini, M. G. 1954. *Riv. Biol.* (*Perugia*) **46**:29. (*196*)
Romanowska, E. (*290*)
Romanowska, E. 1961. *Nature* **191**:1408. (*291*)
Romanovska [Romanowska], E., and Watkins, W. M. 1963. *Biochem. J.* **87**:37P. (*177*)
Rommeney, G. 1934. Thesis, Würzburg. (*134*)
Ronchi, S. (*52*)
Rondinini, R. (*134*)
Rondle, C. J. M. (*329*)
Rood, R. (*25*)
Ropes, M. W. (*186, 229, 230, 237*)
Ropes, M. W., Robertson, W. van B., Rossmeisl, E. C., Peabody, R. B., and Bauer, W. 1947. *Acta Med. Scand.* Suppl. 196, p. 700. (*232*)
Rosato, R. R., and Cameron, J. A. 1964. *Biochim. Biophys. Acta* **83**:113. (*118*)
Rose, C. S. (*28, 82, 157, 167, 269, 286, 293, 294*)
Rose, C. S., and György, P. 1956. *Federation Proc.* **15**:339. (*181*)
Rose, C. S., Kuhn, R., Zilliken, F., and György, P. 1954. *Arch. Biochem. Biophys.* **49**:123. (*157*)
Rose, H. M., (*344, 346, 348, 353*)
Rose, N. R. (*302, 303*)
Rose, N. R., and Witebsky, E. 1955. *J. Immunol.* **75**:282. (*302*) 1956. *J. Immunol.* **76**:417. (*302*)
Rose, W. C., and Fierke, S. S. 1942. *J. Biol. Chem.* **143**:115. (*32*)
Roseman, S. (*4, 7, 12, 15, 21, 24, 26, 27, 37–39, 41, 42, 44, 57, 65, 82, 95, 124, 126, 163, 173, 175, 189, 377*)
Roseman, S. 1956. *Federation Proc.* **15**: 340. (*17*) 1957. *J. Biol. Chem.* **226**: 115. (*39*) 1959. *Ann. Rev. Biochem.* **28**:545. (*46, 58*) 1960. *In* Springer, 1960a. (*335*) 1962. *Proc. Natl. Acad. Sci. U.S.* **48**:437. (*26, 82*)
Roseman, S., and Dorfman, A. 1951. *J. Biol. Chem.* **191**:607. (*157, 158, 162, 167, 168*) 1952. *J. Biol. Chem.* **199**: 345. (*197*)
Roseman, S., Hayes, F., and Ghosh, S. 1960. *Federation Proc.* **19**:85. (*24*)
Roseman, S., Pearson, F., and Dorfman, A. 1949. *Federation Proc.* **8**:245. (*197*)
Roseman, S., Moses, F. E., Ludowieg, J., and Dorfman, A. 1953. *J. Biol. Chem.* **203**:213. (*4, 65, 70*)
Roseman, S., Ludowieg, J., Moses, F. E., and Dorfman, A. 1954. *J. Biol. Chem.* **206**:665. (*4, 49, 65, 70*)
Roseman, S., Davidson, E. [A.], Blumenthal, H. [J.], and Dockrill, M. 1958. *Bacteriol. Proc.* **58**:107. (*7*)
Roseman, S., Jourdian, G. W., Watson, D., and Rood, R. 1961. *Proc. Natl. Acad. Sci. U.S.* **47**:958. (*25*)
Rosen, O., Hoffman, P., and Meyer, K. 1960. *Federation Proc.* **19**:147. (*207*)
Rosen, S. M. (*128*)
Rosenberg, A., and Chargaff, E. 1958. *J. Biol. Chem.* **233**:1323. (*122*)
Rosenberg, A. J. (*222*)
Rosenberg, A. J. 1948. *Compt. Rend.* **226**:1751. (*34*)
Rosenberg, T. (*197, 226*)
Rosenfield, R. E. (*292*)
Rosenfield, R. E., Haber, G. V., and Gilbert, H. S. 1960. *Vox Sanguinis* **5**(n.s.):182. (*284*)
Rosenthal, R. L., and Benedek, A. L. 1950. *Am. J. Physiol.* **161**:505. (*245*)
Rosevear, J. W., and Smith, E. L. 1958. *J. Am. Chem. Soc.* **80**:250. (*86*) 1961. *J. Biol. Chem.* **236**:425. (*83, 86*)
Rosselet, J. P. (*366*)
Rossignol, B. (*83*)
Rossmeisl, E. C. (*232*)

Roth, J. S. (*387*)
Roth, J. S. 1953. *Arch. Biochem. Biophys.* **44**:265. (*224, 225*)
Roth, L. W., Shepperd, I. M., and Richards, R. K. 1954. *Proc. Soc. Exptl. Biol. Med.* **86**:315. (*266*)
Rothfus, J. A. 1961. *Federation Proc.* **20**: 383. (*83*)
Rothfus, J. A., and Smith, E. L. 1963. *J. Biol. Chem.* **238**:1402. (*83*)
Rott, R. (*171*)
Rouillard, L. M. (*290*)
Rouser, G. (*13*)
Routh, J. I. (*321*)
Rowlands, W. T. (*307*)
Roy, A. B. 1956. *Biochem. J.* **62**:41. (*208*)
Royal, G. C., Ferguson, L. C., and Sutton, T. S. 1953. *J. Immunol.* **71**:22. (*295*)
Rozenfel'd, E. L., Poznanskaya, A. A., and Rudakova, N. K. 1959. *Dokl. Akad. Nauk SSSR* (*Dokl. Biochem.*) **125**:109. (*329*)
Rubin, A., Springer, G. F., and Hogue, M. J. 1954. *Cancer Res.* **14**:456. (*384*)
Rubin, O. (*201*)
Rubini, J. R., Stahmann, M. A., and Rasmussen, A. F., Jr. 1951. *Proc. Soc. Exptl. Biol. Med.* **76**:659. (*373*)
Rudakova, N. K. (*329*)
Rüde, E., and Goebel, W. F. 1962. *J. Exptl. Med.* **116**:73. (*325*)
Rueff, F. (*382*)
Ruelius, H. W. (*333*)
Ruhenstroth-Bauer, G. (*379*)
Ruhenstroth-Bauer, G., and Fuhrmann, G. F. 1961. *Z. Naturforsch.* **16b**:252. (*382*)
Ruhenstroth-Bauer, G., Kübler, W. Fuhrmann, G. F., and Rueff, F. 1961. *Klin. Wochschr.* **39**:764. (*382*)
Runnström, J. 1930. *Arkiv Zool.* **21B**(No. 8):1 (*369*) 1949. *Advan. Enzymol.* **9**: 241. (*368*) 1950. *Exptl. Cell Res.* **1**: 304. (*368*) 1951. *Harvey Lectures, Ser. 46* (*1950–1951*), p. 116. (*312*)
Runnström, J., and Immers, J. 1956. *Exptl. Cell Res.* **10**:354. (*312, 369*)
Runnström, J., and Kriszat, G. 1950. *Exptl. Cell Res.* **1**:355. (*368*)
Runnström, J., and Wicklund, E. 1950. *Arkiv Zool.* **1**:179 (*369*)
Ruppender, H. (*15*)
Russell, B. E. (*189*)
Russo, G., and Terranova, T. 1953. *Boll. Soc. Ital. Patol.* **3**:52. (*393*)

S

Sabo, J., Oberlander, L., and Enquist, I. F. 1964. *Surg. Gynec. Obstet.* **119**: 559. (*377*)
Saddington, S. M. (*211*)
Sagin, J. F. (*327*)
Saito, M. (*19, 116*)
Sakakura, K. (*231*)
Saldeen, T. 1963. *Acta Pathol. Microbiol. Scand.* Suppl. 162. (*393*)
de Salegui, M., Rizvi, S., Holley, H. L., and Pigman, W. 1962. *Federation Proc.* **21**:171. (*237*)
Salganik, R. I., Tomsons, V. P., and Protas, L. K. 1963. *Vopr. Virusol.* **8**:(No. 2) 155. (*365*)
Sall, T. (*28, 29*)
Salmi, A. (*9*)
Salmon, S. (*199*)
Saltmarsh-Andrew, M. (*128*)
Saltmarsh-Andrew, M. J. (*128*)
Salton, M. R. J. 1955. *J. Gen. Microbiol.* **13**:iv. (*115*) 1956. *Biochim. Biophys. Acta* **22**:495. (*184*) 1957. *Bacteriol. Rev.* **21**:82. (*182*)
Salton, M. R. J., and Ghuysen, J.-M. 1957. *Biochim. Biophys. Acta* **24**:160. (*85*) 1960. *Biochim. Biophys. Acta* **45**:355. (*88, 164, 182, 184*)
Salton, M. R. J., and Milhaud, G. 1959. *Biochim. Biophys. Acta* **35**:254. (*88*)
Salton, M. R. J., and Pavlik, J. G. 1960. *Biochim. Biophys. Acta* **39**:398. (*87*)
Sampson, P. (*56, 73, 83, 188, 195, 198, 199, 203–207*)
Sandblom, P. 1944. *Acta Chir. Scand.* **60**, Suppl. 89. (*376*)
Sanders, A. C. (*193, 194*)
Sanders, C. (*14, 385*)
Sanderson, A. R. (*113, 168, 314*)
Sanderson, A. R., Juergens, W. G., and Strominger, J. L. 1961. *Biochem. Biophys. Res. Commun.* **5**:472. (*314*)

Sanderson, A. R., Strominger, J. L., and Nathenson, S. G. 1962. *J. Biol. Chem.* **237**:3603. (*168, 314*)
Sanderson, M. (*245*)
Sandson, J. (*237*)
Sanger, R. (*269, 273, 274, 292, 300*)
Sanger, R. 1955. *Nature* **176**:1163. (*292*)
Sarcione, E. J. 1962. *Biochemistry* **1**: 1132. (*100*) 1963. *Arch. Biochem. Biophys.* **100**:516. (*43, 100*) 1964. *J. Biol. Chem.* **239**:1686. (*103*)
Sasaki, H. (*108, 289*)
Sasaki, T. (*394*)
Sato, G. (*372*)
Sato, M. (*128*)
Sato, T., Fukuyama, T., Suzuki, T., and Yoshikawa, H. 1956. *Seikagaku* **27**: 672. (*53*)
Sato, T., Suzuki, T., Fukuyama, T., and Yoshikawa, H. 1958. *J. Biochem.* (*Tokyo*) **45**:237. (*74*)
Satomura, Y., Okada, S., and Fukumoto, J. 1957. *Nippon Nogeikagaku Kaishi* **31**:281. (*88*)
Saunders, A. M., Mathews, M. B., and Dorfman, A. 1962. *Federation Proc.* **21**:A-26e. (*331*)
Saxén, E. (*373, 374*)
Scaife, J. F. 1964. *Can. J. Biochem.* **42**: 555. (*250*)
Scapa, S. (*52, 53*)
Schachman, H. K. (*222*)
Schäfer, W. (*171*)
Schanen, J. M. (*33, 384, 385*)
Schaub, R. E. (*157*)
van der Scheer, J. (*270, 318*)
van der Scheer, J., Wyckoff, R. W. G., and Clarke, F. H. 1941. *J. Immunol.* **40**:173. (*306*)
Scheid-Seydel, L. (*102*)
Scheiffarth, F., Götz, H., and Warnatz, H. 1958. *Clin. Chim. Acta* **3**:535. (*308*)
Scheline, R. R. (*392*)
Scheppler, N. (*83*)
Scherp, H. W. (*317, 324*)
Scherp, H. W. 1939. *J. Immunol.* **37**:469. (*324*) 1960. *In* Springer, 1960a. (*324*)
Scherp, H. W., and Rake, G. 1935. *J. Exptl. Med.* **61**:753. (*324*) 1945. *J. Exptl. Med.* **81**:85. (*324*)
Schiatti, P. (*8*)
Schiemann, O., and Casper, W. 1927. *Z. Hyg.* **108**:220. (*267*)
Schiff, F. 1931. "Über die gruppenspezifischen Substanzen des menschlichen Körpers." Jena: G. Fischer. (*270, 277*) 1934. *Z. Immunitätsforsch.* **82**: 46. (*297*)
Schiff, F., and Adelsberger, L. 1924. *Z. Immunitätsforsch.* **40**:335. (*270, 278, 287, 329*)
Schiff, F., and Burón, F. A. 1935. *Klin. Wochschr.* **14**:710. (*274*)
Schiff, F., and Sasaki, H. 1932. *Klin. Wochschr.* **11**:1426. (*108*) 1932a. *Z. Immunitätsforsch.* **77**:129. (*289*)
Schiff, F., and Weiler, G. 1931. *Biochem. Z.* **235**:454. (*269*)
Schiffmann, E. (*324*)
Schiffman, G. (*284, 287*)
Schiffman, G., Howe, C., and Kabat, E. A. 1958. *J. Am. Chem. Soc.* **80**:6662. (*316*)
Schiffman, G., and Kabat, E. A. 1961. *Federation Proc.* **20**:A-67a. (*278*)
Schiffman, G., Kabat, E. A., and Leskowitz, S. 1962. *J. Am. Chem. Soc.* **84**:73. (*278*)
Schiffman, G., Kabat, E. A., and Thompson, W. 1964. *Biochemistry* **3**:113. (*280*) 1964a. *Biochemistry* **3**:587. (*279, 288*)
Schiller, S. 1959. *Biochim. Biophys. Acta* **32**:315. (*148*)
Schiller, S., Benditt, E. P., and Dorfman, A. 1952. *Endocrinology* **50**:504. (*137, 141*)
Schiller, S., and Dorfman, A. 1956. *Proc. Soc. Exptl. Biol. Med.* **92**:100. (*135*) 1959. *Biochim. Biophys. Acta* **31**:278. (*245*)
Schiller, S., Slover, G. A., and Dorfman, A. 1961. *Biochem. Biophys. Res. Commun.* **5**:344. (*46, 49, 68*)
Schiller, S., Mathews, M. B., Goldfaber, L., Ludowieg, J., and Dorfman, A. 1955. *J. Biol. Chem.* **212**:531. (*72, 77*)
Schiller, S., Mathews, M. B., Cifonelli,

J. A., and Dorfman, A. 1956. *J. Biol. Chem.* **218**:139. (*52, 65, 69, 70, 72, 77*)
Schilling, J. A. (*80*)
Schindler, R. 1960. *Z. Tropenmed. Parasitol.* **11**:71. (*195*)
Schjeide, O. A. (*371*)
Schleuter, R. J. (*357*)
Schlossman, S. F., and Kabat, E. A. 1962. *J. Exptl. Med.* **116**:535. (*334*)
Schmid, D. O. (*295*)
Schmid, K. (*83, 86, 348, 352*)
Schmid, K., Bencze, W. L., Nussbaumer, T., and Wehrmüller, J. O. 1959. *J. Biol. Chem.* **234**:529. (*86*)
Schmidt, A. (*231*)
Schmidt, G. (*311*)
Schmidt, H. (*158, 288, 320*)
Schmidt, H. 1959. *Fortschr. Serol.* p. 362. (*267, 332*)
Schmidt, J. 1964. *Zentr. Bakteriol. Parasitenk. Abt. I. Orig.* **193**:179. (*200*) 1964a. *Zentr. Bakteriol. Parasitenk. Abt. I. Orig.* **193**:318. (*200*) 1964b. *Zentr. Bakteriol. Parasitenk. Abt. I. Orig.* **194**:59. (*200*) 1965. *Zentr. Bakteriol. Parasitenk. Abt. I. Orig.* **195**:326. (*200*) 1965a. *Zentr. Bakteriol. Parasitenk. Abt. I. Orig.* **195**: 331. (*200*)
Schmidt, W. C. 1952. *J. Exptl. Med.* **95**: 105. (*319*)
Schmidt-Lange, W., and Bucherer, H. 1938. *Arch. Hyg. Bakteriol.* **120**:304. (*182*)
Schmiedeberg, [G. E.] O. 1891. *Arch. Exptl. Pathol. Pharmakol.* **28**:355. (*45, 78*)
Schmith, K., and Faber, V. 1949. *Acta Endocrinol.* **3**:310. (*187*)
Schmitz-Moormann, P. 1964. *Z. Physiol. Chem.* **338**:74. (*310*)
Schneider, G. 1964. *Ergebn. Allgem. Pathol.* **44**:1. (*310*)
Schneider, H. (*311*)
Schneider, L. (*344, 346, 348*)
Schneider, M. D. 1954. *Proc. Soc. Exptl. Biol. Med.* **85**:32. (*322*)
Schneiderman, H. (*192, 238*)
Schneir, M. (*171, 173, 176–178*)
Schneir, M., Winzler, R. J., and Rafelson, M. E., Jr. 1962. *Biochem. Prep.* **9**:1. (*172*)
Schoenberg, M. D., Brooks, R. E., Hall, J. J., and Schneiderman, H. 1950. *U.S. Atomic Energy Comm., Tech. Inform. Div., UCLA-83, Aug. 7, 1950.* (*238*) 1951. *Arch. Biochem.* **30**:333. (*192, 238*)
Schoenheimer, R. (*336*)
Schoenheimer, R., Ratner, S., Rittenberg, D., and Heidelberger, M. 1942. *J. Biol. Chem.* **144**:545. (*336*)
Scholtissek, C., Rott, R., and Schäfer, W. 1961. *Z. Naturforsch.* **17b**:222. (*171*)
Schor, J. M. (*275*)
Schramm, G. (*172, 174, 176, 177, 348, 352*)
Schramm, G., and Mohr, E. 1959. *Nature* **183**:1677. (*172, 339, 352*)
Schreibman, I. (*53, 55*)
Schröder, V. 1931. *Z. Immunitaetsforsch.* **75**:77. (*270*)
Schubert, M. (*78, 252*)
Schütte, E. (*87, 182*)
Schütte, E., and Greiling, H. 1955. *Z. Physiol. Chem.* **302**:55. (*194*)
Schütte, E., and Krisch, K. 1958. *Z. Physiol. Chem.* **311**:121. (*87*)
Schulhof, K. (*302*)
Schultze, H. E. 1941. *Biochem. Z.* **308**: 266. (*306*) 1958. *Deut. Med. Wochschr.* **83**:1742. (*306*)
Schultze, H. E., and Heide, K. 1960. *In* "Medizinische Grundlagenforschung" (K. F. Bauer, ed.), Vol. 3, p. 351. (*305*)
Schultze, H. E., Schwick, G., Sonnet, J., Heremans, J., and Michaux, J. L. 1960. *Klin. Wochschr.* **38**:62. (*307*)
Schultz-Haudt, S. D., and Eeg-Larsen, N. 1961. *Biochim. Biophys. Acta* **46**: 311. (*101*) 1961a. *Biochim. Biophys. Acta* **51**:560. (*101*)
Schultze, H. E. (*307*)
Schulze, W. (*52*)
Schuster, R. (*287*)
Schuster, R. 1963. *Strahlentherapie* **121**:580. (*250*) 1964. *Strahlentherapie* **123**:177. (*249*)

Schwartz, D. E. (*264*)
Schwarz, V. (*125*)
Schwarzweiss, H., and Tomcsik, J. 1948. *Proc. Soc. Exptl. Biol. Med.* **69**:558. (*296*) 1949. *Proc. Soc. Exptl. Biol. Med.* **72**:693. (*296*)
Schweinitz, H. (*385*)
Schwenk, E. (*187*)
Scott, G. H. 1943. *Biol. Symp.* **10**:277. (*381*)
Scott, K. G. 1963. *Ann. N.Y. Acad. Sci.* **103**:285. (*392*)
Scott, K. G., Scheline, R. R., and Stone, R. S. 1958. *Cancer Res.* **18**:927. (*392*)
Scott, S. S. (*111*)
Seaman, G. V. F. (*373, 381, 382*)
Seaman, G. V. F., and Heard, D. H. 1960. *J. Gen. Physiol.* **44**:251. (*373*)
Searls, R. L. 1965. *Develop. Biol.* **11**: 155. (*80*)
Seastone, C. V. (*187*)
Seastone, C. V. 1939. *J. Exptl. Med.* **70**: 361. (*330*)
Seegers, W. H. (*263*)
Seegers, W. H. 1953. *Harvey Lectures 1951–52*), p. 180. (*262*) 1955. *Advan. Enzymol.* **16**:23. (*262–264*)
Seemann, J. [H. C.]. 1898. *Arch. Verdauungskr.* **4**:275. (*311*)
Segard, E. (*83*)
Segonzac, G. (*197*)
Seibert, F. B., Seibert, M. V., Atno, A. J., and Campbell, H. W. 1947. *J. Clin. Invest.* **26**:90. (*394*)
Seibert, M. V. (*394*)
Seifter, J., and Baeder, D. H. 1954. *Proc. Soc. Exptl. Biol. Med.* **86**: 709. (*216*)
Seifter, J., Baeder, D. H., and Beckfield, W. J. 1954. *Proc. Soc. Exptl. Biol. Med.* **85**:444. (*331*)
Seifter, J., Baeder, D. H., and Begany, A. J. 1949. *Proc. Soc. Exptl. Biol. Med.* **72**:277. (*224*)
Seifter, J., and Warren, G. H. 1950. *Proc. Soc. Exptl. Biol. Med.* **74**:796. (*393*)
Seifter, S. (*90, 197*)
Seitz, W. (*258*)
Sela, M. (*222*)
Sela, M., and Arnon, R. 1960. *Biochem. J.* **77**:394. (*336*)
Sela, M., and Steiner, L. A. 1963. *Biochemistry* **2**:416. (*200*)
Selden, R. (*149*)
Sellers, A. L. (*99*)
Sellinger, O. Z., Beaufay, H., Jacques, P., Doyen, A., and de Duve, C., 1960. *Biochem. J.* **74**:450. (*166*)
Selye, H. (*142–144, 152*)
Selye, H. 1940. *Anat. Record* **76**:145. (*148*) 1944. *Arch. Dermatol. Syphilis* **50**:261. (*153*)
Selye, H., and Friedman, S. 1940. *Am. J. Cancer* **38**:558. (*149*)
Selye, H., Harlow, C., and McKeown, T. 1935. *Proc. Soc. Exptl. Biol. Med.* **32**:1253. (*149*)
Sergent, C. (*311*)
Setlow, R. B., and Doyle, B. 1955. *Radiation Res.* **2**:15. (*192, 239*)
Seto, J. T., Nishi, Y., Hickey, B. J., and Rasmussen, A. F., Jr. 1961. *Virology* **13**:13. (*353*)
Shall, S. 1955. *S. African J. Med. Sci.* **20**:41. (*146*)
Shapira, R. (*235*)
Shapiro, B., and Wertheimer, E. 1943. *Biochem. J.* **37**:397. (*122*)
Sharon, N. 1957. *Nature* **179**:919. (*319*)
Sharon, N., and Jeanloz, R. W. 1959. *Biochim. Biophys. Acta* **31**:277. (*319*)
Sharon, N., and Seifter, S., 1964. *J. Biol. Chem.* **239**:PC 2398. (*90*)
Shatton, J. and Schubert, M. 1954. *J. Biol. Chem.* **211**:565. (*78*)
Shaw, D. R. D. 1957. *Biochem. J.* **66**:56P. (*113*)
Shear, M. J. (*389*)
Shear, M. J., and Turner, F. C. 1943. *J. Natl. Cancer Inst.* **4**:81. (*367, 389*)
Sheffner, A. L. 1963. *Ann. N.Y. Acad. Sci.* **106**:298. (*238*)
Sheinfeld, S. (*224, 225*)
Shen, T. M. (*264*)
Sheppard, E., and Wright, I. S. 1954. *Arch. Biochem. Biophys.* **52**:426. (*261*)
Shepperd, I. M. (*266*)
Sherman, E. (*316*)

Sherman, J. H. (*363*)
Sherman, T. F. (*232, 234*)
Sherrington, C. S. (*142*)
Sherwood, N. P. Russell, B. E., Jay, A. R., and Bowman, K. 1949. *J. Infect. Diseases* **84**:88. (*189*)
Shetlar, M. R. (*80, 85*)
Shetlar, M. R. 1961. *Ann. N.Y. Acad. Sci.* **94**:44. (*97, 102*)
Shetlar, M. R., Capps, J. C., and Hern, D. L. 1964. *Biochim. Biophys. Acta* **83**:93. (*100*)
Shetlar, M. R., Erwin, C. P., and Everett, M. R. 1950. *Cancer Res.* **10**:445. (*394*)
Shetlar, M. R., Hern, D., Bradford, R. H., and Endecott, B. 1961. *Biochim. Biophys. Acta* **53**:615. (*97*)
Shilo, M. 1957. *Biochem. J.* **66**:48. (*171*)
Shimazu, Y. (*34*)
Shimizu, F. (*26, 27, 82*)
Shiota, T., Blumenthal, H., Disraely, M. N., and McCann, M. P. 1962. *Arch. Biochem. Biophys.* **96**:143. (*39*)
Shipley, R. A. (*134, 140, 142*)
Shipp, V. G. (*63*)
Shockman, G. D., Kolb, J. J., and Toennies, G. 1958. *J. Biol. Chem.* **230**: 961. (*114*)
Shorb, M. S. (*285*)
Shore, B. 1955. *Proc. Soc. Exptl. Biol. Med.* **88**:73. (*215*)
Shore, B., Nichols, A. V., and Freeman, N. K. 1953. *Proc. Soc. Exptl. Biol. Med.* **83**:216. (*215, 259*)
Shrivastava, D. L. 1961. *In* "Immunochemical Approaches to Problems in Microbiology" (M. Heidelberger and O. J. Plescia, eds.), p. 135. New Brunswick, N.J.; Rutgers. (*325*)
Shuey, E. W. (*82*)
Shulman, S. (*303*)
Shulman, S., Rose, N. R., and Witebsky, E. 1960. *J. Lab. Clin. Med.* **55**:733. (*303*)
Shuman, C. R., and Finestone, A. J. 1950. *Proc. Soc. Exptl. Biol. Med.* **73**:248. (*188*)
Shurley, H. M. (*80*)
Sickles, G. (*300*)
Siegel, M. (*268, 317*)
Signer, E. R. (*222*)
Siimes, M. (*250*)
Silberberg, S., Goodman, M., Kefalides, N. A., and Winzler, R. J. 1955. *Proc. Soc. Exptl. Biol. Med.* **90**:641. (*309*)
Silbert, J. E. 1962. *Biochem. Biophys. Res. Commun.* **9**:266. (*105*) 1963. *J. Biol. Chem.* **238**:3542. (*80, 105*) 1964. *J. Biol. Chem.* **239**:1310. (*80*)
Silbert, J. E., and Brown, D. H. 1961. *Biochim. Biophys. Acta* **54**:590. (*19, 75, 97*)
Silbert, J. E., Nagai, Y., and Gross, J. 1965. *J. Biol. Chem.* **240**:1509. (*200*)
da Silva Sasso, W. (*149*)
Silver, R. K. (*348*)
Silverman, J. L. 1963. *Biochim. Biophys. Acta* **78**:94. (*104*)
Simmonds, D. H. (*341, 342*)
Simon-Reuss, I. (*382*)
Simonton, J. (*259*)
Simonton, Y. (*371*)
Simpson, I. M. N. (*125*)
Simpson, M. E. (*52, 85*)
Simpson, W. L. (*391, 393*)
Sinai, C. R. (*200*)
Singer, S. J. 1965. *In* "The Proteins" (H. Neurath, ed.), Vol. 3, p. 269. New York: Academic Press. (*306*)
Singer, S. J., and Campbell, D. H. 1952. *J. Am. Chem. Soc.* **74**:1794. (*267*)
Singer, S. J., Timasheff, S. N., and Kirkwood, J. G. 1952. *J. Am. Chem. Soc.* **74**:5985. (*252*)
Singh, K. P. (*331*)
Singher, H. O., and Marinelli, L. 1945. *Science* **101**:414. (*50, 52*)
Siniscalco, M. (*108*)
Siwiński, S. (*154*)
Skanse, B., and Sundblad, L. 1943. *Acta Physiol. Scand.* **6**:37. (*230, 235, 236*)
Skarnes, R. C., and Watson, D. W. 1955. *J. Bacteriol.* **70**:110. (*224, 225*)
Skinner, C. E., and Dravis, F. 1937. *Ecology* **18**:391. (*181, 182*)
Skipski, V. P. (*311*)
Slein, M. W., Cori, G. T., and Cori, C. F. 1950. *J. Biol. Chem.* **186**:763. (*122*)

Slonimski, P. (*139*)
Slover, G. A. (*46, 49, 68*)
Small, W. (*78*)
Smart, C. L. (*76*)
Smelser, G. K. 1959. *Trans. N.Y. Acad. Sci.* **21**:575. (*52, 55*)
Smelser, G. K., and Ozanics, V. 1957. *Am. J. Ophthalmol.* **44**:(No. 4, Part II, Oct.), 102. (*55*)
Smirnow, N. (*106*)
Smith, C. (*116*)
Smith, D. B. (*333*)
Smith, D. E. 1958. *Proc. Soc. Exptl. Biol. Med.* **97**:872. (*246*)
Smith, D. E., and Lewis, Y. S. 1953. *Proc. Soc. Exptl. Biol. Med.* **82**: 208. (*246*) 1954. *Proc. Soc. Exptl. Biol. Med.* **85**:306. (*246*) 1954a. *Proc. Soc. Exptl. Biol. Med.* **87**: 515. (*246*) 1958. *Experientia* **14**: 335. (*246*)
Smith, E. E. B. (*49*)
Smith, E. E. B., and Mills, G. T. 1954. *Biochim. Biophys. Acta* **13**:386. (*19, 45, 47*)
Smith, E. E. B., Munch-Petersen, A., and Mills, G. T. 1953. *Nature* **172**: 1038. (*49*)
Smith, E. E. B., Mills, G. T., Bernheimer, H. P., and Austrian, R. 1958. *Biochim. Biophys. Acta* **28**:211. (*48*) 1958a. *Biochim. Biophys. Acta* **29**: 640. (*48, 50*) 1960. *J. Biol. Chem.* **235**:1876. (*45*)
Smith, E. J., and Wheat, R. W. 1960. *Arch. Biochem. Biophys.* **86**:267. (*19*)
Smith, E. L. (*83, 86*)
Smith, E. L. 1958. *J. Biol. Chem.* **233**: 1392. (*232*)
Smith, E. L., Kimmel, J. R., Brown, D. M., and Thompson, E. O. P. 1955. *J. Biol. Chem.* **215**:67. (*182*)
Smith, F. C. (*267*)
Smith, F. C., and Marrack, J. 1930. *Brit. J. Exptl. Pathol.* **11**:494. (*308*)
Smith, G. N. (*197*)
Smith, H. P. (*263*)
Smith, P. A. J. (*259*)
Smith, P. N. (*82*)
Smith, R. T. (*261*)
Smithies, O. 1955. *Biochem. J.* **61**:629. (*309*) 1959. *Advan. Protein Chem.* **14**:65. (*309*)
Smithies, O., and Connell, G. E. 1959. *In* "Ciba Foundation Symposium, Biochemistry of Human Genetics, 1959" (G. E. W. Wolstenholme and C. M. O'Connor, eds.), p. 178. London: Churchill. (*308*)
Smolelis, A. N., and Hartsell, S. E. 1949. *J. Bacteriol.* **58**:731. (*183*)
Smyth, E. M. (*229, 330*)
Smyth, I. M. (*394*)
Snell, E. E. (*113, 322*)
Snell, N. S. (*183*)
Snellman, B. (*387*)
Snellman, O. (*231*)
Snellman, O., Sylvén, B., and Julén, C. 1951. *Biochim. Biophys. Acta* **7**:98. (*263*)
Soda, T. 1934. *Bull. Chem. Soc. Japan* **9**:83. (*208*) 1936. *J. Fac. Sci., Univ. Tokyo Sect. I* **3**:149. (*208*)
Soda, T., and Egami, F. 1933. *Bull. Chem. Soc. Japan* **8**:148. (*208*) 1934. *J. Chem. Soc. Japan* **55**:256. (*208*) 1938. *Bull. Chem. Soc. Japan* **13**:652. (*266*) 1938a. *J. Chem. Soc. Japan* **59**:1202. (*202, 208*) 1941. *J. Chem. Soc. Japan* **62**:256. (*208*)
Soda, T., and Hattori, C. 1931. *Bull. Chem. Soc. Japan* **6**:258. (*208*)
Soda, T., and Yoshida, A. 1948. *J. Chem. Soc. Japan* **69**:119. (*202*) 1948a. *J. Chem. Soc. Japan* **69**:121. (*202*)
Soda, T., Katsura, T., and Yoda, O. 1940. *J. Chem. Soc. Japan* **61**:1227. (*202, 208*)
Sodd, M. A. (*120–122*)
Soike, K. F. (*176*)
Sokol, F., Blaškovič, D., and Križanová, O. 1961. *Acta Virol. (Eng. ed.)* **5**: 153. (*171*)
Solms, J., and Hassid, W. Z. 1957. *J. Biol. Chem.* **228**:357. (*19*)
Sols, A. (*16*)
Sols, A. 1956. *Biochim. Biophys. Acta* **19**:144. (*14*)
Sols, A., and Crane, R. K. 1954. *J. Biol. Chem.* **210**:581. (*13*)

Soodak, M. (*57*)
Soodak, M. 1955. *Bacteriol. Proc.* **55**:131. (*15, 37, 40*)
Sørensen, A. N., Rendel, J., and Stone, W. H. 1954. *J. Immunol.* **73**:407. (*295*)
Sorenson, C. W., and Wright, I. S. 1950. *Circulation* **2**:658. (*266*)
Sorkin, E. (*323, 384*)
Sorkin, E., Boyden, S. V., and Rhodes, J. M. 1956. *Helv. Chim. Acta* **39**: 1684. (*323*)
Sorkin, E., and Fjelde, A. 1956. *Giorn. Ital. Chemioterap.* **3**:355. (*384*)
Soru, E., and Ionescu-Stoian, F. 1965. *J. Chromatog.* **17**:538. (*200*)
Spaun, J. 1951. *Acta Pathol. Microbiol. Scand.* **29**:416. (*326*)
Spearing, C. W. (*171, 175*)
Spencer, B. (*202, 205, 207, 208, 210*)
Spensley, P. C. (*197, 226*)
Spensley, P. C., and Rogers, H. J. 1954. *Nature* **173**:1190. (*220, 223, 225, 226*)
Spicer, S. S. (*396*)
Spier, H. W. (*197*)
Spik, G. (*83*)
Spiro, R. G. 1958. *J. Biol. Chem.* **233**: 546. (*377*) 1959. *J. Biol. Chem.* **234**: 742. (*4, 95, 102*) 1960. *J. Biol. Chem.* **235**:2860. (*372*) 1962. *J. Biol. Chem.* **237**:646. (*85, 89*)
Spizizen, J. (*90*)
Spolter, L., and Marx, W. 1958. *Federation Proc.* **17**:314. (*74*) 1959. *Biochim. Biophys. Acta* **32**:291. (*61, 74*) 1961. *Federation Proc.* **20**:162. (*75*)
Spolter, L., Rice, L. I., and Marx, W. 1963. *Biochim. Biophys. Acta* **74**: 188. (*80*)
Sporn, J. (*100*)
Springer, G. F. (*270, 271, 287, 290, 291, 295, 296, 298, 311, 329, 384*)
Springer, G. F. 1956. *J. Immunol.* **76**: 399. (*272, 275, 285, 297, 326*) 1956a. *Naturwissenschaften* **43**:93. (*272, 275, 297, 326*) 1956b. "Polysaccharides in Biology, Transactions of the First Conference" (G. F. Springer, ed.). New York: Josiah Macy, Jr. Foundation. (*333*) 1958. *In* "Ciba Foundation Symposium, Chemistry and Biology of Mucopolysaccharides, 1958" (G. E. W. Wolstenholme and M. O'Connor, eds.), p. 216. Boston: Little, Brown. (*272, 298*) 1958a. *Acta Haematol.* **20**:147. (*272*) 1959. "Polysaccharides in Biology, Transactions of the Fourth Conference, 1958" (G. F. Springer, ed.). New York: Josiah Macy, Jr. Foundation. (*46*) 1960. *Klin. Wochschr.* **38**:513. (*272*) 1960a. "Polysaccharides in Biology, Transactions of the Fifth Conference, 1959" (G. F. Springer, ed.). New York: Josiah Macy, Jr. Foundation. (*313, 320, 321, 324, 334, 335*) 1963. *Bacteriol. Rev.* **27**:191. (*274, 280, 287, 293, 295, 296, 311, 329, 336*) 1965. *Proc. Intern. Congr. Soc. Blood Transfusion, 10th, Stockholm, 1963.* (*284, 291, 294, 298, 329*) 1965a. *Symp. German Soc. Physiol. Chem., 15th, 1964.* (*284, 291, 298*)
Springer, G. F., and Ansell, N. J. 1958. *Klin. Wochschr.* **36**:442. (*290*) 1958a. *Proc. Natl. Acad. Sci. U.S.* **44**:182. (*290, 358*) 1959. *Proc. 7th Congr. Intern. Soc. Blood Transfusion, Rome, 1958,* p. 697. (*290*) 1960. *Federation Proc.* **19**:A-70. (*289, 300*)
Springer, G. F., Desai, P. R., and Kolecki, B. 1964. *Biochemistry* **3**: 1076. (*275, 281, 299, 333*)
Springer, G. F., and Frank, S. M. 1962. *Federation Proc.* **21**:A-67c. (*296*)
Springer, G. F., and György, P. 1955. *Klin. Wochschr.* **33**:627. (*294*)
Springer, G. F., and Hahn, N. J. Ansell 1962. *Proc. 8th Congr. Intern. Soc. Blood Transfusion, Tokyo, 1960,* p. 219. (*289, 300*)
Springer, G. F., and Horton, R. E. 1964. *J. Gen. Physiol.* **47**:1229. (*289, 300*)
Springer, G. F., Horton, R. E., and Forbes, M. 1959. *J. Exptl. Med.* **110**:221. (*272, 300*)
Springer, G. F., and Hotta, K. 1963. *Federation Proc.* **22**:539. (*290, 291*) 1964. *Abstr. 6th Intern. Congr. Biochem.* II–183. (*291*)

Springer, G. F., Nichols, J. H., and Callahan, H. J. 1964. *Science* **146:** 946. (*280, 298, 299*)

Springer, G. F., Nichols, J. H., and Kolecki, B. 1964. *Abstr. Am. Chem. Soc. Meeting, 147th, Philadelphia,* p. 13c. (*284, 325*)

Springer, G. F., and Rapaport, M. 1957. *Proc. Soc. Exptl. Biol. Med.* **96**:103. (*296*)

Springer, G. F., and Readler, B. [L.] 1961. *Excerpta Med.* **42**(*No.75*): 57. (*273, 296, 297*)

Springer, G. F., Readler, B. [L.], and Williamson, P. 1961. *Federation Proc.* **20**:A-30d. (*276, 298, 299*)

Springer, G. F., Rose, C. S., and György, P. 1954. *J. Lab. Clin. Med.* **43:**532. (*269, 281, 286, 293, 294*)

Springer, G. F., and Schuster, R. 1964. *Vox Sanguinis* **9**:589. (*287, 329*) 1964a. *Klin. Wochschr.* **42**:821. (*287, 329*)

Springer, G. F., and Stalder, K. 1961. *Nature* **191**:187. (*290*)

Springer, G. F., and Tegtmeyer, H. 1964. *Nature* **203**:298. (*271*)

Springer, G. F., and Tritel, H. 1962. *Science* **138**:687. (*287, 328, 329, 336*)

Springer, G. F., Tritel, H., and Leuterer, W. 1963. *Proc. Intern. Congr. Microbiol. Montreal, 1962,* E32A, 12. (*272*)

Springer, G. F., and Williamson, P. 1962. *Biochem. J.* **85**:282. (*275, 281, 333*) 1963. *Vox Sanguinis* **8**:177. (*275, 276, 278, 281, 333*)

Springer, G. F., Williamson, P., and Brandes, W. C. 1961. *J. Exptl. Med.* **113**:1077. (*271, 272, 290, 297, 299, 311, 325, 327, 333*)

Springer, G. F., Williamson, P., and Readler, B. L. 1961. *Proc. 8th Congr. European Soc. Haematology, Vienna, 1961,* p. 487. (*276, 298, 299*) 1962. *Ann. N.Y. Acad. Sci.* **97**:104. (*276, 298, 299*)

Springer, G. F., Williamson, P., and Ruelius, H. W. 1960. *Proc. 7th Congr. European Soc. Haematology, London, 1959,* Part II, No. 2, p. 1235. (*333*)

Springer, G. F., Takahashi, T., Kolecki, B., and Desai, P. 1964. *Federation Proc.* **23**:274. (*298, 333*)

Sribney, M., and Kennedy, E. P. 1958. *J. Biol. Chem.* **233**:1315. (*122*)

Srinivasan, S., and Quastel, J. H. 1958. *Science* **127**:143. (*29, 82*)

Stacey, M. (*56, 89, 264, 311, 316, 317, 323, 329, 336*)

Stacey, M. 1957. *Biochemistry* (*USSR*) **22**:226. (*58*)

Stacey, M., and Barker, S. A. 1960. "Polysaccharides of Micro-organisms." London: Oxford. (*312, 317*)

Stacey, M., and Woolley, J. M. 1940. *J. Chem. Soc.* p. 184. (*311*)

Stadtman, E. R. (*12, 57*)

Stahmann, M. A. (*225, 362, 373*)

Stahmann, M. A., and Gothoskor, S. S. 1958. *Phytopathology* **48**:262. (*363*)

Stalder, K. (*290*)

Stalder, K., and Springer, G. F. 1960. *Federation Proc.* **19**:A-70. (*270, 291*) 1962. *Proc. 8th Congr. European Soc. Haematology, Vienna, 1961,* p. 489. (*290, 291*)

Stanacev, N. Z., and Chargaff, E. 1962. *Biochim. Biophys. Acta* **59**:733. (*127*)

Stanier, J. E. (*232*)

Stanier, R. Y. 1947. *J. Bacteriol.* **53**:297. (*181*)

Stanley-Brown, M. (*265*)

Stanton, H. T., Jr. (*197*)

Stanworth, D. R. (*307*)

Starr, P. (*266*)

Staub, A. M. (*333*)

Staub, A. M., and Tinelli, R. 1960. *Bull. Soc. Chim. Biol.* **42**:108. (*333*)

Staveley, J. M. (*289, 292*)

Steddon, L. M. (*52*)

Steele, B. F. (*267*)

Stefanini, M. (*260*)

Stefanini, M. 1953. *Am. J. Med.* **14**:64. (*262*)

Stefanini, M., and Dameshek, W. 1955. "The Hemorrhagic Disorders: A Clinical and Therapeutic Approach." New York: Grune. (*262*)

Stefanini, M., Dameshek, W., and Bernfeld, P. 1953. *Clin. Res. Proc.* **1**:69. (*261*)
Steffen, G. L. (*313*)
Steigman, A. J. (*142*)
Stein, E. (*54*)
Stein, E. A. (*181*)
Steinberg, B. M. (*40*)
Steiner, K. 1929. *Arch. Dermatol. Syphilis* **157**:446. (*153*) 1931. *Arch. Dermatol. Syphilis* **162**:577. (*153*)
Steiner, L. A. (*200*)
Stekker, K. (*188*)
Stellwagen, E., and Schachman, H. K. 1962. *Biochemistry* **1**:1056. (*222*)
Stenlid, G. 1954. *Physiol. Plantarum* **7**: 173. (*14*)
Stephenson, O. (*197*)
Stern, K. G. *In* Springer, 1956b. (*333*)
Sternberg, M. (*199*)
Sternieri, E. 1962. *Farmaco (Pavia), Ed. Sci.* **17**:511. (*200*)
Stevens, C. L., Blumbergs, P., Daniher, F. A., Wheat, R. W., Kujomoto, A., and Rollins, E. L. 1963. *J. Am. Chem. Soc.* **85**:3061. (*44*)
Stevens, C. O., Tolbert, B. M., and Reese, F. E. 1963. *Arch. Biochem. Biophys.* **102**:423. (*184*)
Stevens, G. D. (*363*)
Stevens, M. F. (*306*)
Stewart, D. K. R. (*363*)
Stewart, F. W. (*394*)
Stjernström, L. (*237, 238*)
Stock, C. C. (*199*)
Stoffel, W. (*308*)
Stoker, M. G. P. (*381*)
Stokinger, H. E., Carpenter, C. M., and Plack, J. 1944. *J. Bacteriol.* **47**:149. (*323*)
Stokinger, H. E., and Heidelberger, M. 1937. *J. Exptl. Med.* **66**:251. (*302, 303*)
Stokstad, E. L. R. (*266*)
Stolkowski, J., and Rosenberg, A. J. 1953. *Bull. Soc. Chim. Biol.* **35**:529. (*222*)
Stone, J. D. (*171, 338, 339*)
Stone, J. D. 1947. *Australian J. Exptl. Biol. Med. Sci.* **25**:137. (*339*) 1948. *Australian J. Exptl. Biol. Med. Sci.* **26**:287. (*339*) 1949. *Australian J. Exptl. Biol. Med. Sci.* **27**:337. (*338*) 1949a. *Australian J. Exptl. Biol. Med. Sci.* **27**:557. (*355*)
Stone, J. D., and Ada, G. L. 1950. *Brit. J. Exptl. Pathol.* **31**:275. (*339*)
Stone, R. S. (*392*)
Stone, W. H. (*294, 295*)
Storaasli, J. P. (*245*)
Storey, I. D. E. (*45, 47*)
Storey, I. D. E., and Dutton, G. J. 1955. *Biochem. J.* **59**:279. (*45, 47*)
Stormont, C. 1949. *Proc. Natl. Acad. Sci. U.S.* **35**:232. (*294*)
Stoughton, R. B. (*52*)
Strange, R. E., and Dark, F. A. 1956. *Biochem. J.* **62**:459. (*115*) 1956a. *Nature* **177**:186. (*163*) 1957. *J. Gen. Microbiol.* **16**:236. (*88*)
Strange, R. E., and Kent, L. H. 1959. *Biochem. J.* **71**:333. (*23*)
Strannegard, O. (*200*)
Stratton, F., and Renton, P. H. 1959. *Brit. Med. J.* **2**:244. (*269, 273, 300*)
Straumfjord, J. V., Jr., and Hummel, J. P. 1959. *Cancer Res.* **19**:913. (*381*)
Strömberg, H. E., and Dohlman, C.-H. 1959. *Acta Ophthalmol.* **37**:112. (*53*)
Strominger, J. L. (*47, 53, 60–62, 69, 73, 75, 84, 90, 91, 111, 112, 116, 117, 148, 168, 169, 193, 204–206, 314*)
Strominger, J. L. 1955. *Biochim. Biophys. Acta* **17**:283. (*22, 60, 148*) 1958. *Biochim. Biophys. Acta* **30**:645. (*23*) 1959. *J. Biol. Chem.* **234**:1520. (*82, 113*) 1960. *Physiol. Rev.* **40**:55. (*45*) 1962. *J. Biol. Chem.* **237**:1388. (*22, 148*) 1962a. *Federation Proc.* **21**:134. (*314*)
Strominger, J. L., and Mapson, L. W. 1957. *Biochem. J.* **66**:567. (*48*)
Strominger, J. L., and Threnn, R. H. 1959. *Biochim. Biophys. Acta* **36**:83. (*111, 114*)
Strominger, J. L., Threnn, R. H., and Scott, S. S. 1959. *J. Am. Chem. Soc.* **81**:3803. (*111*)
Strominger, J. L., Kalckar, H. M., Axel-

rod, J., and Maxwell, E. S. 1954. *J. Am. Chem. Soc.* **76**:6411. (*47*)
Strominger, J. L., Maxwell, E. S., Axelrod, J., and Kalckar, H. M. 1957. *J. Biol. Chem.* **224**:79. (*47*)
Strong, L. E. (*374*)
Stróżecka, K. (*290*)
Stumpf, P. K. (*123*)
Südhof, H., and Abraham, S. 1957. *Arch. Biochem. Biophys.* **71**:221. (*95*)
Sugiura, H. T. (*387*)
Sugo, T. (*106*)
Sulman, F. (*301*)
Summers, C. G. (*264*)
Sundblad, L. (*65, 230–237*)
Sundblad, L. 1953. *Acta Soc. Med. Upsaliensis* **58**:113. (*187, 193, 233*)
Suntzeff, V. (*381*)
Suomi, W. (*122*)
Sussman, M. (*330*)
Sussman, M., and Osborn, M. J. 1964. *Proc. Natl. Acad. Sci. U.S.* **52**:81. (*125*)
Sutliff, W. D. (*267*)
Sutton, T. S. (*295*)
Suzuki, K. 1964. *Biochem. Biophys. Res. Commun.* **16**:88. (*126*)
Suzuki, K., and Korey, S. P. 1963. *Biochim. Biophys. Acta* **78**:388. (*126*)
Suzuki, S. (*84*)
Suzuki, S. 1960. *J. Biol. Chem.* **235**:3580. (*193, 195, 204, 207*) 1962. *J. Biol. Chem.* **237**:1393. (*22*)
Suzuki, S., and Strominger, J. L. 1959. *Biochim. Biophys. Acta* **31**:283. (*61, 69, 148*) 1960. *J. Biol. Chem.* **235**: 257. (*60, 61, 69, 148, 204–206*) 1960a. *J. Biol. Chem.* **235**:267. (*61, 148*) 1960b. *J. Biol. Chem.* **235**:274. (*61, 148*) 1960c. *J. Biol. Chem.* **235**:2768. (*193, 204, 206*)
Suzuki, S., Trenn [Threnn], R. H., and Strominger, J. L. 1961. *Biochim. Biophys. Acta* **50**:169. (*62, 73, 75*)
Suzuki, T. (*53, 74*)
Suzuki, T., and Sakakura, K. 1953. *Mie Med. J.* **3**:197. (*231*)
Svennerholm, L. 1962. *Biochem. Biophys. Res. Commun.* **9**:436. (*126, 311*)
Swanson, A. L. (*197*)
Swyer, G. I. M. 1947. *Biochem. J.* **41**: 409. (*192*) 1947a. *Nature* **160**:433. (*192*) 1948. *Biochem. J.* **42**:32. (*197*)
Swyer, G. I. M., and Emmens, C. W. 1947. *Biochem. J.* **41**:29. (*187, 193*)
Sykes, J. F. (*149*)
Sylvén, B. (*263, 390*)
Sylvén, B. 1940. *Acta Radiologica* **21**: 206. (*246*) 1941. *Acta Chir. Scand.* **86**:Suppl. 66 (*391*) 1945. *Acta Radiol.* **26**:Suppl. 59, p. 5. (*376, 391, 392*) 1946. *Acta Obstet. Gynecol. Scand.* **25**:189. (*149*)
Sysma, M. J. (*321*)
Szabó, D. (*85*)
Szasz, G. (*371*)
Szirmai, J. A. (*65, 134–140, 147*)
Szirmai, J. A. 1949. *Anat. Record* **105**: 337. (*134, 137–140, 147*) 1962. *Protein Metabolism: Intern. Symp., Leyden, June, 1962* (*129, 151*) 1954. "Bijdrage tot de Kennis van het Mucoide Bindweefsel." Gravenhageni: Vitgeverij Excelsior. (*129, 138, 139, 151*) 1956. *J. Histochem. Cytochem.* **4**:96. (*134, 135, 137, 138*) 1956a. *Proc. Soc. Exptl. Biol. Med.* **93**:92. (*136–140, 147*) 1957. *Acta Endocrinol.* **25**:225. (*136*)
Szirmai, J. A., and Balazs, E. A. 1958. *Acta Histochem.* Suppl. I, p. 56. (*134, 139*)
Szulman, A. E. 1960. *J. Exptl. Med.* **111**: 785. (*289*)

T

Tabor, H., Mehler, A. H., and Stadtman, E. R. 1953. *J. Biol. Chem.* **204**:127. (*12, 57*)
Taha, B. (*105*)
Taipale, E. (*394*)
Takagi, T. (*112, 184, 199, 222*)
Takahashi, N. (*208*)
Takahashi, N., and Egami, F. 1960. *Biochim. Biophys. Acta* **38**:375. (*204, 207*) 1961. *Biochem. J.* **80**:384. (*204, 208*)
Takahashi, N., and Suzuki, S. 1962. *Biochim. Biophys. Acta* **63**:344. (*84*)
Takahashi, T. (*298, 333*)

Takahashi, T., and Springer, G. F. 1964. *Abstr. Am. Chem. Soc. 147th Natl. Meeting, Philadelphia, 1964,* p. 13c. (*298*)
Takaku, F. (*43, 106*)
Takamura, K. (*53*)
Takao, K. 1923. *Z. Physiol. Chem.* **131:** 307. (*34*)
Takeda, S. (*308*)
Takemitsu, Y. 1961. *Kyushu J. Med. Sci.* **12**:251. (*52, 54*)
Takemoto, K. K. (*363*)
Takemoto, K. K., and Fabisch, P. 1963. *Proc. Soc. Exptl. Biol. Med.* **114:** 811. (*363*)
Takemoto, K. K., and Liebhaber, H. 1961. *Virology* **14**:456. (*363*) 1962. *Virology* **14**:456. (*363*)
Takemoto, K. K., and Spicer, S. S. 1965. *Ann. N.Y. Acad. Sci.* **130**(Art. 1): 365. (*396*)
Takeya, K., Hisatsune, K., and Inoue, Y. 1963. *J. Bacteriol.* **85**:24. (*323*)
Tal, C., Laufer, A., and Zlotnick, A. 1964. *Brit. J. Exptl. Pathol.* **45**:323. (*309*)
Talanti, S. (*200*)
Talmage, R. V. 1947. *Anat. Record* **99:** 91. (*151*) 1947a. *Anat. Record* **99:** 571. (*151*) 1947b. *J. Exptl. Zool.* **106**:281. (*151*)
Tamm, I. (*342, 346*)
Tamm, I., Bugher, J. C., and Horsfall, F. L., Jr. 1955. *J. Biol. Chem.* **212:** 125. (*342*)
Tamm, I., and Horsfall, F. L., Jr. 1952. *J. Exptl. Med.* **95**:71. (*99, 304*)
Tamura, J. (*392*)
Tamura, M. (*128*)
Tanaka, K., Bertolini, M., and Pigman, W. 1964. *Biochem. Biophys. Res. Commun.* **16**:404. (*83, 344*)
Tankó, B. 1932. *Biochem. Z.* **247**:486. (*209*)
Tapson, K. J. (*300*)
Taranova, N. P. (*126*)
Tarasiejska, Z., and Jeanloz, R. W. 1958. *J. Am. Chem. Soc.* **80**:6325. (*157*)
Tardieux, P., and Nisman, B. 1952. *Ann. Inst. Pasteur* **82**:458. (*322*)
Tarver, H. 1954. *In* "The Proteins" (H. Neurath and K. Bailey, eds.), Vol. 2, Part B, p. 1199. New York: Academic Press (*92*)
Tarver, H., Armstrong, F. B., Debro, J. R., and Margen, S. 1961. *Ann. N.Y. Acad. Sci.* **94**:23. (*99*)
Tausche, F. G. (*54*)
Taylor, A. C. 1961. *Exptl. Cell Res.* Suppl. 8, p. 154. (*373*)
Taylor, D. J. (*34*)
Taylor, H. E. (*149*)
Taylor, H. L. (*374*)
Tchertkova, F. A. (*200*)
Tegtmeyer, H. (*271*)
Telford, R. (*274*)
Telser, A. (*80*)
Tempelis, C. H., and Lysenko, M. G. 1957. *Exptl. Parasitol.* **6**:31. (*196*)
Terplan, K. (*302*)
Terranova, T. (*393*)
Tessari, L. 1959. *Naturwissenschaften* **46**:265. (*6*)
Thamsen, J. (*231*)
Thannhauser, S. J. (*311*)
Thomas, J. (*207*)
Thomas, L., Smith, R. T., and Von Korff, R. 1954. *Proc. Soc. Exptl. Biol. Med.* **86**:813. (*261*)
Thomas, M. A. W. (*86, 238, 344*)
Thompson, C. M. (*366*)
Thompson, E. O. P. (*182*)
Thompson, J. S. (*300*)
Thompson, R. 1941. *A.M.A. Arch. Ophthalmol.* **25**:491. (*182*)
Thompson, W. (*279, 280*)
Thomsen, O. 1927. *Z. Immunitätsforch.* **52**:85. (*293*) 1929–30. *Hereditas* **13:** 121. (*272*)
Thorpe, N. O. (*306*)
Thorsell, W. (*197*)
Threnn, R. H. (*62, 73, 75, 111, 114*)
Thudichum, J. L. W. 1884. "A Treatise on the Chemical Composition of Brain." Cited by H. Thierfelder and E. Klenk, "Die Chemie der Cerebroside und Phosphatide." Berlin: Springer, 1930. (*119*)
Tiedemann, H. (*157, 160, 281*)
Tillett, W. S. (*268, 307, 317*)
Tillett, W. S., and Francis, T., Jr. 1929.

J. Exptl. Med. **50**:687. (*267, 268, 317*) 1930. *J. Exptl. Med.* **52**:561. (*267, 268, 307, 317*)
Tillett, W. S., Goebel, W. F., and Avery, O. T. 1930. *J. Exptl. Med.* **52**:895. (*317*)
Timasheff, S. N. (*252*)
Tinelli, R. (*333*)
Tiselius, A. (*306*)
Tiselius, A., and Kabat, E. A. 1939. *J. Exptl. Med.* **69**:119. (*305*)
Tkacz, L. (*53*)
Tobimatsu, G. (*34*)
Toda, Y. (*323*)
Todd, A. R. (*157, 162*)
Toennies, G. (*114*)
Tolbert, B. M. (*184*)
Tolksdorf, S., McCready, M. H., McCullagh, D. R., and Schwenk, E. 1949. *J. Lab. Clin. Med.* **34**:74. (*187*)
Tomasz, A., and Borek, E. 1959. *Proc. Natl. Acad. Sci. U.S.* **45**:929. (*112*) 1960. *Proc. Natl. Acad. Sci. U.S.* **46**:324. (*112*)
Tomcsik, J. 1927. *Magyar Orvosi Arch.* **28**:572; *Chem. Abstr.* **22**:1610, 1928. (*318*) 1945. *Schweiz. Z. Pathol. Bakteriol.* **8**:345. (*287*) 1953. *Ann. Rev. Biochem.* **22**:351. (*312*) 1956. *Bacterial Anat., 6th Symp. Soc. Gen. Microbiol., London, 1956.* (*115*)
Tomita, Y. (*392*)
Tomkins, G. M. (*65*)
Tomsons, V. P. (*365*)
Tonna, E. A., and Cronkite, E. P. 1959. *J. Biophys. Biochem. Cytol.* **6**:171. (*54*) 1960. *J. Gerontol.* **15**:377. (*54*)
Topper, Y. J. 1957. *J. Biol. Chem.* **225**:419. (*10*)
Topper, Y. J., and Lipton, M. M. 1953. *J. Biol. Chem.* **203**:135. (*3, 4, 65, 70*)
Torii, M., Kabat, E. A., and Bezer, A. E. 1964. *J. Exptl. Med.* **120**:13. (*315, 321*)
Torlone, V. (*232, 237*)
Tornheim, J. (*91*)
Torstveit, O. (*141*)
Tóth, G. (*155, 157, 162–164, 167, 182*)
Toth, L. Z. J. (*65*)
Toth, L. Z. J., Balazs, E. A., and Howe, A. F. 1962. *Invest. Ophthalmol.* **1**:797. (*247*)
Touster, O. (*128*)
Tovarnitsky, V. I. (*329*)
Tracey, M. V. (*181*)
Tracey, M. V. 1955. *In* "Modern Methods of Plant Analysis." (K. Paech and M. V. Tracey, eds.), Vol. 2, p. 264. Berlin: Springer. (*182*) 1955a. *Biochem. J.* **61**:579. (*182*)
Trams, E. G. (*311*)
Trautman, R. (*306*)
Trávníček, R. (*188*)
Treffers, H. P. (*267, 274, 336*)
Treffers, H. P. 1944. *Advan. Protein Chem.* **1**:69. (*308*)
Treffers, H. P., and Heidelberger, M. 1941. *J. Exptl. Med.* **73**:125. (*308*) 1941a. *J. Exptl. Med.* **73**:293. (*308*)
Treffers, H. P., Moore, D. H., and Heidelberger, M. 1942. *J. Exptl. Med.* **75**:135. (*306, 308*)
Tritel, H. (*272, 287, 328, 329, 336*)
Tritel, H., and Springer, G. F. 1963. *Federation Proc.* **22**:437. (*287, 329*)
Trivelloni, J. C., Recondo, E., and Cardini, C. E. 1962. *Nature* **195**:1202. (*84*)
Trocca, M. (*116*)
Tronieri, A. (*202*)
Trosper, F. (*176*)
Trotter, W. R., Belyavin, G., and Waddams, A. 1957. *Proc. Roy. Soc. Med.* **50**:961. (*303*)
Trousof, N. (*49*)
Trucco, R. E. (*105, 171*)
Trucco, R. E., and Caputto, R. 1954. *J. Biol. Chem.* **206**:901. (*27, 351*)
Trucco, R. E., and Pardee, A. B. 1958. *J. Biol. Chem.* **230**:435. (*110, 111*)
Tsai, T. (*328*)
Tsugita, A., and Akabori, S. 1959. *J. Biochem.* (*Tokyo*) **46**:695. (*83, 84*)
Tsukamoto, H., Yamamoto, A., and Miyashita, C. 1964. *Biochem. Biophys. Res. Commun.* **15**:151. (*83*)
Tsuyuki, E., Tsuyuki, H., and Stahmann, M. A. 1956. *Proc. Soc. Exptl. Biol. Med.* **91**:318. (*363*)
Tsuyuki, R. (*363*)

Tuba, J. (*394*)
Tull, F. A. (*33, 384, 385*)
Tullner, W. (*142*)
Tunis, M. (*85, 388*)
Tunis, M., and Regelson, W. 1963. *Arch. Biochem. Biophys.* **101**:448. (*388*)
Tuominen, T. (*9*)
Turba, F. (*140*)
Turner, D. H., and Turner, J. F. 1958. *Biochem. J.* **69**:448. (*49*)
Turner, F. C. (*367, 389*)
Turner, J. E. (*94*)
Turner, J. F. (*49*)
Turner, T. (*388*)
Turner, W. A., Jr. (*196*)
Turpeinen, O. (*200*)
Turpeinen, P., Turpeinen, O., and Talanti, S. 1962. *Endocrinology* **70**:731. (*200*)
Turtur, F. (*187*)
Turumi, K.-I., Hamagami, L. T., and Kenkel, H. 1959. *J. Am. Med. Assoc.* **170**:2160. (*307*)
Tuttle, L. P. (*221, 222, 224–227*)
Tyler, A. (*312*)
Tyler, A., 1948. *Physiol. Rev.* **28**:180. (*312*) 1949. *Am. Naturalist* **83**:195. (*312*)
Tyler, H. M., and Lack, C. H. 1964. *Nature* **202**:1114. (*89*)
de Tyssonsk, E. R. (*138–140*)

U

Uchida, T., Robbins, P. W, and Luria, S. E. 1963. *Biochemistry* **2**:663 (*334*)
Udaka, K. (*202*)
Ugo, A. (*145, 146*)
Uhlenbruck, G. (*273, 290, 293, 344, 348, 349, 358*)
Uhlenbruck, G. 1961. *Zentr. Bakteriol. Parasitenk. Abt. I. Ref.* **179**:229. (*293*)
Uhlenbruck, G., and Krüpe, M. 1963. *Z. Immunitaetsforsch.* **124**:342. (*291*)
Uhlenbruck, G., and Schmid, D. O. 1962. *Z. Immunitaetsforsch.* **123**:466. (*295*)
Ujejski, L., and Glegg, R. E. 1955. *Can. J. Biochem. Physiol.* **33**:199. (*302*)
Unger, L. J. (*291, 292*)
Uriel, J. (*102*)
United States Pharmacopoeia 1955. **XV**: 329. (*186, 187*)
Utter, M. F. 1958. *Ann. Rev. Biochem.* **27**:245. (*46*)
Uzman, L. L. 1953. *Arch. Pathol.* **55**:181. (*120*)

V

Vaerman, J. P., and Heremans, J. F. 1959. *Experientia* **15**:226. (*304*)
Vaheri, A. (*372, 373*)
Vaheri, A. 1964. "Heparin and Related Polyionic Substances as Virus Inhibitors." Helsinki: State Serum Institute. (Also published as Suppl. 171, 1964, *Acta Pathol. Microbiol. Scand.*) (*364, 365*)
Vaheri, A., and Cantell, K. 1963. *Virology* **21**:661. (*364*)
Vajda, É. (*157, 164, 182*)
Vajda, J. (*332*)
Valette, G., and Ranson, M. 1954. *Ann. Pharm. Franc.* **12**:761. (*188*)
Valtonen, E. J., Jänne, J., and Siimes, M. 1964. *Acta Dermato-Venereol.* **44**: 269. (*250*)
Vandenbergh, J. G. 1965. *Gen. Comp. Endocrinol.* **5**:31. (*154*)
Vandendriessche, L. 1956. *Arch. Biochem. Biophys.* **65**:347. (*224–226*)
Van der Schoot, J. B. (*106*)
Van Heyningen, R. (*274*)
Van Holde, K. E. (*222*)
Van Leeuwen, G. (*102, 303, 307*)
Van Slyke, D. D. 1929. *J. Biol. Chem.* **83**:425. (*217*)
Van Tamelen, E. E., Dyer, J. R., Carter, H. E., Pierce, J. V., and Daniels, E. E. 1956. *J. Am. Chem. Soc.* **78**:4817. (*163*)
Varga, L. (*239–242, 244*)
Varma, S. N., Schwarz, V., and Simpson, I. M. N. 1962. *Biochem. J.* **85**:546. (*125*)
Vasseur, E. 1947. *Arkiv Kemi* **25B**:1. (*312*) 1948. *Acta Chem. Scand.* **2**: 900. (*312*) 1952. "The Chemistry and Physiology of the Jelly Coat of the Sea Urchin Egg." Stockholm:

Kihlstrom. (*312*) 1952a. *Acta Chem. Scand.* **6**:376. (*368*)

Vasseur, E., and Immers, J. 1949. *Arkiv Kemi* **1**:253. (*312*) 1949a. *Arkiv Kemi* **1**:39. (*368*)

Vaubel, E. 1933. *J. Exptl. Med.* **58**:63. (*62*)

Vaughan, J. (*52*)

Vaughan, J. H., and Kabat, E. A. 1954. *J. Immunol.* **73**:205. (*335*)

Vazquez, J. J. (*99*)

Vazquez, J. J., and Dixon, F. J. 1956. *J. Exptl. Med.* **104**:727. (*310*)

Vegeto, A. (*392*)

Veldkamp, H. 1952. *Nature* **169**:500. (*181*) 1955. *Mededel. Landbouwhogeschool Wageningen* **55**:127. (*35, 181, 182*)

Veninga, T. S. (*249*)

Veninga, T. S., and Brinkman, R. 1962. *Intern. J. Radiation Biol.* **5**:283. (*249*)

Venturi, V. M. 1953. *Acta Pharmacol. Toxicol.* **9**:93. (*188*)

Verachtert, H., Bass, S. T., and Hansen, R. G. 1964. *Biochem. Biophys. Res. Commun.* **15**:158. (*84*)

de Verdier, C.-H. (*23*)

Verne, J., Weill, R., Ceccaldi, P. F., and de Charpal, O. 1952. *Compt. Rend. Soc. Biol.* **146**:1558. (*54*)

Verne, J., Bescol-Liversac, J., Droz, B., and Olivier, L. 1956. *Compt. Rend. Soc. Biol.* **150**:1770. (*54*)

Vestermark, A. (*5, 53, 71*)

Vilar, O. (*54*)

Villanueva, J. R. (*90*)

Vincent, D., and Segonzac, G. 1953. *Compt. Rend. Soc. Biol.* **147**:1776. (*197*) 1956. *Compt. Rend. Soc. Biol.* **150**:447. (*197*)

Vincent, D., Segonzac, G., and Issandou-Carles, R. 1954. *Compt. Rend. Soc. Biol.* **148**:1075. (*197*)

Vincent, J. 1954. *Arch. Biol.* (*Liège*) **65**: 531. (*54*) 1955. "Recherches sur la constitution de l'os adulte." Bruxelles: Arscia. (*54*) 1957. *Arch. Biol.* (*Liège*) **68**:561. (*54*)

Vinter, V. 1963. *Experientia* **19**:307. (*118*)

Virchow, [R.]. 1851. *Verh. Phys.-Med. Ges. Würzburg* **2**:314. (*134*)

Vogt, A. (*309*)

Vogt, A., and Kochem, H.-G. 1960. *Z. Zellforschg. Mikroskop. Anat.* **52**: 640. (*309, 310*)

Vogt, P. K. 1963. *Cancer Res.* **23**:1519. (*381*)

Volk, W. A., and Ashwell, G. 1963. *Biochem. Biophys. Res. Commun.* **12**: 116. (*44*)

Voluyskaya, E. N., Cheburkina, N. V., Tovarnitsky, V. I., and Nikolskaya, I. N. 1959. *Vopr. Med. Khim.* **5**:147. (English summary). (*329*)

Von Korff, R. (*261*)

Voronin, G. N. 1959. *Dokl. Akad. Nauk SSSR* **131**:425; *Chem. Abstr.* **54**: 14326h, 1960. (*54*)

Voss, H. (*385*)

Voss, H. 1964. *Zentr. Bakteriol. Parasitenk. Abt. I. Orig.* **193**:1. (*365*)

W

Wachs, E. F. (*141*)

Wada, Y., Tamura, J., Tomita, Y., and Yamada, M. 1955. *Gann* **46**:397. (*392*)

Wada, T., Ohara, H., Sasaki, T., Nakajima, J., and Yachi, A. 1957. *Gann* **48**:305. (*394*)

Waddams, A. (*303*)

Wadel, J. (*248*)

Wadström, L. B. (*215*)

van Wagenen, G. (*142, 143, 145, 146, 152*)

Wagman, G. H. (*366*)

Wagman, G. H., and Weinstein, M. J. 1964. *J. Med. Chem.* **7**:800. (*366*)

Waksman, B. H. (*273*)

Waksman, S. A., and Woodruff, M. B. 1942. *J. Bacteriol.* **44**:373. (*182*)

Waksman, S. A., Reuszer, H. W., Carey, C. L., Hotchkiss, M., and Renn, C. E. 1933. *Biol. Bull.* **64**:183. (*181*)

Walaas, E. (*102*)

Walaas, O., Borrebaek, B., Kristiansen, T., and Walaas, E. 1960. *Biochim. Biophys. Acta* **40**:562. (*102*)

Waldenström, J. 1944. *Acta Med. Scand.* **117**:216. (*307*)

Walker, B. E. 1961. *J. Embryol. Exptl. Morphol.* **9**:22. (*55*)

Walker, P. G. (*17, 30, 88, 91, 155–163, 166*)

Walker, P. G., Woollen, J. W., and Heyworth, R. 1961. *Biochem. J.* **79**:288. (*159–163*)

Walker, P. G., Woollen, M. E., and Pugh, D. 1960. *J. Clin. Pathol.* **13**: 353. (*157, 160, 166*)

Wallach, D. F. H., and Eylar, E. H. 1961. *Biochim. Biophys. Acta* **52**:594. (*128, 382*)

Wallach, D. F. H., and de Perez Esandi, M. V. 1964. *Biochim. Biophys. Acta* **83**:363. (*383*)

Wallas, C. H., and Strominger, J. L. 1963. *J. Biol. Chem.* **238**:2264. (*116*)

Wallenius, G., Trautman, R., Franklin, E. C., and Kunkel, H. G., 1956. *Federation Proc.* **15**:378. (*306*)

Walop, J. N. (*172, 353*)

Walop, J. N., Boschman, T. A. C., and Jacobs, J. 1960. *Biochim. Biophys. Acta* **44**:185. (*352*)

Walshe, J. M., DeCarli, L., and Davidson, C. S. 1958. *Clin. Sci.* **17**:26. (*32*)

Walter, A. W. (*268, 317*)

Walter, H. (*100*)

Walter, H., Haurowitz, F., Fleischer, S., Lietze, A., Cheng, H. F., Turner, J. E., and Friedberg, W. 1957. *J. Biol. Chem.* **224**:107. (*94*)

Walter, K. (*301*)

Walther, W. W. (*300*)

Walton, K. W. (*211, 254, 265*)

Walton, K. W. 1952. *Brit. J. Pharmacol.* **7**:370. (*224, 266*) 1955. *Brit. Med. Bull.* **11**:62. (*263–265*)

Warburton, M. F. (*289*)

Ward, W. H. (*183*)

Warnatz, H. (*308*)

Warrack, G. H. (*187*)

Warren, G. H. (*393*)

Warren, G. H., and Durso, J. G. 1951. *Endocrinology* **48**:408. (*187*)

Warren, G. H., Durso, J. G., and Levin, N. R. 1948. *Endocrinology* **43**:48. (*187*)

Warren, G. H., Seifter, J., and Glassman, J. M. 1962. *Nature* **194**:770. (*197*)

Warren, L. (*126*)

Warren, L. 1959. *J. Biol. Chem.* **234**:1971. (*172*) 1964. *Biochim. Biophys. Acta* **83**:129. (*105*)

Warren, L., and Blacklow, R. S. 1962. *Biochem. Biophys. Res. Commun.* **7**: 433. (*26*)

Warren, L., and Felsenfeld, H. 1961. *Biochem. Biophys. Res. Commun.* **4**:232. (*24*) 1961a. *Biochem. Biophys. Res. Commun.* **5**:185. (*25*) 1962. *J. Biol. Chem.* **237**:1421. (*25*)

Warren, L., and Spearing, C. W. 1960. *Biochem. Biophys. Res. Commun.* **3**: 489. (*171, 175*)

Warren, S. (*54*)

Waszczenko-Zacharczenko, E. (*271*)

Watanabe, K. 1936. *J. Biochem.* (*Tokyo*) **24**:297. (*157, 165*) 1936a. *J. Biochem.* (*Tokyo*) **24**:305. (*158*) 1936b. *J. Biochem.* (*Tokyo*) **24**:315. (*158, 159*)

Waters, E. T., Markowitz, J., and Jaques, L. B. 1938. *Science* **87**:582. (*332*)

Watkins, W. M. (*168, 177, 274, 275, 277, 279–281, 283, 284, 286, 287, 292, 316*)

Watkins, W. M. 1953. *Biochem. J.* **54**: xxxiiiP. (*107, 281*) 1956. *Biochem. J.* **64**:21P. (*107, 287*) 1959. *Biochem. J.* **71**:261. (*157, 160, 167, 168*)

Watkins, W. M., Kościelak, J., and Morgan, W. T. J. 1964. *Proc. Intern. Soc. Blood Trans., 9th, Mexico City, 1962,* p. 213. (*270*)

Watkins, W. M., and Morgan, W. T. J. 1952. *Nature* **169**:825. (*277, 333*) 1954. *Brit. J. Exptl. Pathol.* **35**:181. (*274*) 1955. *Nature* **175**:676. (*280*) 1956. *Nature* **178**:1289. (*316*) 1956–1957. *Acta Genet. Statist. Med.* **6**: 521. (*276, 284*) 1957. *Nature* **180**: 1038. (*283, 284*) 1959. *Vox Sanguinis* **4**:97. (*107, 168*) 1962. *Vox Sanguinis* **7**:129. (*277, 280, 281, 284, 317*) 1964. *Proc. Intern. Soc. Blood Trans., 9th, Mexico City, 1962,* p. 230. (*292*)

Watkins, W. M., Zarnitz, M. L., and

Kabat, E. A. 1962. *Nature* **195**:1204. (*280, 298*)
Watson, D. (*25*)
Watson, D. R. (*27*)
Watson, D. W. (*224, 225*)
Watson, R. G., Marinetti, G. V., and Scherp, H. W. 1958. *J. Immunol.* **81**: 337. (*324*)
Watson, R. G., and Scherp, H. W. 1958. *J. Immunol.* **81**:331. (*324*)
Wattenberg, L. W., and Glick, D. 1949. *J. Biol. Chem.* **179**:1213. (*197*)
Watts, G. T., Grillo, H. C., and Gross, J. 1958. *Ann. Surg.* **148**:153. (*373*)
Webb, M. (*101*)
Weber, E. (*123*)
Weber, G. (*224*)
Weber, G. F. (*357*)
Weber, M. J. (*89*)
Webster, M. E. (*22, 163, 193, 194, 326, 327*)
Wegelius, O. (*392*)
Wegelius, O., and Lamberg, B.-A. 1960. *Acta Endocrinol.* **33**:473. (*55*)
Wehrmüller, J. O. (*86*)
Weibull, C. 1958. *Acta Pathol. Microbiol. Scand.* **42**:324. (*111*)
Weicker, H., Huhnstock, K., and Grässlin, D. 1964. *Clin. Chim. Acta* **9**:19. (*106*)
Weicker, H., Dain, J. A., Schmidt, G., and Thannhauser, S. J. 1960. *Federation Proc.* **19**:219. (*311*)
Weide, U. 1952. Thesis, München. (*151*)
Weidel, W. (*88, 90, 182*)
Weidel, W. 1964. *Angew. Chem* **76**:801. (*313*)
Weidel, W., Frank, H., and Martin, H. H. 1960. *J. Gen. Microbiol.* **22**:158. (*114, 313*)
Weidel, W., and Katz, W. 1961. *Z. Naturforsch.* **16b**:156. (*182*)
Weidel, W., and Primosigh, J. 1957. *Z. Naturforsch.* **12b**:421. (*42*) 1958. *J. Gen. Microbiol.* **18**:513. (*88*)
Weidinger, A. (*139*)
Weigle, W. O. (*99*)
Weil, A. J., and Sherman, E. 1939. *J. Immunol.* **36**:139. (*316*)
Weil, R. 1916. *J. Immunol.* **1**:19. (*333*)
Weiler, G. (*269*)
Weill, P. 1919. *Folia Haematol.* **23**:185. (*391*)
Weill, R. (*54*)
Weimer, H. E., Mehl, J. W., and Winzler, R. J. 1950. *J. Biol. Chem.* **185**:561. (*309*)
Weimer, H. E., Quinn, F. A., Redlich-Moshin, J., and Nishihara, H. 1957. *J. Natl. Cancer Inst.* **19**:409. (*394*)
Weinfeld, H., and Tunis, M. 1960. *J. Biol. Chem.* **235**:1668. (*85*)
Weinstein, M. J. (*366*)
Weinstein, M. J., Luedemann, G. M., Oden, E. M., Wagman, G. H., Rosselet, J. P., Marquez, J. A., Coniglio, C. T., Charney, W., Herzog, H. L., and Black, J. 1963. *J. Med. Chem.* **6**:463. (*366*)
Weisbrod, F. G. 1950. *J. Lab. Clin. Med.* **35**:408. (*394*)
Weiser, D. (*281*)
Weiser, R. S. (*87, 164, 182*)
Weiss, B. 1955. *Federation Proc.* **14**:482. (*119*) 1956. *J. Biol. Chem.* **223**:523. (*119*)
Weiss, L. (*382*)
Weiss, L. 1959. *Exptl. Cell Res.* **17**:508. (*373*) 1961. *Nature* **191**:1108. (*374*) 1963. *Biochem. Soc. Symp.* (*Cambridge, Engl.*) **22**:40. (*373*)
Weissbach, A. (*49*)
Weissmann, B. (*164, 189, 194, 198*)
Weissmann, B. 1955. *J. Biol. Chem.* **216**: 783. (*29, 189, 192, 193, 197*)
Weissmann, B., Hadjiioannou, S., and Tornheim, J. 1964. *J. Biol. Chem.* **239**:59. (*91*)
Weissmann, B., and Meyer, K. 1953. *Federation Proc.* **12**:287. (*189*)
Weissmann, B., Meyer, K., Sampson, P., and Linker, A. 1954. *J. Biol. Chem.* **208**:417. (*188*)
Welch, A. D. (*294*)
Wells, H. G. (*305, 311*)
Wells, H. G. 1911. *J. Infect. Diseases* **9**: 147. (*311*)
Welsch, M. 1947. "Phénomènes d'antibiose chez les actinomycètes." Ge-

intlowx: J. Ducolt. (*88*) 1958. *J. Gen. Microbiol.* **18**:491. (*88*)
Welsch, M., and Ghuysen, J.-M. 1953. *Compt. Rend. Soc. Biol.* **147**:1659. (*88*)
Wengle, B. (*80*)
Wenner, C. (*376*)
Wenzel, M. (*182*)
Wenzel, M., Lenk, H.-P., and Schütte, E. 1961. *Z. Physiol. Chem.* **327**:13. (*182*)
Werle, E., Turtur, F., and Bauereis, R. 1949. *Biochem. Z.* **319**:337. (*187*)
Werner, A. (*216, 265, 371*)
Werner, G. H. (*348*)
Werner, I. (*344*)
Werner, I. 1949. *Acta Physiol. Scand.* **19**: 27. (*91*)
Wertheim, E. M. (*241*)
Wertheimer, E. (*122*)
Werthessen, N. T., Berman, S., Greenberg, B. E., and Gargill, S. L. 1945. *J. Urol.* **54**:564. (*193*)
Weseli, D. F. (*295*)
West, G. B. (*246*)
Westerborn, O. (*54*)
Westin, B., and Odeblad, E. 1959. *Acta Pathol. Microbiol. Scand.* **45**:129. (*54*)
Westin, B., Allgén, L.-G., and Odeblad, E. 1959. *Acta Pathol. Microbiol. Scand.* **45**:123. (*52*)
Westphal, E. 1891. "Über Mastzellen." *In* "Farbenanalytische Untersuchungen" (P. Ehrlich, ed.), p. 17. Berlin: Hirschwald. (*391*)
Westphal, O. (*333*)
Westphal, O. 1957. *In* "Polysaccharides in Biology, Transactions of the Second Conference, 1956" (G. F. Springer, ed.), p. 115. (*325*) 1957a. *In* "Physiologische Chemie. Ein Lehr-und Handbuch," Vol. IIb: "Der Stoffwechsel" (B. Flaschenträger and E. Lehnartz, eds.), p. 894. Berlin: Springer. (*267*)
Westphal, O., and Lüderitz, O. 1954. *Angew. Chem.* **66**:407. (*325*)
Westphal, O., and Schmidt, H. 1952. *Ann. Chem.* **575**:84. (*158, 288, 320*)
Wetter, L. R. (*333*)
Wetter, L. R., Cohn, M., and Deutsch, H. F. 1952. *J. Immunol.* **69**:109. (*333*)
Wexler, I. B. (*334*)
Wheat, R. W. (*14, 19, 44*)
Wheat, R. W. 1956. *Bacteriol. Proc.* **56**: 109. (*22*)
Wheat, R. W., and Davidson, E. A. 1963. *Biochem. Prep.* **10**:52. (*14*)
Wheat, R. W., and Rollins, E. 1962. *Abstr. Am. Chem. Soc., 141st Meeting, Washington, D.C. March, 1962,* p. 22c. (*23, 30*)
Wheeler, L. M. (*197*)
Whistler, R. L., and Smart, C. L. 1953. "Polysaccharide Chemistry" New York: Academic Press. (*76*)
White, B. N., Shetlar, M. R., Shurley, H. M., and Schilling, J. A. 1965. *Biochim. Biophys. Acta* **101**:97. (*80*)
White, F. H., Jr. (*222*)
White, F. H., Jr. 1961. *J. Biol. Chem.* **236**:1353. (*222*)
White, G. J., and Sussman, M. 1963. *Biochim. Biophys. Acta* **74**:179. (*330*)
White, S. (*259, 371*)
White, W. F. (*357*)
Whitehouse, M. (*53*)
Whitehouse, M. W. (*46, 52, 53*)
Whitehouse, M. W., and Boström, H. 1961. *Biochem. Pharmacol.* **7**:135. (*69*) 1962. *Biochem. Pharmacol.* **11**: 1175. (*53*)
Whiteside, R. E. (*327*)
Whiteside, R. E., and Baker, E. E. 1959. *J. Immunol.* **83**:687. (*327*) 1960. *J. Immunol.* **84**:221. (*327*)
Whitley, R. W. (*187, 196*)
Whitney, J. G., and Grula, E. A. 1964. *Biochem. Biophys. Res. Commun.* **14**:375. (*118*)
Whitten, W. K. (*357*)
Whitten, W. K. 1948. *Australian J. Sci. Res. Ser. B. Biol. Sci.* **1**:388. (*301, 356*)
Wick, A. N. (*14, 378, 385*)
Wick, A. N., Drury, D. R., Nakada, H. I., Barnet, H. N., and Morita, T. N. 1955. *J. Biol. Chem.* **213**:907. (*14, 378*)

Wicklund, E. (*369*)
Wicklund, E. 1954. *Arkiv Zool.* **6**:485. (*312*)
Wide, L., and Gemzell, C. A. 1960. *Acta Endocrinol.* **35**:261. (*301*) 1962. *In* "Ciba Foundation Colloquia on Endocrinology," Vol. 14: "Immunoassay of Hormones" (G. E. W. Wolstenholme and M. P. Cameron, eds.), p. 296. (*301*)
Widholm, O. (*301*)
Wiedersheim, M. (*211*)
Wiegandt, H. (*311*)
Wieghard, C. W. (*314, 321*)
Wieghard C. W., and Julianelle, L. A. 1935. *J. Exptl. Med.* **62**:23. (*314, 321*)
Wiener, A. S. 1943. "Blood Groups and Transfusion," (3rd edition), pp. 332–360. Springfield, Ill.: Thomas. (*273*) 1944. *Proc. Soc. Exptl. Biol. Med.* **56**: 173. (*267*) 1951. *J. Immunol.* **66**:287. (*272*) 1961. "Advances in Blood Grouping." New York: Grune. (*269, 273, 306*)
Wiener, A. S., and Gordon, E. B. 1953. *Am. J. Clin. Pathol.* **23**:429. (*273, 274*)
Wiener, A. S., and Herman, M. 1939. *J. Immunol.* **36**:255. (*290*)
Wiener, A. S., and Wexler, I. B. 1952. *Bacteriol. Rev.* **16**:69. (*334*)
Wiener, A. S., Unger, L. J., Cohen, L., and Feldman, J. 1956. *Ann. Internal Med.* **44**:221. (*291, 292*)
Wilander, O. (*73*)
Wiley, C. E. (*224–226*)
Wilkens, H. J. (*376*)
Willers, J. M. N., Michel, M. F., Sysma, M. J., and Winkler, K. C. 1964. *J. Gen. Microbiol.* **36**:95. (*321*)
Williams, C. A. (*267*)
Williams, H. T. G. (*52*)
Williams, J. H. (*157, 385*)
Williams, J. M. (*317*)
Williams, O. B. (*181*)
Williams, R. T. 1959. "Detoxication Mechanisms," 2d ed. New York: Wiley. (*47*)
Williamson, A. R., and Zamenhof, S. 1963. *Federation Proc.* **22**:239. (*325*) 1963a. *J. Biol. Chem.* **238**:2255. (*44*)
Williamson, P. (*271, 272, 275, 276, 278, 281, 290, 297–299, 311, 325, 327, 333*)
Wilson, A. T. 1945. *J. Exptl. Med.* **81**: 593. (*319*)
Wilson, C. W. 1965. *Brit. J. Radiol.* **38**:271. (*250*)
Wilson, D. W. (*300, 301*)
Wilson, G. S. (*372*)
Wilson, G. S., and Miles, A. A. 1955. *In* "Topley and Wilson's Principles of Bacteriology and Immunity," 4th ed. Vol. II, p. 1223. Baltimore: Williams & Wilkins. (*272*)
Wilson, L. G., and Bandurski, R. S. 1956. *Arch. Biochem. Biophys.* **62**: 503. (*56*)
Wilson, V. (*175–177, 179*)
Wilson, V. W., Jr. (*171, 173, 178*)
Wilson, V. W., Jr., and Rafelson, M. E., Jr. 1962. *Federation Proc.* **21**:249. (*172, 177*) 1963. *Biochem. Prep.* **10**: 113. (*172*)
Wilson, W. L. (*251, 367*)
Wiltbank, J. N. (*149*)
Wilzbach, K. E. 1957. *J. Am. Chem. Soc.* **79**:1013. (*67*)
Winitz, M., Birnbaum, S. M., and Greenstein, J. P. 1957. *Arch. Biochem. Biophys.* **72**:437 (*33*)
Winkert, J. W., and Gordon, A. S. 1960. *Biochim. Biophys. Acta* **42**:170. (*85*)
Winkler, K. C. (*321*)
Winterstein, A. (*266*)
Winzler, R. (*173*)
Winzler, R. J. (*93, 94, 96, 97, 100, 102, 128, 172, 175, 177, 290, 309, 342–344, 346, 352, 357*)
Winzler, R. J. 1955. *In* "Methods of Biochemical Analysis" (D. Glick, ed.), Vol. 2, p. 279. New York: Interscience. (*91*) 1960. *In* "The Plasma Proteins" (F. W. Putnam, ed.), Vol. 1, p. 309. New York: Academic Press. (*91, 306, 378*)
Winzler, R. J., and Smyth, I. M. 1948. *J. Clin. Invest.* **27**:617. (*394*)
Wise, S. (*63*)
Wiser, R. (*123*)

Witebsky, E. (*302, 303*)
Witebsky, E. 1929. *Naturwissenschaften* **17**:771. (*302*)
Witebsky, E., Rose, N. R., and Shulman, S. 1958. *Lancet* **I**:808. (*303*)
Witebsky, E., Rose, N. R., Terplan, K., Paine, J. R., and Egan, R. W. 1957. *J. Am. Med. Assoc.* **164**:1439. (*302*)
Witt, D. H. (*270*)
Wizerkaniuk, M. (*53, 55*)
Wohlfart, G. (*391, 392*)
Wolf, G. 1952. "Chemical Induction of Cancer." Cambridge, Mass: Harvard. (*391*)
Wolfe, J. B. (*188, 193–195, 203, 204*)
Wolfe, J. B., Britton, B. B., and Nakada, H. I. 1957. *Arch. Biochem. Biophys.* **66**:333. (*37*)
Wolfe, L. S. 1961. *Biochem. J.* **79**:348. (*121, 128*)
Wolfe, R. G. (*89*)
Wolff, I., and Springer, G. F. 1964. *Federation Proc.* **23**:296. (*271, 311*)
Wolff, L. K. 1927. *Z. Immunitaetsforsch.* **50**:88. (*182*)
Wolfrom, M. L. (*332*)
Wolfrom, M. L., and McNeely, W. H. 1945. *J. Am. Chem. Soc.* **67**:748. (*217, 264*)
Wolfrom, M. L., Shen, T. M., and Summers, C. G. 1953. *J. Am. Chem. Soc.* **75**:1519. (*264*)
Wolfrom, M. L., Montgomery, R., Karabinos, J. V., and Rathgeb, P. 1950. *J. Am. Chem. Soc.* **72**:5796. (*264*)
Wolfrom, M. L., Gibbons, R. A., and Huggard, A. J. 1957. *J. Am. Chem. Soc.* **79**:5043. (*217*)
Wong, H. Y. C., and Hawthorne, E. W. 1954. *Am. J. Physiol.* **179**:419. (*142*)
Wong, H. Y. C., Lavenda, N., and Hawthorne, E. W. 1954. *Am. J. Physiol.* **178**:269. (*142*)
Wood, J. E. (*324*)
Woodard, H. Q. (*249*)
Woodin, A. M. 1952. *Biochem. J.* **51**: 319. (*209*)
Woodruff, M. B. (*182*)
Woodward, G. E., Cramer, F. B., and Hudson, M. T. 1953. *J. Franklin Inst.* **256**:577. (*14*)
Woodward, G. E., and Hudson, M. T. 1953. *J. Franklin Inst.* **255**:556. (*14*)
Woollen, J. W. (*159–163*)
Woollen, J. W., Heyworth, R., and Walker, P. G. 1961. *Biochem. J.* **78**:111. (*158, 159, 161, 163*)
Woollen, J. W., Walker, P. G., and Heyworth, R. 1961. *Biochem. J.* **79**:294. (*17, 88, 156–160, 163*)
Woollen, M. E. (*157, 166*)
Woolley, J. M. (*311*)
Work, E. (*109, 110*)
Work, E. 1957. *Nature* **179**:841. (*108*)
Worrel, C. S. (*197*)
Wortman, B. 1961. *J. Biol. Chem.* **236**: 974. (*75*)
Wortman, B., and Strominger, J. L. 1957. *Am. J. Ophthalmol.* **44**:Part II (No. 5, Nov.), p. 291. (*53*)
Wotherspoon, N. (*234*)
Wright, G. G., Jr. 1942. *J. Infectious Dis.* **70**:103. (*308*)
Wright, I. S. (*261, 266*)
Wu, Y.-C. (*83, 89*)
Wuhrmann, F. H., Wunderly, C., and Hässig, A. 1950. *Brit. J. Exptl. Pathol.* **31**:507. (*307*)
Wuhrmann, F., Wunderly, C., Hässig, A., and Hugentobler, F. 1949. *Helv. Med. Acta* **16**:279. (*307*)
Wulwek, W. (*157*)
Wunderly, C. (*307*)
Wyckoff, R. W. G. (*306*)

Y

Yachi, A. (*394*)
Yamada, M. (*392*)
Yamagiwa, K., and Ichikawa, K. 1916. *Japan. Z. Krebsforsch.* **10**:1. (*391*)
Yamakawa, T., and Iida, T. 1953. *Japan. J. Exptl. Med.* **23**:327. (*270*)
Yamakawa, T., and Irie, R. 1960. *J. Biochem.* (*Tokyo*) **48**:919. (*270*)
Yamakawa, T., Irie, R., and Iwanaga, M. 1960. *J. Biochem.* (*Tokyo*) **48**:490. (*270, 288*)
Yamakawa, T., Yokoyama, S., and

Handa, N. 1963. *J. Biochem. (Tokyo)* **53**:28. (*311*)
Yamamoto, A. (*83*)
Yamamoto, S., Kogure, T., Ichikawa, H., and Iseki, S. 1963. *Gunma J. Med. Sci.* **12**:6. (*298*)
Yamashina, I. (*83, 86, 91, 96, 128*)
Yamashina, I. 1956. *Acta Chem. Scand.* **10**:1666. (*86*)
Yamashina, I., and Izumi, K. 1962. *In* "Biochemistry and Medicine of Mucopolysaccharides" (F. Egami and Y. Oshima, eds.), p. 39. Tokyo: University of Tokyo, Research Association of Mucopolysaccharides. (*86*)
Yamashina, I., and Makino, M. 1962. *J. Biochem. (Tokyo)* **51**:359. (*83, 86*)
Yamashina, I., Ban-I, K. [Katsuko, B.], and Makino, M. 1963. *Biochim. Biophys. Acta* **78**:382. (*83*)
Yamashina, I., Izumi, K., and Naka, H. 1964. *J. Biochem. (Tokyo)* **55**:652. (*128*)
Yamazaki, I. (*235*)
Yang, J. T. (*253*)
Yankley, A. (*259, 371*)
Yarenshko, N. T. (*200*)
Yariv, J. (*311*)
Yielding, K. L., Tomkins, G. M., and Bunim, J. J. 1957. *Science* **125**:1300. (*65*)
Yoda, O. (*202, 208*)
Yokoyama, M., Trams, E. G., and Brady, R. O. 1963. *J. Immunol.* **90**:372. (*311*)
Yokoyama, S. (*311*)
Yoshida, A. (*202*)
Yoshikawa, H. (*53, 74*)
Yositake, M. 1939. *J. Biochem. (Tokyo)* **30**:423. (*32*) 1939a. *J. Biochem. (Tokyo)* **30**:439. (*32*)
Yosizawa, Z. 1962. *In* "Biochemistry and Medicine of Mucopolysaccharides" (F. Egami and Y. Oshima, eds.), Tokyo: University of Tokyo, Research Association of Mucopolysaccharides. (*278*)
Yosizawa, Z., and Miki, T. 1963. *Proc. Japan Acad.* **39**:187. (*277*)
Yost, D. M. (*50*)
Young, B. G. (*225*)
Young, B. G., and Mora, P. T. 1960. *Virology* **12**:493. (*363*)
Young, F. E., and Spizizen, J. 1963. *J. Biol. Chem.* **238**:3126. (*90*)
Young, G. O. (*308*)
Young, L. (*50, 54, 69*)
Yu, P.-C. (*340, 344*)
Yuki, H., and Fishman, W. H. 1963. *J. Biol. Chem.* **238**:1877. (*195*)

Z

Zachariae, F. (*389*)
Zachariae, F. 1958. *Acta Endocrinol.* **29**: 118. (*149*)
Zachariae, F., and Jensen, C. E. 1958. *Acta Endocrinol.* **27**:343. (*389*)
Zakarian, L. M. 1962. *Lab. Delo* **8**: No. 3, 36. (*200*)
Zakrzewski, K. (*270*)
Zakrzewski, Z. 1932. *Z. Krebsforsch.* **36**: 513. (*369, 386*) 1933. *Arch. Exptl. Zellforsch.* **13**:152. (*368*) 1933a. *Bull. Intern. Acad. Polonaise Sci. Lettres, Classe Med., 1932*, p. 238. (*386*)
Zambotti, V. (*8, 48, 52, 70*)
Zambotti, V., Castellani, A. A., and Schiatti, P. 1956. *Boll. Soc. Ital. Biol. Sper.* **32**:1138. (*8*)
Zambotti, V., Castellani, A. A., and De Bernard, B. 1957. *Rend. Ist. Lombardo Sci. Lettere, Part I: Classe Sci. Mat. Nat.* **91**:614. (*70*)
Zamenhof, S. (*44, 325*)
Zarnitz, M. L. (*280, 299*)
Zarnitz, M. L., and Kabat, E. A. 1960. *J. Am. Chem. Soc.* **82**:3953. (*299*)
Zavázal, V. 1957. *Experientia* **13**:359. (*331*)
Zechmeister, L. (*155*)
Zechmeister, L., and Tóth, G. 1939. *Enzymologia* **7**:165. (*155, 162, 163, 167*)
Zechmeister, L., Tóth, G., and Vajda, É. 1939. *Enzymologia* **7**:170. (*157, 164, 182*)
Zeleznick, L. D., Boltralik, J. J., Barkulis, S. S., Smith, C., and Heymann, H. 1963. *Science* **140**:400. (*116*)

SUBJECT INDEX

B

C

D

H

M

T

U

V